QUATERNARY EVOLUTION OF THE GREAT LAKES

Edited by

P.F. Karrow and P.E. Calkin

1985

P.F. Karrow
Department of Earth Sciences
University of Waterloo
Waterloo, Ontario N2L 3G1

P.E. Calkin
Department of Geological Sciences
State University of New York at Buffalo
4240 Ridge Lea Road
Amherst, New York 14226

International Standard Book Number: 0-919216-29-3

Canadian Cataloguing in Publication Data

Main entry under title:

Quaternary evolution of the Great Lakes

(The Geological Association of Canada special paper; 30)
Papers of a symposium on the quaternary evolution of the
Great Lakes held in London, Ont., 1984.
Summaries in English and French.
ISBN 0-919216-29-3

1. Geology, Stratigraphic — Quaternary — Congresses.
2. Geology — Great Lakes — Congresses. I. Karrow, P.F.,
1930-   II. Calkin, Parker E. (Parker Emerson, 1933-
III. Geological Association of Canada. IV. Series.

QE696.Q37 1985   551.7′9′0977   C86-093127-7

Geological Association of Canada
Department of Earth Sciences,
Memorial University of Newfoundland,
St. John's, Newfoundland
Canada A1B 3X5

Printed by: Johanns Graphics, Waterloo

The GEOLOGICAL ASSOCIATION OF CANADA is Canada's
national society for the geosciences. It was established in 1947 to
advance geology and its understanding among both professionals
and the general public. The GAC membership of 3000 includes representatives of all geological disciplines from across Canada and
many parts of the world employed in government, industry and
academia. There are specialist divisions for environmental earth sciences, geophysics, mineral deposits, paleontology, Precambrian,
sedimentology, tectonics, and volcanology. Regional sections of
GAC have been set up in Victoria, Vancouver, Edmonton, Winnipeg, and St. John's, and there are affiliated groups in Toronto and
the Maritimes.

GAC activities include the organization and sponsorship of con-
ferences, seminars, short courses, field trips, lecture tours, and stu-
dent and professional awards and grants. The Association publishes
the quarterly journal *Geoscience Canada* and the quarterly newsletter *Geolog,* a *Special Paper* series, Short Course Notes, and several other continuing series. GAC also maintains liaison with other
earth science societies and provides advice to government and the
public on geological issues. The Assoiation was incorporated under
the Canada Corporations Act in January, 1984. For information
contact: Geological Association of Canada, Department of Earth
Sciences, Memorial University of Newfoundland, St. John's, Newfoundland A1B 3X5, Canada.

L'Association géologique du Canada est la société nationale
canadienne pour les sciences de la Terre. Créée en 1947, elle a
comme double objectif de faire progresser la géologie et de sen-
sibiliser les spécialistes et les membres du grand public aux sciences
de la Terre. Ses trois mille membres représentent toutes les disciplines géologiques; ils viennent de toutes les régions du Canada et de
nombreux autres pays; ils oeuvrent dans le secteur public, dans le
secteur industriel et dans le monde universitaire. L'Association
comprend des divisions de spécialistes en géophysique, en gise-
ments minéreaux, en paléontologie, en Précambrien, en sédimen-
tologie, en tectonique, en volcanologie et en sciences de la Terre
touchant à l'environnement. Des sections régionales existent à Victoria, Vancouver, Edmonton, Winnipeg et St. John's, et des groupes
affiliés se sont constitués à Toronto et dans les provinces maritimes.

Les activités de l'Association géologique du Canada comprennent
l'organisation et le parrainage de conférences, de colloques, de
cours de formation de courte durée, de visites sur le terrain et de
tournées de conférences. Elle décerne des octrois et des bourses aux
étudiants et aux personnes qui travaillent dans le domaine des
sciences de la Terre. L'Association publie un journal trimestriel,
Geoscience Canada, et un bulletin trimestriel d'information,
Geolog, une série de mémoires, des notes de cours et diverses autres
séries de publications. Elle assure en outre la liaison avec d'autres
sociétés en sciences de la Terre et fournit des conseils au gouverne-
ment et au grand public sur des questions géologiques. L'Association a été constituée en corporation en janvier 1984, en vertu de la
Loi sur les corporations canadiennes.

Pour renseignements: Association géologique du Canada, Dé-
partment of Earth Sciences, Memorial University of Newfoundland,
St. John's (Terre-Neuve), A1B 3X5, Canada.

CONTENTS

PREFACE

The history of the North American Great Lakes is one of the classic stories of the Quaternary Period, the youngest major interval of geologic time. The five major basins Superior, Michigan, Huron, Erie, and Ontario share a common ancestry in preglacial valleys formed in rocks of contrasting hardness. Topographic relief in the region had a major effect on the patterns of ice flow. The ice margin took on a markedly lobate form, with major projections, or lobes, extending generally southwestward into each of the basins. During the melting of the ice, retreat was down into the basins and generally northeastward, while glacial lakes formed around the margins of the shrinking ice lobes. Overflow channels were frequently replaced by lower outlets as the ice retreated, with drainage reversals during temporary ice readvances. The complex paleogeography resulted in a complex series of interconnected glacial lakes, often shared between basins; commonly a lake in one basin drained into a different lake in another basin. The working out of the relationships between numerous lakes has occupied the attention of many workers for several generations.

While there are reports of studies extending back into the early nineteenth century, there was a major increase in attention to the lake development late in the century, which has lasted more or less up to the present. The complexity of the derived history presents a challenge to the geomorphologist and Earth historian. The effects of the lakes are of concern to engineers and planners dealing with the geological materials of the region, to biogeographers concerned with the dispersal and distribution of plants and animals, and to archeologists, who have followed the migrations and settlements of the Paleo-Indian along the shores of the glacial lakes. The late Indian settlers developed population densities among the highest in the Americas, a condition still evident today with the region's industrialization and numerous cities. Early European explorers were drawn along the Great Lakes waterways, which gave them access to the interior of the continent. The former and present drainage, intimately related to the history of glaciation, profoundly affects commerce in the region today.

The first major synthesis of Great Lakes history was that of Leverett and Taylor in United States Geological Survey Monograph 53 (1915). Early in the period after the development of radiocarbon dating, a revised version was presented by J.L. Hough (Geology of the Great Lakes, 1958). Most recently, D.S. Fullerton has assembled much detailed information, including an assessment of hundreds of radiocarbon dates, into a large chart with notes (U.S.G.S. Prof. Paper 1089, 1980); it did not include the Lake Superior basin. Summary versions appear in most accounts of North American glacial history, such as Flint (1971) and Prest (1970).

The present collection of papers had its inspiration at a symposium on Lake Agassiz held at the annual meeting of the Geological Association of Canada in Winnipeg, Manitoba, in 1982. The papers of that symposium have appeared as G.A.C. Special Paper 26 "Glacial Lake Agassiz" (1983). A sequel symposium on the "Quaternary Evolution of the Great Lakes" was held at the annual meeting in London, Ontario, in 1984. This volume is the result of that symposium.

Papers in this volume are arranged by lake basin, opening with a discussion of the effects and timing of a gift of water to the Great Lakes system from drainage events in Lake Agassiz. Each basin is dealt with first in a summary review paper followed by the results of more recent and more specific studies. This volume has been prepared at a time of renewed controversy about the role of uplift in the region. Readers will note that there are inconsistencies in many events or interpretations. In spite of the efforts of an army of people over more than a century, there is still much to be learned before a consensus is reached. We hope that this volume will stimulate new studies. It is clear from the continuing and the newest controversies that many more reliable basic data are needed — seemingly mundane facts such as accurate shoreline elevations which allow isobase trends to be defined, not to mention the need for many more reliable radiocarbon dates from sites with well-defined stratigraphy. Studies of associated fossils and paleosols need much expansion to yield the full range of paleoenvironmental information. We can therefore say that the future is as bright as ever for the researcher dealing with Great Lakes history.

The preparation of this volume has benefitted greatly from the cooperation of authors, reviewers, and the various persons we worked with in the G.A.C. Publications Committee. We gratefully acknowledge this help, as well as financial support from the Geological Survey of Canada and the Natural Sciences and Engineering Research Council. The Canadian-American Studies Committee of the State University of New York at Buffalo provided funds to help in the editorial process. Pierrette Turcotte undertook the major editing of résumés. We also appreciated the assistance of B.H. Feenstra in organizing and running the meeting sessions in London in May, 1984.

P.F. Karrow
P.E. Calkin

We would also like to thank Patricia Sheahan for preparing an index for this volume.

Quaternary Evolution of the Great Lakes,
edited by P.F. Karrow and P.E. Calkin,
Geological Association of Canada Special Paper 30, 1985

GLACIAL LAKE AGASSIZ
AND ITS INFLUENCE
ON THE GREAT LAKES

James T. Teller

Department of Earth Sciences, University of Manitoba, Winnipeg, Manitoba R3T 2N2

ABSTRACT

Glacial Lake Agassiz came into existence about 11 700 B.P., after ice of the Red River-Des Moines Lobe retreated north of the Hudson Bay-Mississippi River divide, allowing water to be impounded in the Red River valley. During the early Cass and Lockhart Phases, overflow was south into the Mississippi River basin. As ice retreated northward, Lake Agassiz expanded into Manitoba and northwestern Ontario, depositing fine-grained sediment in the offshore, deep-water areas and coarser sediment along the shoreline and at the mouths of rivers along the western side of the basin.

Shortly after 11 000 B.P., lower outlets into the Superior basin were uncovered by retreating ice, and the level of the lake fell in a series of steps, as water poured eastward into the Great Lakes. The resulting low water Moorhead Phase ended about 9900 B.P. as the Marquette glacial advance crossed the Superior basin to the Upper Peninsula of Michigan and again blocked these eastern outlets. Overflow returned to the Mississippi River watershed briefly, but by about 9500 B.P. the eastern outlets into the Superior basin had again become ice free, initiating the Nipigon Phase. Water levels fell abruptly at this time, and a series of catastrophic bursts, each of which released up to 4000 km³ of water in less than a year or two, flooded through the Nipigon basin to Lake Superior. By 8500 B.P., ice had retreated far enough to allow Lake Agassiz to overflow across northern Ontario into Lake Ojibway, by-passing the Great Lakes.

The influence of Lake Agassiz overflow on the Great Lakes lasted from 10 900 to 8500 B.P., except for a few hundred years around the time of the Marquette glacial advance at 9900 B.P. Sedimentation in the Superior basin probably was most affected by this overflow, and much of the upper grey clay there may reflect the 1000-year-long Nipigon Phase. A brief period of spillover from the Superior basin at 10 900 to 10 800 B.P. carried Lake Agassiz waters into the Michigan basin. Although the Lake Agassiz overflow spilled mainly from the Superior basin into the Huron basin, the sediment record in the main Huron basin suggests that it must have been largely confined to the North Channel (north of Manitoulin Island) before overflowing through the North Bay outlet to the Ottawa River valley. Lake Agassiz water that reached the Huron basin prior to the opening of the North Bay outlet, between about 10 900 to 10 500 B.P., may have overflowed into the Erie basin through Lake Algonquin.

RÉSUMÉ

Le lac glaciaire Agassiz s'est formé vers 11 700 B.P. après que la glace du lobe de la rivière Rouge et du lobe de Des Moines a retraité au nord de la ligne de partage des eaux entre la baie d'Hudson et le fleuve Mississippi. Ceci a permis aux eaux du lac de s'endiguer dans la vallée de la rivière Rouge. Au début des phases Cass et Lockhart, les eaux débordaient vers le sud jusqu'au bassin du fleuve Mississippi. Tandis que la glace reculait vers le nord, le lac Agassiz s'étendait à l'intérieur du Manitoba et dans le nord-ouest ontarien déposant des sédiments fins en eaux profondes et des sédiments plus grossiers le long du littoral et à l'embouchure des rivières situées du côté ouest du bassin.

Peu de temps après 11 000 B.P., la glace, en reculant, a libéré des exutoires plus bas dans le bassin du lac Supérieur. Ainsi, alors que les eaux se déversaient vers l'est jusqu'aux Grands Lacs, le niveau du lac baissait graduellement. Ce niveau d'eau basse, la phase Moorhead, s'est terminé vers 9900 B.P. à l'époque où l'avancée glaciaire de Marquette franchissait le bassin du lac Supérieur pour s'immobiliser sur la haute péninsule de lac Michigan, bloquant ainsi les exutoires à l'est. Ce n'est que vers 9500 B.P. que les eaux lacustres se déverseront de nouveau vers l'est après une brève période de drainage vers le bassin du Mississippi. C'est en effet à cette période que les exutoires de l'est se libéraient de la glace, inaugurant ainsi la phase Nipigon. A ce moment, le niveau des eaux a baissé brusquement et une série de torrents catastrophiques, chacun pouvant libérer quelques 4000 km³ d'eau en moins d'un ou deux ans, inondaient périodiquement l'étendue du bassin Nipigon jusqu'au lac Supérieur. Pas plus tard que 8500 ans B.P. la glace reculait assez profondément pour permettre au lac Agassiz de déborder dans le nord de l'Ontario atteignant le lac Ojibway en contournant les Grands Lacs.

L'influence qu'a eu le débordement du lac Agassiz sur les Grands Lacs s'est fait sentir tout au cours de la période entre 10 900 et 8500 B.P., à l'exception de quelques centaines d'années durant l'avancée glaciaire de Marquette. Ce débordement a sans doute eu un effet très marqué sur la sédimentation dans le bassin du lac Supérieur et l'argile grise qui est présente dans les couches supérieures appartient probablement au millénaire de la phase Nipigon. Entre 10 900 et 10 800 ans B.P. on constate une brève période de débordement du lac Supérieur durant laquelle les eaux du lac Agassiz étaient dirigées vers le bassin du lac Michigan. Quoique la majeure partie des eaux de débordement du lac Supérieur aient été dirigées vers le bassin du lac Huron, la colonne sédimentaire dans le principal bassin huronien indique que cet envahissement s'est effectué en très grande partie par le canal Nord (au nord de l'île Manitoulin) pour ensuite se déverser dans la vallée de l'Outaouais par l'exutoire de North Bay. L'eau du lac Agassiz qui a atteint le bassin du lac Huron avant l'ouverture de l'exutoire de North Bay a inondé le bassin du lac Érié par le lac Algonquin.

INTRODUCTION

During the retreat of late Wisconsinan ice from North America, there were six Great Lakes. These lakes, from Lake Agassiz in the west to Lake Ontario in the east, linked together the drainage of more than half a continent. Meltwater entering Lake Agassiz from the glacial margin of central Canada, which extended more than 1800 km from the Rocky Mountains of Alberta to Lake Superior, inundated a total of nearly 1 000 000 km² in Manitoba, Saskatchewan, Ontario, North and South Dakota, and Minnesota (Fig. 1). The area of the Lake Agassiz drainage basin exceeded 2 000 000 km², which is three times the drainage area of all the modern Great Lakes.

Lake Agassiz depended on the Laurentide ice sheet for its existence, forming whenever rivers of central Canada that flowed toward Hudson Bay were dammed by glacial ice. Fluctuations in the areal extent of the ice controlled the size and depth of glacial Lake Agassiz, not only by providing the northern and eastern borders to the lake throughout most of its history, but also by influencing isostasy and outlet availability.

The history of this lake, the distribution of its sediments, and its role in influencing regional climate, deglaciation, and the other Great Lakes is complex. Over its 4000-year late Wisconsinan history, the lake spanned more than 12° of latitude and 16° of longitude, intercepting water and sediment discharge from most of the western Hudson Bay watershed, including that derived from the western Laurentide ice sheet. For part of its history, overflow from the lake was south via the Minnesota and Mississippi River valleys to the Gulf of Mexico; at other times, overflow was east through the Great Lakes system to the St. Lawrence valley and the North Atlantic Ocean.

The history of glacial Lake Agassiz, the largest but shortest-lived of the Great Lakes, is summarized in this paper. Although we are only beginning to recognize the effect of the thousands of cubic kilometres of water that, in only a few years, overflowed into the other Great Lakes, an understanding of the nature and timing of the link between Lake Agassiz and all other lakes "downstream" is essential for an understanding of the system as a whole and of its component parts.

SUMMARY OF LAKE AGASSIZ HISTORY

Introduction

Whenever ice in the Hudson Bay basin dammed the rivers of central Canada, water flooded the lowlands across northern Manitoba and Ontario. This must have occurred dozens of times during the Quaternary, although the stratigraphic record throughout the region is so incomplete and discontinuous that the actual number of lake events, like the actual number of glaciations, probably never will be known. Overflow from the proglacial lake initially may have been eastward around the ice in northern Ontario, perhaps at first to James Bay, but eventually would have been directed southeastward to the Ottawa River valley and into the St. Lawrence. As ice advanced south to the continental divide between the Hudson Bay and St. Lawrence watersheds, north of Lake Superior, the level of this proglacial lake rose, inundating increasingly higher elevations to the south. Overflow into Lake Superior was initiated at this time, and continued until the outlets to that basin were closed by advancing ice. Once a glacial barrier covered northwestern Ontario, all waters from the Hudson Bay basin flowed south into the Mississippi River watershed, rather than east into the Great Lakes. Eventually, ice pushed south over the divide between the Hudson Bay and Mississippi basins, which extended across North Dakota and Minnesota, displacing all water impounded north of the divide. Until the glacial margin retreated north again, meltwater and normal runoff from central Canada discharged to the Gulf of Mexico.

The progressive evolution in the distribution of proglacial waters during glacier buildup and expansion applies not only to late Wisconsinan events that began, perhaps, 25 000 years ago, but also to the early phases of all Quaternary glaciations. Likewise, the proglacial lake phases in the Hudson Bay watershed that developed during the retreating phase of continental glaciation, and which are described in the following sections, may be applicable, at least in a general way, to all Quaternary glaciations.

Early Phases

After the maximum advance of late Wisconsinan ice into central Iowa at 14 000 B.P. (Ruhe, 1969), the margin of the Des Moines Lobe began to retreat northward toward the Lake Agassiz basin, which probably had been filled with ice for more than 10 000 years. The retreat was rapid, but was interrupted many times by surging of the Red River and James River lobes southward through the lowlands of the Red River valley (Clayton and Moran, 1982; Fenton *et al.*, 1983; Clayton *et al.*, 1985). At times during the earliest retreat phases, these surges completely displaced the newly

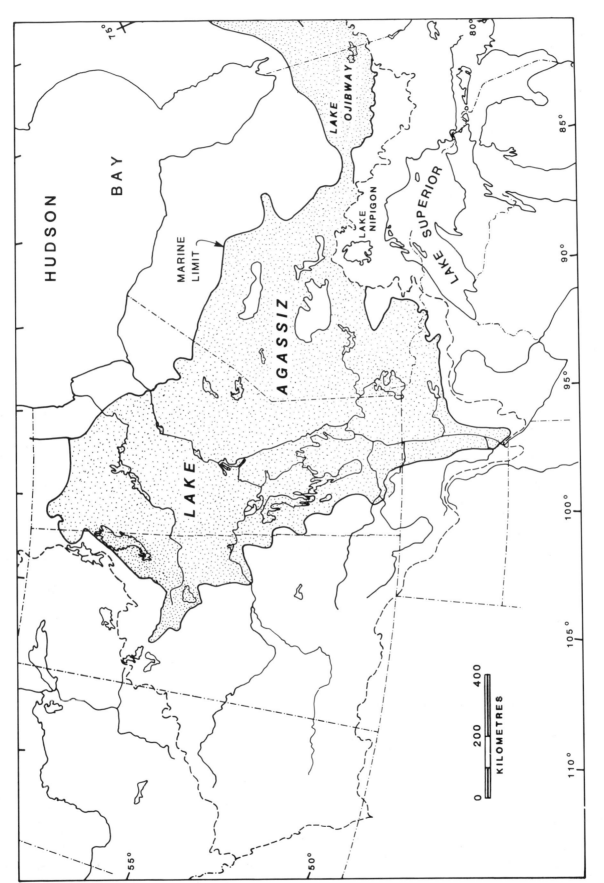

Figure 1. Total area above sea level covered by Lake Agassiz during all post-glacial phases (after Teller *et al*., 1983). Outline of the Lake Agassiz and Lake Ojibway drainage basins is shown by the dashed line (Teller and Thorleifson, 1983).

formed proglacial lake at the southern end of the Lake Agassiz basin, thus aborting the establishment of a "permanent" body of water (Fig. 2). This see-saw battle between ice and water – in which at least six surges, advancing at more than 2 km/yr, were driven back north by rapid calving and melting (Clayton et al., 1985) – progressively shifted northward until the southern part of the basin became permanently ice free. By about 11 700 B.P., Lake Agassiz was established in the southern end of the basin (Fig. 3).

The initial phases of Lake Agassiz, referred to as the Cass Phase and Lockhart Phase, overflowed south into the valley of the Minnesota River and then to the Mississippi River at Minneapolis, although a brief period of eastward overflow along the glacial margin toward Duluth, Minnesota, may have occurred initially (Hobbs, 1983; Fenton et al., 1983, Fig. 7c). By 11 500 B.P., ice in the Red River valley had wasted north at least to the International Boundary. Following several more surges down the axis of the Red River valley, the glacial margin retreated into central Manitoba (Fig. 4); Lake Agassiz now stretched 700 km from its northern boundary to the southern (River Warren) outlet, whose elevation was being lowered by erosion (Matsch, 1983). Beaches formed along the margins of this rapidly changing body of water, although we now realize that the simple model of strandline formation, such as described by Upham (1895) and Johnston (1946), is not fully applicable to the complexities associated with a pulsating ice margin (Fenton et al., 1983).

During the Cass and Lockhart Phases, silty clay was deposited in the deeper, offshore areas of the lake; in places, this sediment contains ice-rafted clasts. The thick lacustrine units associated with this period of Lake Agassiz history, when the lake was overflowing into the Mississippi River basin, have been described in detail in many publications (e.g., Moran, 1972; Harris et al., 1974; Teller, 1976; Arndt, 1977; Teller and Fenton, 1980) and have been summarized in Clayton and Moran (1982) and Fenton et al. (1983). Coarser-grained underflow fans were built along the western side of the lake basin – mainly off the mouths of the Sheyenne, Pembina-Souris, and Assiniboine Rivers (Brophy and Bluemle, 1983; Kehew and Clayton, 1983; Klassen, 1983a) – where runoff from precipitation and glacial melting from much of central Canada entered the lake.

Moorhead Phase

Shortly after 11 000 B.P., the Lockhart Phase came to an end as the glacial margin wasted north of Thunder Bay, Ontario, allowing Lake Agassiz to overflow eastward into Lake Superior and drop below the level of the southern outlet. A series of still lower outlets, just west of the Nipigon basin, were opened as ice retreated farther north, and the level of Lake Agassiz fell in a series of steps as water discharged through the Nipigon basin to Lake Superior.

According to Clayton (1983), water in the largely ice-free Superior basin initially overflowed into Lake Michigan. During most of this phase, however, Lake Superior was near the Minong level, and overflow was eastward past Sault Ste. Marie to Lake Huron (Drexler et al., 1983; Clayton, 1983).

Once Lake Agassiz began to overflow eastward into Lake

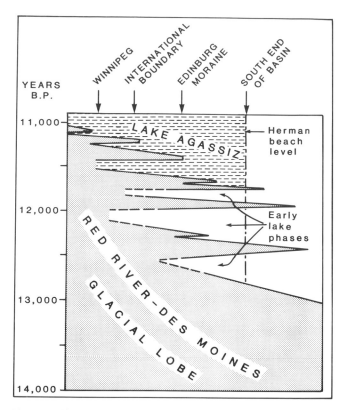

Figure 2. Fluctuations in the retreating margin of the Red River-Des Moines Lobe, showing the development of Lake Agassiz in the southern end of the basin during the Cass and Lockhart Phases, 11 700 to 10 900 B.P. All glacial and lacustrine events are based on lithostratigraphic units. After Fenton et al. (1983).

Superior, initiating the Moorhead Phase, its level rapidly declined, exposing much of the lake floor in the southern part of the basin by 10 500 B.P. Buried fluvial sediment on the floor of the lake occurs as far north as the International Boundary (Arndt, 1977), and a pedogenic horizon in the Lake Manitoba basin (Teller and Last, 1981, 1982) indicates that the lake could not have been deeper than 20 m at Winnipeg during the lowest level of the Moorhead Phase (Fig. 5); thus, there was a decrease in depth of more than 150 m in only a few hundred years. In northwestern Ontario, an unconformity developed on the previously deposited lacustrine sediment (Johnston, 1915; Elson, 1967) and fluvial and organic matter accumulated in places on this subaerially exposed surface.

The details of overflow through the eastern outlets into Lake Superior at this time are not well known, mainly because the record there has been destroyed by later glacial and fluvial events. Water first spilled over the continental divide through the Kashabowie-Seine channel west of Thunder Bay (Teller and Thorleifson, 1983). The Dog River channel, about 40 km to the north, may also have carried part of this early Moorhead Phase overflow (Elson, 1967; Teller and Thorleifson, 1983). Continued ice wastage uncovered the lower elevations west of Lake Nipigon, more than 100 km to the north, allowing overflow to spill into the Nipigon basin and then south to the Superior basin. As described by Thorleifson (1983) and summarized in Teller and Thorleifson (1983), establishing which of the five channel complexes west of Lake Nipigon carried overflow is dependent on knowing their elevations during the Moorhead Phase, which are a function of how much isostatic rebound had occurred by this time. In brief, if there had been substantial crustal rebound of the eastern outlet area, it would have been necessary for the northern, lower channels to carry overflow in order for lake levels to have fallen enough to expose the floor of the Lake Agassiz basin over such a large region to the west (Fig. 5). If crustal rebound had been less, the glacial margin would not have had to retreat as far north to uncover

outlets that were low enough to allow this to occur. Although numerous beaches must have formed around the margins of Lake Agassiz as its level declined during the Moorhead Phase, most of those described and shown by Upham (1895), Johnston (1946), Elson (1967), and Teller and Thorleifson (1983) probably were formed during the later, Nipigon Phase of the lake's history; most Moorhead Phase strandlines were probably destroyed by subsequent fluctuations in the level of the lake.

Emerson Phase

Ice readvanced across the region about 9900 B.P., pushing

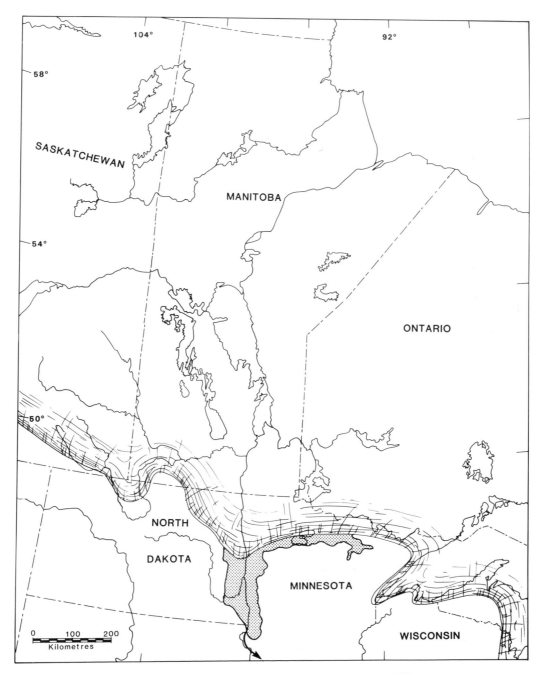

Figure 3. Lake Agassiz, about 11 600 B.P. After Clayton (1983).

across the Lake Superior basin into Michigan, and closing the eastern outlets of Lake Agassiz. The time of this (Marquette) advance is well dated in both the Lake Superior basin, where wood is buried by glacial sediment (e.g., Drexler *et al.*, 1983; Clayton, 1983), and in the Lake Agassiz basin, where wood and peat on the Moorhead Phase unconformity are buried by lacustrine sediment (e.g., Elson, 1967; Clayton and Moran, 1982; Fenton *et al.*, 1983).

Lake Agassiz rose at least to the Campbell level and began again to overflow through the southern outlet toward the Gulf of Mexico (Fig. 6). The lake covered about 350 000 km² at this time. Silty clay of the Sherack Formation and its

correlatives was deposited over the older lacustrine sediment and the Moorhead Phase unconformity (Harris *et al.*, 1974; Teller, 1976; Fenton *et al.*, 1983; Teller and Last, 1982). All of these sediments are grey, and are distinct from the interlaminated red clays that were deposited in the eastern part of the basin during this time, when a proglacial lake (Lake Kam) overflowed from the Superior basin into Lake Agassiz (Rittenhouse, 1934; Antevs, 1951; Zoltai, 1961, 1965; Elson, 1967; Teller and Thorleifson, 1983; Fig. 6 and 7).

Saarnisto (1974, 1975) reviews the evidence for time of retreat of ice from the Superior basin, including a number of

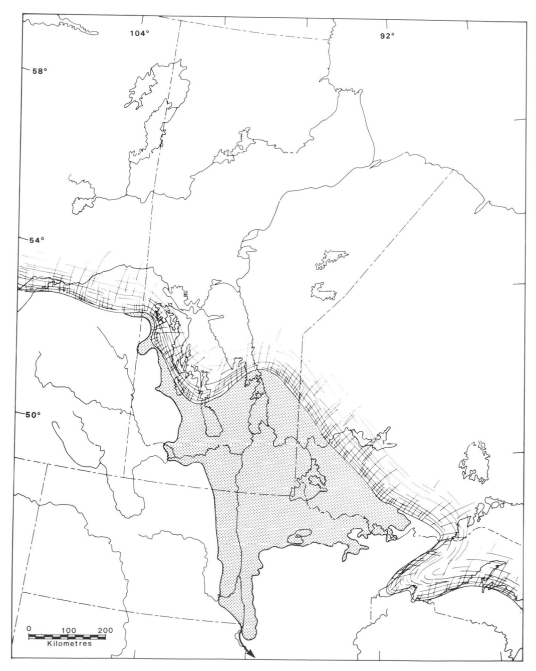

Figure 4. Lake Agassiz, about 11 000 B.P. After Teller *et al.* (1983) and Clayton (1983).

radiocarbon dates between 9000 and 9400 B.P. along the north shore of the basin, and concludes, as had Zoltai (1965) and Elson (1967), that the eastern outlets from Lake Agassiz reopened by about 9500 B.P. This ended the Emerson Phase.

Nipigon Phase

The level of Lake Agassiz declined rapidly, in a series of steps, as progressively lower outlets west of the Nipigon basin were undammed. In a span of a thousand years, between about 9500 and 8500 B.P., the lake fell nearly 200 m from the lower Campbell level where it stood at the start of the Nipigon Phase, to the Gimli level which is the lowest beach formed by Lake Agassiz when it overflowed into Lake Superior via the Nipigon basin. Thorleifson (1983) details the use of these channels and their interrelationship with the glacial margin and crustal rebound during the Nipigon Phase.

The canyons through which the lake drained during this time and the boulder alluvium deposited by this overflow are described by Teller and Thorleifson (1983) and Thorleifson (1983). Their calculations indicate that discharges through each of a series of 17 channel complexes commonly exceeded 100 000 m^{3}s^{-1}, resulting in very rapid declines in lake level before equilibrium outflow was established; more than

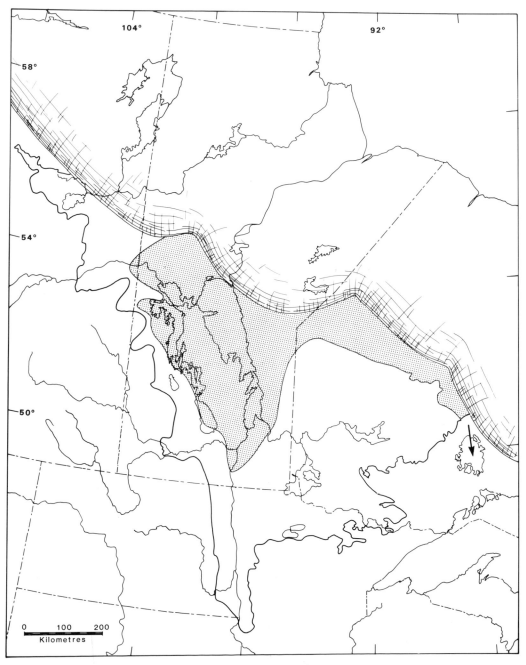

Figure 5. Lake Agassiz, about 10 200 B.P.

20 new strandlines were built, probably in only a few decades each, during these stable (equilibrium) lake levels. These catastrophic bursts of overflow resulted from periodic failure of the ice dam that lay west of Lake Nipigon over the divide between the Lake Agassiz-Lake Superior basins (Teller, 1981; Teller and Thorleifson, 1983).

The volume of some of these catastrophic bursts exceeded 3000 km³, about seven times the present volume of Lake Erie. If there had been no overflow from the Lake Superior basin at these times, the depth of water in that basin would have risen by more than 36 m. Given that the spillways from Lake Superior to the Mississippi River (the Brule and Portage channels) and into the Lake Michigan basin (Huron Mountain channels) were well above the level of the lake at this time (Clayton, 1983), all overflow must have been eastward to Lake Huron by Sault Ste. Marie and east through the North Bay outlet to the Ottawa River valley (Prest, 1970).

Calculations by Teller and Thorleifson (1983) indicate that each time a new, lower outlet through the Nipigon basin to the Superior basin became free of ice, it took less than two years for Lake Agassiz to fall from one level to another. Thus, during the Nipigon Phase, more than 20 bursts of overflow, estimated to have varied from 500 to 4000 km³ each, entered the Lake Superior basin near Thunder Bay. Equilibrium flow from Lake Agassiz to Superior, roughly estimated to have averaged 50 000 m³s⁻¹ (Teller and Thor-

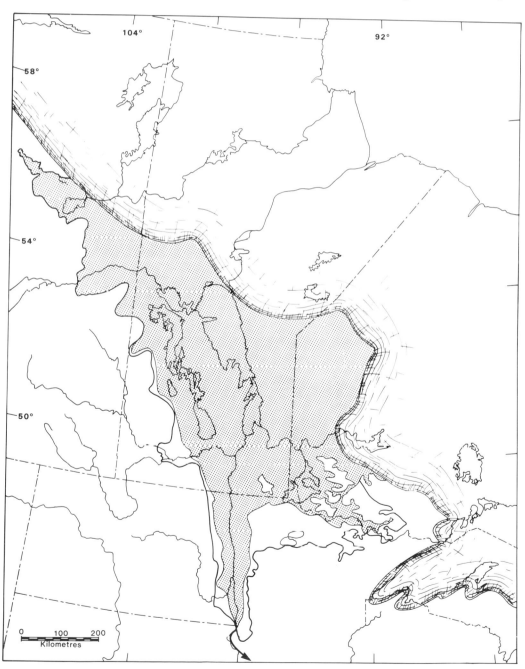

Figure 6. Lake Agassiz, about 9900 B.P. After Teller *et al.* (1983).

leifson, 1983), probably lasted only a few decades before another, still lower overflow channel was opened, allowing another flood of water to spill into the Superior basin.

By about 8500 B.P., ice had retreated north of the Nipigon basin and the divide between the Superior and Hudson Bay (Lake Agassiz) watersheds. The Nipigon Phase came to an end when Lake Agassiz overflow no longer discharged into the Superior basin, but instead bypassed the Great Lakes along the glacial margin in northern Ontario before flowing into the St. Lawrence through the Ottawa River valley (Prest, 1970; Vincent and Hardy, 1979).

Ojibway Phase

After Lake Agassiz overflow was directed toward the east into proglacial Lake Ojibway (Fig. 1), about 8500 B.P., there appears to have been no further discharge of water from the 2 000 000 km² watershed of Lake Agassiz into any of the Great Lakes. Overflow from the western Great Lakes, which drained from Lake Huron through the North Bay outlet, joined with overflow from the combined Lake Agassiz-Lake Ojibway system, and discharged down the Ottawa River valley, entering the St. Lawrence valley at Montreal (e.g., Prest, 1970; Vincent and Hardy, 1979).

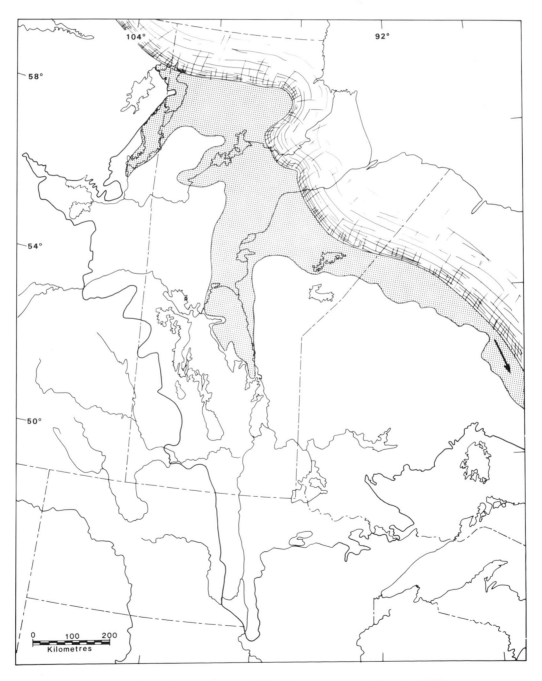

Figure 7. Lake Agassiz, about 8300 B.P. In part from Klassen (1983b).

By this time Lake Agassiz had receded from its southern basin and was considerably reduced in size from its maximum of about 350 000 km² during the Emerson Phase. The glacial margin now lay across northeastern Manitoba and northern Ontario, with Lake Agassiz occupying the deglaciated Hudson Bay lowlands and adjacent lowlands along its edge (Fig. 7). By about 7700 B.P., Lake Agassiz had begun "to drain into the Tyrrell Sea via channels beneath and around the now stagnant Hudson lobe" (Klassen, 1983b, p. 111). Vincent and Hardy (1979) indicate that Lake Ojibway began to discharge north into the Tyrrell Sea (near James Bay) about 7900 B.P. The final drainage of Lake Agassiz occurred about 7500 B.P. (Klassen, 1983b).

INFLUENCE OF LAKE AGASSIZ ON THE OTHER GREAT LAKES

Introduction

The history of eastward overflow from Lake Agassiz is important to our understanding of late glacial events in the Great Lakes. Furthermore, deposition in the Mississippi River delta may have been influenced by overflow from Lake Agassiz. The previous sections described the interrelationship of glacial and lacustrine events in the Lake Agassiz basin. Figure 8 summarizes the chronology of overflow into the Mississippi River, Great Lakes, and St. Lawrence valley.

Although it is apparent that the catastrophic bursts of overflow from Lake Agassiz, as well as the normal, equilibrium overflow, must have influenced sedimentation in some of the Great Lakes basins, much work remains to be done in order to clearly identify the role of this water. In fact, only very recently has it been recognized that Lake Agassiz contributed volumes of water to the Great Lakes that were large in proportion to the masses of water in these basins. For example, the volume of a 3000 km³ Lake Agassiz flood would have been more than 20% of the total volume of water in the Superior basin at the Minong level and even greater than the volume in the Huron basin at this time.

A full evaluation of the influence of Lake Agassiz on the other Great Lakes is not possible at this time. Such an evaluation would require synthesizing the data from six great lakes and their surrounding watersheds. Correlation is a problem because this interrelated system spans half a continent and because radiocarbon dates are scarce throughout much of this region. Paleomagnetic correlation of off-shore sediments may prove helpful (Mothersill, 1983, 1984; Johnson and Fields, 1984).

In the following sections I only attempt to identify some of the effects in the Great Lakes that may have resulted from Lake Agassiz overflow. Although overflow must have occurred repeatedly throughout the Pleistocene − whenever ice impounded water in the lowlands of central Canada and the U.S. − there is little record of these events in the region. My speculations on the link between west and east will be confined to the last episode of deglaciation between about 11 700 B.P. and 7500 B.P. If this serves to promote discussion, stir controversy, or to encourage Great Lakes researchers to look west, I will have accomplished my goal.

Lake Superior Basin

The basin most influenced by overflow from glacial Lake Agassiz was the Lake Superior basin. Although there have been a number of major studies on this basin, the nature of its sedimentary record and the chronology of events are still not well known.

Clearly, the Moorhead and Nipigon phases of Lake Agassiz, 10 900 to 9900 B.P. and 9500 to 8500 B.P. (Fig. 8), respectively, have been important in the sedimentary history of Lake Superior. Lake levels must have risen abruptly during each catastrophic burst of overflow from Lake Agassiz − when an additional thousand or more cubic kilometres of water were introduced to the basin in only a few years − and then have fallen once equilibrium flow between the two basins was resumed. Controlling the rise in level of Lake Superior during most of these floods would have been the overflow channel at Sault Ste. Marie. Shoreline sedimentation, as well as offshore sedimentation, would have been affected by both the change in water level and the influx of sediment during the flood. The complexities of shoreline development (e.g., Farrand, 1960; Drexler, 1981), which are partly a result of isostasy, glacial margin position elsewhere in the Great Lakes, and the natural destructive action of lake level rises on former shorelines, preclude a discussion of strandline development as related to Lake Agassiz in this paper. In general terms, water in the Superior basin must have been well below the Duluth level, near the Minong level, during Moorhead Phase overflow from Lake Agassiz (Clayton, 1983). During the later, Nipigon Phase overflow, Lake Superior levels were normally at or below the Minong (Drexler et al., 1983; Clayton, 1983), eventually falling to the Houghton lower level by about 8500 B.P. (Farrand, 1960).

A number of cores from the offshore regions of Lake Superior have penetrated sediment deposited during the late glacial and early postglacial period (e.g., Farrand, 1969a,b; Dell, 1972, 1974; Mothersill and Fung, 1972; Maher, 1977; Mothersill, 1979). The typical sequence of lacustrine sediment overlies red till of the last glaciation. Farrand (1969a,b), Mothersill and Fung (1972), and Dell (1972, 1974) describe this sequence as follows:

> brown silt and clay
> grey clay (non-laminated)
> grey clay varves
> red clay varves
> red clay and silt (laminated)
> red till

Beneath the red till is a complex of red lacustrine and glacial sediment in some parts of the basin.

If we assume that the red till represents the Marquette glaciation, which crossed the basin to the Upper Peninsula of Michigan about 9900 B.P., then the basal red lacustrine units must have been deposited sometime after this ice had retreated back north, perhaps beginning as early as 9800 B.P. Farrand (1969a,b) suggests that the gradual upward transition from red to grey varves, with the grey colour making its first appearance in the coarser part of the couplet, indicates that a new source of grey sediment had become available. This transition may be related to the influx of meltwater from glaciers depositing grey calcareous till along the north

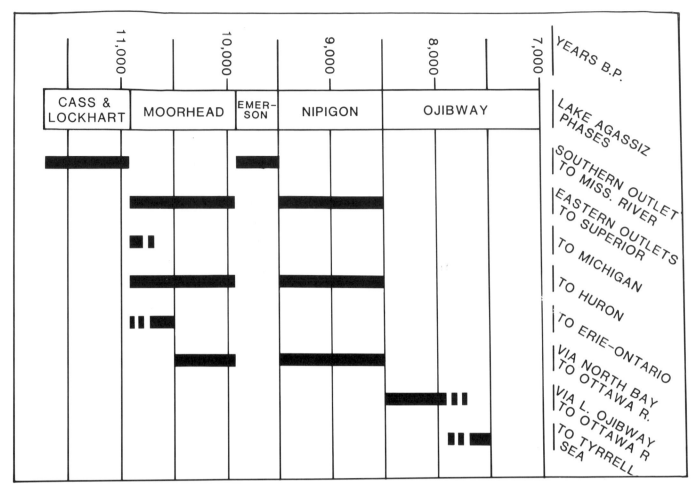

Figure 8. Routing of overflow from glacial Lake Agassiz.

shore of the lake (Farrand, 1969a; Dell, 1972, 1974) or to the first influence of overflow from Lake Agassiz, or both. If it took less than 300 years to deposit the dominantly red clays and silts, as Farrand (1969a) suggests, then the dominating influence of the grey, northern source, materials began about 9500 B.P.

The "varved" nature of the red and grey clays may not be strictly a function of seasonality (in the sense that the fine-grained laminae formed below a frozen surface of Lake Superior and the coarse-grained laminae formed during the ice-free season), but of periodic influxes of Lake Agassiz overflow and, possibly, glacial meltwater. Of course, discharge from Lake Agassiz may have varied on a seasonal basis, but was interrupted from time to time by bursts of overflow as new outlets became ice free.

In my interpretation, the end of "varve" deposition and the start of non-laminated sedimentation coincided with the end of the Nipigon Phase of Lake Agassiz overflow into the Superior basin, about 8500 years ago. On the basis of paleomagnetic chronology, Mothersill (1984) has dated the top of the "varved" sequence at 8200 B.P. The sedimentation rate in the Superior basin since this time has been markedly lower (Farrand, 1969a; Mothersill and Fung, 1972; Maher, 1977).

Lake Huron Basin

Throughout most of its postglacial history, Lake Superior overflowed into Lake Huron via the St. Marys River at Sault Ste. Marie. Therefore, notable hydrological events in the Superior basin would have influenced sedimentation in the Huron basin and its overflow channels.

During the Moorhead and Nipigon Phases of Lake Agassiz, a large continuous volume of overflow, punctuated by periodic bursts of catastrophic discharge, entered Lake Superior and passed east into Lake Huron (Fig. 8). Most overflow was northeastward through the North Bay outlet to the Ottawa River valley (e.g., Leverett and Taylor, 1915; Prest, 1970), although overflow during the early Moorhead Phase of Lake Agassiz (11 000 to 10 500 B.P.), which corresponds to the late Algonquin phase in the Huron basin, probably was south into Lake Erie through the Port Huron outlet (Karrow et al., 1975) (Fig. 8). Throughout the Nipigon Phase (9500 to 8500 B.P.), when Lake Agassiz overflowed into the Great Lakes, water levels in the Huron basin were low and water occupied only the deeper parts of the basin (Hough, 1962; Prest, 1970; Lewis and Anderson, 1984). The water level in the Huron basin probably began to fall about 10 500 B.P. (Karrow et al., 1975), reaching its low water Stanley Phase (Hough, 1955) by 9500 B.P. (Saarnisto, 1975;

Wayne and Zumberg, 1965). As isostatic rebound raised the northern side of the basin, water gradually deepened (the "Nipissing transgression") until it "rose above the Sault Ste. Marie threshold about 7000 B.P. and waters in the Superior basin were drowned to the same common level" (Saarnisto, 1975, p. 318). A return to overflow through the southern, Port Huron, outlet began well after the end of Lake Agassiz influx, perhaps about 5500 B.P. (Lewis, 1969; Eschman and Karrow, 1985; Anderson and Lewis, 1985).

The sequence of offshore sediment in the western Huron basin was described by Hough (1955, 1962) as follows:

> buff clay
> grey clay (laminated)
> red clay (laminated)
> red clay, with zones of fine sand and silt
> red clay, with grey colour bands
> red till

In cores from depths of less than 70 m from the lake's present surface, there is an unconformity between the red and grey clay, and the upper part of the normal deep-water red clay is occasionally missing. A thin zone of sand and pebbles generally overlies this unconformity, which Hough (1962) interpreted as reflecting the low-water Stanley Phase.

Even though the impact of overflow from Lake Agassiz, which periodically introduced 500 to 4000 km^3 bursts of water into the western end of Lake Superior, must have been diminished by the time it crossed the Superior basin and passed through the St. Marys River outlet, the sedimentary record in the Huron basin should reflect these events. It is possible, however, that much of the influx from Lake Superior may have bypassed the main Huron basin during the Stanley low-water Phase, spilling mainly into North Channel (north of Manitoulin Island) before exiting northeastward through the North Bay outlet.

If the unconformity between the red and grey clay does represent the break in sedimentation during the Stanley Phase in the main Huron basin, then the coarser grey-coloured units in the underlying red clay may reflect flood events during the Moorhead Phase of Lake Agassiz. In this interpretation, the overflow from Lake Agassiz during the younger, Nipigon Phase would have influenced the grey clay sequence. If overflow into the Huron basin during the Stanley Phase was confined to the North Channel until differential rebound allowed discharge into the main basin, this influence would have been minimal, perhaps only occurring during major Lake Agassiz floods. The absence of any distinctive coarse units in the laminated grey clay in the western part of the main basin (Hough, 1955; 1962) suggests that Lake Agassiz waters may have by-passed the main basin at this time.

Lake Michigan Basin

By 11 000 B.P., ice had retreated from the Lake Michigan basin (e.g., Saarnisto, 1974) and from the other Great Lakes' basins everywhere east of Lake Superior (Mickelson et al., 1983). By about 10 900 B.P., the glacial margin along the northwestern side of the Superior basin had retreated far enough to allow overflow from Lake Agassiz and initiation of the Moorhead Phase.

During the early part of the Moorhead Phase, when the level of Lake Superior was highest, water may have briefly spilled south into the Lake Michigan basin (Clayton, 1983). In only a few years, however, water in the Superior basin fell below the threshold level and all overflow went eastward into the Huron basin (Fig. 8). At about this time, outflow from the Michigan basin, which had previously been south through the Chicago outlet, shifted to the Mackinac channel and into the Huron basin, initiating the Chippewa low water phase (e.g., Prest, 1970); the interrelationship of events in these lake basins at this time, however, is very complex, as noted by Fullerton (1980).

The push of ice across the Superior basin during the Marquette advance, about 9900 B.P., again closed the eastern outlets of Lake Agassiz. Although meltwater and overflow from proglacial lakes must have discharged south into the Michigan basin when this ice lay across the Upper Peninsula of Michigan, water levels in the Superior basin had fallen below these spillways by the time the eastern outlets of Lake Agassiz were re-opened during the Nipigon Phase. Thus, only during the early Moorhead Phase of Lake Agassiz, shortly after 11 000 B.P., did water from Lake Agassiz enter the Michigan basin.

Many cores from Lake Michigan have been studied and interpreted (e.g., Hough, 1958; Lineback et al., 1972; Wickham et al., 1978). Lineback et al. (1979) propose that the grey "varved" clays of the Superior basin, which I have interpreted as being related to Lake Agassiz influx during the Nipigon Phase, 9500 to 8500 B.P., are equivalent to the Wilmette Bed of the Lake Michigan Formation. This bed is also a grey clay, confined largely to the deeper part of the basin, and is underlain and overlain by red lacustrine sediment. The top of the Wilmette Bed is marked by "one of the major sedimentological discontinuities in the Lake Michigan Formation" and is overlain by clays reworked during a regressive phase of Lake Michigan "as the water level dropped toward the Chippewa low stage" (Lineback et al., 1979, p. 790). If the red till below the grey "varved" clay in the Superior basin was deposited during the Marquette advance, 9900 to 9500 B.P., then these "varves" cannot be correlated with the Wilmette Bed because water levels apparently were not high enough to overflow from the Superior basin into the Michigan basin at that time (Clayton, 1983). Although the Wilmette Bed may correlate with overflow from the Superior basin, either it is related to the brief high-water level in that basin shortly after 11 000 B.P. (at which time Lake Agassiz may have contributed water at the start of the Moorhead Phase) or to water related to the Marquette advance about 9900 B.P. (at which time there was no contribution from Lake Agassiz). Drexler et al. (1983) believe the Wilmette Bed was deposited between 11 000 and 10 000 B.P., during deglaciation of the Upper Peninsula.

Any influence of Lake Agassiz waters on the sediments of the Michigan basin probably was minor, and even Lake Superior waters must not have strongly affected sedimentation. Although the grey Wilmette Bed may reflect this influence, other beds of the Lake Michigan Formation, grey or red, may represent overflow from the Superior basin.

Lake Erie and Ontario Basins

Once the North Bay outlet from Lake Huron was opened at about 10 500 B.P. (Karrow *et al.*, 1975), all overflow from the Huron, Michigan, Superior, and Agassiz basins was directed northeastward to the Ottawa River valley and into the St. Lawrence valley, thus by-passing the Erie and Ontario basins. Because Lake Agassiz first overflowed into the Superior basin during the Moorhead Phase, which began shortly after 11 000 B.P., it was only between this time and the opening of the North Bay outlet at 10 500 B.P. that water from Lake Agassiz could have spilled through the Port Huron outlet into Lake Erie (Fig. 8). In turn, water from the Erie basin overflowed into the Ontario basin and to the Champlain Sea in the St. Lawrence Valley.

The level of water in the Erie basin may have declined after the North Bay outlet was opened (Lewis, 1969; Coakley and Lewis, 1985), gradually rising during the next several thousand years as a result of crustal rebound (e.g., Calkin and Feenstra, 1985). The Ontario basin also experienced a period of reduced water supply after the North Bay outlet was opened, although this was superposed on an overall rising trend that followed the post-Lake Iroquois low-water phase about 11 400 B.P. (Anderson and Lewis, 1985).

The influence of Lake Agassiz, during the brief period between about 10 900 and 10 500 B.P. when its waters may have drained through the Erie and Ontario basins, probably was small. Although the catastrophic bursts of overflow from Lake Agassiz were several times the volume of water in the Erie and Ontario basins, the impact of such a flood, more than a thousand kilometres to the west in the drainage system, would have been greatly attenuated by the time it reached the Erie basin. Nevertheless, discharge from the Huron basin would have increased and there may be some indication of this period of Lake Agassiz overflow in the sedimentary record of the Erie and Ontario basins.

The Champlain Sea

Studies of molluscs, ostracods, and foraminifera in sediments of the Champlain Sea have allowed the identification of several paleoenvironmental episodes (Elson, 1969; Fillon and Hunt, 1974; Cronin, 1977; Corliss *et al.*, 1982). During the earliest phase, between about 12 500 B.P. and 11 000 B.P., arctic species dominated and conditions became increasingly more saline. Between 11 000 and 10 600 B.P. a distinct and abrupt faunal change, from arctic to cold-temperate types, occurred in the Champlain Sea (Elson, 1969; Cronin, 1977). The shift to warmer conditions and to distinctly less saline waters at this time is confirmed by oxygen isotope ratios (Corliss *et al.*, 1982). "The beginning of the rapid isotopic decrease at approximately 10 900 yr B.P. marks the onset of the largest environmental change in the history of the Champlain Sea..." (Corliss *et al.*, 1982, p. 325). A major influx of water is demanded by this change (Cronin, 1977; Corliss *et al.*, 1982).

Coincident with this rapid environmental change was the influx of a large volume of water to the Great Lakes from Lake Agassiz. Initially, this influx may have overflowed through the Erie and Ontario basins, but later discharged via the North Bay-Ottawa River valley outlet from the Huron basin (Fig. 8). In addition, the geotechnical properties of some of the Champlain Sea clays indicate that, following rapid burial, they must have undergone a very rapid period of erosion (unloading) in order to explain the relationship of preconsolidation pressure with depth in the clays (Quigley *et al.*, 1983). Graham and Teller (1984) suggest that the volume and timing of Lake Agassiz floodwater could explain this rapid unloading, in which up to 20 m of sediment was eroded in less than a century. Catto *et al.* (1982) concluded that a large part of the discharge through the Ottawa River valley to the Champlain Sea, which was responsible for depositing the highest terraces between 10 500 and 8500 B.P., came from Lake Agassiz.

SUMMARY

Lake Agassiz was a very large body of water that overflowed into the Great Lakes during much of late glacial and early postglacial time. Initially, this proglacial lake spilled southward into the Minnesota River valley, which drained into the Mississippi River. By 10 900 B.P., the glacial margin had retreated far enough north to open the eastern outlets into the Superior basin. During the Moorhead Phase, 10 900 to 9900 B.P., the level of Lake Agassiz fell more than 150 m in a series of steps, as progressively lower outlets west of the Nipigon basin were opened. Very early in this phase, water in the Superior basin overflowed into the Michigan basin. This was followed by a brief period of overflow into the Erie-Ontario basins via Lake Huron (Fig. 8). By about 10 500 B.P., the North Bay outlet from the Huron basin became ice-free, and all overflow from Lake Agassiz, Lake Superior, Lake Michigan, and Lake Huron discharged northeastward through this outlet into the Ottawa River valley. The record in the Champlain Sea after 10 900 B.P. reflects the increase in discharge from the Great Lakes that resulted, at least in part, from the contributions of Lake Agassiz.

About 9900 B.P., the Marquette glacial advance pushed south across the Lake Superior basin to the Upper Peninsula of Michigan, again blocking the eastern outlets of Lake Agassiz. The level of Lake Agassiz rose and expanded over the large southern part of the basin, which had become dry during the Moorhead Phase of low water. Until the eastern outlets were reopened, overflow from Lake Agassiz was through the southern outlet.

As the glacial margin wasted back north after 9500 B.P., the eastern outlets from Lake Agassiz were opened in a series of steps, allowing more than a dozen catastrophic bursts of water to surge through the progressively lower channels west of the Nipigon basin and into Lake Superior. Although an equilibrium flow developed between each burst, during which time a new strandline developed in the Lake Agassiz basin, the volume of water that overflowed into the Superior basin during each catastrophic burst was much larger. Calculations indicate that 500 to 4000 km^3 of overflow spilled through each newly opened outlet in only a year or two, with rates of discharge commonly exceeding 100 000 m^{3}s^{-1}. During this, the Nipigon Phase of Lake Agassiz, a sequence of grey clays was deposited in the Superior basin; water levels in this basin may have risen rapidly in response to the floods. The evidence suggests that most overflow from the Superior to the Huron basin was into North Channel and out through the North Bay outlet, by-passing the main Huron basin during much of the Stanley low-water phase of that lake.

By about 8500 B.P., the glacial margin had retreated north of the divide between the Superior and Hudson Bay (Lake Agassiz) basins, allowing Lake Agassiz to overflow eastward across northern Ontario and into the St. Lawrence. This ended the influence that Lake Agassiz had on the Great Lakes. Lake Agassiz finally drained into the Tyrrell Sea about 7500 B.P.

ACKNOWLEDGEMENTS

I am indebted to the many researchers, past and present, who have studied Lake Agassiz and the Great Lakes; only a small number of their publications have been cited in this paper. Discussions with Lee Clayton over the past 15 years have contributed greatly to my understanding of both the glacial and lacustrine processes in the region and the history of this ancient lake. Steve Moran and Mark Fenton also played an important role in helping shape my views about Lake Agassiz. Recently, Harvey Thorleifson has provided thoughtful and challenging ideas that have influenced my opinions. In addition, I would like to thank John Elson, Harvey Thorleifson, and Lee Clayton for reviewing this paper, and Ron Pryhitko for drafting the illustrations.

REFERENCES

Anderson, T.W., and Lewis, C.F.M., 1985, Postglacial Water-Level History of the Lake Ontario Basin: in Karrow, P.F., and Calkin, P.E., eds., Quaternary Evolution of the Great Lakes: Geological Association of Canada Special Paper 30.

Antevs, E., 1951, Glacial Clay in Steep Rock Lake, Ontario, Canada: Geological Society of America Bulletin, v. 62, p. 1223-1262.

Arndt, B.M., 1977, Stratigraphy of Offshore Sediment of Lake Agassiz, North Dakota: North Dakota Geological Survey Report of Investigation 60, 58 p.

Brophy, J.A., and Bluemle, J.P., 1983, The Sheyenne River: its Geological History and Effects on Lake Agassiz: in Teller, J.T., and Clayton, Lee, eds., Glacial Lake Agassiz: Geological Association of Canada Special Paper 26, p. 173-186.

Calkin, P.E., and Feenstra, B.H., 1985, Evolution of the Erie-basin Great Lakes: in Karrow, P.F., and Calkin, P.E., eds., Quaternary Evolution of the Great Lakes: Geological Association of Canada Special Paper 30.

Catto, N.R., Patterson, R.J., and Gorman, W.A., 1982, The Late Quaternary Geology of the Chalk River Region, Ontario and Quebec: Canadian Journal of Earth Sciences, v. 19, p. 1218-1231.

Clayton, Lee, 1983, Chronology of Lake Agassiz Drainage to Lake Superior: in Teller, J.T., and Clayton, Lee, eds., Glacial Lake Agassiz: Geological Association of Canada Special Paper 26, p. 291-307.

Clayton, Lee, and Moran, S.R., 1982, Chronology of Late Wisconsinan Glaciation in Middle North America: Quaternary Science Reviews, v. 1, p. 55-82.

Clayton, Lee, Teller, J.T., and Attig, J.W., 1985, Surging of the Southwestern Part of the Laurentide Ice Sheet: Boreas, v. 14, p.

Coakley, J.P., and Lewis, C.F.M., 1985, Postglacial Lake Levels in the Erie Basin: in Karrow, P.F., and Calkin, P.E., eds., Quaternary Evolution of the Great Lakes: Geological Association of Canada Special Paper 30.

Corliss, B.H., Hunt, A.S., and Keigwin, L.D., 1982, Benthonic Foraminiferal Fauna and Isotopic Data for the Postglacial Evolution of the Champlain Sea: Quaternary Research, v. 17, p. 325-338.

Cronin, T.M., 1977, Late-Wisconsin Marine Environments of the Champlain Valley (New York, Quebec): Quaternary Research, v. 7, p. 238-253.

Dell, C.I., 1972, The Origin and Characteristics of Lake Superior Sediments: Proceedings 15th Conference on Great Lakes Research, International Association for Great Lakes Research, p. 361-370.

———, 1974, The Stratigraphy of Northern Lake Superior Late-Glacial and Postglacial Sediments: Proceedings 17th Conference on Great Lakes Research, International Association for Great Lakes Research p. 179-192.

Drexler, C.W., 1981, Outlet Channels for the Post-Duluth Lakes in the Upper Peninsula of Michigan: Ph.D. Thesis, University of Michigan, Ann Arbor, 226 p.

Drexler, C.W., Farrand, W.R., and Hughes, J.D., 1983, Correlation of Glacial Lakes in the Superior Basin with Eastward Discharge Events from Lake Agassiz: in Teller, J.T., and Clayton, Lee, eds., Glacial Lake Agassiz: Geological Association of Canada Special Paper 26, p. 309-329.

Elson, J.A., 1967, Geology of Glacial Lake Agassiz: in Mayer-Oakes, W., ed., Life, Land, and Water: Winnipeg, Manitoba, University of Manitoba Press, p. 36-95.

———, 1969, Radiocarbon dates, Mya arenaria Phase of the Champlain Sea: Canadian Journal Earth Sciences, v. 6, p. 367-372.

Eschman, D.F., and Karrow, P.F., 1985, Huron Basin Glacial Lakes: A Review: in Karrow, P.F., and Calkin, P.E., eds., Quaternary Evolution of the Great Lakes: Geological Association of Canada Special Paper 30.

Farrand, W.R., 1960, Former Shorelines in Western and Northern Lake Superior Basin: Ph.D. Thesis, Ann Arbor, Michigan, University of Michigan, 226 p.

———, 1969a, The Quaternary History of Lake Superior: Proceedings 12th Conference on Great Lakes Research, International Association for Great Lakes Research, p. 181-197.

———, 1969b, Late-Glacial and Postglacial Sedimentation in the Deep Basins of Lake Superior, USA: Mitteilungen International Vereiningen Limnologie, v. 17, p. 34-42.

Fenton, M.M., Moran, S.R., Teller, J.T., and Clayton, Lee, 1983, Quaternary Stratigraphy and History in the Southern Part of the Lake Agassiz Basin: in Teller, J.T., and Clayton, Lee, eds., Glacial Lake Agassiz: Geological Association of Canada Special Paper 26, p. 49-74.

Fillon, R.F., and Hunt, A.S., 1974, Late-Pleistocene Benthonic Foraminifera of the Southern Champlain Sea: Paleotemperature and Paleosalinity Indications: Maritime Sediments, v. 10, p. 14-18.

Fullerton, D.S., 1980, Preliminary Correlation of Post-Erie Interstadial Events (16 000–10 000 Radiocarbon Years Before Present), Central and Eastern Great Lakes Region, and Hudson, Champlain, and St. Lawrence Lowlands, United States and Canada: United States Geological Survey Professional Paper 1089, 52 p.

Graham, J., and Teller, J.T., 1984, Leda Clay from Deep Boreholes at Hawkesbury, Ontario. Part I: Geology and Geotechnique: Discussion: Canadian Geotechnical Journal, v. 21, p. 733-734.

Harris, K.L., Moran, S.R., and Clayton, Lee, 1974, Late Quaternary Stratigraphic Nomenclature, Red River Valley, North Dakota and Minnesota: North Dakota Geological Survey Miscellaneous Series 52, 47 p.

Hobbs, H.C., 1983, Drainage Relationships of Glacial Lakes Aitkin and Upham and Early Lake Agassiz in Northeastern Minnesota: in Teller, J.T., and Clayton, Lee, eds., Glacial Lake Agassiz: Geological Association of Canada Special Paper 26, p. 245-259.

Hough, J.L., 1955, Lake Chippewa, a Low Stage of Lake Michigan Indicated by Bottom Sediments: Geological Society of America Bulletin, v. 66, p. 957-968.

————, 1958, Geology of the Great Lakes: Urbana, Illinois, University of Illinois Press, 313 p.

————, 1962, Lake Stanley, a Low Stage of Lake Huron Indicated by Bottom Sediments: Geological Society of America Bulletin, v. 73, p. 613-620.

Johnson, T.C., and Fields, F., 1984, Paleomagnetic Dating of Postglacial Sediment, Offshore Lake Superior, Minnesota-Wisconsin, U.S.A.: Chemical Geology, v. 44, p. 253-265.

Johnston, W.A., 1915, Rainy River District, Ontario: Surficial Geology and Soils: Geological Survey of Canada Memoir 82, 95 p.

————, 1946, Glacial Lake Agassiz, with Special Reference to the Mode of Deformation of the Beaches: Geological Survey of Canada Bulletin 7, 20 p.

Karrow, P.F., Anderson, T.W., Clarke, A.H., Delorme, L.D., and Sreenivasa, M.R., 1975, Stratigraphy, Paleontology, and Age of Lake Algonquin Sediments in Southwestern Ontario, Canada: Quaternary Research, v. 5, p. 49-87.

Kehew, A.E., and Clayton, Lee, 1983, Late Wisconsinan Floods and Development of the Souris-Pembina Spillway System in Saskatchewan, North Dakota, and Manitoba: in Teller, J.T., and Clayton, Lee, eds., Glacial Lake Agassiz: Geological Association of Canada Special Paper 26, p. 187-209.

Klassen, R.W., 1983a, Assiniboine Delta and the Assiniboine-Qu'Appelle Valley System—Implications Concerning the History of Lake Agassiz in Southwestern Manitoba: in Teller, J.T., and Clayton, Lee, eds., Glacial Lake Agassiz: Geological Association of Canada Special Paper 26, p. 211-229.

————, 1983b, Lake Agassiz and the Late Glacial History of Northern Manitoba: in Teller, J.T., and Clayton, Lee, eds., Glacial Lake Agassiz: Geological Association of Canada Special Paper 26, p. 97-115.

Leverett, F., and Taylor, F.B., 1915, The Pleistocene of Indiana and Michigan and the History of the Great Lakes: United States Geological Survey Monograph 53, 529 p.

Lewis, C.F.M., 1969, Late Quaternary History of Lake Levels in the Huron and Erie Basins: Proceedings 12th Conference on Great Lakes Research, International Association for Great Lakes Research, p. 250-270.

Lewis, C.F.M., and Anderson, T.W., 1984, Early Holocene Lake Levels in the Huron Basin: Comparative Uplift Histories of Basins and Sills in a Rebounding Glacial Marginal Depression: Geological Association of Canada Program with Abstracts, v. 9, p. 84.

Lineback, J.A., Dell, C.I., and Gross, D.L., 1979, Glacial and Postglacial Sediments in Lakes Superior and Michigan: Geological Society of America Bulletin, v. 90, p. 781-791.

Lineback, J.A., Gross, D.L., and Meyer, R.P., 1972, Geologic Cross Sections Derived from Seismic Profiles and Sediment Cores from Southern Lake Michigan: Illinois Geological Survey Environmental Geology Note 54, 43 p.

Maher, L.J., 1977, Palynological Studies in the Western Arm of Lake Superior: Quaternary Research, v. 7, p. 14-44.

Matsch, C.L., 1983, River Warren, the Southern Outlet of Glacial Lake Agassiz: in Teller, J.T., and Clayton, Lee, eds., Glacial Lake Agassiz: Geological Association of Canada Special Paper 26, p. 231-244.

Mickelson, D.M., Clayton, Lee, Fullerton, D.S., and Borns, H.W, 1983, The Late Wisconsin Glacial Record of the Laurentide Ice Sheet in the United States: in Porter, S.C., ed., The Late Pleistocene: Minneapolis, University of Minnesota Press, p. 3-37.

Moran, S.R., 1972, Subsurface Geology and Foundation Conditions in Grand Forks, North Dakota: North Dakota Geological Survey Miscellaneous Series 44, 18 p.

Mothersill, H.S., 1979, The Paleomagnetic Record of the Late Quaternary Sediments of Thunder Bay: Canadian Journal Earth Sciences, v. 16, p. 1016-1023.

————, 1983, Results from the Great Lakes: in Creer, K.M., and Tucholka, P., eds., Geomagnetism of Baked Clays and Recent Sediments: New York, Elsevier, p. 223-231.

————, 1984, Paleomagnetic Columns: a Method for Time-Parallel Correlation and Absolute Dating of Late Quaternary Sequences of the Great Lakes Area: in Mahaney, W.C., ed., Correlation of Quaternary Chronologies: Norwich, England, GeoBooks, p. 91-101.

Mothersill, J.S., and Fung, P.C., 1972, The Stratigraphy, Mineralogy, and Trace Element Concentrations of the Quaternary Sediments of the Northern Lake Superior Basin: Canadian Journal Earth Sciences, v. 9, p. 1725-1755.

Prest, V.K., 1970, Quaternary Geology of Canada: in Douglas, R.J.W., ed., Geology and Economic Minerals of Canada: Geological Survey of Canada, Economic Geology Report 1, Fifth Edition, p. 676-764.

Quigley, R.M., Gwyn, Q., White, O., Rowe, R., Haynes, J., and Bohdanowicz, A., 1983, Leda Clay from Deep Boreholes at Hawkesbury, Ontario. Part I: Geology and Geotechnique: Canadian Geotechnical Journal, v. 20, p. 288-298.

Rittenhouse, G., 1934, A Laboratory Study of an Unusual Series of Varved Clays from Northern Ontario: American Journal of Science, v. 28, p. 110-120.

Ruhe, R.V., 1969, Quaternary Landscapes in Iowa: Ames, Iowa, Iowa State University Press, 255 p.

Saarnisto, M., 1974, The Deglaciation History of the Lake Superior Region and its Climatic Implications: Quaternary Research, v. 4, p. 316-339.

————, 1975, Stratigraphic Studies on the Shoreline Displacement of Lake Superior: Canadian Journal Earth Sciences, v. 12, p. 300-319.

Teller, J.T., 1976, Lake Agassiz Deposits in the Main Offshore Basin of Southern Manitoba: Canadian Journal Earth Sciences, v. 13, p. 27-43.

————, 1981, The Catastrophic Drainage of Glacial Lake Agassiz: Geological Society America, Abstracts with Programs, v. 13, no. 7, p. 565.

Teller, J.T., and Fenton, M.M., 1980, Late Wisconsinan Glacial Stratigraphy and History of Southeastern Manitoba: Canadian Journal Earth Sciences, v. 17, p. 19-35.

Teller, J.T., and Last, W.M., 1981, Late Quaternary History of Lake Manitoba, Canada: Quaternary Research, v. 16, p. 97-116.

————, 1982, Pedogenic Horizons in Lake Sediments: Earth Surface Processes and Landforms, v. 7, p. 367-379.

Teller, J.T., and Thorleifson, L.H., 1983, The Lake Agassiz-Lake Superior Connection: in Teller, J.T., and Clayton, Lee, eds., Glacial Lake Agassiz: Geological Association of Canada Special Paper 26, p. 261-290.

Teller, J.T., Thorleifson, L.H., Dredge, L.A., Hobbs, H.C., and Schreiner, B.T., 1983, Maximum Extent and Major Features of Lake Agassiz: *in* Teller, J.T., and Clayton, Lee, eds., Glacial Lake Agassiz: Geological Association of Canada Special Paper 26, p. 43-45.

Thorleifson, L.H., 1983, The Eastern Outlets of Lake Agassiz: M.Sc. Thesis, Winnipeg, University of Manitoba, 87 p.

Upham, W., 1895, The Glacial Lake Agassiz: United States Geological Survey Monograph 25, 658 p.

Vincent, J-S., and Hardy, L., 1979, The Evolution of Glacial Lakes Barlow and Ojibway, Quebec and Ontario: Geological Survey of Canada Bulletin 316, 18 p.

Wayne, W.J., and Zumberge, J.H., 1965, Pleistocene Geology of Indiana and Michigan: *in* Wright, H.E., and Frey, D.G., eds., The Quaternary of the United States: Princeton, New Jersey, Princeton University Press, p. 63-84.

Wickham, J.T., Gross, D.L., Lineback, J.A., and Thomas, R.L., 1978, Late Quaternary Sediments of Lake Michigan: Illinois Geological Survey Environmental Geology Note 84, 26 p.

Zoltai, S.C., 1961, Glacial History of Part of Northwestern Ontario: Proceedings Geological Association Canada, v. 13, p. 61-83.

————, 1965, Glacial Features of the Quetico-Nipigon Area, Ontario: Canadian Journal Earth Sciences, v. 2, p. 247-269.

Quaternary Evolution of the Great Lakes,
edited by P.F. Karrow and P.E. Calkin,
Geological Association of Canada Special Paper 30, 1985

LATE WISCONSINAN AND HOLOCENE HISTORY
OF THE LAKE SUPERIOR BASIN

William R. Farrand
Department of Geological Sciences, The University of Michigan, Ann Arbor, Michigan 48109

Christopher W. Drexler
Western Division, Exxon Corporation, Englewood, Colorado 80110

ABSTRACT

During the last decade or so interpretations of the late Quaternary history of Lake Superior have changed more drastically than those of the lower Great Lakes. Constraints on the Lake Superior chronology have been imposed by dated inputs from glacial Lake Agassiz and by the availability of drainage outlets across northern Michigan and in the North Bay, Ontario, area. The most striking revision calls for a late-glacial ("Marquette") readvance that nearly refilled the basin about 10 000 B.P. Eastward drainage from Lake Agassiz flowed through the Superior basin into the Michigan and Huron lake basins, both before and after the Marquette maximum. Glacial Lake Minong, the first Holocene lake to approximate the present outline of Lake Superior, developed diachronically upon ice retreat from the Marquette stand – earliest in the southeast corner of the basin (Whitefish Bay area) and only later in the west, after the ice front retreated from Keweenaw Point. Catastrophic floods scoured bedrock channels in the Huron Mountains (northern Michigan) early in this retreat. Subsequently, catastrophic discharges from Lake Agassiz were responsible for cutting down the Lake Minong sill (between Gros Cap and Nadoway Point).

Sediments cored from the deep basins record events beginning with the Marquette event. Red till is followed by red lake beds, then some 1300 grey varves, and finally homogeneous grey and brown clays. Red till and lake clays do not occur in the northern part of the basin, i.e., east of Thunder Bay. It has been proposed that the spread of grey clays throughout the basin, and even at times into the Lake Michigan basin, is largely the result of catastrophic flooding from Lake Agassiz.

Around 5000 B.P. the Nipissing Great Lakes formed impressive shoreline features all around the basin. Some of these are now uplifted at least 30 m (100 ft) in the northeast. Lake Superior was finally separated from Lake Huron-Michigan about 2000 years ago by the continuing isostatic uplift of the Sault Ste. Marie threshold.

RÉSUMÉ

Dans les 10 dernières années, l'interprétation de l'histoire quaternaire du lac Supérieur a été remise en question beaucoup plus que celles des autres Grands Lacs. La chronologie du lac Supérieur est basée non seulement sur des datations au carbone − 14 obtenues dans le bassin même, mais aussi sur des données venant des bassins avoisinants: ceux du lac Agassiz et du lac Huron. En plus, le comportement des exutoires du nord de l'état de Michigan et de la région de North Bay en Ontario contrôle les variations du niveau lacustre. L'élément le plus frappant dans la nouvelle interprétation est l'introduction de la notion d'une réavancée glaciaire tardive, le stade de Marquette, qui a quasi-totalement rempli le bassin du lac Supérieur vers 10 000 ans B.P. Avant cette poussée de glace les eaux du lac Agassiz se sont déversées à travers le bassin du lac Supérieur jusque dans les bassins des lacs Michigan et Huron. Au maximum du stade de Marquette les eaux du lac Agassiz, aussi bien que celles de la partie occidentale du lac Supérieur, se sont drainées vers le sud-ouest pour se jeter dans le bassin versant du fleuve Mississippi.

De nouveau, pendant le recul du front glaciaire après le maximum du stade de Marquette, les eaux du lac Supérieur ont retrouvé des exutoires vers le sud-est. Tout d'abord, elles ont surcreusé des chenaux rocheux dans les montagnes Huron (à l'ouest de Marquette au Michigan), au fur et à mesure que cette région a été libérée par le glacier. Puis, le drainage s'est effectué par le chenal d'Au Train-Whitefish, passant vers le sud jusqu'à la baie Green du lac Michigan. Ensuite, les eaux du lac Supérieur se sont écoulées le long du front glaciaire pour se jeter dans le lac Minong qui existait dans la partie sud-est du bassin (baie de Whitefish). Enfin, le retrait du glacier a dégagé tout le bassin du lac Supérieur (à la phase Minong) et libéré des exutoires orientaux du lac Agassiz. En même temps, des torrents catastrophiques se sont déversés depuis le bassin du lac Agassiz dans le bassin du lac Supérieur alors à un niveau inférieur à celui du lac Minong. Il est bien possible que ce drainage catastrophique ait érodé le seuil du lac Minong, probablement morainique, qui devait exister entre le Gros Cap et la pointe Nadoway près de Sault Ste-Marie.

Depuis ce temps-là le soulèvement isostatique, d'abord au Sault Ste-Marie, ensuite à l'exutoire de North Bay (à l'est de la baie georgienne), a contrôlé les niveaux lacustres dans le bassin du lac Supérieur. Le niveau maximum atteint pendant cet épisode était celui de Nipissing vers 5000 ans B.P. Les formes de relief créées pendant la phase Nipissing (cordons littoraux, falaises) sont impressionnantes tout autour du bassin. Ensuite, l'érosion de l'exutoire du lac Huron (rivière St-Clair) a entraîné une baisse dans le niveau des lacs Huron, Michigan et Supérieur, jusqu'à ce que le lac Supérieur soit séparé de nouveau du lac Huron par l'émergence du seuil du Sault Ste-Marie vers 2000 ans B.P.

Les sédiments des bas-fonds du lac Supérieur, disponibles par les forages, peuvent être corrélés aux événements de cette histoire, en commençant avec l'avancée de Marquette. De bas en haut, les carottes révèlent un till rouge, suivi de sédiments lacustres rouges, stratifiés, et même varvés. Les sédiments rouges passent par transition aux sédiments gris: tout d'abord on retrouve à peu près 1300 varves grises, suivies d'une couche d'argile grise, sans stratification apparente et finalement d'une couche d'argile brune. Dans la partie nord du bassin, c'est-à-dire à l'est de Thunder Bay, on ne retrouve pas de sédiments rouges. Pour expliquer cette répartition on propose que l'argile grise ait été introduite dans le bassin du lac Supérieur, et même par moments dans le bassin du lac Michigan, par des torrents catastrophiques originaires du lac Agassiz.

INTRODUCTION

Although our personal involvement with the geology of Lake Superior goes back about 25 years and 10 years, respectively, the present review owes a tremendous debt to our colleagues and friends of recent years who have advanced our knowledge of the Superior basin in a superior way, as well as to our predecessors, beginning with Louis Agassiz himself, who was preaching the gospel of ice ages in these waters about 150 years ago. This presentation will draw heavily on the contributions of these colleagues, living and departed.

When investigating in the Lake Superior area in the late 1950s, one could consider the area in relative isolation, not worrying about contemporaneous events to the east or west because little was known in detail about those adjacent areas. This is no longer the case. The late Quaternary history of the Superior basin is highly constrained by well-studied events in the Lake Agassiz basin to the west and in the Lake Michigan and Lake Huron basins to the south. Moreover, the major outlines of deglacial history to the north and east are now well drawn. These comments should not be taken to imply that everything is now known about Lake Superior's history. Important questions still remain unanswered. For example, the coast between Michipicoten and Marathon never has been mapped in detail, and in the southwest the pre-Marquette stratigraphy must be unraveled in the third dimension, rather than by geomorphology alone, because it has been buried or submerged.

DEFINITIONS

Stratigraphic terminology dealing with the changing levels of former lakes is still not satisfactorily or uniformly applied. Clayton (1983, p. 294-296) found it necessary to define his terms, and this represents a significant step in the right direction in dealing with lakes, lake levels, and lake phases. Since we feel that there is still some ambiguity, we would like to clarify and justify our usage of terms in this paper.

Lake. A present-day or reconstructed geomorphic feature, namely "any inland body of standing water occupying a depression in the Earth's surface, generally of appreciable size..." (Bates and Jackson, 1980, p. 347). The level of such a water body may be variable with time.

Glacial Lake. A lake whose existence at a given level depends on an ice barrier at some point on its periphery, i.e., blocking potentially lower outlets.

Morpho-sedimentary features. These may be either depositional (beaches, deltas, lake-bottom sediments, etc.) or erosional (wave-cut bluffs, outlet channels, etc.). These lithostratigraphic and allostratigraphic features (North American Commission, 1983) form the basis for reconstructing the paleogeomorphic form and the geologic history of former levels of former lakes.

Lake level. An inferred water plane within a given lake basin reconstructed on the basis of morpho-sedimentary features. A given level should be related to a specified outlet, if any, but levels and outlets should be named independently because more than one level may have been controlled by a single outlet or vice-versa. Moreover, whereas an outlet is an observable feature, a former lake level must be inferred. Former lake levels may be no longer horizontal because of crustal deformation, such as glacial rebound. Lake "stage" is not considered an appropriate synonym for "level" because "stage" is restricted to chronostratigraphic usage in the North American Stratigraphic Code (North American Commission, 1983, Article 74).

Lake Phase. The time during which a given lake level or group of levels was functional. A lake phase may be time-transgressive, for example, existing in one part of a lake basin at first and then expanding to other parts as a bounding ice margin retreats. Such a "phase" is properly a diachronic unit of the North American Stratigraphic Code (Articles 91 and 93) based on "material referents", such as morpho-sedimentary features (above). Clayton (1983, p. 294) calls phases "geologic-event units", but the latter term is not part of the North American Stratigraphic Code. He goes on appropriately to emphasize that lake phases are "important episodes in the history of the lake" and that ideally the names given to lakes, outlets, lake levels, and lake phases should all be independent of each other in order to avoid ambiguity. We concur fully with Clayton's ideas, but we wish to emphasize that phases are units of time. Unfortunately in current practice many lake phases are named from lake levels, e.g., the Minong shoreline and the Minong Phase. Herein we distinguish between the Early Minong

Phase and the (main) Minong Phase, but we have opted not to introduce a new, independent set of phase terms at this time as long as there is no ambiguity.

HISTORY OF THE STUDY OF LAKE SUPERIOR

Only 11 years after the history-making *Discours de Neuchâtel* (1837) in which he pronounced his theory of ice ages, Louis Agassiz was floating in a canoe on Lake Superior observing ancient lake terraces and glacial striae, as well as collecting all sorts of fish, mammals, and plants for his museum at Harvard University (Agassiz, 1850). However, the first detailed study of former shorelines on the Superior coast was by A. C. Lawson (1893) who cruised along the north shore from Sault Ste. Marie to Duluth spirit-levelling the old shorelines at 48 localities. His conclusion that the former shorelines were still horizontal was quickly challenged by F. B. Taylor (1895, 1897), who travelled inland on the Canadian Pacific Railway. A bit later Frank Leverett (1929) summarized the knowledge of former shorelines (and moraines) to that date, but he did not discuss the shorelines in Ontario above the Nipissing beach.

The next significant work was the dissertation of G. M. Stanley (1932) who discussed in detail the abandoned strands of Isle Royale and investigated the mainland in search of correlatives of the strongly developed Fort Brady (now Minong) beaches that he had found on the island. Stanley's later work on Lake Superior was never published, except for an abstract (Stanley, 1941). Still later, R. P. Sharp (1953), added a very detailed study of former shorelines in Cook County, Minnesota, but the stretch of shoreline that he studied was too limited to establish firm correlations with distant parts of the basin. Finally, in the late 1950s, the dissertation of the senior author was devoted to detailed observations in northern Wisconsin, Minnesota, and the north shore in Ontario, but it depended on the earlier work of Leverett and Stanley for correlations with the southeastern part of the basin (Farrand, 1960).

The latest generation of students has added greatly to the previous observations and interpretations, and has been able to take advantage of better maps and an increasing number of radiocarbon dates as a basis for correlation. The first of these was S. C. Zoltai (1965, 1967). His extensive mapping of glacial deposits and lake sediments throughout the wilderness of western Ontario identified numerous moraines and placed firmer limits on the northern and eastern extent of Lake Agassiz and Lake Superior. J. D. Hughes (1963) mapped in detail the central Keweenaw Peninsula, worked out details of drainage channels in the Marquette-Munising area, and capitalized on the interpretation of the Gribben buried forest (Hughes, 1971, 1978). In these same years investigations of the bottom sediments in Lake Superior were pursued at the University of Michigan and the University of Minnesota (Zumberge and Gast, 1961; Farrand, 1969; Dell, 1971, 1975, 1976).

M. Saarnisto (1974, 1975) added important insights to the late-glacial history of Lake Superior in the course of his valuable palynological studies in the eastern part of the basin. Next, R. P. Futyma (1981) and C. W. Drexler (1981), working in adjacent areas of Michigan's Upper Peninsula, added

considerable information on the extent of glacial Lake Algonquin and on the drainage history of the Post-Duluth lakes, respectively. Most recently Drexler *et al.* (1983) have detailed the nature of the Marquette readvance, and Cowan (1985) has studied the Sault Ste. Marie (Ontario) area in detail.

Finally, it must be granted that much of this present summary would not be possible without the recent publication of the Geological Association of Canada's Lake Agassiz symposium papers, especially the contributions by Teller and Thorleifson (1983) and Clayton (1983). These authors have contributed valuable advice and criticism to us, which we hope is faithfully reflected in this paper.

GEOGRAPHIC SETTING OF THE LAKE SUPERIOR BASIN

Lake Superior is the largest of all the present-day Great Lakes in North America, and has in fact the largest surface area of any freshwater lake in the world (Fig. 1). It is called "Superior" (*supérieur*, French), however, because it is the uppermost of the chain of Great Lakes. The present surface area of Lake Superior is about 82 260 km², and its volume is about 12 258 km³ (Showers, 1979, p. 158, 170).

The floor of the present lake lies mostly at depths of greater than 150 m (Farrand, 1969), and the eastern half differs considerably from the western. In the east the bedrock floor of the lake is thinly covered with glacial drift (15 m or less) and is marked by a conspicuous dendritic pattern of deep bedrock troughs, oriented more or less north-south (Fig. 1). In the west, by contrast, the bedrock surface is overlain by drift well in excess of 300 m thick near the Minnesota shore (Farrand, 1969), but deep bedrock troughs occur there as well, as revealed by seismic profiling (Farrand, 1969; Wold *et al.*, 1982, p. 260).

Pleistocene sediments on the floor of the lake have been cored (Farrand, 1969), revealing a regular sequence that begins in red clayey or sandy till, passes upward through red lacustrine sediments into a thick series of grey varves (at least 1300 varve years), and is overlain by homogeneous grey clays and, in the southern part of the basin, brown muds. A current summary of the characteristics of these sediments with extensive references can be found in Wold *et al.* (1982, p. 265-267).

The late-Pleistocene chronology of the sub-lake drift, to the extent known by coring, was formerly considered to begin with red till of Valderan age (Farrand, 1969) or, in current terminology, of early Greatlakean age. However, since the recognition of the Marquette readvance of about 10 000 B.P., it must be considered more likely that the red till was deposited at that time and that the red and grey lake beds all postdate 10 000 B.P.

The topographic rim is generally rather high all around the basin except in the vicinity of the present outlet at Sault Ste. Marie. The bedrock rapids in the St. Marys River now control the water level at about 183 m (602 ft) above sea level. Adjacent to the river there is a drift-covered lowland, some 11 km wide at its narrowest point and generally not exceeding 215 m (700 ft) above sea level.

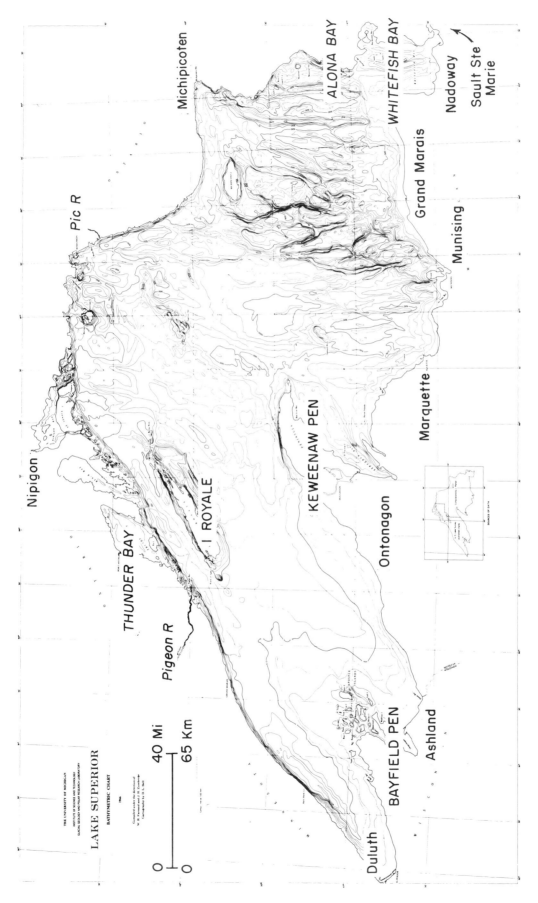

Figure 1. Index map of Lake Superior showing bottom contours and names of places discussed in the text. Bathymetry after Farrand (1969).

GLACIATION IN THE LAKE SUPERIOR BASIN

Although the Superior basin must have been invaded by the Laurentide ice sheet repeatedly throughout the Quaternary Period, the stratigraphic record appears to be restricted to Late Wisconsinan time. One of the prime aims of the 1961-1962 coring program initiated by Zumberge and Gast (1961) was to probe areas of thick glacial drift on the lake floor in search of pre-Wisconsinan deposits, for example, in the area off the Minnesota coast where the drift is as much as 500 m thick (Wold *et al.*, 1982, p. 261). Coring in that area penetrated 209 m (686 ft.) of sediment without encountering the bedrock floor. No deposits were sampled that could not be most reasonably attributed to the Wisconsinan Stage. In fact all were probably Late Wisconsinan in age (Farrand, 1969). The red tills penetrated in coring most likely reflect the multiplicity of red tills recently investigated in northern Wisconsin (Need *et al.*, 1981; Clayton, 1983).

Whenever the margin of the Laurentide ice sheet retreated north of the south rim of the basin, meltwater would have been ponded to form a glacial lake. The lake would have overflowed at the lowest possible point along the rim, as discussed in the following section on outlets. As far as the direct record of glacial lakes is concerned, our discussion of glaciation can begin in post-Twocreekan time, i.e., post 11 800 B.P. These glacial events have been recently revised and summarized by Clayton and Moran (1982), Clayton (1983), and for the southeastern part of the basin by Drexler *et al.* (1983). The post-Twocreekan glacier advance completely filled the basin (Fig. 2a) in the form of two ice lobes split by the Keweenaw Peninsula. The Superior lobe reached the position of the Nickerson moraine southwest of Duluth, and the Lake Michigan-Green Bay lobe moved southward across the northern peninsula of Michigan, ultimately reaching the Two Rivers moraine at Manitowoc, Wisconsin, about 11 800 B.P. Glacial lakes are postulated to have

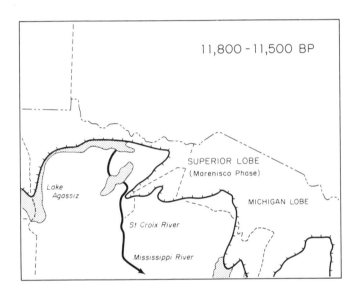
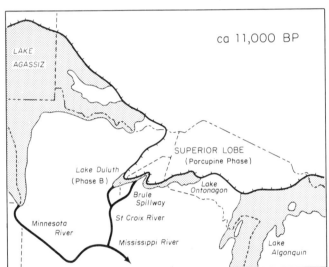
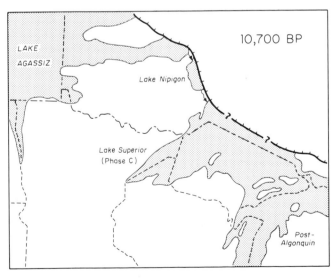
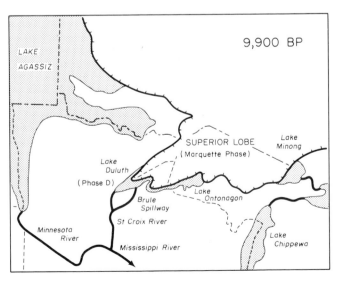

Figure 2. Glacial lakes and contemporaneous ice margins at 11 800 to 11 500, about 11 000, 10 700, and 9900 years B.P. in Lake Superior and adjacent regions. Modified after Clayton (1983).

existed near and southwest of Duluth as the ice front oscillated in the early stages of retreat from the Nickerson moraine. However, shorelines of these lakes have largely been obliterated by subsequent glacier or lacustrine activity associated with the Marquette readvance about 10 000 B.P. Conceivably sub-till lacustrine deposits that can be ascribed to these early lakes will be found in deep exposures or in drilling. In fact, lake beds that alternate with red tills in the deep core recovered off Silver Bay, Minnesota, may fall into this category (Farrand, 1969).

The Marquette readvance (Fig. 2d) is a new element, recently added to the glacial history of the Superior basin. Some problematic radiocarbon dates on wood in till had been known for some time (Black, 1976), but it was the discovery of the Gribben Lake buried forest (Hughes, 1978) and the detailed field work of Hughes (1971) and Drexler (1981; also Drexler et al., 1983) that demonstrated the validity of a major readvance of the Laurentide ice about 10 000 B.P. From a retreatal position somewhere in the northern part of the Superior basin the ice front moved south to the Michigan shores of the present lake. Numerous dates on wood (Clayton, 1983; Drexler et al., 1983) fix the culmination of this advance tightly at 10 000 B.P. or just slightly younger, and they demonstrate its correlation with well-dated events in the Lake Agassiz basin.

The exact position of the Marquette advance in the southwestern corner of the basin is still debated, although Clayton (1983, p. 301) now states that he has traced its margin "nearly to Duluth". If it did not pass Duluth, there would have been a glacial lake − the latest phase of glacial Lake Duluth − trapped between the Marquette ice front and the southwestern basin rim.

Several separate morainal segments have been identified with the Marquette readvance. Of greatest importance because of its association with the buried Gribben Forest Bed is a moraine, Grand Marais I, that can be traced eastward from Marquette, Michigan, nearly to Whitefish Point (Fig. 3). It was outwash from this moraine that buried the forest. Drexler has recognized two retreatal positions (Grand Marais II and III) just inside the outermost moraine, showing minor adjustments of the ice front during which time discharge of lake waters from the western part of the Superior basin began to pour eastward and southward into Lake Michigan. This drainage initiated the Post-Duluth Phase (Sub-Duluth through Huron Mountain lake levels; Farrand, 1960; Drexler, 1981, p. 216). As the ice was melting back from Grand Marais III, discharge from western Lake Superior was passing directly along the ice front and entering Lake Minong, which was expanding in the southeastern corner of the basin.

In the southwestern part of the Superior basin (i.e., northern Wisconsin), the Marquette front is represented by the inner Saxon (Lake View) ice margin of Clayton (1983, p. 301). In contrast to the Marquette-Munising-Grand Marais sector, the ice front retreated rapidly from northern Wisconsin, and the Post-Duluth lakes expanded as far north as the international border (Pigeon River) and Isle Royale, more than 200 km, within a century or two. This rapid retreat is based on the difference in the northern limits of glacial Lake Duluth and Lake Beaver Bay, the first to reach the

Pigeon River area. On the average, each Post-Duluth lake, including Beaver Bay, lasted only about a decade (see below).

The next ice margins of importance to lake history are those in the Thunder Bay-to-Lake Nipigon area (Fig. 2c). Moraines associated with those margins have been mapped by Zoltai (1965, 1967) and discussed by Teller and Thorleifson (1983) in connection with the opening of eastern outlets from Glacial Lake Agassiz. Two ice lobes are recognized. Ice flowing east-northeast to west-southwest covered the Lake Nipigon basin and formed the Nipigon moraine that lies more or less along the west shore of present-day Lake Nipigon. The Nipigon lobe was contiguous with another lobe just west of Lake Nipigon, the ice of which moved nearly due south and built the Kaiashk moraine. (A number of other local names are applied to moraines in these lobes, but they need not concern us here; see Zoltai, 1965.)

As the ice front retreated from the Nipigon and Kaiashk moraines, an interlobate tract gradually opened and low land was exposed, allowing eastward drainage from Lake Agassiz to pass via the Nipigon basin into Lake Superior. The result was catastrophic discharge, which is discussed under the following section on outlets.

The final stand of the ice front that concerns the lakes in the Superior basin was at the Nakina moraine, which lies just north of the Superior-Hudson Bay drainage divide. It dammed a relatively small ice-marginal lake, Lake Nakina, that drained westward into an early high stage of Lake Nipigon and perhaps was confluent with one of the post-Minong levels of the Superior basin (Zoltai, 1967, p. 522) in the headwaters of the Pic River valley. The Nakina ice margin persisted long enough to prevent the establishment of any connection between Glacial Lake Barlow-Ojibway and the Superior basin.

GLACIAL LAKE OUTLETS AROUND THE SUPERIOR BASIN

The present outlet from the Lake Superior basin, the St. Marys River, lies in a lowland area that has, in fact, been the location of the only outlet from Superior for some 9500 years. The next higher pass across the Superior bedrock rim is the Au Train-Whitefish channel, which heads near Au Train Bay, west of Munising, Michigan, and leads southward into Green Bay at Little Bay de Noc (Fig. 3). This bedrock trough, which has a divide at about 234 m (768 ft.) above sea level (Leverett, 1929, p. 69) probably functioned repeatedly to carry drainage from the western Superior basin into the Lake Michigan basin at times when the Sault area was blocked by an ice sheet. The most recent use of this channel was during the Post-Duluth Phase (Drexler et al., 1983) shortly after 10 000 B.P.

In the southwestern corner of the basin are two higher outlet channels that functioned when the Superior Basin was nearly filled with glacier ice. The most prominent of these is the Brule outlet on the west side of the Bayfield Peninsula in Wisconsin, leading south via the St. Croix River valley to the Mississippi River (Fig. 2b and 2d). Its divide is presently about 312 m (1022 ft.) above sea level. A second, and smaller, outlet is found southwest of Duluth; this is the Portage (formerly "Moose Lake") outlet, the floor of which is about 320 m (Fig. 2b and 2d). Both the Brule and the Portage outlets are low enough to have drained Glacial Lake Duluth, which in that area stood at 331 m (1085 ft.) above sea level, according to Farrand (1960), or somewhat lower (323 m) according to newer observations by Clayton (1983 and pers. commun.). Although the Portage outlet is much smaller, and at the Duluth level would have been much shallower than the Brule outlet, the two outlets should have functioned simultaneously whenever the lake stood at the Duluth level. However, the Portage outlet would have functioned alone at times when the ice front plugged the Brule outlet, as pointed out by Clayton (1983).

None of the above-mentioned outlets has been significantly uplifted by glacial rebound since they were last functioning. That is not the case, however, for outlets on the northwestern basin rim. The latter area, which links the history of the Lake Agassiz basin, has been recently studied and summarized by Teller and Thorleifson (1983). The first of these outlets drained a small ice-marginal lake, Lake Kaministikwia, westward into glacial Lake Agassiz (Emerson Phase). Glacial Lake Kaministikwia was dammed in the

reentrant between the Dog Lake and Marks moraines west of Thunder Bay, Ontario. The overflow was near the southeastern corner of Lac des Mille Lacs, an area that has rebounded some 100 m since the outlet last functioned.

Finally, there is a group of drainage channels west of Lake Nipigon that also connected Lake Agassiz and lakes in the Superior basin, but in this case the drainage was from Agassiz into Superior. There are actually five groups of channel complexes, mapped by Teller and Thorleifson (1983), that functioned successively as the front of the ice sheet retreated from the area. One is shown schematically in Figure 2c. Depending on the relative lake levels in the two basins, drainage through these channels could have been in either direction, given that the southern outlets of the lakes Duluth and Agassiz are about the same altitude (300 to 325 m). However, because glacier retreat in the eastern Superior basin preceded that in the area west of Lake Nipigon, the Superior levels dropped earlier allowing higher level lakes in the Agassiz basin to drain eastward to Superior.

As postulated by Teller and Thorleifson (1983), the outflow through the Nipigon channels must have been catastrophic. As each channel (or complex of channels) was freed

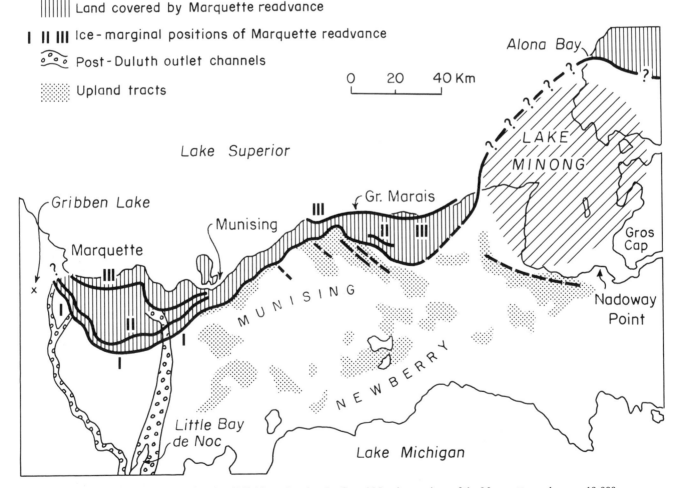

Figure 3. Eastern Upper Peninsula of Michigan showing the Grand Marais moraines of the Marquette readvance, 10 000 to 9800 B.P. and associated drainage outlets for Post-Duluth lakes. Note also the upland tracts formerly considered to be the Newberry and Munising moraines. At this time glacial Lake Minong was restricted to the Whitefish Bay Area. After Drexler *et al.* (1983).

of its icy barrier, initial discharges in excess of 100 000 m³/s ensued. Some 4000 km³ of Lake Agassiz water entered the Superior basin in less than 2 years (Teller and Thorleifson, 1983, p. 286-287). This influx would have dissipated across the broad surface of Lake Superior, conceivably raising its surface nearly 50 m for a brief interval. If Lake Superior was broadly connected with lakes Michigan and Huron at the time of the catastrophic discharge, e.g., during the Algonquin Phase of the Great Lakes, then all three basins (with some 200 000 km² surface area) might have experienced a brief surge of some 20 m. To our knowledge, no field evidence of such a surge has been detected.

In the case of the latest episode, early in the Nipigon Phase of Lake Agassiz, the catastrophic discharge would have entered the Minong level of Lake Superior, which was maintained by a barrier of glacial drift across Whitefish Bay (details below). That barrier had apparently been maintained for some centuries, but must have been cut down rapidly when the flood surge passed through. The evidence for such erosion is seen in the high, concave scarps at Nadoway Point (Michigan), as pointed out previously by Saarnisto (1975), although he was not then aware of the flood surge mechanism responsible for the erosion. In detail, the erosion at Nadoway Point may have been episodic, being renewed when each new outburst occurred west of Lake Nipigon. It may not be a mere coincidence that five drainage outlets are recognized by Teller and Thorleifson (1983) and that five or six discrete lowerings of level in the Superior basin are suggested by mapped shorelines between the Minong and

Houghton levels (Farrand, 1960; Teller and Thorleifson, 1983, Fig. 3).

Although it has been suggested (Prest, 1970) that there "perhaps" was overflow from Lake Barlow-Ojibway (north of the continental divide in the Hudson Bay basin) into Lake Superior, neither Farrand (1960) nor Zoltai (1967) see evidence for it.

GLACIOISOSTATIC REBOUND

The shoreline diagrams discussed in the following section show the progressive rise of water planes in a northerly direction beginning from a point near Duluth. The extreme southwest corner of the basin, including the areas of the Brule and Portage outlets, appeared to Farrand (1960) not to have been tilted since the last time that the lake stood at the Duluth shoreline, that is, since the Marquette readvance. However, on the basis of more detailed study and better maps, Clayton (1983, Fig. 9) now thinks the Duluth water plane is slightly tilted all the way to the Portage outlet.

The pattern of rebound as depicted by isobases drawn on the former water planes fits coherently into the regional pattern of uplift (Teller and Thorleifson, 1983, Fig.1). The isobases shown here (Fig. 4) for Lake Washburn, a middle level of the Post-Duluth Phase, and for Lake Minong, are taken from Farrand (1960, Pl. III) with some minor adjustment of the Minong isobases to bring them into agreement with Stanley's Minong data (G. M. Stanley, pers. commun.). The difference in altitude between the Washburn and Minong isobases in Figure 4 reflects the drop in lake level

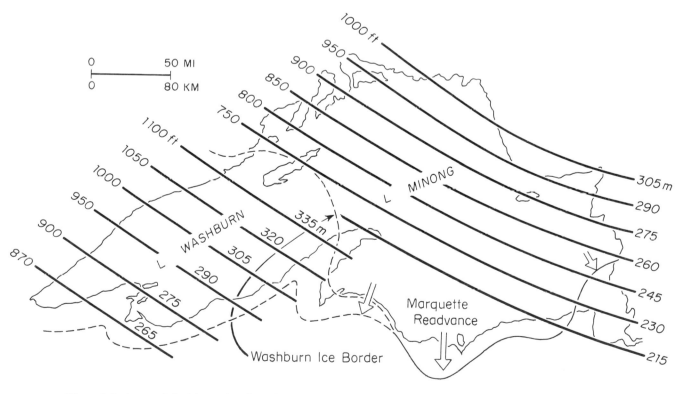

Figure 4. Isobases of glacioisostatic rebound on the Washburn and Minong water planes. The inferred ice border of Lake Washburn shows the rapid retreat that took place in the western basin while the ice front remained on the Michigan coast in the east. Modified from Farrand (1960).

during the century or so that separates those lakes in time.

Glacial rebound also played a role in determining the relative position of a former shoreline relative to today's water surface. This is especially critical for lakes with outlets in the Sault Ste. Marie area, that is, along one side of the basin with respect to the direction of maximum tilt. Since the maximum rebound occurred in the northeast, the isobase passing through the Sault outlet trends northwestward across the lake approximately to the international border at Pigeon River (Fig. 4). With ongoing uplift, all water planes with an outlet at the Sault will tend to be drowned southwest of the Sault-Pigeon River isobase (Fig. 5a). For this reason the Houghton low-stage shoreline is completely submerged throughout the United States portion of the Superior shoreline, and the Minong shoreline can be traced southwestward into Minnesota only about as far as Grand Portage, beyond which it is intersected by the stronger and younger Nipissing shoreline, and finally plunges below present water level (Fig. 5a; see also Farrand, 1960, Pl. II). The Houghton shoreline in the southwestern corner of the basin should lie at about 110 m (360 ft.) above sea level, that is, submerged under some 73 m of water.

Finally, isostatic rebound appears to be continuing in the Superior basin, as well as across northern Huron and Ontario basins. Apparent vertical movement determined by the study of lake gauges (Coordinating Committee, 1977) shows the northeastern corner of the basin rising 27 cm per century and the Duluth area subsiding 21 cm per century relative to Point Iroquois, which is at the head of the St. Marys River (Fig. 6). Thus, the total differential movement from southwest to northeast is about 48 cm per century.

GLACIAL LAKE SEQUENCE IN THE SUPERIOR BASIN

Having reviewed the topographic configuration of the basin, the lobation and timing of Late Wisconsinan ice movements, and the positions of possible outlets and their uplift, as well as connections with the Lake Agassiz basin, we can now summarize the succession of glacial lakes that occurred in various parts of the basin (Fig. 7).

Western Superior Basin

Lakes earlier than the Greatlakean Subage, that is, those which have been completely overrun by a subsequent ice advance, will not be discussed here. The earliest lakes for which we still have a record of both shorelines and deposits were narrow ice-marginal lakes ponded between the ice front and the bedrock highlands in western northern Michigan and northern Wisconsin. Meltwater was trapped in several embayments between the Keweenaw Peninsula and Duluth. Overflow occurred from east to west from one embayment into the next through bedrock channels, through channels one wall of which was formed by the ice front, or even directly across the surface of the thin edge of the ice sheet (e.g., Drexler, 1981, p. 91).

These ice-marginal lakes were discussed and mapped by Leverett (1929, p. 55-57). Glacial Lake Ontonagon (western Michigan) spilled westward into glacial Lake Ashland, whose discharge passed across the axis, or around the end,

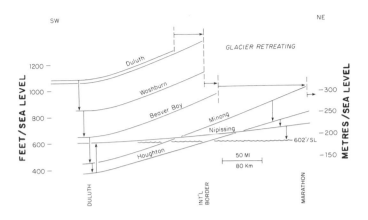

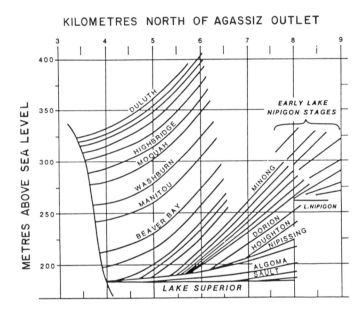

Figure 5. Shoreline-relation diagrams for the western part of the Superior basin. 5a) Generalized diagram emphasizing glacier retreat and the submergence of Houghton and Minong shorelines south of the international border (Pigeon River-Sault isobase). After Farrand (1969). 5b) More complete diagram emphasizing relations with the Lake Nipigon basin. After Teller and Thorleifson (1983).

of the Bayfield Peninsula into glacial Lake Brule, the drainage of which flowed southward through the Brule outlet into the St. Croix River (Fig. 2b and 2d). Farther west was glacial Lake Nemadji which discharged via the Portage (Moose Lake) outlet, ultimately into the St. Croix River also. As the ice front retreated from the intervening bedrock highs, these lakes merged with each other, forming glacial Lake Duluth, discharging at its higher levels through both Brule and Portage outlets, but utilizing only the Brule outlet at its lower levels. This scenario of narrow, ice-marginal lakes expanding into a unified Duluth-type glacial lake must have occurred repeatedly during oscillations of the ice front. The visible evidence of these lakes, however, is restricted to those lakes that formed upon retreat from the Nickerson and related moraines, about 11 500 B.P. and those lakes created and de-

stroyed by the Marquette advance and retreat, about
10 000 B.P.

The name "Glacial Lake Duluth" was first proposed by
F. B. Taylor, according to Leverett (1929, p. 57), for the
prominent beaches in the city of Duluth. Leverett *(ibid.)*
recognized that Lake Duluth expanded rapidly northward
upon ice retreat and that the northern and eastern beaches of
Lake Duluth were not only somewhat younger, but also
slightly lower in altitude (when corrected for rebound) than
the highest Duluth beach in the southwest. He attributed this
state of affairs to downcutting of the Brule outlet during the
lifetime of Lake Duluth.

The Duluth beach is the most prominent shoreline, above
the Nipissing, in the western Lake Superior basin. However,
it is not strongly developed in comparison to some Lake
Agassiz or Lake Algonquin shorelines of similar age (cf.
Clayton, 1983, p. 294). Some of its strength around and
southwest of Duluth may be attributed to the possibility that
it was occupied twice – during the retreats from the Nickerson moraine first and then later at the time of the Marquette
readvance. Throughout the rest of the basin the earlier Lake
Duluth shoreline features (Phase B of Clayton, 1983) would
have been destroyed by the Marquette advance.

As mentioned above, the ice front retreated more rapidly
from the western basin than it did from the Marquette area.
Thus, the water level remained at the Duluth levels (now 331
to 314 m or 1085 to 1030 ft. above sea level at the west end of
the basin) until ice retreat in the Huron Mountains-
Marquette area exposed outlets lower than the Brule outlet.
At that time lake levels began to fall stepwise as different

TABLE I

**POST-DULUTH LAKES IN THE WESTERN BASIN OF
LAKE SUPERIOR**

Name	Original Level (metres/feet)	Reference
Sub-Duluth	307/1007	Farrand, 1960, p. 26
Tamarack	300/975(?)	Hughes, 1963, p. 208
Highbridge	291/954	Farrand, 1960, p. 27
Moquah	280/920	Farrand, 1960, p. 28
Washburn	261/855	Farrand, 1960, p. 29
Manitou	233/765	Farrand, 1960, p. 20
Beaver Bay	198/650	Farrand, 1960, p. 33
Shelter Bay	? *	Drexler, 1981, p. 216
Huron Mountain	? *	Drexler, 1981, p. 176

* Original levels now drowned below Lake Superior.

outlets were opened or were deepened by erosion; the details
of this Post-Duluth Phase are given by Drexler (1981) and
reviewed in Drexler *et al.* (1983). The Post-Duluth Phase was
brief. Some nine named lake levels (Fig. 5b and Table I) are
recognized within the interval 9800 to 9700 B.P., thus explaining the faintness of geomorphic development of their
shorelines (Clayton, 1983, p. 294).

The latest of the Post-Duluth lakes, glacial Lake Huron
Mountain of Drexler (1981), discharged along the ice front as
it retreated from the Grand Marais III moraine into glacial
Lake Minong, then occupying the southeastern corner of the
basin (Fig. 3).

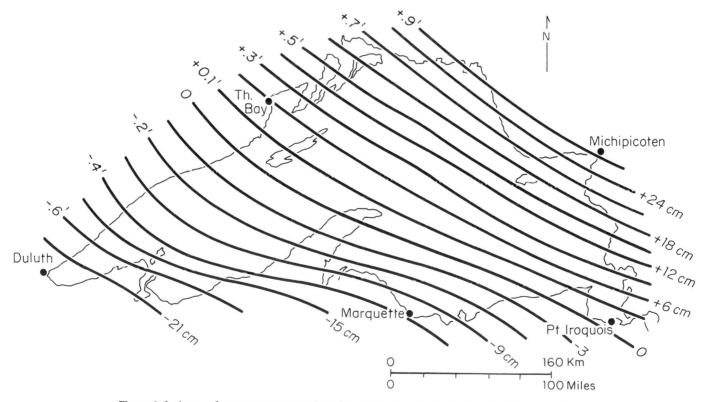

Figure 6. Isobases of contemporary warping of the Lake Superior basin based on lake-gauge data.
After Coordinating Committee (1977). Rates are in centimetres and feet per century.

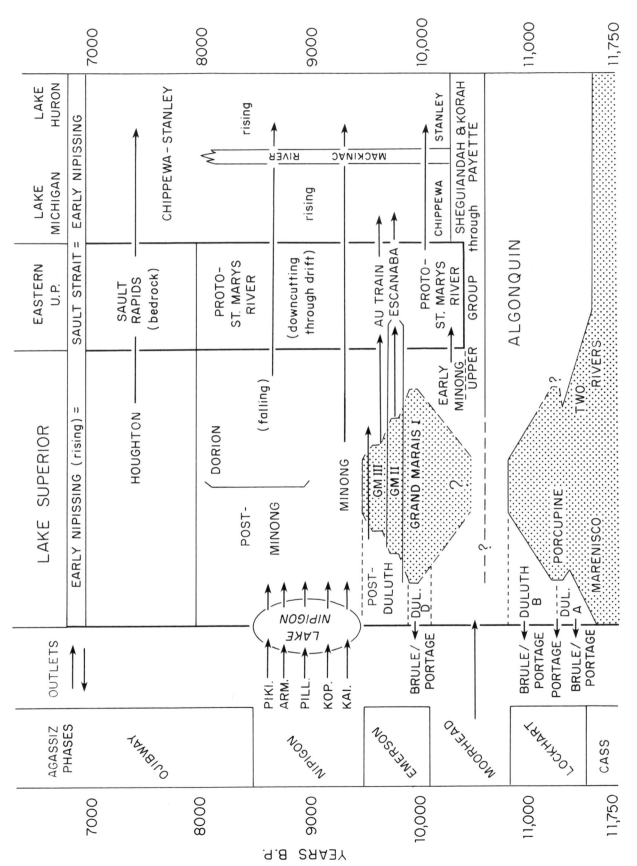

Figure 7. Chronological chart of ice-sheet fluctuations and glacial lake phases in the Superior basin and their relations with adjacent areas, based on numerous sources, but primarily Drexler *et al.* (1983), Clayton (1983), and Teller and Thorleifson (1983). Stippled: ice sheet present.

Eastern Superior Basin

Before pursuing the story of Lake Minong, it is necessary to review the lake development in the southeast. Following the initial Greatlakean advance to the Two Rivers moraine in the Lake Michigan basin at 11 800 B.P., the ice front began its northward retreat with glacial Lake Algonquin lapping against it on the south. As the ice front retreated across the Niagara Escarpment, which forms the topographic backbone of the eastern part of Michigan's Upper Peninsula, ice recession may have slowed. In any case, Lake Algonquin was very shallow in this area so that extensive outwash deltas were formed (Fig. 2c). These are the extensive, high-level sand plains of the eastern Upper Peninsula (Futyma, 1981). This episode of retarded retreat was part of Saarnisto's (1974) scenario for an "Algonquin Stadial," a concept now rejected by Drexler et al. (1983).

Also rejected, moreover, is the concept that the higher, rolling tracts of the eastern Upper Peninsula, south of the Grand Marais moraines, are in fact synchronous belts of end moraines. They were discussed by Leverett (1929, p. 49-53) and named "Newberry" and "Munising" by Bergquist (1936); see Figure 3. Drexler has determined that some of these high areas are, in fact, bedrock hills and others are composed largely of outwash (Drexler et al., 1983). The Newberry and Munising "moraines" formed an important part of Hough's (1958) reconstruction of Lake Algonquin history. He saw them as marking ice barrier positions that prevented Lake Algonquin from flooding into the Superior basin, a concept also adopted by Farrand (1960). It is now recognized that the main Algonquin shoreline encircles these "morainic" uplands (Futyma, 1981), a conclusion not in agreement with Hough's notion.

In summary, the only late-Wisconsinan (Greatlakean) ice border known in the eastern Upper Peninsula is the Grand Marais moraine (I, II and III). Thus, Lake Algonquin washed across all the peninsula east of the meridian of Munising and

into the Superior basin prior to the Marquette advance. Only the highest hills would have been emergent as islands in Lake Algonquin. Any Algonquin shorelines that may have formed in the Superior basin were effaced by the Marquette advance. Shorelines previously identified as "Algonquin" in Cook County, Minnesota, and in the Thunder Bay area (Leverett, 1929, p. 59; Sharp, 1953) must postdate the Marquette advance and belong to the Post-Duluth Phase (Farrand, 1960, p. 102-106).

Algonquin and some post-Algonquin shorelines are mapped along the Canadian shore north of Sault Ste. Marie, as well as in the Upper Peninsula of Michigan. Along the Ontario coast they are found only as far north as Alona Bay (Fig. 8). North of that point the Minong shoreline is the highest lacustrine feature. The Alona Bay vicinity, therefore, appears to mark the limit of the Marquette readvance along the eastern border of the Superior basin. It is not known where the ice front was located at the time of maximum retreat in Lake Algonquin time. It must have been at or north of Alona Bay in the east and somewhere in the Lake Nipigon basin in the north, in order to allow eastward drainage from the Agassiz basin (Moorhead Phase).

TABLE II

POST-ALGONQUIN LAKES IN THE LAKE HURON AND EASTERN SUPERIOR BASINS

Name	Original Level (metres/feet)	Reference
Upper Group	ca. 170/555	Leverett and Taylor, 1915, p. 416
Wyebridge	165/540	Stanley, 1936, p. 1948
Penctang	155/510	Stanley, 1936, p. 1948
Cedar Point	150/493	Stanley, 1936, p. 1948
Payette	142/465	Stanley, 1936, p. 1948
Sheguiandah	134/440(?)	Hough, 1958, p. 234-5
Korah	122/400(?)	Hough, 1958, p. 234-5

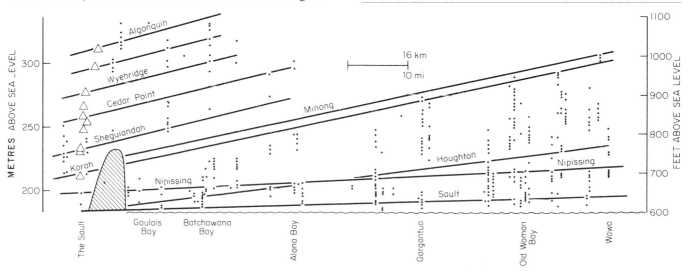

Figure 8. Detailed shoreline-relation diagram for the east coast of Lake Superior from Sault Ste. Marie to Michipicoten Harbor. The bearing of this diagram is N 21°E. For clarity, not all post-Algonquin and post-Minong shorelines have been drawn. Note particularly that the Minong, Houghton, and Sault water planes are restricted to the Superior basin by a barrier in the Nadoway Point-Gros Cap area, as explained in the text. Modified from Farrand (1960). Large triangles in Sault area from Cowan (1985).

During Algonquin time, lake levels in the eastern part of the basin, and presumably in the western basin too, were controlled by Lake Algonquin's outlets at Chicago and Port Huron. Subsequently lake levels in the Michigan and Huron basins began to fall as lower outlets east of Georgian Bay were deglaciated (Prest, 1970; Harrison, 1972), creating the post-Algonquin levels in the Huron basin (Stanley, 1936; and Table II). Comparable levels are known in the Lake Michigan basin. The lowest, Lake Chippewa, was separated from Lake Stanley by dry land and the Mackinac River in the area of the present Straits of Mackinac (Stanley, 1938).

Glacial Lake Minong

Lake Minong was named by Stanley (1941) for prominent beaches on Isle Royale ("Minong" in the Chippewa language) that he correlated with the highest ancient shorelines of the northern and eastern coasts of Lake Superior. He thus recognized that Lake Minong was the first late-or postglacial lake (for which shoreline evidence still remains) to approximate the present coastal configuration of Lake Superior. In his dissertation Stanley (1932) had called this same lake "Fort Brady" because of its apparent continuity with the Fort Brady water plane (a post-Algonquin level) in the Sault Ste. Marie area. Because of conceptual differences, however, Stanley (1936) later argued that Minong and Fort Brady were not the same lake, and subsequently the name "Fort Brady" dropped out of usage. Still later, the original type-Fort Brady beach, just west of Sault Ste. Marie, Ontario, became the type-Korah beach of Hough (1958, p. 234-236), the lowest of the named post-Algonquin levels prior to Lake Stanley. However, its altitude is in question; see Cowan (1985).

The question of which post-Algonquin lakes penetrated into the Superior basin has been the subject of some difference of opinion, in part brought about by the terminological complications reviewed in the preceding paragraph. It appears that the Payette and Sheguiandah beaches can be followed to Alona Bay (Fig. 8), but the next lower shoreline at that point correlates with the Minong shoreline as recognized by Stanley (1932, 1941). In the absence of any obvious barrier between Lake Huron and Lake Superior in the Sault area and a slightly different interpretation of shoreline tilt, Farrand (1960, p. 94) suggested that the Minong water plane was confluent with Lake Sheguiandah at Sault Ste. Marie. With the application of radiocarbon dating to the post-Algonquin sequence and with the recognition of the Marquette readvance and its dating, it became obvious that Lake Minong and Lake Sheguiandah were not correlatives (Prest, 1970; Saarnisto, 1975; Drexler, 1981, p. 261-263). In brief, the North Bay outlet was open and, therefore, lake levels in the Michigan and Huron basins were well below the Sheguiandah level before the Marquette advance brought Lake Minong into existence.

Given the fact that the Minong water plane intersects the Sault area about 40 m above the present outlet sill (Fig. 8), Saarnisto (1975) recognized that there must have been a barrier that retained the water in the Superior basin at the Minong level while the Huron basin lakes were falling. He proposed a barrier of glacial drift between Gros Cap (On-

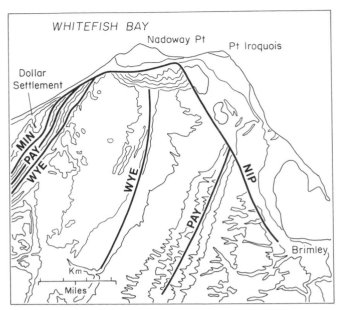

Figure 9. Topographic map of Nadoway Point and Point Iroquois, showing truncation of the Wyebridge, Payette, and Minong shorelines, presumably by catastrophic floods from Lake Agassiz in post-Minong time. (Base map: United States Geological Survey Brimley and Strongs quadrangles, 1:62 500).

tario) and Nadoway Point (Michigan), on the southeastern side of Whitefish Bay. Gros Cap is a heavily eroded bedrock headland, but Nadoway Point is built largely of unconsolidated sediment that has impressive traces of recent erosion (Fig. 9). The upland that terminates at Nadoway Point is crossed by shorelines of the post-Algonquin Upper Group, Wyebridge(?), and Payette. The latter two are abruptly truncated at Nadoway Point by concave scarps, at the base of which is the Nipissing bluff. At first glance one might attribute all the erosion of the high bluffs to Nipissing wave action. However, the east-facing bluff, overlooking Monocle and Spectacle lakes and Point Iroquois, is not likely to be a wave-cut bluff because it is sheltered from the prevailing winds. In fact, the Nipissing features in the area of Point Iroquois appear to be largely constructional, not erosional. Thus, the prominent bluff on the east side of Nadoway Point can be interpreted as the result of dissection of a barrier some time after the Payette Phase.

Moreover, the date of downcutting of the Nadoway Point-Gros Cap sill can be refined further. In the Pendills Lake embayment immediately west of Nadoway Point a bench at about 213 to 219 m (700 to 720 ft.) above sea level can be seen below the Wyebridge and Payette shorelines (Fig. 9). Like the latter, it is truncated at Nadoway Point, on one hand, and by the Nipissing beach along Pendills Bay, on the other. This feature at 213 to 219 m is a good candidate for the Minong shoreline; it occurs only west of Nadoway Point, that is on the Superior side, not to the east on the Lake Huron slope. Thus, one can conclude that the cutting of the steep bluffs of Nadoway Point occurred during or after the Minong Phase, and brought about the demise of that lake. As described earlier, the catastrophic floods released from Lake Agassiz through the Nipigon channels could have supplied the erosive force necessary to cut through the Minong sill.

Concerning the initiation of Lake Minong, perhaps there is still some reality in Farrand's (1960) correlation of Minong and Sheguiandah. One can see in the shoreline diagram (Fig. 8) that the Minong water plane is only slightly lower than the Sheguiandah level and apparently followed it closely in time. Recall that during Algonquin and early post-Algonquin time the ice front was receding well into the Superior basin, allowing the post-Algonquin lakes, at least through Shequiandah, to transgress there as well (as shown in Fig. 8). As the ice began to advance once more on its way to the Marquette maximum (Grand Marais moraine) it expelled the lake waters from the basin except in the extreme southwest (Lake Duluth) and southeast (Lake Minong) and obliterated the traces of all former shorelines north of its most advanced position, i.e., north of Alona Bay on Figure 8. Since the Minong shoreline is the highest one found on drift of Marquette age, the Nadoway-Gros Cap sill must have already been cut down to the Minong level during the post-Algonquin ice retreat. In other words, it would appear that just after the time of the Sheguiandah level the lakes in the

Huron and Superior basins were separated by the Nadoway Point sill. In the Huron basin the water continued to fall through the Korah to the Stanley level, but the Superior basin lake remained perched close to the former Sheguiandah level. We suggest that this phase be called ''Early Minong'' since it preceded the maximum of the Marquette advance. Lake level during the Early Minong Phase and the main Minong Phase appears not to have changed appreciably.

At the time of the Grand Marais moraine (Marquette maximum about 10 000 B.P.) glacial Lake Minong was about twice the size of the present Whitefish Bay. It expanded rapidly, however, as the ice front pulled back across the lake, probably accelerated by calving in the deep waters of the lake. When the retreating Marquette ice cleared the tip of the Keweenaw Peninsula, Lake Minong would have rapidly expanded westward to the Minnesota and Wisconsin shores, and very soon thereafter to the northern (Ontario) shore where it produced the highest shoreline features found there about 9500 B.P. (Saarnisto, 1975; Drexler et al., 1983).

Therefore, the main level of glacial Lake Minong, which as

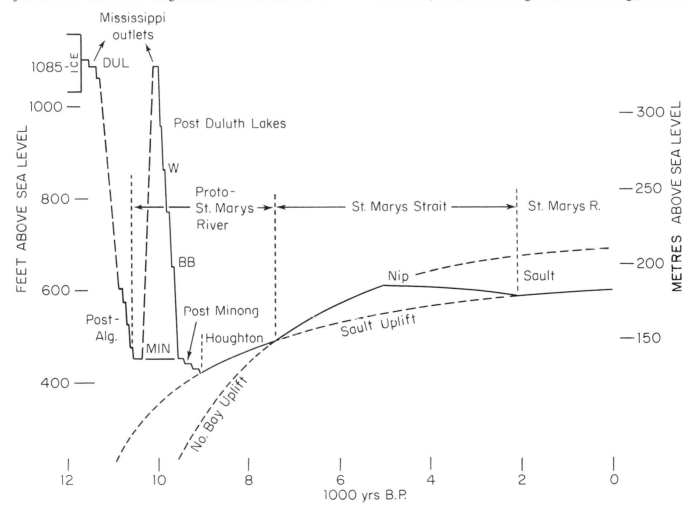

Figure 10. Curves of water level in the Lake Superior basin prior to rebound. The ''spike'' at 10 000 B.P. occurred only in the western basin, while the eastern basin remained at the Minong level. DUL=Duluth, POST-ALG=Post-Algonquin, MIN=Minong, W=Washburn, BB=Beaver Bay, NIP=Nipissing. Modified from Farrand (1969).

conceived by Stanley touched all the shores of the Superior basin, was achieved diachronically between about 9800 and 9500 B.P. However, the Early Minong level was apparently established somewhat earlier, synchronously with or immediately following the Sheguiandah level, perhaps around 10 400 B.P. (± 200 years, given the constraints of Lake Algonquin and North Bay history; Karrow *et al.*, 1975).

Post-Minong History

As discussed above, the catastrophic floods of Lake Agassiz water that entered the Superior basin as the Marquette Phase ice freed the Lake Nipigon area were the probable causes of downcutting of the Nadoway Point sill. Lake level was lowered in five or six steps from the Minong to the Houghton levels, the latter being stabilized when the present bedrock sill in the St. Marys River was reached. Thus, the Houghton low level in the Superior basin came into existence well after the extremely low Chippewa and Stanley levels to the south (Fig. 7), as a number of previous workers have concluded in recent years. In fact, the Chippewa and Stanley levels were already rising, because of rebound of the North Bay outlet, while Superior waters were still falling toward the Houghton minimum.

Ultimately the North Bay outlet rebounded to the level of the Sault barrier, which was rebounding more slowly (Fig. 10), and the waters of lakes Huron-Michigan and the Superior basin were once again confluent at the same level about 7500 B.P. Saarnisto (1975) places this event at about 7000 B.P. The waters continued to rise, moreover, as North Bay had not yet rebounded to the altitude (184 m or 605 ft. above sea level) of the abandoned southern outlets of Michigan and Huron, at Chicago and Port Huron, respectively. The latter event initiated the three-outlet phase of the Nipissing Great Lakes, perhaps as early as 5500 B.P., but more likely closer to 4700 B.P. (Cowan, 1978), and produced some of the most spectacular geomorphic features found along any ancient shoreline in the Superior basin.

Following the Nipissing maximum, lake levels began to fall throughout the upper Great Lakes as downcutting of the Port Huron outlet took place. The Algoma level was common to all three basins, but at 2200 B.P. the falling water level in Lake Huron dropped below the rebounding sill at the Sault (Fig. 10). At that time the Superior and Huron basins were once again separated by the St. Marys River (Farrand, 1962; Saarnisto, 1975). This event brought into being the Sault level (Fig. 5b, 8, 10) within the Superior basin, and subsequently the Sub-Sault level (Farrand, 1960, p. 58-61), the latter being barely above the reach of present-day storm waves on the north shore.

In a number of localities around the northern part of the Superior basin distinct levels of these youngest shorelines (Algoma, Sault and Sub-Sault) do stand out, but in many other places there are essentially continuous corrugated surfaces below the main Nipissing beach, composed of one beach ridge after the other, each at a slightly lower altitude, all the way down to present lake level. This situation reflects the continuing process of glacial rebound upon which was superposed oscillations of lake level, perhaps climatically induced.

SUMMARY

The late Quaternary history of Lake Superior that can be reconstructed from tangible field evidence is limited to post-Twocreekan time, and even for the early part of this interval the record is not very clear. The Greatlakean ice advance completely filled the Superior basin, reaching the Nickerson moraine in the Duluth area. Retreat from this position allowed narrow marginal lakes to form that ultimately expanded into glacial Lake Duluth (Phases A and B of Clayton, 1983) discharging to the Mississippi drainage by way of the Brule outlet in Wisconsin and to a limited extent by way of the Portage outlet in Minnesota. A major ice retreat then followed that deglaciated most or all of the Superior basin, and certainly the area west of Lake Nipigon, so that Lake Agassiz (Moorhead Phase) could drain eastward through Superior and into the Algonquin and post-Algonquin lakes of the Michigan and Huron basins.

A rapid readvance (Marquette) of the Superior lobe ensued, reaching the south shores of the basin about 10 000 B.P., forming the Grand Marais moraines in Michigan and the inner Saxon moraine in Wisconsin. Apparently the southwesternmost corner of the basin was not reached by the Marquette advance, and a final stand of glacial Lake Duluth (Phase D of Clayton, 1983) occurred there. Lake Duluth expanded rapidly northward as the ice retreated, being lowered slightly by erosion of the Brule outlet. As the ice front began to pull back from the Grand Marais moraines, the water in the western basin found outlets eastward, first through the Escanaba River, then through the Au Train-Whitefish trough into Green Bay, and later directly along the ice front into glacial Lake Minong, which was at that time limited to the southeastern corner of the basin.

Once the ice sheet retreated into the deeper part of the eastern basin, it dissipated rapidly, probably by calving, and glacial Lake Minong expanded to fill the entire Superior basin about 9500 B.P. While Lake Minong was still relatively small, it was retained behind a barrier of glacial drift between Nadoway Point and Gros Cap, about 40 m above the present level of the Sault rapids. Ice retreat not only allowed Lake Minong to expand, but also opened the eastern outlets (Nipigon Phase) of Lake Agassiz once again, allowing catastrophic floods to rush into Lake Minong eroding its outlet down to its ultimate (bedrock) level (Lake Houghton).

The subsequent history of the Superior basin was controlled largely by glacioisostatic rebound of the North Bay outlet (east of Lake Huron) and of the Sault sill. At first the rising waters of the Nipissing Great Lakes flooded into the Superior basin, but later they were excluded as the Sault sill became emergent. Thus Lake Superior was separated from Lake Huron about 2200 B.P. (Farrand, 1962). Rebound is still causing the northeastern part of the basin to rise relative to the southwest.

REFERENCES

Agassiz, Louis, 1850, Lake Superior: Its Physical Character, Vegetation, and Animals Compared to Those of Other and Similar Regions: Boston, Gould, Kendall and Lincoln, 428 p.

Bates, Robert L., and Jackson, J.A., Ed., 1980, Glossary of Geology, Second Edition: Falls Church, Virginia, American Geological Institute, 749 pages.

Bergquist, S.C., 1936, The Pleistocene History of the Tahquamenon and Manistique Drainage Region of the Northern Peninsula of Michigan: Michigan Geological Survey Publication 40, Geological Series 34, part 1, p. 7-148.

Black, R.F., 1976, Quaternary Geology of Wisconsin and Contiguous Upper Michigan: in Mahaney, W.C., ed., Quaternary Stratigraphy of North America: Stroudsburg, Pennsylvania, Dowden, Hutchinson and Ross, Inc., p. 93-117.

Clayton, Lee, 1983, Chronology of Lake Agassiz Drainage to Lake Superior: in Teller, J.T., and Clayton, Lee, eds., Glacial Lake Agassiz: Geological Association of Canada Special Paper 26, p. 291-307.

Clayton, Lee, and Moran, S.R., 1982, Chronology of Late Wisconsinan Glaciation in Middle North America: Quaternary Science Reviews, v. 1, p. 55-82.

Coordinating Committee on Great Lakes Basic Hydraulic and Hydrologic Data, 1977, Apparent Vertical Movement over the Great Lakes: Detroit District, United States Corps of Engineers, 70 p.

Cowan, W.R., 1978, Radiocarbon dating of Nipissing Great Lakes Events near Sault Ste. Marie, Ontario: Canadian Journal of Earth Sciences, v. 15, p. 2026-2030.

_____, 1985, Deglacial Great Lakes Shorelines at Sault Ste. Marie, Ontario: in Karrow, P.F., and Calkin, P.E., eds., Quaternary Evolution of the Great Lakes: Geological Association of Canada Special Paper 30.

Dell, C.I., 1971, Late Quaternary Sedimentation in Lake Superior: Ph.D. Dissertation, University of Michigan, Ann Arbor, Michigan, 184 p.

_____, 1975, Relationships of Till to Bedrock in the Lake Superior Region: Geology, v. 3, p. 563-564.

_____, 1976, Sediment Distribution and Bottom Topography of Southeastern Lake Superior: Journal of Great Lakes Research, v. 2, p. 164-176.

Drexler, C.W., 1981, Outlet Channels for the Post-Duluth Lakes in the Upper Peninsula of Michigan; Ph.D. Dissertation, University of Michigan, Ann Arbor, Michigan, 295 p.

Drexler, C.W., Farrand, W.R., and Hughes, J.D., 1983, Correlation of Glacial Lakes in the Superior Basin with Eastward Discharge Events from Lake Agassiz: in Teller, J.T., and Clayton, Lee, eds., Glacial Lake Agassiz: Geological Association of Canada Special Paper 26, p. 261-290.

Farrand, W.R., 1960, Former Shorelines in Western and Northern Lake Superior Basin: Ph.D. Dissertation, University of Michigan, Ann Arbor, Michigan, 266 p.

_____, 1962, Postglacial Uplift in North America: American Journal of Science, v. 260, p. 181-199.

_____, 1969, The Quaternary History of Lake Superior: Proceedings 12th Conference on Great Lakes Research, International Association of Great Lakes Research, p. 181-197.

Futyma, R.P., 1981, The Northern Limits of Lake Algonquin in Upper Michigan: Quaternary Research, v. 15, p. 291-310.

Harrison, J.E., 1972, Quaternary Geology of the North Bay-Mattawa Region: Geological Survey of Canada Paper 71-26, 37 p.

Hough, J.L., 1958, Geology of the Great Lakes: University of Illinois Press, Urbana, Illinois, 313 p.

Hughes, J.D., 1963, Physiography of a Six Quadrangle Area in the Keweenaw Peninsula North of Portage Lake: Ph.D. Dissertation, Northwestern University, Evanston, Illinois, 228 p.

_____, 1971, Post-Duluth Stage Outlet from the Lake Superior Basin: Michigan Academician, v. 3, no. 4, p. 71-77.

_____, 1978, Marquette Buried Forest 9850 Years Old: Abstract for the American Association for the Advancement of Science Annual Meeting, February 12-17,

Karrow, P.F., Anderson, T.W., Clarke, A.H., Delorme, L.D., and Sreenivasa, M.R., 1975, Stratigraphy, Paleontology, and Age of Lake Algonquin Sediments in Southwestern Ontario, Canada: Quaternary Research, v. 5, p. 49-87.

Lawson, A.C., 1893, Sketch of the Coastal Topography of the North Side of Lake Superior with Special Reference to the Abandoned Strands of Lake Warren: Geological and Natural History Survey of Minnesota, 20th Annual Report, 1891, p. 181-289.

Leverett, F., 1929, Moraines and Shorelines of the Lake Superior Basin: United States Geological Survey Professional Paper 154-A, 72 p.

Leverett, F., and Taylor, F.B., 1915, The Pleistocene of Indiana and Michigan and the History of the Great Lakes: United States Geological Survey Monograph 53, 529 p.

Need, E.A., Johnson, M.D., and Michelson, D.M., 1981, Till Stratigraphy and Glacial History along the Western Shoreline of Wisconsin's Bayfield Peninsula: Geological Society of America Abstracts with Programs, v. 13, no. 6, p. 311.

North American Commission on Stratigraphic Nomenclature, 1983, North American Stratigraphic Code: American Association of Petroleum Geologists Bulletin, v. 67, p. 841-875.

Prest, V.K., 1970, Quaternary Geology of Canada, in Douglas R.J.W., ed., Geology and Economic Minerals of Canada Chapter 12: Geological Survey of Canada, Economic Geology Report No. 1, Fifth Edition, p. 675-764.

Saarnisto, M., 1974, The Deglaciation History of the Lake Superior Region and Its Climatic Implications: Quaternary Research, v. 4, p. 316-339.

_____, 1975, Stratigraphic Studies on the Shoreline Displacement of Lake Superior: Canadian Journal of Earth Sciences, v. 12, p. 300-319.

Sharp, R.P., 1953, Shorelines of the Glacial Great Lakes in Cook County, Minnesota: American Journal of Science, v. 251, p. 109-139.

Showers, V., 1979, World Facts and Figures: New York, Wiley-Interscience, 757 p.

Stanley, G.M., 1932, Abandoned Strands of Isle Royale and Northeastern Lake Superior: Ph.D. Dissertation, University of Michigan, Ann Arbor, Michigan, 158 p.

_____, 1936, Lower Algonquin Beaches of Penetanguishene Peninsula: Geological Society of America Bulletin: v. 47, p. 1933-1960.

_____, 1938, The Submerged Valley through Mackinac Straits: Journal of Geology, v. 46, p. 966-974.

_____, 1941, Minong Beaches and Water Plane in Lake Superior Basin (Abstract): Geological Society of America Bulletin, v. 52, p. 1935.

Taylor, F.B., 1895, The Nipissing Beach on the North Superior Shore: American Geologist, v. 15, p. 304-314.

_____, 1897, Notes on the Abandoned Beaches of the North Coast of Lake Superior: American Geologist, v. 20, p. 111-128.

Teller, J.T., and Thorleifson, L.H., 1983, The Lake Agassiz-Lake Superior Connection: in Teller, J.T., and Clayton, Lee, eds., Glacial Lake Agassiz: Geological Association of Canada Special Paper 26, p. 261-290.

Wold, R.J., Hutchinson, D.R., and Johnson, T.C., 1982, Topography and Surficial Structure of Lake Superior Bedrock as Based on Seismic Reflection Profiles: Geological Society of America Memoir 156, p. 257-272.

Zoltai, S.C., 1965, Glacial Features of the Quetico-Nipigon Area, Ontario: Canadian Journal of Earth Sciences, v. 2, p. 247-269.

_____, 1967, Glacial Features of the North-Central Lake Superior Region, Ontario: Canadian Journal of Earth Sciences, v. 4, p. 515-528.

Zumberge, J.H., and Gast, P., 1961, Geological Investigations in Lake Superior: Geotimes, v. 6, p. 10-13.

Quaternary Evolution of the Great Lakes,
edited by P.F. Karrow and P.E. Calkin,
Geological Association of Canada Special Paper 30, 1985

DEGLACIAL GREAT LAKES SHORELINES
AT SAULT STE. MARIE, ONTARIO

W.R. Cowan

Palliser Environmental & Terrain Services Inc., 9859 Palistone Road, S.W., Calgary, Alberta T2V 3W1

ABSTRACT

At Sault Ste. Marie, Ontario, (lat. 46°31'N; long. 84°20'W) there is a very well developed suite of raised shoreline features ranging from barrier bar deposits to erosional scarps. The gross geology of the sequence is that of a delta having an uppermost water plane represented by a large barrier bar at 309 to 311 m a.s.l. Subsequent lower water levels resulted in the erosion and reworking of the deltaic sediments into a series of erosional scarps and depositional bars, depending on the type of sediment, aspect, and length of time the water remained at any specific level.

Level surveys were carried out on those features occurring between the Nipissing Great Lakes shoreline (198 m) and the Main Algonquin level (309 m). Of the upper Algonquin levels a strong feature is present at 295 m which is correlated with the Upper Orillia level. Lower Algonquin levels are suggested as follows: Wyebridge (275 m), Penetang (265 m), Cedar Point (257 m), and Payette (247 m). The Sheguiandah level is placed at 233 m and the Korah at 210 m. In addition, numerous shoreline levels are present at intermediate positions. These are interpreted as representing either single events, such as storms, or sites prone to shoreline development over short time spans.

RÉSUMÉ

À Sault Ste-Marie en Ontario (lat. 46°31'N; long 84°20'W) on peut observer une série de formes de rivages surélevés allant des formes d'accumulation de cordons littoraux aux escarpements d'érosion. Dans l'ensemble, la géologie de la région se résume à un delta où le niveau d'eau maximum atteint est représenté par un cordon littoral situé à une altitude de 309 à 311 m au-dessus du niveau de la mer. Par la suite, les niveaux d'eau inférieurs ont entraîné l'érosion et le remaniement des sédiments deltaïques en une série d'escarpements d'érosion ou d'accumulation en cordons littoraux. La forme résultante dépend du type de sédiment, de l'orientation et de la durée de chaque plan d'eau à une altitude donnée.

Des levées d'arpentage ont été effectuées sur les formes rencontrées sur les rivages du lac Nipissing (198 m) et de la phase principale du lac Algonquin (309 m). Sur les plus hauts rivages du lac Algonquin une forme bien définie se retrouve à 295 m d'altitude et est ici corrélée avec le haut niveau Orillia. Les niveaux inférieurs du lac Algonquin sont: Wyebridge (275 m), Penetang (265 m), Cedar Point (257 m), et Payette (247 m) d'altitude. Le niveau Sheguiandah est situé à 233 m d'altitude et celui de Korah à 210 m. En plus de ces niveaux, plusieurs autres lignes de rivage se rencontrent à des positions intermédiaires. Elles sont alors interprétées soit comme des évènemetns uniques, soit comme des plages de tempêtes ou encore comme des sites favorables au développement riverain pendant une courte période de temps.

INTRODUCTION

The spectacular raised shorelines of the deglacial Great Lakes at Sault Ste. Marie, Ontario, (Fig. 1) have been the subject of geological discussion for more than a century. This is because Sault Ste. Marie is strategically situated between the Lake Superior and Lake Huron basins and because it is located on a very common route of travel. In 1976 the writer was commissioned by the Ontario Geological Survey to map the Quaternary sediments of the Sault Ste. Marie area (N.T.S. 41 K NE). During this survey level lines were run over several suites of shoreline features to determine their elevations. The results of these surveys are presented herein and major lake levels interpreted with respect to classic Great Lakes history and recent work in adjoining areas. As such, it is intended as a contribution of site-specific data rather than as a synthesis of lake history in the area. This paper will consider only beach levels between the Nipissing and Algonquin phases.

Lines were run with a self-levelling surveying level using geodetic bench marks and road spot heights for control; these control points allow survey accuracy to about 30 cm. Water plane levels were placed at the top of depositional bar features and at the break in slope at the base of erosional scarps; these are estimated to provide water planes to an accuracy of about one metre under ideal conditions. How-

TABLE I

INTERPRETATION OF
SAULT STE. MARIE BEACH LEVELS
WITH RESPECT TO THOSE OF
SLY AND LEWIS (1972) FROM NORTHERN
MANITOULIN ISLAND

Sault Ste. Marie this study		Manitoulin Island Sly and Lewis (1972)		Huron Basin Lakes
(m)	(ft.)	(m)	(ft.)	
309	1015	309	1013	Main Algonquin
302?	990?	—	—	Ardtrea
295	966 - 968	287 - 296	940 - 970	Upper Orillia
?	?	—	—	Lower Orillia
275?	902?	271 - 276	890 - 905	Wyebridge
265	868	267	875	Penetang
257	842 - 844	259	850	Cedar Point
247	810 - 812	244	800	Payette
233±	763 - 768	233	765	Sheguiandah
210	690 - 694	212	695	Korah
198	650	198	650	Nipissing

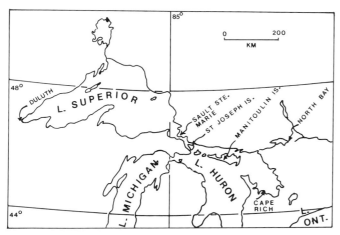

Figure 1. Location of Sault Ste. Marie.

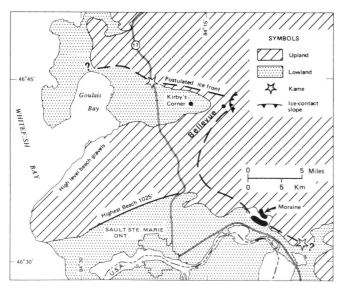

Figure 2. Postulated ice-frontal position at about the time of Main Lake Algonquin. From Cowan (1976, p. 135).

ever, storm features can create large perturbations if not recognized. For instance, modern Lake Superior storm beaches may be in excess of 2.5 m above mean lake levels and have been reported at more than four metres above mean lake level.

GEOLOGY

Bedrock geology dominates the physiographic setting at Sault Ste. Marie. The area shown as uplands on Figure 2 and the Gros Cap Highland on Figure 3 is underlain by Early to Late Precambrian rocks of plutonic, volcanic and sedimentary origin. The drift-covered lowlands to the south of these highlands are underlain by Cambrian or Late Precambrian red sandstone of the Jacobsville Formation.

The primary Quaternary feature present is a massive barrier bar-deltaic complex (Fig. 3) developed on the south side of the Gros Cap Highland and fed by southward-flowing meltwaters derived from ice on the Gros Cap Highland. It seems that the delta complex formed with ice in the immediate vicinity (Fig. 2) and at a water plane in which a barrier bar system was built at about 309 to 312 m (1015 to 1025 ft.). The degree of development of this feature has led most writers to conclude that it represents the Main Algonquin shoreline (Hough, 1958; Prest, 1970; Cowan, 1976; Futyma, 1981), though Saarnisto (1974) considered it to be the first high post-Main Algonquin phase shoreline. Lower shorelines are developed on this feature.

Radiocarbon dates presented by Saarnisto (1974) indicate that deglaciation of the area probably took place about 11 000 B.P. The ice-marginal position during the highest water level (Main Algonquin) is shown in Figure 2 (Cowan, 1976, p. 135) and implies that the Main Algonquin phase occupied at least a sizeable part of Whitefish Bay in eastern Lake Superior. This differs from Hough's (1958, p. 220) interpretation in which he placed the ice in Whitefish Bay and the ice front at the delta front (west) side of an ice-contact delta near Bellevue, rather than the ice on the upland with the ice front at the ice-contact face (east side), i.e., on the opposite side. This ice-marginal position is similar to that shown by Drexler et al. (1983) for their late-glacial readvance to the Grand Marais Moraine which is about 1 000 years younger. The degree of development of the bar and contained gravels implies a large lake of considerable consequence and duration.

SHORELINE LEVELS

Numerous writers have observed and commented on the shoreline features at Sault Ste. Marie. However, the work of Lawson (1893) and Hough (1958) provides the most germane information with respect to the present study. Lawson (1893, p. 281-282) surveyed the raised beaches with a wye level and provided his data in feet above Lake Superior to two decimal places; his data are rounded and given in feet above sea level in Figure 4. Hough (1958, p. 235) used an altimeter and a road spot height to obtain the elevations shown on Figure 4; he also named the Korah beach and stage after the hamlet of Korah which is now within the City of Sault Ste. Marie.

The writer carried out 15 survey transects with a self-levelling level including one transect which followed the same road as Hough's. Survey transects were laid out following the mapping of all beaches in the area, bearing in mind the location of survey control points, and it is believed that good coverage was obtained. In Figure 4, beach features are broken into major and minor groups. The major features consist of either recurring groups of elevations from different transects or large well-defined bluffs. Minor features consist primarily of single occurrences of shoreline features or relatively minor bluffs or bars which perhaps reflect peculiarities of site, aspect, materials, or storms.

Visual inspection of Figure 4 indicates that the present survey data are more similar to those of Lawson than to those of Hough. Furthermore, several of Hough's key levels do not show up in Lawson's very detailed work nor in that of the present study. The reason for this is unexplainable, instrumental, or the result of subjective siting of survey points, particularly the base of erosional scarps. It is known that both Lawson and the writer used the base of erosional scarps to determine water planes; however, Hough's usage is not so clear as he tends to refer to terraces. Similarly, some discrepancies exist between elevations given by Hough (1958) for Manitoulin Island and those of Sly and Lewis (1972). For the purpose of this paper the writer's data are considered to be broader based than the older data and perhaps more accurate.

DISCUSSION

The barrier bar system at Sault Ste. Marie has been measured by numerous scientists as having its highest level between 309 and 311 m a.s.l. (1015 and 1020 ft.) with the highest value being reported at 313 m (1026 ft.). It is suggested here that 309 m (1015 ft.) is probably a good average value with higher beach gravels being the result of storms.

Most writers have considered this massive bar as representing the Main Lake Algonquin phase on the basis of its size and development. However, Saarnisto (1974) argued that this beach represents the first post-Main Algonquin stage on the basis of correlation with Chapman's (1954) shoreline measurements east of Lake Huron and on the basis of lake-bottom radiocarbon dates from Prince Lake (ca. 290 m) and Upper Twin Lake (ca. 302 m) near Sault Ste. Marie. Both lakes are below the highest shore level at Sault Ste. Marie and Saarnisto believed these dates (10 650 ± 265; HEL – 400: 10 800 ± 360; GSC – 1715) to be too young to represent Main Algonquin. However, recent data provided

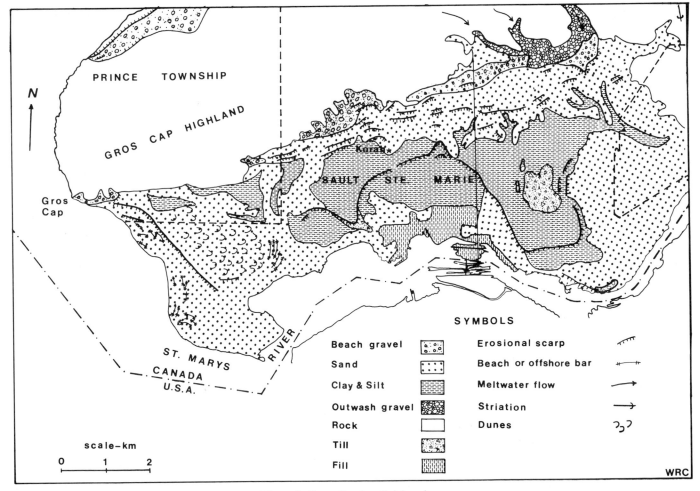

Figure 3. Generalized surficial geology.

by Karrow *et al.* (1975, p. 79) suggest that the Main Algonquin high water levels were in existence between 11 200 and 10 400 B.P., which would accommodate Saarnisto's radiocarbon dates.

Futyma (1981) also studied Lake Algonquin shorelines throughout eastern northern Michigan and concluded that the highest beach at Sault Ste. Marie, Ontario, is Main Algonquin, as is the highest beach on Manitoulin Island at 309 m (1013 ft.) based on his construction of isobases. Lewis (in Sly and Lewis, 1972) considered the uppermost beach near Little Current, Manitoulin Island to be Main Algonquin. Accepting this interpretation, the present study data are directly comparable with those near Little Current as both Main Algonquin and Nipissing levels are within one metre of each other at the two sites. Table I correlates the present study data with those of Manitoulin Island (Sly and Lewis, 1972).

From the top of the bar at Sault Ste. Marie descending to 274 m (900 ft.) there are numerous erosional bluffs or scarps (Fig. 4), all apparently indicating erosion of the bar complex as water levels lowered. Some of these are undoubtedly storm features; however, a recurring scarp is present at 295 m (966 to 968 ft.) which was also recorded by Lawson (1893) as a "good terrace". This is interpreted here as the Upper Orillia beach which Deane (1950) described as the strongest of the Upper Algonquin beaches. If this is so, then minor recurring features at about 302 m (990 ft.) may represent the Ardtrea beach.

No strong beach is present which appears to represent the Lower Orillia beach. It probably is present as one of the numerous features occurring between 274 and 291 m (900 and 954 ft.).

Within the present data, the Lower Algonquin beaches are enigmatic as very few data concur with Hough's interpretation: furthermore, Hough's data do not fit well with the Manitoulin Island data presented by Sly and Lewis (1972). The most significant feature is a high bluff having a base at 257 m (between 842 and 844 ft.) a.s.l. This is judged to be the Cedar Point level and the 247 m level (810 to 812 ft.) the Payette level. A strong beach occurring at 265 m (868 ft.), but measured at only one site on a well-developed suite of beaches, is interpreted as representative of the Penetang level. This is somewhat lower than Hough placed it and is also lower than the Manitoulin Island data. Finally, the

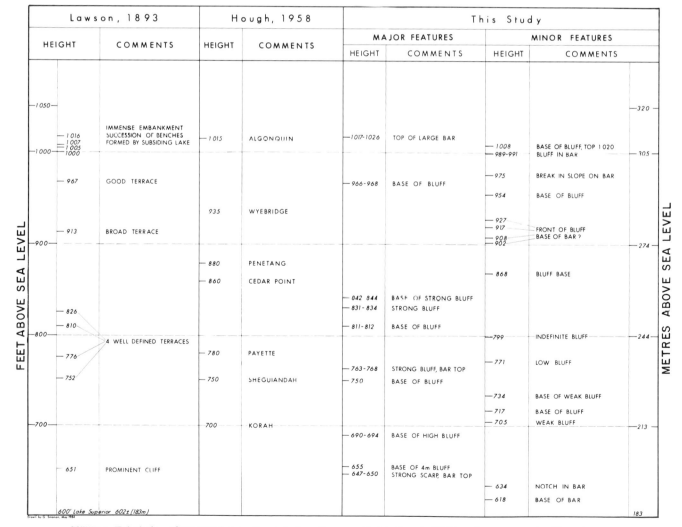

Figure 4. Tabulation of surveyed shoreline data from Lawson (1893), Hough (1958) and present study. Elevations are given in units of original measurement (feet).

Wyebridge level is placed at 275 m (902 ft.) with some question as this level represents a strong bluff which was only encountered at one site. This is considerably below the Wyebridge level given by Hough (935 ft.), which appears to be placed too high when compared with Harrison's (1972) uplift curves.

Though a beach is present at 228 m (750 ft.) (Hough's Sheguiandah beach), a much stronger feature is present at 233 m (763 to 768 ft.) which the writer prefers to equate with Sheguiandah. This agrees very closely with the level suggested by Sly and Lewis (1972) for the Sheguiandah beach on northern Manitoulin Island (233 m).

The Korah beach was defined at Sault Ste. Marie by Hough (1958) at an altitude of 213 m (700 ft.). No beach was found at this level during the present survey; however, well-developed scarps occur between 210 and 212 m (690 and 694 ft.) and these are considered to be the Korah. These are very comparable with northern Manitoulin Island (Sly and Lewis, 1972; 212 m). According to Hough (1958, p. 236), the Korah beach is the same as that termed Fort Brady by Leverett and Taylor (1915).

Finally, the Nipissing beach is extremely well developed and occurs at 198 m.

The above interpretation of water planes at Sault Ste. Marie does not include the recurring beach levels at 254 m and 200 m as well as numerous features which were encountered at only one site. Many of these are storm features, while others must go unexplained for now. Also, very few of these beaches have correlations in the Superior basin because ice apparently was present over much of it as recently as 10 000 B.P. (Drexler et al., 1983). Consequently only the Nipissing and Korah levels occupied both the Huron and Superior Basins; the Korah phase has been correlated with the Minong phase of the Superior basin by Drexler et al. (1983) although Farrand (1969) previously correlated the Sheguiandah level with the Minong (see also Farrand and Drexler, 1985).

CONCLUSION

The Sault Ste. Marie area exhibits a broad array of raised beaches which have been measured by numerous writers, each recording new levels. Most of the upper beaches are developed in unconsolidated sand which is more prone to short term erosion and redistribution than is clay, till, or rock. This may explain the profusion of beaches of limited areal extent or development. One could conclude that a series of beaches developed in sandy terrain may not be suitable for reference sections or control sections. Unfortunately, in many Shield areas these are the only sites upon which multiple beaches are developed.

The models upon which Upper and Lower Algonquin series are based have been in existence for one-quarter to one-half century without serious re-examination of the type areas or of the models which they represent.

The present study concludes that the uppermost beach at Sault Ste. Marie is that of Main Algonquin and has attempted to relate the beach sequence at Sault Ste. Marie more closely with the established sequence for Lake Huron than has been done previously; however, there remain numerous questions due to large data gaps.

ACKNOWLEDGEMENTS

This work is published with the permission of V.G. Milne, Director of the Ontario Geological Survey. Instrumental survey work was carried by B.H. Ainsworth and the writer. Additional information was provided by B.E. Broster, Senior Assistant during the geological mapping program. The paper was reviewed by W.R. Farrand, P.F. Karrow, and G.J. Larson.

REFERENCES

Chapman, L.J., 1954, An Outlet of Lake Algonquin at Fossmill Ontario: Proceedings of the Geological Association of Canada, v. 6, part 2, p. 61-68.

Cowan, W.R., 1976, Quaternary Geology of the Sault Ste. Marie area, District of Algoma: in Milne, V.G., Cowan, W.R., Card, K.D., and Robertson, J.A., eds., Summary of Field work, 1976, by the Geological Branch: Ontario Division of Mines Miscellaneous Publication MP67, p. 134-136.

Deane, R.E., 1950, Pleistocene Geology of the Lake Simcoe District, Ontario: Geological Survey of Canada Memoir 256, 108 p.

Drexler, C.W., Farrand, W.R., and Hughes, J.D., 1983, Correlation of Glacial Lakes in the Superior Basin with Eastward Discharge Events from Lake Agassiz: in Teller, J.T., and Clayton, L., eds., Glacial Lake Agassiz: Geological Association of Canada Special Paper 26, p. 309-329.

Farrand, W.R., 1969, The Quaternary History of Lake Superior: Proceedings 12th Conference on Great Lakes Research, International Association for Great Lakes Research, p. 181-197.

Farrand, W.R., and Drexler, C.W., 1985, Late Wisconsinan and Holocene History of the Lake Superior Basin: in Karrow, P.F., and Calkin, P.E., eds., Quaternary Evolution of the Great Lakes: Geological Association of Canada, Special Paper 30.

Fytyma, R.P., 1981, The Northern Limits of Glacial Lake Algonquin in Upper Michigan: Quaternary Research, v. 15, p. 291-310.

Harrison, J.E., 1972, Quaternary Geology of the North Bay-Mattawa Region: Geological Survey of Canada Paper 71-26, 37 p.

Hough, J.L., 1958, Geology of the Great Lakes: Urbana, Illinois, University of Illinois Press, 313 p.

Karrow, P.F., Anderson, T.W., Clarke, A.H., Delorme, L.D., and Sreenivasa, M.R., 1975. Stratigraphy, Paleontology, and Age of Lake Algonquin Sediments in Southwestern Ontario, Canada: Quaternary Research, v. 15, p. 49-87.

Lawson, A.C., 1893, Sketch of the Coastal Topography of the North Side of Lake Superior with Special Reference to the Abandoned Strands of Lake Warren (The Greatest of the Late Quaternary Lakes of North America): in Winchell, N.W., ed., The Geological and Natural History Survey of Minnesota, 20th Annual Report for the Year 1892, Minnesota State Geologist, p. 181-289.

Leverett, F. and Taylor, F.B., 1915, The Pleistocene of Indiana and Michigan and the History of the Great Lakes: United States Geological Survey Monograph 53, 529 p.

Prest, V.K., 1970, Quaternary Geology of Canada: in Douglas, R.J.W., ed., Geology and Economic Minerals of Canada: Geological Survey of Canada, Economic Geology Report No. 1, Fifth Edition, p. 676-764.

Saarnisto, M., 1974, The Deglaciation History of the Lake Superior Region and its Climatic Implications: Quaternary Research, v. 4, p. 316-339.

Sly, P.G., and Lewis, C.F.M., 1972, The Great Lakes of Canada – Quaternary Geology and Limnology: 24th International Geological Congress, Field Excursion A43 Guidebook, 92 p.

Quaternary Evolution of the Great Lakes,
edited by P.F. Karrow and P.E. Calkin,
Geological Association of Canada Special Paper 30, 1985

LATE WISCONSINAN AND HOLOCENE HISTORY
OF THE LAKE MICHIGAN BASIN

Ardith K. Hansel
Illinois State Geological Survey, 615 East Peabody, Champaign, Illinois 61820
David M. Mickelson
Department of Geology and Geophysics, University of Wisconsin-Madison, Madison, Wisconsin 53706
Allan F. Schneider
Department of Geology, University of Wisconsin-Parkside, Kenosha, Wisconsin 53141
Curtis E. Larsen
U.S. Geological Survey, Reston, Virginia 22092

ABSTRACT

Glacial Lake Chicago formed during late Wisconsinan deglaciation when ice extended into the Lake Michigan basin but still blocked northern outlets at or near the Straits of Mackinac. The lake drained southward across the Valparaiso Morainic System near Chicago. Deglaciation of the northern outlets permitted eastward drainage through the lower channels and consequent lowering of the lake level. Lake Chicago probably was at the Glenwood level (195 m, 640 ft.) twice, originally between 14 500 and 13 500 B.P. and again between 13 000 and 12 200 B.P. It fell below the modern lake level (177 m, 580 ft.) during the Two Creeks retreat, after 12 000 B.P., and it then rose to the Calumet level (189 m, 620 ft.) as the Two Rivers ice margin advanced, about 11 800 B.P. The short-lived Calumet phase probably ended when the Straits were deglaciated, shortly before 11 000 B.P. Subsequent deglaciation opened successively lower outlets across isostatically depressed southern Ontario; consequently, the lake level dropped to the low Chippewa level (116 m, 380 ft.) about 10 000 B.P. As differential isostatic rebound raised the northern outlets, the Lake Nipissing transgression reactivated the southern outlets at Port Huron and Chicago and the lake rose to the Toleston level (184 m, 605 ft.) between 5000 and 4000 B.P. Incision of the Port Huron outlet resulted in a gradual lowering to the Algoma level (179 m, 587 ft.) about 3800 B.P. and a subsequent lowering to the modern Lake Michigan level about 2500 B.P.

RÉSUMÉ

Le lac proglaciaire Chicago s'est formé lorsque la glaciation continentale couvrait le bassin du lac Michigan et bloquait les exutoires septentrionaux aux ou près des détroits de Mackinac. Le trop plein de ce lac se déchargeait par un exutoire méridional traversant la moraine Valparaiso près de Chicago. Lorsque les détroits ont été libres de glace le niveau du lac a baissé car l'eau s'est alors déversée par les exutoires nordiques moins élevés. Le lac Chicago a atteint son niveau Glenwood (195 m, 640 pieds) probablement deux fois: une première fois entre 14 500 et 13 500 B.P. puis à nouveau entre 13 000 et 12 200 B.P. Il descendit sous son niveau actuel (177 m, 580 pieds) lors de la retraite de Two Creeks qui débuta vers 12 000 B.P. pour ensuite atteindre le niveau Calumet (189 m, 620 pieds) lors de l'avancée glaciaire de Two Rivers vers 11 800 B.P. Cette courte phase Calumet se termina sans doute avec la déglaciation des détroits il y a un peu moins de 11 000 ans. La retraite glaciaire qui suivit, libéra des exutoires de plus en plus bas dans le sud de l'Ontario alors isostatiquement déprimé. En conséquence, le niveau du lac s'abaissa au bas niveau de Chippewa (116 m, 380 pieds) il y a environ 10 000 ans. Alors que le soulèvement isostatique élevait les altitudes des exutoires septentrionaux, la transgression du Nipissing réactivait les exutoires méridionaux à Port Huron et Chicago et le lac s'élevait au niveau Toleston (184 m, 605 pieds) entre 5000 et 4000 B.P. Le surcreusement de l'exutoire de Port Huron créa il y a environ 2500 ans un abaissement graduel jusqu'au niveau Algoma (179 m, 587 pieds) autour de 3800 B.P. et une baisse successive de la surface lacustre jusqu'au niveau actuel du lac Michigan.

INTRODUCTION

A series of lakes of different sizes and levels developed during and after late Wisconsinan deglaciation in the Lake Michigan basin. Evidence for these lake events comes from observations of the extent and altitudes of wave-cut cliffs, beaches, spits, and deltas, and from the altitudes of abandoned lake outlets. Differential isostatic rebound during and after deglaciation changed the altitudes of these features, and the history of rebound in the basin is not known in detail. Radiocarbon dating has progressed considerably since the studies of Bretz and Hough in the 1950s and 1960s; presentation of a summary of the new radiocarbon chronology is the main emphasis in this paper. Our discussion focuses on radiocarbon-dated stratigraphy in the southern Lake Michigan area, the type area for many of the lake events and an area in which the effects of differential isostatic rebound are minimal.

The chronology of events in the Lake Michigan basin is summarized in Figure 1. Lithostratigraphic units in the area surrounding and beneath Lake Michigan record the principal glacial and lake phases in the basin. These phases are based on time-transgressive events and represent episodes of glacial and lake history. The names associated with the lakes that occupied the Lake Michigan basin during the past 16 000 years are indicated in Figure 1; the phases of lake history that we propose here are also indicated. The lake levels and the inlets and outlets associated with the lake history are also shown. The radiocarbon age assignments to the lake phases represent estimates based on our interpretation of the available radiocarbon evidence for events in the Lake Michigan basin area. The ages of some of the glacial and lake phases are not closely limited by radiocarbon measurements.

The lake chronology in the Lake Michigan basin proposed in Figure 1 is discussed in the main part of the paper. Mechanisms of lake level changes, relationships of glacial and lake events, and the effect of differential isostatic rebound on the lake history are discussed first.

Mechanisms of Lake Level Changes

Glacial and postglacial lake levels changed because of: 1) advance and retreat of ice margins that blocked or uncovered outlets, 2) downcutting of outlets, 3) major increases and decreases in the volume of water entering the lake, and 4) differential isostatic changes in the altitudes of parts of the basin or outlets. Generally, these mechanisms worked in combination to control events.

After the formation of the Valparaiso Morainic System, a proglacial lake called Lake Chicago formed when glacial ice still extended into the Lake Michigan basin and blocked outlets at or near the Straits of Mackinac. Lake Chicago drained by way of an outlet through the Valparaiso Morainic System and the Tinley Moraine southwest of Chicago. This outlet consisted of two trans-morainic channels (Des Plaines and Sag channels, Fig. 2) leading southwestward to the Illinois River and ultimately to the Mississippi River. When eastward drainage of lakes in the Lake Huron, Lake Saginaw, and Lake Erie basins was obstructed by ice, the Chicago outlet also served as the "ultimate" outlet for water from the lakes that drained into Lake Chicago by way of the glacial Grand Valley across central Michigan (Fig. 3a, 3b, 3d).

Major fluctuations of the ice margin within the Lake Michigan basin occurred between 15 500 and 11 000 B.P. These fluctuations can be separated into three main glacial advance phases (the Cary, Port Huron, and Two Rivers advances) and two recessional phases (the Cary Port Huron

and Two Creeks recessions) (Fig. 1). During the recessional phases, the ice margin probably withdrew north of the Lower Peninsula of Michigan. Initial drainage was eastward through an inferred outlet in the Indian River lowland. Later it may have been through the Straits of Mackinac (Fig. 3c, 3e). When these outlets were deglaciated, the water level in the Lake Michigan basin was lowered because water in the contemporaneous lake in the Lake Huron basin drained eastward through still lower outlets – perhaps south to Lake Ypsilanti (Kunkle, 1963) or east through the Trent Valley.

Shoreline features occur at three distinct levels in the southwestern Lake Michigan area, and on the basis of these strands Leverett (1897) distinguished three main high levels of Lake Chicago: the Glenwood level at 195 m (640 ft.), the Calumet level at 189 m (620 ft.), and the Toleston level at 183 to 184 m (600 to 605 ft.). The lowering of the lake to progressively lower levels generally has been attributed to episodic downcutting of the Chicago outlet (e.g., Leverett, 1897; Alden, 1902; Goldthwait, 1908; Wright, 1918; Bretz, 1951, 1955; Hough, 1958), although explanations for the pauses interrupting downcutting have varied.

The most recent and most widely accepted explanation for lake level stabilization is the outlet control model of Bretz (1951, 1955), who argued that the lake level during each phase was governed by the threshold altitude of the outlet. Bretz speculated that the lake level was stabilized during the Glenwood and Calumet phases because erosion-resistant boulder lags formed in the outlet channels and retarded incision. He asserted that the boulder lags formed when discharge came solely from Lake Chicago and that they were swept away when discharge increased greatly owing to the addition of drainage from glacial lakes in the Lake Huron, Lake Saginaw, and Lake Erie basins. After deglaciation uncovered a lower outlet for the eastern lakes and the channels at Chicago had been downcut to bedrock, the lake was stabilized at the Toleston level.

An alternative to the outlet-control model is that of temporary lake level stabilization that was adjusted to the depth and width (cross-section) of the Chicago outlet. Like the modern St. Clair River outlet of Lake Huron, which prior to 1890 had an historic sill depth 6 m below the mean lake level, the Chicago outlet channel also probably had a considerable depth during the Glenwood and Calumet phases. Therefore, the bedrock sill of the channel (now at 180 m, 590 ft.) may have been reached earlier in the history of Lake Chicago than thought previously. The level of the lake may have fluctuated due to large increases and decreases in the volume of water in the lake basin (Wright, 1918). The flow through the channel, rather than a specific threshold altitude, probably controlled the lake levels because the altitude of the threshold at any given time provided only a lower limit to the lake level. For example, the depth of water flowing through the channel may have been near 9 m when the lake was at the Calumet level, but only 3 to 4 m when it was at the Toleston level.

A second alternative explanation of lake level changes involves possible, but as yet undocumented, differential isostatic uplift of the southern Lake Michigan area following deglaciation. If differential uplift was responsible for the re-

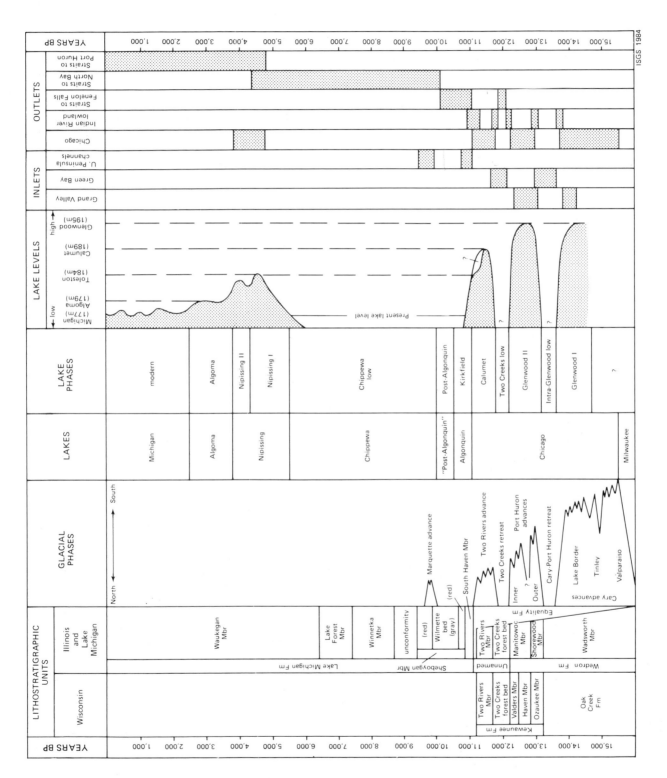

Figure 1. Chronology in the Lake Michigan basin. Shaded area indicates times inlets and outlets were used. Radiocarbon ages are estimates.

cord of lake level changes, the Glenwood and Calumet levels could represent times when isostatic changes were offset by changes in discharge (Larsen, 1985a). Incision of the channel into the Valparaiso Morainic System and the Tinley Moraine thus may have occurred largely in response to differential uplift.

The final retreat of the ice margin from the Straits resulted in coalescence of lakes in the Lake Michigan, Lake Huron, and Lake Superior basins. The outlet of this lake, known as Lake Algonquin, was at Fenelon Falls, east of Georgian Bay, in southern Ontario. According to some current interpretations (Eschman and Karrow, 1985; Finamore, 1985), the Fenelon Falls (Kirkfield) outlet was raised by differential uplift enough to reactivate the southern outlets at Chicago and Port Huron before the ice margin had retreated far enough to open still lower outlets near North Bay, Ontario. Kaszycki (1985), on the other hand, argues that the Main Algonquin water plane projected to a level approximately 46 m below present lake level in the vicinity of Port Huron and that the Kirkfield (Fenelon Falls) outlet was the sole point of discharge for Lake Algonquin prior to the deglaciation of the South River outlet near North Bay. Field evidence to support re-use of the Chicago outlet at this time (Main Algonquin) has not been found in the southern Lake Michigan area. We suggest that after the ice margin withdrew from the Straits, successively lower outlets were uncovered, and the lake level continued to fall, until the lowest (Chippewa) level was reached when the North Bay outlet was deglaciated.

The Nipissing transgression resulted from differential isostatic rebound north of the southern lake basins. The rebound caused reoccupation of the southern outlets at Chicago and Port Huron. Because the Chicago outlet channel had been cut to bedrock previously, it was abandoned when the St. Clair River channel near Port Huron was incised into less resistant glacial drift. The outlet at Port Huron, thereafter, served as the sole outlet for the postglacial upper Great Lakes. As the region continued to recover from the effects of glaciation and isostatic adjustment, further incision of the outlet at Port Huron resulted in lowering of the lake level, thereby creating Lake Algoma (179 m, 587 ft.) and ultimately Lake Michigan (177 m, 580 ft.).

Glacial Events and Lake Levels

Between about 15 500 and 13 500 B.P., ice of several minor readvances, each succeeding advance being of a lesser magnitude than the former, reworked lake sediment and deposited it in the Valparaiso, Tinley, and Lake Border Moraines (Johnson, in press). Several units of grey, clayey till separated by lake sediment are present in Illinois and Wisconsin (Hansel, 1983). These units, called the Wadsworth Till Member of the Wedron Formation in Illinois (Willman and Frye, 1970) and the Oak Creek Formation in Wisconsin (Mickelson et al., 1984), show no evidence that drainage entered the Lake Michigan basin from the Lake Superior basin between advances.

After 13 500 B.P., the ice margin evidently retreated far enough to allow drainage through the Indian River lowland and the Straits of Mackinac. One or both of these northern

outlets may have been used during each subsequent episode of ice margin retreat. When glacial ice was at its position of maximum expansion during the later Port Huron and Two Rivers advances, the ice margin occupied a relatively unstable position on the mid-lake high in the Lake Michigan basin; it probably was in relatively shallow water, and the glacier bed sloped northward. Thinning of the ice sheet or a rise in the lake level would have caused very rapid calving (Mickelson et al., 1981). Channels in the Indian River lowland and on the floor of Lake Michigan, near the Straits of Mackinac, may have been cut by catastrophic floods when the ice margin calved far enough northward to allow drainage across that lowland. It is even possible that the late glacial ice-margin fluctuations were enhanced by rising and falling levels of the lake.

Units of till, called the Ozaukee, Haven, and Valders Members of the Kewaunee Formation in Wisconsin and the Manitowoc and Shorewood Till Members of the Wedron Formation in the Lake Michigan basin, were deposited in rapid succession between about 13 000 and 12 500 B.P. (Acomb et al., 1982; Lineback et al., 1974, 1979). The lithologic character of these red, clayey till units suggests that red clay from the Lake Superior basin was deposited in the Green Bay-Fox River lowland and the Lake Michigan basin before and/or during the Port Huron advances and it then was reworked by Green Bay Lobe and Lake Michigan Lobe ice.

The Glenwood level was abandoned either before or as a result of the Two Creeks retreat, which began about 12 200 B.P. When the northern outlet(s) were opened, the lake level was lowered to an altitude below that of present Lake Michigan. The Two Rivers ice advance, which began about 11 800 B.P., blocked the northern outlets and caused a rise to the Calumet level and flooding of Picea trees of the Two Creeks forest before the Two Rivers till was deposited. Lake Chicago was lowered from the Calumet level after the retreat of the Two Rivers ice margin, and it was replaced by Lake Algonquin when water in the Lake Michigan and Lake Huron basins became confluent. When the ice margin had later retreated from the Upper Peninsula of Michigan, Lake Algonquin extended into the Lake Superior basin.

The red and grey clay units of the South Haven and Sheboygan Members of the Lake Michigan Formation probably were deposited between 11 000 and 9500 B.P. (Fig. 1). Red clay likely entered the Lake Michigan basin as the ice margin retreated from the Upper Peninsula of Michigan about 11 000 B.P., and it entered again during the Marquette advance of the Superior Lobe ice between 10 000 and 9700 B.P. (Clayton, 1983; Drexler et al., 1983). Between 11 000 and 10 000 B.P., when the Upper Peninsula was free of ice, lake drainage and red clay from the Superior basin could not have entered the Lake Michigan basin because the levels of eastward-draining Lake Algonquin and the post-Algonquin lakes were below those of the channels across the Upper Peninsula. As Drexler et al. (1983) have suggested, when drainage from the Lake Superior basin was cut off and the lake level was low in the Lake Michigan basin, the grey clay of the Wilmette Bed probably was deposited (Fig. 1).

Differential Isostatic Rebound and Lake History

Shore features of former lakes in the Lake Michigan basin are discontinuous today because many were destroyed or obscured by more recent ice advances, shore erosion, dune development, and human modification. Thus, it is difficult to trace the shorelines and to evaluate the effect of isostatic rebound on lake levels in the basin. Despite early work by Chamberlin (1877), Goldthwait (1906, 1907, 1908), Leverett and Taylor (1915), and Alden (1918), and later evaluations by Bretz (1951), Hough (1966), and Evenson (1973), the uplift history in the basin remains a puzzle.

During the Glenwood and Calumet phases, the outlet was at the south end of the lake, and one would expect that the altitudes of the shorelines would rise northward because of differential rebound. The latest analysis of rebound in the Lake Michigan basin, however, suggests that no tilting of shorelines occurred south of Sheboygan, Wisconsin, on the west side of the lake and south of the Indiana/Michigan state line on the east side (Evenson, 1973). Although Leverett and Taylor (1915) recognized a rise in altitude of the Glenwood shoreline from 195 m to 201 m between the Michigan/Indiana state line and Muskegon, Michigan, a similar change was not noted in Wisconsin by either Goldthwait (1907) or Alden (1918). These observations suggested to Evenson that isobases run north-northwest/south-southeast across the southern half of the lake, and that shorelines on both sides of the lake are flat at 195 m, rise to 201 m, and then are flat at this altitude between Muskegon and Manistee on the Michigan side of the basin (Evenson, 1973). Evenson concluded that Calumet shorelines are not deformed. He pointed out that it is difficult to reconcile these observations with what is known about the pattern of ice margin retreat. Recently, Taylor (1985) presented evidence of uplifted Glenwood and Calumet shorelines in the Manistee-Frankfort area along the eastern shore of Lake Michigan.

Shore features at the 184 m (Toleston) level are present on the Haven and Valders tills south of Two Rivers, Wisconsin. On the Door Peninsula in Wisconsin, beaches interpreted as Main Algonquin and post-Algonquin shore features rise rapidly northward; those interpreted as Lake Nipissing beaches have been inferred to be horizontal south of Washington Island in Wisconsin and south of Traverse Bay in Michigan (Goldthwait, 1908; Leverett and Taylor, 1915). The Main Algonquin and Nipissing shorelines appear to converge to the 184 m level at Chicago. As Hough (1953) noted, none of the old beaches in the northern parts of the Lake Michigan or Lake Huron basins can be traced to a junction with any beaches in the southern parts of the basins because the old beaches on both sides of the lake (where they supposedly approach horizontality) have been removed by erosion.

The above observations and interpretations appear to be irreconcilable with recent studies that indicate that both the northern and southern parts of the basin currently are undergoing differential uplift (e.g., see Clark and Persoage, 1970; Coordinating Committee on Great Lakes Basic Hydraulic and Hydrologic Data, 1977). Furthermore, ongoing uplift has raised the Nipissing and Algoma terraces at Port Huron above contemporaneous terraces at Chicago (Larsen, 1985a).

The effect of isostatic rebound on lake events cannot be resolved until the nature of rebound in the basin is better understood. Investigators have attempted to correlate beaches in various parts of the basin with outlets since Goldthwait (1907, 1908) and Leverett and Taylor (1915) originally mapped shore features but the correlations are not firmly established. Beaches mapped as Glenwood and Calumet may be beaches of later phases, and the Main Algonquin shoreline may plunge beneath the Lake Nipissing shorelines in the area where the shorelines of the two lake phases supposedly converge. Furthermore, there is no closely limiting radiocarbon age control for many of the high beaches in the central and northern parts of the lake basin. For these reasons, relative age determination of glacial and lake phases based on the relationship of deposits to shoreline levels is tenuous.

GLACIAL LAKE CHICAGO

Lake Chicago occupied the southern part of the Lake Michigan basin at various times between 15 000 and 11 000 B.P. after retreat of the ice margin from the Valparaiso Morainic System. The lake was named by Leverett in 1897, when he first distinguished the three main high levels of the lake. In designating the lake "stages" (now referred to as phases or lake levels), Leverett selected geographic names of localities on or near the three most prominent shorelines at the south end of Lake Michigan in northeastern Illinois and northwestern Indiana (Fig. 2). Unfortunately, the type area of Lake Chicago has been overlooked by more recent workers in their reconstruction of the sequence of events that accompanied retreat of the Wisconsinan ice margin in the Lake Michigan basin. We refocus attention to this critical type area.

Pre-Glenwood Phases

The oldest recognized beaches of Lake Chicago are those of the Glenwood level. According to Bretz (1951, 1955), the Glenwood level post-dated the moraine dam that was created when the ice margin readvanced to the position of the Tinley Moraine on the proximal slope of the older Valparaiso Morainic System (Fig. 2) and deposited outwash as a valley train in the outlet channels. Following Leverett (Leverett and Taylor, 1915), Bretz (1951) cited evidence that drainage from a pre-Glenwood lake, called "incipient Lake Chicago", cut a channel through the Tinley Moraine, and he inferred that the boulder lag that formed as a result of the drainage stabilized the later Glenwood level at 195 m. Some investigators inferred that earlier and higher lake events occurred during ice margin retreat from the Valparaiso Morainic System (e.g., Atwood and Goldthwait, 1908; Cressey, 1928; Ekblaw, 1931; Hough, 1958; Schneider, 1968). However, if those higher and earlier events occurred, much of the morphologic evidence for the lake events apparently was destroyed by the readvance of the ice margin to the position of the Tinley Moraine. Hough (1958, p. 164) referred to a post-Valparaiso, pre-Tinley lake as "Early Lake Chicago." A still earlier (pre-Valparaiso) lake in the Lake Michigan basin, called glacial Lake Milwaukee, has been recognized

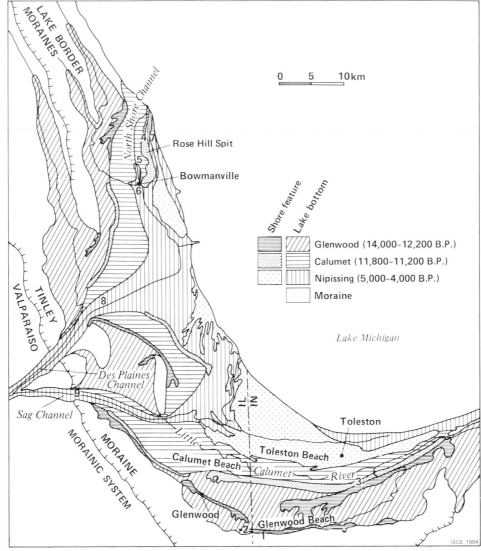

Figure 2. Map of reference area (type area) for Lake Chicago and Glenwood, Calumet, and Toleston beaches. Modified from Alden (1902), Schneider and Keller (1970), and Willman (1971). Numbers refer to locations of radiocarbon dates listed in Table I.

on the basis of lithologic and stratigraphic evidence (Schneider, 1983; Schneider and Need, 1983), but no shoreline features or radiocarbon dates are available to verify the level, extent, and exact age of any pre-Lake Chicago lakes.

Glenwood I Phase of Lake Chicago

The Glenwood I phase of Lake Chicago began shortly after 14 500 B.P., when the ice margin had retreated from the Tinley Moraine. The closely spaced moraines of the Lake Border Morainic System probably were formed early in this phase. Fullerton (1980, pl. 1) introduced the term "border lakes" (phase) for this episode. During this phase, Lake Chicago was probably small and crescentic; it was dammed by the southern margin of the Lake Michigan Lobe ice and it received ice marginal drainage from the east and west (Fig. 3a). Retreat of the ice margin from the Lake Border Moraines caused Lake Chicago to expand northward

(Fig. 3b). The lake attained its maximum extent just prior to deglaciation of a northern outlet channel, about 13 500 B.P. Proglacial drainage from Saginaw Lobe ice and possibly Huron and Erie Lobe ice probably discharged into Lake Chicago by way of the glacial Grand Valley during the Glenwood I phase. Whether or not Lake Chicago actually stabilized at the Glenwood (195 m) level during the Glenwood I phase remains uncertain because all dated Glenwood sediments represent the Glenwood II phase.

Intra-Glenwood Low Phase

The intra-Glenwood low phase (Fig. 1, 3c) corresponds with the Cary-Port Huron retreat (the Mackinaw Interstade of Dreimanis and Karrow, 1972). During this retreat, between 13 500 and 13 000 B.P., the ice margin probably wasted north of the Straits of Mackinac and red clay from the Lake Superior basin was transported into the Lake Michigan

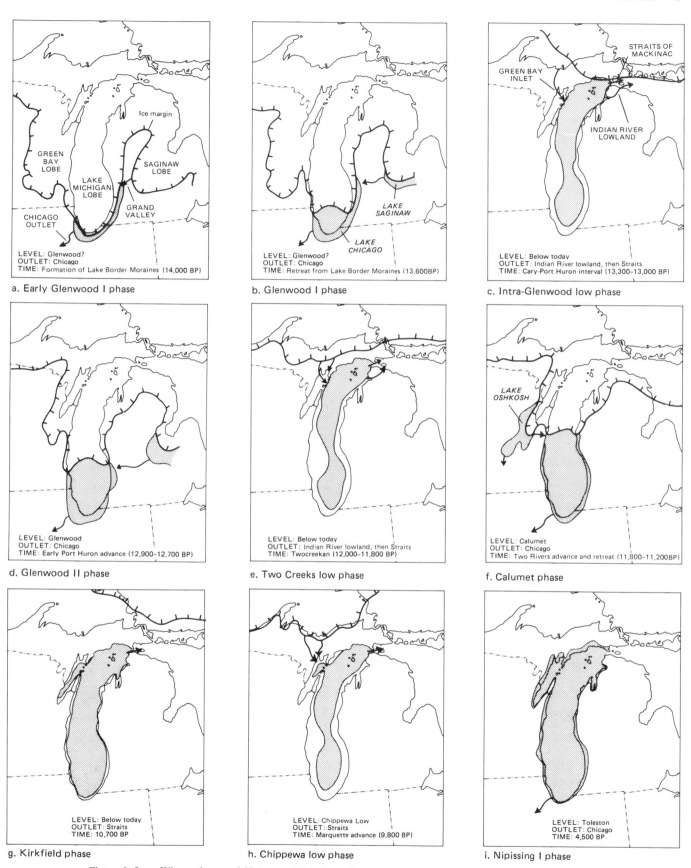

a. Early Glenwood I phase

b. Glenwood I phase

c. Intra-Glenwood low phase

d. Glenwood II phase

e. Two Creeks low phase

f. Calumet phase

g. Kirkfield phase

h. Chippewa low phase

i. Nipissing I phase

Figure 3. Late Wisconsinan and Holocene lake phases in the Lake Michigan basin. Radiocarbon ages are estimates. a) Early Glenwood I phase b) Glenwood I phase c) Intra-Glenwood low phase d) Glenwood II phase e) Two Creeks low phase f) Calumet phase g) Kirkfield phase h) Chippewa low phase i) Nipissing I phase

basin. Hough (1958, 1963, 1966) regarded the Glenwood to be a multiphase lake, and he suggested (1963) that a "possible low stage" developed during the Cary-Port Huron ice retreat. Possible evidence of a low level had been reported earlier by Workman (1925). Hough was not able to document the existence of this low-level event, however, because of the uncertainty of correlations of beaches, discrepancies in radiocarbon dates from the Dyer spit, and the lack of evidence for the extent of ice margin retreat between the Cary and Port Huron readvances.

The intra-Glenwood low phase thus remained conjectural until Farrand *et al.* (1969) discovered a buried bryophyte bed south of the Straits of Mackinac in Cheboygan County, Michigan. On the basis of the oldest radiocarbon dates of the mosses, they concluded that the Straits of Mackinac were deglaciated during the Cary-Port Huron retreat, but not during the Two Creeks retreat. They indicated an age of 13 000 to 12 500 B.P. for the bryophyte bed (Farrand *et al.*, 1969), but the age subsequently was reported to be about 13 300 B.P. (Farrand and Eschman, 1974). The reliability of the dates was questioned by Fullerton (1980).

Glenwood II Phase of Lake Chicago

A readvance of the Lake Michigan Lobe ice margin in early Port Huron time closed the northern outlet, thereby initiating the Glenwood II phase and reactivating the Chicago outlet shortly after 13 000 B.P. (Fig. 1, 3d). This phase is recorded by deposits of the Dyer spit and by the Glenwood beach in its type area; both occur at 195 m at Dyer, Indiana (Table I, Fig. 2). Wood from deposits in these landforms ranged in age from 12 650 ± 350 to 12 220 ± 350 B.P. (Schneider and Reshkin, 1970; Table I). Further possible evidence of the Glenwood II phase consists of shoreline features and lacustrine sediments that overlie the red, clayey Port Huron till (Evenson, 1973; Evenson *et al.*, 1973; Mickelson and Evenson, 1975; Taylor, 1977, 1978; Evenson and Taylor, 1981; Acomb *et al.*, 1982). No radiocarbon dates are available to verify the age of the shorelines, however.

Both Bretz (1951, 1955, 1964) and Hough (1966) assigned the Glenwood-Calumet transition to Port Huron time and inferred that an influx of water from ice-dammed lakes in the eastern basins caused downcutting of the Chicago outlet. Alternatively, Lake Chicago may have risen to and stabilized at the Glenwood level during the Glenwood II phase because of the added discharge from eastern lakes, and then may have been lowered when a lower northern outlet was opened and the eastern lakes drained eastward.

The Glenwood level may have been abandoned before retreat of the Port Huron ice margin in the Lake Michigan basin uncovered a lower outlet and initiated the Two Creeks low phase. Evidence of the pre-Two Creeks Calumet I phase of Bretz (1951, 1959) has not been observed in the type area of the Calumet phase in the southern part of the Lake Michigan basin. All dated landforms at the Calumet level are post-Two Creeks in age (Fig. 2, Table I). Eschman and Farrand (1970) and Evenson (1973; Evenson *et al.*, 1973) argued that a Calumet level was formed in pre-Two Creeks time because the lowest terraces of pre Two Creeks Lake Warren

have been traced through the glacial Grand Valley to the Calumet level (189 m) in the Lake Michigan basin.

Two Creeks Low Phase

The Two Creeks low phase began before 12 000 B.P., when the Port Huron ice margin had retreated far enough to open a lower outlet to the northeast. The forest bed at Two Creeks, Wisconsin, provided evidence for the low-level phase, which was named accordingly (Thwaites and Bertrand, 1957; Hough, 1958). Broecker and Farrand (1963) suggested a period of 200 radiocarbon years (11 950-11 750 B.P.) for the growth of the forest, and Fullerton (1980) concluded that initial growth of the forest began no earlier than 12 000 B.P.

Lake Algonquin in the Lake Huron basin was contemporaneous with the Two Creeks low phase and the lakes in both basins (Michigan and Huron) ultimately drained through the region east of Georgian Bay in Ontario. Some investigators have interpreted the stratigraphy at the Cheboygan County bryophyte site in Michigan as indicating that the Straits of Mackinac were covered by ice throughout the Two Creeks interval (Farrand *et al.*, 1969; Farrand and Eschman, 1974; Evenson *et al.*, 1976). However, Fullerton (1980) noted that this interpretation is wholly dependent on the assignment of a Cary-Port Huron age to the bryophyte bed and that that age assignment is equivocal. For this reason, in Figure 3e the ice margin is shown with both the Indian River lowland and the Straits serving as possible outlets.

In the type area of Lake Chicago evidence for a low lake event was first recognized by Andrews (1870), who noted the presence of peat and wood beneath the Rose Hill spit at Evanston, Illinois. This feature is a 25 km-long spit that was formed southward into Lake Chicago from a headland near Wilmette (Fig. 2). Its highest part consists of a ridge at an altitude of 187 to 189 m, and it is considered to be an extension of the Calumet shoreline (Andrews, 1870; Leverett, 1897; Alden, 1902; Baker, 1920; Bretz, 1939, 1955; Willman, 1971). Baker (1912) correlated the deposits beneath the spit at Evanston with a silt bed in an area west of the spit near Bowmanville (Fig. 2). The silt bed contained wood and shells and it was exposed during excavation of the North Shore Channel to the Chicago River. On the basis of these deposits, Baker (1912) proposed that a low-water phase that he named the Bowmanville stage (Baker, 1920; 1926) existed between the Glenwood and Calumet phases. Although Baker's interpretation of the deposits at Evanston and Bowmanville as evidence for a low-water phase was questioned (Goldthwait, 1908; Leverett and Taylor, 1915; Alden, 1918; Hough, 1958), Bretz (1951) correlated the Bowmanville phase with the well-established Two Creeks low phase.

Hansel recently examined the stratigraphy and collected organic material from sites in the southern Lake Michigan area. Baker's stratigraphy, as well as the faunal and macrobotanical collection he made in 1910 during the excavation of the North Shore Channel, were re-examined. Thirty new radiocarbon dates on material from either the Baker collection or new sites were measured at the Illinois State Geologi-

TABLE I
SELECTED RADIOCARBON DATES, SOUTHERN LAKE MICHIGAN BASIN

Location No.	Years BP	Lab No.	Material	Altitude (a.s.l.)	Comments	References
1 Glenwood Beach						
	12 400 ± 300	IU-62	wood	*ca.* 195 m	Below eolian sand overlying fine- to medium-grained lacustrine deposits.	Schneider and Reshkin, 1970
2 Dyer Spit						
	12 650 ± 350	W-140	wood	<191 m	From peat in lagoon deposits beneath spit deposits.	Rubin and Suess, 1955
	12 220 ± 350	W-161	wood	<191 m	From spit deposits.	Rubin and Suess, 1955
	12 660 ± 140	ISGS-1190	wood	<192 m	Above till beneath spoil; may have been out of place.	C. L. Liu, (pers. commun.)
3 Calumet Beach						
	11 815 ± 640	IU-67	wood	*ca.* 814 m	From thin peat horizon in sand and gravel below lacustrine sediments.	Schneider and Reshkin, 1982
	9110 ± 640	IU-68	wood	*ca.* 187 m	From peat and gravel bed that underlies 3 m of lacustrine and/or eolian sand.	Schneider and Reshkin, 1982
	10 890 ± 560	IU-69	wood	*ca.* 186 m	From thin clay and peat layer in sand 1 m below IU-68.	Schneider and Reshkin, 1982
	11 740 ± 100	ISGS-1147	driftwood	<189 m	From sand and gravel beneath eolian sand.	C. L. Liu, (pers. commun.)
4 Rose Hill Spit						
	11 610 ± 70	ISGS-985	driftwood	*ca.* 183 m	From lacustrine sediment beneath distal part of spit.	C. L. Liu, (pers. commun.)
	11 000 ± 80	ISGS-1097	driftwood	*ca.* 183 m	From lacustrine sediment beneath distal part of split.	C. L. Liu, (pers. commun.)
	11 740 ± 270	ISGS-1117	wood	182.7 m	With peat in carbonaceous sand underlying a gravel layer beneath spit deposits.	C. L. Liu, (pers. commun.)
	11 180 ± 160	ISGS-1121	wood	183.3 m	With peat and twigs in fine sand and silt beneath distal part of spit.	C. L. Liu, (pers. commun.)
	11 870 ± 100	ISGS-1137	driftwood	182.6 m	From fine sand and silt at base of the main ridge of spit.	C. L. Liu, (pers. commun.)
	11 810 ± 90	ISGS-1159	wood	182.6 m	In gravel lag on till *ca.* 1 m below fine sand at base of spit.	C. L. Liu, (pers. commun.)
	11 250 ± 180	ISGS-1165	driftwood	<182.5 m	With detrital peat interbedded in fine sand and silt beneath lakeward part of spit.	C. L. Liu, (pers. commun.)
	11 630 ± 120	ISGS-1180	driftwood	182.0 m	At base of fine sand above till beneath lakeward part of spit.	C. L. Liu, (pers. commun.)
5 North Shore Channel (Stations 33, 37; Baker, 1920)						
	* 8590 ± 140	ISGS-927	*picea* cones	178.8 m	Station 37, Stratum IV; in interstratified sand and silt.	C. L. Liu, (pers. commun.)
	*11 010 ± 130	ISGS-934	wood	178.3 m	Station 33, Stratum VI; in solid layer beneath interstratified silt and sand; 30 cm below ISGS-950.	C. L. Liu, (pers. commun.)
	*10 570 ± 180	ISGS-950	wood	178.6 m	Station 33, Stratum VIII; from thin silt layer below sand.	C. L. Liu, (pers. commun.)
6 North Shore Channel (Bowmanville deposits; Baker, 1920)						
	* 4330 ± 75	ISGS-266	shells	177.4 m	Station 1, Stratum III; from *Unio* bed beneath silt and above sand and gravel bed.	C. L. Liu, (pers. commun.)
	* 5580 ± 70	ISGS-928	wood	176.7 m	Station 9, Stratum VII; from peaty silt with plant remains and shells below *Unio* bed; 10 cm below ISGS-961.	C. L. Liu, (pers. commun.)
	* 5420 ± 90	ISGS-953	wood	177.0 m	Station 27, Stratum II; from silt bed overlain by sand and gravel bed with *Unios*.	C. L. Liu, (pers. commun.)
	* 4690 ± 90	ISGS-959	shells	177.3 m	Station 16, Stratum IV; from sand and gravel bed with *Unios*.	C. L. Liu, (pers. commun.)
	* 4550 ± 70	ISGS-961	shells	176.8 m	Station 9, Stratum VIII; from *Unio* bed; above ISGS-928	C. L. Liu, (pers. commun.)
7 Graceland Spit						
	4030 ± 150	W-725	wood	*ca.* 177 m	Log from beach gravel 4.5 to 6 m below surface and 1 m above till.	Rubin and Alexander, 1960
	4970 ± 180	ISGS-987	paleosol	180.7 m	Developed in silt and fine sand between calcareous silts beneath 1 m of sand and gravel.	C. L. Liu, (pers. commun.)
8 Ogden Ditch (Baker, 1920)						
	* 4640 ± 80	ISGS-970	shells	192.7 m	*Unios* in silt above peat bed.	C. L. Liu, (pers. commun.)
9 Sag Channel						
	6280 ± 70	ISGS-960	peat	177.7 m	Test borehole sample; from 48 cm peat bed overlain by silt and underlain by clay with molluscs and gastropods.	C. L. Liu, (pers. commun.)

NOTE: Locations shown by number on Figure 2.

*Samples collected by Baker.

cal Survey Radiocarbon Laboratory. These data (8 samples) revealed that wood in and beneath the Rose Hill spit in the Evanston area ranged in age from 11 870 ± 100 to 11 000 ± 80 B.P.; wood and shells from the Bowmanville deposits collected by Baker ranged from 5580 ± 70 to 4330 ± 75 B.P. (Fig. 2, Table I). The deposits beneath the Rose Hill spit are Two Creeks and post-Two Creeks in age and the Bowmanville deposits are middle Holocene. However, the presence of Two Creeks wood associated with peat beneath the sediments of the Rose Hill spit (Table I, ISGS-1117) confirms the existence of the Two Creeks low phase in the type area of Lake Chicago, as reported by Schneider and Reshkin (1982; Table I, IU-67). This indicates that the Two Creeks low phase antedated formation of the Calumet features such as the Rose Hill spit and the Calumet beach in the type area of the Calumet phase.

Calumet Phase

The Calumet phase, a result of the Two Rivers ice advance, represents a rise to the 189 m level of Lake Chicago (Figs. 1, 3f). Lake sediments between the Two Creeks forest bed and the younger Two Rivers till in Wisconsin record the rise of lake level with the advance of the Two Rivers ice margin. Driftwood at the base of the spit, ranging in age from 11 870 ± 100 to 11 610 ± 70 B.P. (Fig. 2, Table I), indicates that the Rose Hill spit is post-Two Creeks in age; the altitude of the main ridge suggests that it was formed when Lake Chicago was at the Calumet level. Wood that is Two Creeks and younger also occurs in Calumet beach deposits in the type area near Liverpool, Indiana (Schneider and Reshkin, 1982; Fig. 2, Table I). It provides further evidence that the Calumet deposits in the type area of the phase are post-Two Creeks in age and that that phase corresponds to the Calumet II phase of Bretz (1951, 1955, 1959). The Calumet shoreline is not represented by obvious cut terraces in the type area, as are the Glenwood and Toleston shorelines; this suggests that the Calumet phase was relatively short-lived. An age of 11 800 to 11 200 B.P. is suggested for the Calumet phase (Fig. 1).

Although Leverett (1897) regarded the Toleston level to be a "stage" of Lake Chicago, he expressed doubt that the Toleston beach (184 m level) was formed in a proglacial lake. He observed that, in contrast to the Glenwood and Calumet beaches, the Toleston beaches contain abundant molluscan fossils. Taylor (p. 330 in Leverett and Taylor, 1915) indicated that the Toleston beach may have been formed in part in Lake Chicago and in part in Lake Algonquin. Recognition of Toleston and/or Algonquin features in the southern Lake Michigan basin is problematic because lakes supposedly were at the 184 m level at least three times — during the Toleston, Main Algonquin, and Nipissing phases (Hough, 1958, p. 166). Figure 2 and Table I illustrate that, like the Bowmanville phase deposits, some dated landforms formerly attributed to the Toleston phase are middle Holocene and they were formed during the Nipissing transgression. Karrow (1980) reported a similar occurrence of beaches at the 184 m (supposed Main Algonquin) level in the southern Lake Huron basin.

Conclusive evidence of a Toleston phase of Lake Chicago has not been found in its type area. Baker (1912, 1920)

suggested that the lower distal part of the Rose Hill spit, at an altitude of 183 to 186 m, was formed when Lake Chicago was lowered from the Calumet level to the Toleston level. Driftwood and detrital peat are interbedded with silt and fine sand beneath the lakeward and distal parts of the spit, and wood samples were dated at 11 250 ± 180 B.P. (ISGS-1165) and 11 180 ± 160 B.P. (ISGS-1121) (Table I). Thus, deposition of the sand and gravel in the lower part of the Rose Hill spit may have occurred approximately 11 000 B.P. or earlier. Because Lake Chicago ceased to exist when the Straits were deglaciated and because that event has not been precisely dated — although generally it is placed prior to 11 000 B.P. (Evenson *et al.*, 1976; Karrow, 1978; Fullerton, 1980) — it is not clear whether the lower part of the Rose Hill spit relates to a Toleston level of Lake Chicago.

GLACIAL LAKE ALGONQUIN

When the ice margin retreated from the Straits, probably shortly before 11 000 B.P., water in the Lake Michigan and Lake Superior basins became confluent with Lake Algonquin in the Lake Huron basin. According to the current model, Lake Algonquin was in the Main (or late) Algonquin phase (at the 184 m level) during this time (Fullerton, 1980); however, shore features of this phase have not been identified in the southern parts of the Lake Michigan and Lake Huron basins. The apparent absence of Algonquin landforms has been attributed to intensive Lake Nipissing waves and currents (Karrow, 1980).

Dated sediments in the southern Lake Michigan area suggest that the lake level was below an altitude of 184 m (the assumed Main Algonquin level) during the Main Algonquin phase (from about 11 200 to 10 400 B.P., according to Karrow *et al.*, 1975). Spruce wood and cones from silt at an altitude of 178 to 180 m at Baker's (1920) Stations 33 and 37 on the North Shore Channel (Fig. 2, Table I) ranged in age from 11 010 ± 130 to 8590 ± 140 B.P. Deposition at this locality possibly was alluvial, and the range of dates and the stratigraphy suggest that the lake level was below the 184 m (Main Algonquin) level between 11 000 and 8600 B.P. Wood from a peat bed at South Haven, Michigan, at an altitude of 179 m yielded a date of 10 900 ± 160 B.P. (Lowdon and Blake, 1975) and it provides additional evidence for a level below 184 m in the southern Lake Michigan basin during Main Algonquin time.

We suggest that when the ice margin retreated from the Lake Michigan basin, Lake Algonquin drained through the relatively lower Fenelon Falls outlet, which was below the 184 m Toleston level. In the type area of Lake Chicago, there appears to be no clear evidence to support assumptions that Lake Algonquin drained through the Chicago outlet or that the lake stabilized at the Toleston level prior to the Nipissing transgression in the middle Holocene. Therefore, we suggest that the Kirkfield phase occurred in the Lake Michigan basin from about 11 000 to 10 500 B.P. and that drainage was through the Straits to the Fenelon Falls outlet (Fig. 1, 3g). The Kirkfield phase in the Lake Michigan basin corresponds in time with the Main Algonquin phase in the Lake Huron basin (Eschman and Karrow, 1985), but we suggest that lake level in the confluent lake basins was below the 184 m level.

POST-ALGONQUIN GROUP LAKES

Deglaciation of successively lower outlets, as the ice margin retreated northward across isostatically depressed southern Ontario between 10 500 and 10 000 B.P., resulted in formation of a series of successively lower confluent lakes in the upper Great Lakes basins (Terasmae and Hughes, 1960; Lewis, 1969; Harrison, 1972; Saarnisto, 1974; Drexler et al., 1983). These post-Algonquin lakes usually are relegated to an upper group (Lakes Ardtrea, Upper Orillia, and Lower Orillia) and a lower group (Lakes Wyebridge, Penetang, Cedar Point, Payette, Sheguiandah, Korah, and Chippewa). In the Lake Michigan basin they are represented by uplifted shorelines in the northern part of the lake basin. Deglaciation of the North Bay area about 10 000 B.P. (Harrison, 1972; Fullerton, 1980; Drexler et al., 1983) opened an outlet to the St. Lawrence Lowland by way of the Mattawa and Ottawa valleys. Ice margins then ceased to be an important factor in the changing levels of the lakes. Instead, isostatic rebound, climatic change, and outlet downcutting became the dominant variables in the hydrological system.

Stanley (1936, 1937) noted that if isostatically warped terraces below the highest Lake Algonquin terrace in the northern Lake Huron and Lake Michigan basins are projected southward they are below the modern lake surfaces in the southern parts of the basins. These terraces were considered to be evidence of falling post-Algonquin lake levels. Stanley also suggested that an extremely low post-Algonquin level, now known as Lake Stanley, formed in the Lake Huron basin (Hough, 1958, p. 236). Hough (1955, 1958), following Stanley, proposed that an extremely low level, Lake Chippewa, formed in the Lake Michigan basin. An apparent unconformity 107 m below present lake level was attributed to Lake Chippewa. Stanley (1938) proposed that Lake Chippewa drained to the Lake Huron basin through a submerged river channel at the Straits of Mackinac. However, research on ostracode faunas and the sedimentology of the Lake Michigan Formation by Buckley (1974) suggests that during this low lake phase, the water level was not more than 61 m below the present level. Erosion related to the Chippewa level may be represented by an unconformity between the Sheyboygan and Winnetka Members of the Lake Michigan Formation (Fig. 1), but the molluscan faunas may not be indicative of water as shallow as Hough (1955, 1958), suggested (Buckley, 1974; Lineback et al., 1979).

The Chippewa low phase (Fig. 3h) was initiated about 10 000 B.P., when the North Bay outlet was deglaciated, and it was terminated about 5500 B.P., during the Nipissing transgression, when the lake level rose to an altitude above that of the present lake. The Chippewa-Nipissing transition corresponded approximately in time with the end of the Hypsithermal episode of Holocene climatic history, when the warmer and drier conditions of the early Holocene were replaced by cooler and moister conditions in the northern Midwest after 6000 B.P. (Bartlein and Webb, 1982).

POSTGLACIAL LAKES NIPISSING, ALGOMA, AND MICHIGAN

Continued differential uplift progressively raised the altitude of the North Bay outlet. The lake level in the Lake Michigan and Lake Huron basins rose until it reached the altitudes of previously abandoned southern outlets at Chicago and Port Huron, about 5000 B.P. This transgression culminated in the Nipissing episode of the Great Lakes history (Figs. 1, 3i). Water in the Lake Michigan, Lake Huron, and Lake Superior basins was confluent at this time, and initially the Nipissing phase simultaneously drained through three outlets – the North Bay, Port Huron, and Chicago outlets (Lewis, 1969, 1970). Continued differential uplift caused abandonment of the North Bay outlet as it was raised above the altitude of the two southern outlets (Fig. 1).

The post-Chippewa water levels in the Lake Michigan basin were recognized by early writers (e.g., Leverett and Taylor, 1915; Bretz, 1955). However, later workers (Hough, 1958, 1963; Lewis, 1969, 1970), distinguished three distinct middle to late Holocene lake events – Nipissing (5500 to 3800 B.P.), Algoma (3800 to 2500 B.P.), and modern Lakes Michigan and Huron (2500 B.P. to present).

The Nipissing transgression has been dated in both the Lake Huron basin (Dreimanis, 1958; Farrand and Miller, 1968; Lewis, 1969, 1970; Prest, 1970; Cowan, 1978; Terasmae, 1979; Monaghan et al., in review) and the Lake Michigan basin (Winkler, 1962; Larsen, 1974, 1985b; Fraser et al., 1975; Gutscheck and Gonsiewski, 1976). In general, the age control indicates a Nipissing transgression that rose above present lake level between 6000 and 5000 B.P. and attained a maximum level between 4700 and 4000 B.P.

According to Hough, the altitudes of the pre-existing outlets governed the altitude of the Nipissing phase (184 m). Incision of the Port Huron outlet into unconsolidated glacial deposits then caused lowering of the lake to the Algoma level at an altitude of 182 m, and the bedrock-floored Chicago outlet was abandoned. Renewed incision of the Port Huron outlet about 2500 B.P. caused lowering of the lake to the modern Lake Michigan and Lake Huron level (177 m, 580 ft.).

Hough's (1953, 1958, 1963) interpretation of the Nipissing Great Lakes greatly affected subsequent work. Relying on assumed tectonic and isostatic stability of the southern Lake Michigan basin, Hough attempted to reconcile anomalous relationships betwen the Nipissing and Algonquin terraces in the northern and southern extremes of the basin. Nipissing beaches and terraces north of Traverse Bay, Michigan, are upwarped northward by postglacial differential isostatic uplift; those south of Traverse Bay appear to be undeformed. An apparent hinge line (Leverett and Taylor, 1915), or zero isobase, transects the basin at the latitude of Traverse Bay. The area south of the hinge line was considered to have been isostatically stable. Hough assumed that the bedrock-floored Chicago outlet remained at the Toleston-Algonquin altitude of 184 m. Thus, the Nipissing Great Lakes rose to an altitude of 184 m, coincident with the earlier Toleston-Algonquin level.

Two inconsistencies affect Hough's interpretation. First, the altitude of the Chicago outlet channel as originally reported by Leverett (1897, p. 59) was 180 m. Second, studies of recent uplift discussed by Clark and Persoage (1970) and the Coordinating Committee on Great Lakes Basic Hydraulic and Hydrologic Data (1977) indicate that the northern and southern parts of the basin currently are undergoing differential uplift. Data presented by Larsen (1985a) and Kaszycki (1985) seem to invalidate the hinge-line concept. If so, an outlet-control model for the Nipissing Great Lakes, as envisioned by Hough, does not seem plausible.

Detailed stratigraphic studies in the Chicago area during the past decade indicate that the level of the lake fluctuated on a scale of 200 to 300 years during the late Holocene. We believe the Nipissing and Algoma phases were short-lived; high lake-level events were separated by periods when lake levels were lower. Apparently, there were no long periods of stable levels that were governed by occasional rapid incision of outlet channels. During an early Nipissing phase (Nipissing I), the lake attained an altitude of 183 m about 4500 B.P. During a second Nipissing phase (Nipissing II), the lake reached an altitude of 180 m about 4000 B.P. During the Algoma phase, it reached a maximum altitude of 179 m about 3200 B.P. In addition, conspicuous fluctuations as high as 2 m above present lake level occurred about 1500, 1000, and 450 B.P., during a period previously regarded to be one of relatively stable lake levels. A record of late Holocene changes in lake level is preserved in stream-mouth alluvial fills near Zion, Illinois (Larsen, 1974, 1985b).

Comparison of the lake level record with late Holocene pollen and Neoglacial records (Webb and Bryson, 1972; Swain, 1978; Bernabo, 1981; Denton and Karlén, 1973; Curry, 1969; Benedict, 1973; Goldthwait, 1966; Webb *et al.,* 1983; Davis, 1983) suggests that the fluctuations in lake level were climatically related to changes in water volume in the upper Great Lakes basins (Larsen, 1973, 1974, 1985b; Fraser *et al.,* 1975). Thus, during the past 2000 years the lake level appears to have fluctuated around a mean level that was adjusted to the channel depth of the St. Clair River at Port Huron (Larsen, 1985a). Fluctuations during the Nipissing and Algoma phases also can be thought of as climate-related changes in lake level that were adjusted to channel depths. Such an interpretation reconciles the altitude of the bedrock sill of the Chicago outlet (180 m) that has been inferred to have controlled the Nipissing level at an altitude of 184 m (Hough, 1953, 1958, 1963; Lewis, 1969, 1970).

The altitudes of the Nipissing and Algoma terraces and beaches characteristically are lower in the southern Lake Michigan basin than they are in the southern Lake Huron basin (Larsen, 1985a). Ongoing differential uplift has raised the Port Huron outlet above the contemporaneous terraces at Chicago. The outlet incision at Port Huron previously was considered to have been responsible for the lowering from the Nipissing level to the Algoma level and then to the Lake Michigan and Lake Huron level. It probably was a more gradual process: the rate of erosion of the outlet channel partly kept pace with ongoing differential uplift.

CONCLUSIONS AND SUGGESTIONS FOR FURTHER RESEARCH

Although the general history of lakes in the Lake Michigan basin has been known for nearly a century, radiocarbon dates obtained during the past 10 years have changed interpretations of many details. In the Illinois and Indiana part of the basin, where shore features have been least altered by differential uplift, lake levels between 12 500 and 11 000 B.P. and between 6000 B.P. and the present are particularly well dated. Several specific conclusions about lake history are drawn on the basis of radiocarbon dates.

1) A Port Huron age Glenwood II phase is confirmed by dates from the Dyer spit. A Cary age Glenwood I phase is unconfirmed, but a lake must have existed.

2) The Two Creeks low phase is documented in the southern Lake Michigan area by dated sediments beneath the Rose Hill spit. This low-level phase is not the Bowmanville low phase, as was suggested by Baker (1926). The Bowmanville deposits are middle Holocene and they do not represent a low-level phase.

3) A pre-Two Creeks Calumet I phase is unconfirmed, but it may have existed. The Calumet beach in the type area of Lake Chicago and the Rose Hill spit sediments are post-Two Creeks in age and they were deposited during the Calumet II phase of Bretz (1959).

4) All dated sediments associated with Toleston level (184 m) features are middle Holocene in age and they relate to the Nipissing transgression. The 184 m Toleston phase of Lake Chicago and the 184 m Main Algonquin phase of Lake Algonquin are not documented by radiocarbon dates in the southern Lake Michigan area.

Because the uplift history of the Lake Michigan basin is not well known and very few radiocarbon dates have been obtained from the northern part of the basin, determination of the ages of beaches and terraces in Wisconsin and Michigan remains a major problem. For this reason, correlation of shore features northward from the southern part of the basin is conjectural, and without age control of beaches and terraces in the northern part of the basin, correlation of glacial and lake events is tenuous. A greater effort should be made in the future to focus research on the rebound history in the Lake Michigan basin, especially if dates from shore features in the northern part of the basin can be obtained.

Another suggested focus for future research is the relationship of the altitudes of outlets to lake levels. Larsen (1985a) suggests that middle to late Holocene lake-level fluctuations were controlled chiefly by climate-related changes in the volume of water in the lake basin, rather than by episodic outlet incision. The high-level phases lasting no longer than 200 to 300 years occurred betwen periods of lower levels. Large changes in the volume of water entering the Lake Michigan basin occurred during deglaciation of the Great Lakes region. There is good evidence, for instance, that at times the drainage from lakes in the Lake Huron and Lake Erie basins entered the Lake Michigan basin through the glacial Grand Valley and that drainage from the Lake Superior basin entered through channels across the Upper Peninsula of Michigan. Such large and perhaps catastrophic changes in the volume of water entering the basin probably affected lake levels and may have been a more important control of lake level in the basin than was the altitude of the outlet at Chicago.

Recent studies have documented historic uplift, even in the southern parts of the Lake Michigan basin. The possibility that differential isostatic uplift affected outlet incision at Chicago and Port Huron during the late Wisconsinan and Holocene also should be explored.

ACKNOWLEDGEMENTS

We are grateful to C.L. Liu, of the Illinois State Geological Survey Radiocarbon Laboratory, for making available unpublished data and to the U.S. Geological Survey for a joint funding agreement with the Illinois State Geological Survey to study the postglacial geology of the southern Lake Michigan area. We thank Lee Clayton, D.F. Eschman, L.R. Follmer, D.S. Fullerton, P.F. Karrow, C.A. Kaszycki, and W.H. Johnson for discussions and constructive comments on the manuscript.

REFERENCES

Acomb, L.J., Mickelson, D.M., and Evenson, E.B., 1982, Till Stratigraphy and Late Glacial Events in the Lake Michigan Lobe of Eastern Wisconsin: Geological Society of America Bulletin, v. 93, p. 289-296.

Alden, W.C., 1902, Description of the Chicago District, Illinois-Indiana: United States Geological Survey Geologic Atlas, Folio 81, 14 p.

_____, 1918, The Quaternary Geology of Southeastern Wisconsin: United States Geological Survey Professional Paper 106, 356 p.

Andrews, Edmund, 1870, The North American Lakes Considered as Chronometers of Post-Glacial Time: Transactions of the Chicago Academy of Science, v. 2, p. 14.

Atwood, W.W., and Goldthwait, J.W., 1908, Physical Geography of the Evanston-Waukegan Region: Illinois State Geological Survey Bulletin 7, 102 p.

Baker, F.C., 1912, Post-Glacial Life of Wilmette Bay, Glacial Lake Chicago: Transactions of the Illinois Academy of Science, v. 4, p. 108-116.

_____, 1920, The Life of the Pleistocene or Glacial Period as Recorded in the Deposits Laid Down by the Great Ice Sheets: University of Illinois Bulletin, v. 17, no. 14, 476 p.

_____, 1926, Bowmanville Low-Water Stage of Glacial Lake Chicago: Science, New Series, v. 64, p. 249.

Bartlein, P.J., and Webb, Thompson III, 1982, Holocene Climatic Changes Estimated from Pollen Data from the Northern Midwest: in Knox, J.C., ed., Quaternary History of the Driftless Area: Wisconsin Geological and Natural History Field Trip Guidebook 5, p. 67-82.

Benedict, J.B., 1973, Chronology of Cirque Glaciation, Colorado Front Range: Quaternary Research, v. 3, p. 584-599.

Bernabo, J.C., 1981, Quantitative Estimates of Temperature Changes Over the Last 2700 Years in Michigan Based on Pollen Data: Quaternary Research, v. 15, p. 143-159.

Bretz, J.H., 1939, Geology of the Chicago Region, Part I-General: Illinois State Geological Survey Bulletin 65, Part I, 118 p.

_____, 1951, The Stages of Lake Chicago – Their Causes and Correlations: American Journal of Science, v. 249, p. 401-429.

_____, 1955, Geology of the Chicago Region, Part II-The Pleistocene: Illinois State Geological Survey Bulletin 65, 132 p.

_____, 1959, The Double Calumet Stage of Lake Chicago: Journal of Geology, v. 67, p. 675-684.

_____, 1964, Correlation of Glacial Lake Stages in the Huron-Erie and Michigan Basins: Journal of Geology, v. 72, p. 618-627.

Broecker, W.S., and Farrand, W.R., 1963, Radiocarbon Age of the Two Creeks Forest Bed, Wisconsin: Geological Society of America Bulletin, v. 74, p. 795-802.

Buckley, S.B., 1974, Study of Post-Pleistocene Ostracod Distribution in the Soft Sediments of Southern Lake Michigan: Ph.D. Thesis, University of Illinois, Urbana, Illinois, 189 p.

Chamberlin, T.C., 1877, Geology of Wisconsin, v. 2, p. 219-229.

Clark, R.H., and Persoage, N.P., 1970, Some Implications of Crustal Movement in Engineering Planning: Canadian Journal of Earth Sciences, v. 7, p. 628-633.

Clayton, Lee, 1983, Chronology of Lake Agassiz Drainage to Lake Superior: in Teller, J.T., and Clayton, Lee, eds., Glacial Lake Agassiz: Geological Association of Canada Special Paper 26, p. 291-307.

Coordinating Committee on Great Lakes Basic Hydraulic and Hydrologic Data, 1977, Apparent Vertical Movement Over the Great Lakes: Detroit District, United States Army Corps of Engineers, 70 p.

Cowan, W.R., 1978, Radiocarbon Dating Nipissing Great Lakes Events Near Sault Ste. Marie, Ontario: Canadian Journal of Earth Sciences, v. 15, p. 2026-2030.

Cressey, G.B., 1928, The Indiana Sand Dunes and Shore Lines of the Lake Michigan Basin: Geographic Society of Chicago Bulletin 8, 80 p.

Curry, R.R., 1969, Holocene Climatic and Glacial History of the Central Sierra Nevada, California: in Schumm, S.A., and Bradley, W.C., eds., United States Contributions to Quaternary Research: Geological Society of America Special Paper 123, p. 1-47.

Davis, M.B., 1983, Holocene Vegetational History of the Eastern United States: in Wright, H.E., Jr., ed., Late-Quaternary Environments of the United States, v. 2: The Holocene: Minneapolis, University of Minnesota Press, p. 166-181.

Denton, G.H., and Karlén, Wibjorn, 1973, Holocene Climatic Variations – Their Pattern and Possible Cause: Quaternary Research, v. 3, p. 155-205.

Dreimanis, Aleksis, 1958, Beginning of the Nipissing Phase of Lake Huron: Journal of Geology, v. 66, p. 591-594.

Dreimanis, Aleksis, and Karrow, P.F., 1972, Glacial history of the Great Lakes-St. Lawrence Region, the Classification of the Wisconsin(an) Stage, and its Correlatives: 24th International Geological Congress, Montreal, Quaternary Geology, Section 12, p. 5-15.

Drexler, C.W., Farrand, W.R., and Hughes, J.D., 1983, Correlation of Glacial Lakes in the Superior Basin with Eastward Discharge Events from Lake Agassiz: in Teller, J.T., and Clayton, Lee, eds., Glacial Lake Agassiz: Geological Association of Canada Special Paper 26, p. 309-329.

Ekblaw, G.E., 1931, Some Evidences of Incipient Stages of Lake Chicago: Illinois Academy of Science Transactions, v. 23, p. 387-390.

Eschman, D.F., and Farrand, W.R., 1970, Glacial History of the Glacial Grand Valley: in Guidebook for Field Trips: East Lansing, Michigan, Michigan Basin Geological Society, p. 131-157.

Eschman, D.F., and Karrow, P.F., 1985, Huron Basin Glacial Lakes: A Review: in Karrow, P.F. and Calkin, P.E., eds., Quaternary Evolution of the Great Lakes: Geological Association of Canada Special Paper 30.

Evenson, E.B., 1973, Late Pleistocene Shorelines and Stratigraphic Relations in the Lake Michigan Basin: Geological Society of America Bulletin, v. 84, p. 2281-2298.

Evenson, E.B., Eschman, D.F., and Farrand, W.R., 1973, The "Valderan" Problem, Lake Michigan Basin: Midwest Friends of the Pleistocene [Guidebook], 22nd Annual Field Conference, Ann Arbor, University of Michigan, 59 p.

Evenson, E.B., Farrand, W.R., Eschman, D.F., Mickelson, D.M., and Maher, L.J., 1976, Greatlakean Substage – A Replacement for Valderan Substage in the Lake Michigan Basin: Quaternary Research, v. 6, p. 411-424.

Evenson, E.B., and Taylor, L.D., 1981, The "Valders" Problem: National Association of Geology Teachers, East-Central Section, Field Trip Guide, Grand Valley State College, Allendale, Michigan, 57 p.

Farrand, W.R., and Eschman, D.F., 1974, Glaciation of the Southern Peninsula of Michigan – A review: Michigan Academician, v. 7, p. 31-56.

Farrand, W.R., and Miller, B.B., 1968, Radiocarbon Dates on and Depositional Environments of the Wasaga Beach Marl Deposits: Ohio Journal of Science, v. 68, p. 235-239.

Farrand, W.R., Zahner, Robert, and Benninghoff, W.S., 1969, Cary-Port Huron Interstade – Evidence from a Buried Bryophyte Bed. Cheboygan County, Michigan: Geological Society of America Special Paper 123, p. 249-262.

Finamore, P.F., 1985, Glacial Lake Algonquin and the Fenelon Falls Outlet: *in* Karrow, P.F., and Calkin, P.E., eds., Quaternary Evolution of the Great Lakes: Geological Association of Canada Special Paper 30.

Fraser, G.S., Larsen, C.E., and Hester, N.C., 1975, Climatically Controlled High Lake Levels in Lake Michigan and Lake Huron Basins: Anais Academia Brasiliera Ciencias, v. 47, p. 51-66 (Supplemento).

Fullerton, D.S., 1980, Preliminary Correlation of Post-Erie Interstadial Events (16,000-10,000 Radiocarbon Years Before Present), Central and Eastern Great Lakes Region, and Hudson, Champlain, and St. Lawrence Lowlands, United States and Canada: United States Geological Survey Professional Paper 1089, 52 p.

Goldthwait, J.W., 1906, Correlation of the Raised Beaches on the West Side of Lake Michigan: Journal of Geology, v. 14, p. 411-424.

———, 1907, The Abandoned Shore Lines of Eastern Wisconsin: Wisconsin Geological and Natural History Survey Bulletin 17, 134 p.

———, 1908, A reconstruction of Water Planes of the Extinct Glacial Lakes in the Lake Michigan Basin: Journal of Geology, v. 16, p. 459-476.

Goldthwait, R.P., 1966, Evidence from Alaskan Glaciers of Major Climatic Changes: *in* Sawyer, J.S., ed., World Climate from 8000 to 0 B.C.: London, Royal Meteorological Society, p. 40-53.

Gutschick, R.C., and Gonsiewski, J., 1976, Coastal Geology of Mt. Baldy Injiana Dunes National Lakeshore South End of Lake Michigan: *in* Guide book for Fieldtrips, North-Central Section, Geological Society of America Meeting, Western Michigan University, Kalamazoo, p. 40-90.

Hansel, A.K., 1983, The Wadsworth Till Member of Illinois and the Equivalent Oak Creek Formation of Wisconsin: *in* Mickelson, D.M., and Clayton, Lee, eds., Late Pleistocene History of Southeastern Wisconsin: Geoscience Wisconsin, v. 7, p. 1-16.

Harrison, J.E., 1972, Quaternary Geology of the North Bay-Mattawa Region: Geological Survey of Canada Paper 71-26, 36 p.

Hough, J.L., 1953, Revision of the Nipissing Stage of the Great Lakes: Illinois State Academy of Science Transactions, v. 46, p. 133-141.

———, 1955, Lake Chippewa, a Low Stage of Lake Michigan Indicated by Bottom Sediments: Geological Society of America Bulletin, v. 73, p. 613-619.

———, 1958, Geology of the Great Lakes: Urbana, Illinois, University of Illinois Press, 313 p.

———, 1963, The Prehistoric Great Lakes of North America: American Scientist, v. 51, p. 84-109.

———, 1966, Correlation of Glacial Lake Stages in the Huron-Erie and Michigan Basins: Journal of Geology, v. 74, p. 62-77.

Johnson, W.H., in press, Stratigraphy and Correlation of the Glacial Deposits of the Lake Michigan Lobe prior to 14 000 B.P.: *in* Richmond, G.M., and Fullerton, D.S., eds., Quaternary Glaciations in the United States: International Geological Correlation Project 24, Quaternary Glaciations of the Northern Hemisphere.

Karrow, P.F., 1978, Comment on "Greatlakean Substage: A Replacement for Valderan Substage in the Lake Michigan Basin" by E.B. Evenson, W.R. Farrand, D.F. Eschman, D.M. Mickelson, and L.J. Maher: Quaternary Research, v. 9, p 116-118.

———, 1980, The Nipissing Transgression Around Southern Lake Huron: Canadian Journal of Earth Sciences, v. 17, p. 1271-1274.

Karrow, P.F., Anderson, T.W., Clarke, A.H., Delorme, L.D., and Sreenivasa, M.R., 1975, Stratigraphy, Paleontology, and Age of Lake Algonquin Sediments in Southwestern Ontario, Canada: Quaternary Research, v. 5, p. 49-87.

Kaszycki, C.A., 1985, History of Glacial Lake Algonquin in the Haliburton Region, South Central Ontario: *in* Karrow, P.F., and Calkin, P.E., eds., Quaternary Evolution of the Great Lakes: Geological Association of Canada Special Paper 30.

Kunkle, G.R., 1963, Lake Ypsilanti – A Probable Late Pleistocene Low-Lake Stage in the Erie Basin: Journal of Geology, v. 71, p. 72-75.

Larsen, C.E., 1973, Prehistoric Levels of Lake Michigan-Huron: Their Potential in Shoreland Planning: *in* Botts, L., ed., Proceedings of Shoreland Planning Conference, Chicago: Lake Michigan Federation, p. 169-195.

———, 1974, Late Holocene Lake Levels in Southern Lake Michigan: *in* Collinson, Charles, ed., Coastal Geology, Sedimentology, and Management; Chicago and the Nearshore: Illinois State Geological Survey Guidebook Series 12, p. 39-49.

———, 1985a, Lake Level, Uplift, and Outlet Incision, the Nipissing and Algoma Great Lakes: *in* Karrow, P.F., and Calkin, P.E., eds., Quaternary Evolution of the Great Lakes: Geological Association of Canada Special Paper 30.

———, 1985b. A Stratigraphic Study of Beach Features on the Southwestern Shore of Lake Michigan: New Evidence of Holocene Lake Level Fluctuations: Illinois State Geological Survey Environmental Geology Notes 112, 31 p.

Leverett, Frank, 1897, The Pleistocene Features and Deposits of the Chicago Area: Chicago Academy of Science Bulletin 2, 86 p.

Leverett, Frank, and Taylor, F.B., 1915, The Pleistocene of Indiana and Michigan and the History of the Great Lakes: United States Geological Survey Monograph 53, 529 p.

Lewis, C.F.M. 1969, Late Quaternary History of Lake Levels in the Huron and Erie Basins: *in* Proceedings 12th Conference on Great Lakes Research, International Association for Great Lakes Research, p. 250-270.

———, 1970, Recent uplift of Manitoulin Island, Ontario: Canadian Journal of Earth Sciences, v. 7, p. 665-675.

Lineback, J.A., Gross, D.L., and Dell, C.I., 1979, Glacial and Postglacial Sediments in Lakes Superior and Michigan: Geological Society of America Bulletin, Part 1, v. 90, p. 781-791.

Lineback, J.A., Gross, D.L., and Meyer, R.P., 1974, Glacial Tills Under Lake Michigan: Illinois State Geological Survey Environmental Geology Notes 69, 48 p.

Lowdon, J.A., and Blake, Weston, Jr., 1975, Geological Survey of Canada Radiocarbon Dates XV: Geological Survey of Canada Paper 75-7, 32 p.

Mickelson, D.M., Acomb, L.J., and Bentley, C.R., 1981, Possible Mechanism for the Rapid Advance and Retreat of the Lake Michigan Lobe Between 13 000 and 11 000 years B.P.: Annals of Glaciology v. 2, p. 185-186.

Mickelson, D.M., Clayton, Lee, Baker, R.W., Mode, W.N., and Schneider, A.F., 1984, Pleistocene Stratigraphic Units of Wisconsin: Wisconsin Geological and Natural History Survey, 199 p.

Mickelson, D.M., and Evenson, E.B., 1975, Pre-Twocreekan Age of the Type Valders Till, Wisconsin: Geology, v. 3, p. 587-590.

Monaghan, G.W., Faye, L., and Lovis, W.A., in review, Nipissing Transgression in the Saginaw Bay region, Michigan: Canadian Journal of Earth Sciences.

Prest, V.K., 1970, Quaternary Geology of Canada: in Douglas, R.J.W., ed., Geology and Economic Minerals of Canada, Economic Geology Report No. 1: Ottawa, Department of Energy, Mines and Resources, p. 676-764.

Rubin, Meyer, and Alexander, Corrine, 1960, U.S. Geological Survey Radiocarbon Dates V: Radiocarbon, v. 2, p. 129-185.

Rubin, Meyer, and Suess, H.E., 1955, U.S. Geological Survey Radiocarbon Dates II: Science, v. 121, p. 481-488.

Saarnisto, Matti, 1974, The Deglaciation History of the Lake Superior Region and Its Climatic Implications: Quaternary Research, v. 4, p. 316-339.

Schneider, A.F., 1968, History of a Morainal Gap at Valparaiso, Indiana (Abstract): Geological Society of America Special Paper 115, p. 398-399.

_____, 1983, Wisconsinan Stratigraphy and Glacial Sequence in Southeastern Wisconsin: in Mickelsen, D.M. and Clayton, Lee, eds., Late Pleistocene History of Southeastern Wisconsin: Geoscience Wisconsin, v. 7, p. 59-85.

Schneider, A.F., and Keller, S.J., 1970, Geologic Map of the 1° × 2° Chicago Quadrangle, Indiana, Illinois, and Michigan, Showing Bedrock and Unconsolidated Deposits: Indiana Geological Survey Regional Geologic Map 4, Part B, Scale 1:250,000.

Schneider, A.F., and Need, E.A., 1983, Lithologic and Stratigraphic Evidence for a Late Mid-Woodfordian Proglacial Lake in the Lake Michigan Basin: Geological Society of America Abstracts with Programs, v. 15, no. 6, p. 680.

Schneider, A.F., and Reshkin, Mark, 1970, Age and Correlation of the Glenwood Stage of Glacial Lake Chicago: Geological Society of America Abstracts with Programs, v. 2, no. 6, p. 404.

_____, 1982, Identification of the Twocreekan Substage in Indiana: Indiana Academy of Science Proceedings, v. 91, p. 347.

Stanley, G.M., 1936, Lower Algonquin Beaches of Penetanguishene Peninsula: Geological Society of America Bulletin, v. 47, p. 1933-1960.

_____, 1937, Lower Algonquin Beaches of Cape Rich, Georgian Bay: Geological Society of America Bulletin, v. 48, p. 1665-1686.

_____, 1938, The Submerged Valley Through Mackinac Straits: Journal of Geology, v. 46, p. 966-974.

Swain, A.M., 1978, Environmental Changes During the Past 2000 Years in North Central Wisconsin: Analysis of Pollen, Charcoal, and Seeds from Varved Lake Sediments: Quaternary Research, v. 10, p. 55-68.

Taylor, L.D., 1977, Preliminary Analysis of Glacial Stratigraphy in the Vicinity of the Port Huron and Two Rivers Till Sheets, Manistee, Michigan: Geological Society of America Abstracts with Programs, v. 9, no. 5, p. 658.

_____, 1978, Glacial Stratigraphy and Clay Mineralogy of Till and Lacustrine Units Along the East Shore of Lake Michigan: Geological Society of America Abstracts with Programs, v. 10, no. 6, p. 286.

_____, 1985, Geomorphic and Stratigraphic Evidence for Glacial Lake Levels in the Northeastern Lake Michigan Basin and their Relationship to Uplift Curves: Geological Society of America Abstracts with Programs, v. 17, no. 5, p. 329.

Terasmae, Jaan, and Hughes, O.L., 1960, Glacial Retreat in the North Bay Area, Ontario: Science, v. 131, p. 1444-1446.

Terasmae, J., 1979, Radiocarbon Dating and Palynology of Glacial Lake Nipissing Deposits at Wasaga Beach, Ontario: Journal of Great Lakes Research, v. 5, p. 292-300.

Thwaites, F.T., and Bertrand, Kenneth, 1957, Pleistocene Geology of the Door Peninsula, Wisconsin: Geological Society of America Bulletin, v. 68, p. 831-879.

Webb, Thompson, Cushing, E.J., and Wright, H.E., Jr., 1983, Holocene Changes in the Vegetation of the Midwest: in Wright, H.E., Jr., ed., Late Quaternary Environments of the United States, Vol. 2: The Holocene: Minneapolis, University of Minnesota Press, p. 142-165.

Webb, Thompson, and Bryson, R.A., 1972, Late and Postglacial Climatic Change in the Northern Midwest, USA: Quantitative Multivariate Statistical Analyses: Quaternary Research, v. 2, p. 70-115.

Willman, H.B., 1971, Summary of the Geology of the Chicago Area: Illinois State Geological Survey Circular 460, 77 p.

Willman, H.B., and Frye, J.C., 1970, Pleistocene Stratigraphy of Illinois: Illinois State Geological Survey Bulletin 94, 204 p.

Winkler, E.M., 1962, Radiocarbon Ages of Postglacial Lake Clays Near Michigan City, Indiana: Science, v. 137, p. 528-529.

Workman, L.E., 1925, A Pleistocene Section in the Vicinity of the Thorton Reef: M.S. Thesis, University of Chicago, Chicago, Illinois, 25 p.

Wright, G.F., 1918, Explanation of the Abandoned Beaches About the South End of Lake Michigan: Geological Society of America Bulletin, v. 29, p. 235-244.

Quaternary Evolution of the Great Lakes,
edited by P.F. Karrow and P.E. Calkin,
Geological Association of Canada Special Paper 30, 1985

LAKE MILWAUKEE: AN "EARLY" PROGLACIAL LAKE IN THE LAKE MICHIGAN BASIN

Allan F. Schneider

Department of Geology, University of Wisconsin-Parkside, Kenosha, Wisconsin 53141

Edward A. Need

IT Corporation, 4300 W. Brown Deer Road, Milwaukee, Wisconsin 53223

ABSTRACT

Lithologic and stratigraphic evidence from the Milwaukee, Wisconsin, area indicate the existence of a generally unrecognized late Wisconsinan proglacial lake in the Lake Michigan basin. Named "glacial Lake Milwaukee", this lake apparently occupied the southern part of the basin in late mid-Woodfordian time, probably between 14 500 and 15 500 B.P., prior to the earliest phases of glacial Lake Chicago. However, the actual extent and level of Lake Milwaukee are still largely unknown.

The principal lithologic evidence for glacial Lake Milwaukee is a significant difference in grain size between tills of the New Berlin and Oak Creek Formations. Whereas New Berlin till is a very stony, sandy drift that has about 40% silt and clay in its matrix, the younger Oak Creek till contains relatively few stones and nearly 50% more silt and clay. New Berlin till was deposited by ice that crossed southeastern Wisconsin from northeast to southwest and terminated at the Darien Moraine. Lake Milwaukee formed with subsequent ice-marginal retreat. Readvance of the Lake Michigan Lobe from a more easterly direction to its Valparaiso and subsequent Tinley and Lake Border positions resulted in the assimilation of fine-grained Lake Milwaukee sediments and deposition of Oak Creek till. The basal part of the Oak Creek Formation is commonly a water-laid diamicton. Where both New Berlin and Oak Creek tills are exposed along the modern Lake Michigan shoreline, glaciolacustrine clays occur between them. Additional stratigraphic evidence comes from recent geotechnical borings along the lower Milwaukee and Menomonee River valleys which show that New Berlin and Oak Creek tills are generally separated by proglacial lake deposits.

RÉSUMÉ

Des données lithologiques et stratigraphiques provenant de Milwaukee au Wisconsin révèlent l'existence à la fin du Wisconsinien d'un lac proglaciaire jusqu'ici non-reconnu dans le bassin du lac Michigan. Ce lac, ci-après nommé Milwaukee, occupait la partie méridionale du bassin à la fin du Woodfordien moyen, probablement entre 14 500 et 15 000 ans B.P., juste avant l'initiation du lac glaciaire Chicago. Cependant, l'étendue ainsi que le niveau du lac Milwaukee sont peu connus encore aujourd'hui.

L'indice principal pour la reconnaissance du lac glaciaire Milwaukee est la différence significative dans la granulométrie des tills des formations de New Berlin et d'Oak Creek. Alors que le till de New Berlin est un dépôt très blocailleux et sableux avec une teneur d'environ 40% en limons et argiles dans la matrice. Le plus jeune till d'Oak Creek, pour sa part, a une faible teneur en cailloux et contient presque 50% plus de limons et argiles que le till de New Berlin. Les assemblages minéralogiques des deux tills sont aussi quelque peu différents. Le till de New Berlin a été déposé par le sous-lobe Delavan du lobe du lac Michigan. Celui-ci a traversé le sud-ouest du Wisconsin du nord-est au sud-ouest et s'est arrêté à la moraine de Darien. Lors de la période de stagnation glaciaire, une série de sédiments fins glaciolacustres ont été déposés dans le lac Milwaukee dont le rivage nord s'assimilait au front glaciaire. La réavancée du lobe du lac Michigan, d'une direction plus à l'est, vers les positions de Valparaiso puis de Tinley et de Lake Border a entraîné l'incorporation de ces sédiments lacustres dans la charge glaciaire et la déposition du till d'Oak Creek. La portion basale de la formation d'Oak Creek est principalement un diamicton déposé dans l'eau. Lorsque les tills de New Berlin et d'Oak Creek affleurent à un même site le long du rivage actuel du lac Michigan, ils sont séparés par des argiles glaciolacustres. Des données stratigraphiques additionnelles proviennent de forages géotechniques le long des vallées inférieures des rivières Milwaukee et Menomonee. Les forages obtenus par l'intermédiaire du programme d'assainissement des eaux par la ville de Milwaukee indiquent que les tills de New Berlin et d'Oak Creek sont généralement séparés par des sédiments de lacs proglaciaires.

INTRODUCTION

Among the numerous lake phases that played important roles in the complex late-glacial and postglacial history of the Lake Michigan basin were those associated with glacial Lake Chicago. This lake occupied the basin between about 14 000 and 11 000 B.P. Lake Chicago was named nearly 90 years ago by Frank Leverett, who at the same time also named the three main levels or stages of the lake – Glenwood, Calumet, and Toleston. In choosing these names, Leverett (1897) selected localities in northwestern Indiana and northeastern Illinois that were situated on or near prominent beaches south of the Lake Michigan shoreline and north of (behind) the Valparaiso and Tinley Moraines. For more than half a century thereafter, the earliest generally recognized proglacial lake phase in the Lake Michigan basin was the 195-m (640-ft.) Glenwood stage of Lake Chicago. This formed when the Lake Michigan Lobe retreated from the Tinley Moraine (Bretz, 1951, 1955; Hough, 1958, 1963; Wayne and Zumberge, 1965; Willman, 1971). In the classic Leverett and Taylor (1915) monograph, Leverett (p. 225, 227) referred to the formative phase of the Glenwood stage as "incipient Lake Chicago". Bretz (1951) retained this designation for the lake during the time required to erode the Tinley Moraine crest down to the level of the Tinley valley train and develop the boulder armour that he believed would serve to control the semistatic level of the Glenwood phase for the next 1800 years or so.

Earlier (pre-Bretz) students of Lake Chicago (Leverett, 1897, 1899; Salisbury and Alden, 1899; Alden, 1902, 1904, 1906, 1918; Goldthwait, 1906, 1907, 1908, 1909; Atwood and Goldthwait, 1908; Leverett and Taylor, 1915; Wright, 1918; Cressey, 1928) wrote that the Glenwood phase was initiated as the Lake Michigan Lobe withdrew from the Valparaiso Moraine, rather than from the Tinley Moraine, but only because the latter was long regarded to be part of the Valparaiso system rather than a discrete ridge behind the Valparaiso. That the Tinley Moraine marked a distinct readvance of the ice after retreating an unknown distance from the Valparaiso was first recognized by Bretz, who named the moraine (Bretz, 1939) and later discussed the significance of its recognition to the formation of Lake Chicago and its outlet (Bretz, 1951; 1955, p. 107-110). The rather confusing history of nomenclature surrounding the Tinley Moraine, as well as its expression in northern Indiana, was discussed by Schneider (1968a).

In this paper we are concerned not with lake events that followed the establishment of the earliest Glenwood phase (see Hansel *et al.*, 1985), but rather with events that preceded the formation of Lake Chicago. We focus here on available evidence for glacial Lake Milwaukee – an earlier proglacial lake that may well have equaled or exceeded Lake Chicago in size and significance.

PRE-GLENWOOD LAKE PHASES

Although the Glenwood phase is generally regarded to be the earliest recognizable proglacial lake in the Lake Michigan basin, earlier and higher lake levels have been inferred. Cressey (1928) proposed the name "Valparaiso stage" for a narrow, irregularly crescentic pre-Glenwood lake, mostly in

Indiana, with a minimum elevation of 204 m. This was believed to have drained southward through gaps in the Valparaiso Moraine prior to the uncovering of the Chicago outlet at 195 m. Schneider (1968b) presented evidence for still higher lakes in Indiana at levels of about 229 m and 213 m, which also drained southward through Valparaiso gap and eventually into the Kankakee sluiceway. In Illinois, pre-Glenwood Lake Chicago stages were suggested by Atwood and Goldthwait (1908) and by Ekblaw (1931); however, Bretz (1955, p. 108) considered the field evidence supporting these phases to be unconvincing.

More commonly accepted perhaps is Early Lake Chicago, a pre-Glenwood phase named and figured by Hough (1958, 1963). This formed during retreat of ice from the Valparaiso Moraine. Although the evidence for Early Lake Chicago is attributed by Hough (1958, p. 164-165) to Bretz (1951, p. 404-405), it is clear that Bretz (1955, p. 107) himself was not fully convinced of its existence. The elevation of the lake is unknown; no beaches have ever been found because the entire area occupied by Early Lake Chicago was later overridden when the ice readvanced to form the Tinley Moraine. Consequently, some later authors (e.g., Kelley and Farrand, 1967; Fullerton, 1980) have included Early Lake Chicago as a phase in the lake sequence of the Michigan basin; others (Wayne and Zumberge, 1965; Willman, 1971) have apparently chosen not to recognize it. Thwaites and Bertrand (1957) used the name "Early Lake Chicago" in several places, but almost certainly the lacustrine deposits they ascribed to Early Lake Chicago were actually deposited during a second rise to the 195-m level or Glenwood II phase of Lake Chicago (Hough, 1958; Hansel *et al.*, 1985).

Briefly then, although it is not well documented, the earliest proglacial lake phase postulated for the Lake Michigan basin has been Early Lake Chicago. The age of Early Lake Chicago (post-Valparaiso, pre-Tinley) is currently placed at slightly greater than 14 300 B.P. (Fullerton, 1980, pl. 1).

RECOGNITION OF GLACIAL LAKE MILWAUKEE

The existence of a still earlier proglacial lake (a pre-Valparaiso lake) in the Lake Michigan basin is now indicated. This phase was called "glacial Lake Milwaukee" by Schneider (1983, p. 77) because the best known evidence for this lake comes from the Milwaukee, Wisconsin area. Lithologic and stratigraphic evidence for the lake was subsequently summarized by Schneider and Need (1983) and that evidence is presented here in greater detail.

Only a few weeks before this paper was written, we discovered that the name "Glacial Lake Milwaukee" had previously been used by Lawrence Martin nearly 70 years ago. Martin (1916, p. 453-454) used the name for an early (pre-Lake Chicago) "milky-white" proglacial lake in the Lake Michigan basin. He referred to Lake Milwaukee only briefly however, and somewhat indirectly, in his discussion of glacial lakes in the Lake Superior basin. No mention can be found of Lake Milwaukee in his more extensive discussions of eastern Wisconsin and the Lake Michigan coastal zone. Substantive evidence for the lake was not provided.

Thwaites (1950, p. 91) also used the name "Lake Milwaukee" (in quotation marks) and indicated that it was equivalent either to Lake Chicago or to an early Glenwood phase of Lake Chicago; his statement in this regard is ambiguous. Certainly Thwaites did not consider the lake to be pre-Chicago phase, as did Martin (1916, p. 454), who clearly stated that Lake Chicago followed Lake Milwaukee "... some thousands of years later." Thus Thwaites and Bertrand (1957, p. 859) equated Martin's Lake Milwaukee with their Early Lake Chicago, which, as stated above, probably equates with the Glenwood II phase of Lake Chicago.

To our knowledge, the name "glacial Lake Milwaukee" has not appeared elsewhere, except in later, virtually unaltered editions (published in 1932 and 1965) of Martin's original volume. No mention is made of either a glacial Lake Milwaukee or a pre-Glenwood phase of Lake Chicago in Alden's (1918) comprehensive treatment of the Quaternary geology of southeastern Wisconsin. Fortunately our current usage seems to be fully in accord with Martin's original use and concept, and no conflict in priority is involved.

EVIDENCE FOR GLACIAL LAKE MILWAUKEE

According to Hough (1963, p. 90), Early Lake Chicago was "inferred from the evidence of ice retreat and readvance, and from the fact that the till deposit of the readvance contains a higher percentage of silt and clay (lake deposits?) than the older till on which it lies." Glacial Lake Milwaukee is inferred from similar evidence, but the lithologic evidence for Lake Milwaukee is much stronger and in addition it is substantiated by stratigraphic evidence.

Lithologic Evidence

The existence of Lake Milwaukee is based in part on a significant difference in lithology, particularly grain size, between tills of the New Berlin and Oak Creek Formations Fig. 1). The New Berlin Formation (Mickelson et al., 1984), whose surficial distribution is shown in Figure 2, was deposited by the Delavan Sublobe of the Lake Michigan Lobe. This crossed southeastern Wisconsin flowing from northeast to southwest and terminated at the Darien Moraine (Fig. 3; Alden, 1904, 1918; Schneider, 1982, 1983). New Berlin till typically is a gravelly sandy loam. It contains many stones, and its matrix (less than 2 mm) has an average composition of 58% sand, 29% silt, and 13% clay (Table I and Fig. 4). In some places the till is considerably more sandy, containing as much as 70 or 72% sand. Till of equivalent age in northeastern Illinois, called the Haeger Till Member of the Wedron Formation (Willman and Frye, 1970), is also very sandy (Table I).

When the Lake Michigan Lobe subsequently readvanced from a more easterly direction, it laid down a much finer grained deposit named the Oak Creek Formation (Mickelson et al., 1984; Fig. 2), along with the equivalent Wadsworth Till Member of the Wedron Formation (Willman and Frye, 1970) of northeastern Illinois. Oak Creek till is less stony than New Berlin till and has a matrix that contains nearly 50% more silt and clay than New Berlin till (Table I and Fig. 4). Sixty-eight samples of Oak Creek till from southeastern Wisconsin averaged 12% sand, 44% silt, and 44% clay. Till from the oldest moraine containing Oak Creek till, the Valparaiso Moraine, is somewhat coarser grained than

WISCONSIN TERMINOLOGY	ILLINOIS TERMINOLOGY
Kewaunee Formation	Not present
Oak Creek Formation	Wadsworth Till Member of the Wedron Formation
New Berlin Formation (Lake Michigan Lobe) and Horicon Formation (Green Bay Lobe)	Haeger Till Member of the Wedron Formation

Figure 1. Nomenclature of selected late Wisconsinan lithostratigraphic units in southeastern Wisconsin and northeastern Illinois. Wisconsin terminology from Mickelson et al. (1984); Illinois terminology from Willman and Frye (1970).

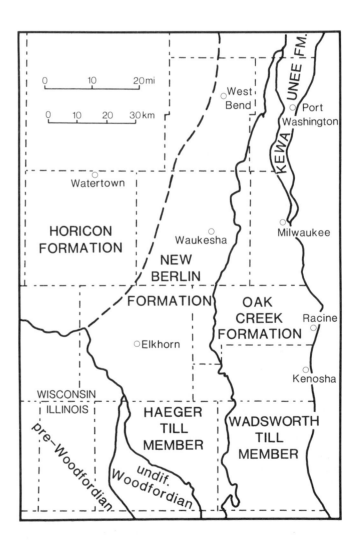

Figure 2. Map of southeastern Wisconsin and adjacent northeastern Illinois showing surficial distribution of late Wisconsinan lithostratigraphic units. Wisconsin names are those used by Mickelson et al. (1984).

till in the younger Tinley and Lake Border Moraines (Fig. 3), probably because the ice came over terrain underlain by the New Berlin Formation. Nevertheless, samples from the Valparaiso Moraine average about 45% more silt and clay than samples of New Berlin till.

The equivalent Wadsworth till of northeastern Illinois has a similar grain-size distribution. Analyses of 98 samples of Oak Creek and Wadsworth tills indicate an average grain-size composition of 11% sand, 43% silt, and 46% clay, as previously reported by Hansel (1983, Table 1).

This extreme difference in grain size between the New Berlin-Haeger and the Oak Creek-Wadsworth till units can best be explained by the erosion and incorporation of the fine-grained lake sediment deposited in the Lake Michigan basin during an ice-free interval. Scouring of the bedrock floor of the lake and assimilation of Devonion shale does not appear to be an adequate explanation, though certainly this must have occurred, as indicated by the abundance of shale chips in the younger till.

Mineralogically, Oak Creek till contains somewhat more illite than New Berlin till. Clay-mineral analyses of fifty-five samples of Oak Creek till by H.D. Glass of the Illinois State Geological Survey averaged 72% illite, 15% expandable clay minerals, and 13% kaolinite plus chlorite. Twenty-six samples of New Berlin till averaged 66% illite and 17% each of expandable clays and kaolinite plus chlorite. We are not prepared to assess the significance, if any, of these differences.

TABLE I
AVERAGE GRAIN-SIZE COMPOSITION OF TILLS, SOUTHEASTERN WISCONSIN AND NORTHEASTERN ILLINOIS. SCHNEIDER'S SAMPLES ARE ALL FROM WISCONSIN; WICKHAM'S SAMPLES AND WILLMAN AND FRYE'S SAMPLES ARE ALL FROM ILLINOIS; HANSEL'S SAMPLES ARE FROM BOTH STATES.

	SAND (%)	SILT (%)	CLAY (%)	N
OAK CREEK-WADSWORTH TILL				
Schneider, 1983	12	44	44	(68)
Hansel, 1983	11	43	46	(98)
Willman & Frye, 1970	12	39	49	(19)
NEW BERLIN-HAEGER TILL				
Schneider, 1983	58	29	13	(15)
Wickham, 1975	45	39	16	(32)
Willman & Frye, 1970	39	39	22	(5)

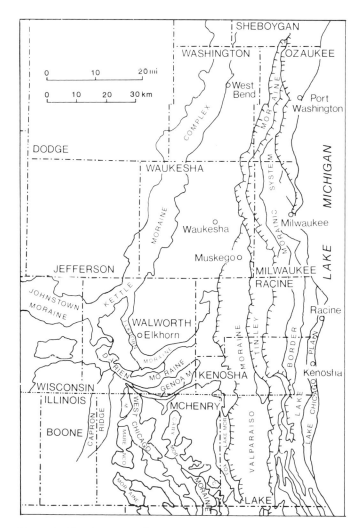

Figure 3. Moraine map of southeastern Wisconsin and adjacent northeastern Illinois. Moraines as shown do not necessarily represent the interpretations of the authors; rather an attempt is made to show relationships mapped by several workers during the past 80 years. Hachured lines represent distal edges of younger rock-stratigraphic units. Compiled from several sources; adapted from Schneider (1983).

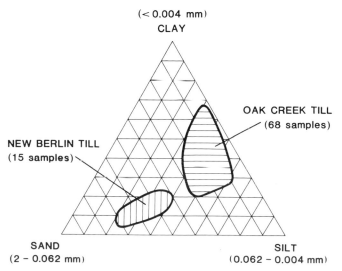

Figure 4. Textural triangle showing grain-size distribution of the matrix (less than 2 mm) of till samples of the New Berlin and Oak Creek Formations.

Stratigraphic Evidence

Stratigraphic evidence for glacial Lake Milwaukee comes from both surface exposures and subsurface data. In the few places along the Lake Michigan shoreline where both New Berlin and Oak Creek tills are exposed, they are commonly separated by fine-grained lake sediments (Fig. 5). The basal part of the Oak Creek till usually grades downward into lacustrine clay or is a water-laid diamicton. The contact between the lake clays and underlying New Berlin till, on the other hand, is usually sharp (Fig. 6). These relationships are best displayed at the St. Francis bluff exposure (Klauk, 1978; Christensen and Schneider, 1984), which was examined by more than fifty Quaternary scientists on the North-Central Geological Society of America glacial geology field trip in May, 1983 (Mickelson *et al.*, 1983).

Toward the south end of the St. Francis exposure, a pink facies of probable Oak Creek till occurs at the base of the Oak Creek Formation. Just above modern lake level the pink till is underlain by 3 to 4 m of well-sorted, medium sand layers that possibly represent Lake Milwaukee beach deposits (Christensen and Schneider, 1984). New Berlin till is below lake level in this part of the exposure but is presumed to underlie the sand sequence.

The subsurface data come from recent geotechnical borings drilled along the lower Milwaukee and lower Menomonee River valleys in connection with the Milwaukee Water Pollution Abatement Program. These borings show that the New Berlin and Oak Creek Formations are generally separated by proglacial lake sediment (Need, 1983, p. 33, Figs. 5, 8, and 9). Borings along the lower Menomonee

Valley particularly reveal both fine-grained and medium-grained lake sediments between the tills (Fig. 7). The fine-grained materials consist of well-sorted clay to silty clay loam which is commonly laminated. The medium-grained sediments are composed of dense silty fine sand with very little clay. Maximum thickness of the lacustrine deposits in these borings is about 12 m.

The suggestion has been made that some of the higher lacustrine units in the borings may also represent Lake Milwaukee sedimentation. While it is probably true that parts of the lake persisted as the ice advanced to the Valparaiso Moraine, it is not possible to state which, if any, of the younger lacustrine units in the borings were indeed deposited in Lake Milwaukee. The Oak Creek Formation characteristically includes fine-grained till and interbedded lacustrine deposits (Mickelson *et al.*, 1984), but detailed interpretation of the many interbedded and interfingering units in the formation has not been undertaken. Based upon its stratigraphic position, unit 4L (Fig. 7) is tentatively thought to represent the Valparaiso advance. If this interpretation is correct, the overlying lake sediments were likely to have been deposited during a somewhat later lake phase (Early Lake Chicago?), rather than in Lake Milwaukee.

EXTENT AND DURATION OF LAKE MILWAUKEE

The depositional record found in the Milwaukee and Menomonee valleys is preserved in a preglacial bedrock lowland (Need, 1983). Thus, the highest elevations of identified Lake Milwaukee sediments in any of the borings is about 150 m. In the borings from the lower Menomonee River valley, the general elevation of the top of the lacustrine sequence is only about 135 m (Fig. 7), or some 42 m below the level of modern Lake Michigan. The highest Lake Mil-

Figure 5. Photograph showing fine-grained lacustrine sediments of glacial Lake Milwaukee (between shovel blades) between till of the New Berlin Formation (below) and till of the Oak Creek Formation. Note that the lower contact of the lake deposits is sharp, whereas the upper contact is gradational. St. Francis bluff exposure; NE1/4 NE1/4 Sec. 23, T. 6 N., R. 22 E., Milwaukee County, Wisconsin.

Figure 6. Photograph showing sharp contact between stony New Berlin till (below shovel blade) and overlying lacustrine clay of glacial Lake Milwaukee. St. Francis bluff exposure; NE1/4 NE1/4 Sec. 23, T. 6 N., R. 22 E., Milwaukee County, Wisconsin.

waukee sediments observed along the Lake Michigan shoreline (Figs. 5 and 6) are only a few metres above lake level. If the sand layers above the pink Oak Creek till are indeed Lake Milwaukee beach deposits, the level of the lake probably was only a few metres above that of the present-day lake. Even the highest known lake phases, Glenwood I and Glenwood II, attained levels only 18 m above present lake level, and their shorelines and depositional records, where still preserved, do not extend very far inland. Thus it seems most unlikely that Lake Milwaukee deposits will be found very far inland. Hopefully, more of the lithostratigraphic record of the lake will eventually be discovered in deep borings along the coast or from the bottom of Lake Michigan. On the other hand, much of that record could well have been destroyed by glacial scouring of the basin during post-Lake Milwaukee ice advances.

Thus the actual extent and level of Lake Milwaukee are unknown. The outline of the lake as shown in Figure 8 is highly conjectural, but we do wish to suggest that the ice front probably backwasted to a position relatively far north in the Lake Michigan basin. The fine-grained deposits of the Oak Creek Formation are known to occur only as far north as southern Sheboygan County (Alden, 1918), where they become buried by red clayey till of the Kewaunee Formation (Figs. 2 and 3). The subsurface stratigraphy north of here is completely unknown, however, and Oak Creek till may be present in the subsurface. It is also possible that the Oak Creek till was largely removed by glacial scouring, just as Lake Milwaukee deposits were eroded and incorporated into the Oak Creek Formation. Much of the Lake Michigan basin may well have been occupied by Lake Milwaukee and received abundant contributions of silt and clay, in order to account for the very high percentage of fine-grained constitutents in the tills of the Valparaiso, Tinley, and Lake Border Moraines. Martin's reference to Lake Milwaukee as

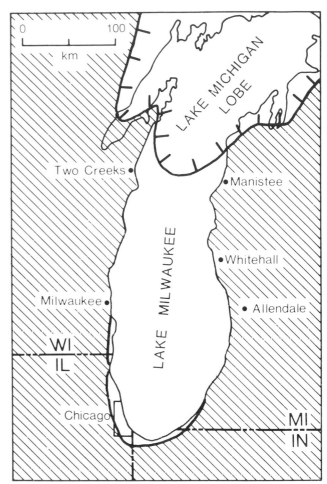

Figure 8. Map of the Lake Michigan basin at about 15 000 B.P. showing hypothetical extent of glacial Lake Milwaukee and its relationship to the Lake Michigan ice lobe.

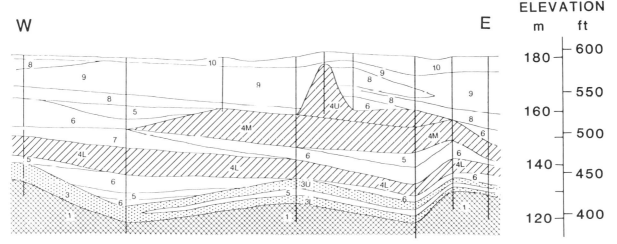

Figure 7. Subsurface cross section of Quaternary deposits along the lower Menomonee River valley. Vertical lines represent selected geotechnical borings used in construction of the cross section; dashed vertical line at west (left) end of section represents data projected from borings not in line of section. Length of section is approximately 1.8 km; vertical exaggeration X 10. Elevations are in metres and feet above mean sea level; approximate level of Lake Michigan is 177 m (580 ft). Deposits identified by number are as follows: 1) Silurian bedrock, 2) Devonian bedrock (not present in this section), 3) New Berlin till (3L, lower unit, 3U, upper unit), 4) Oak Creek till (4L, lower unit, 4M, middle unit, 4U, upper unit), 5) fine-grained lake sediment, 6) medium grained lake sediment, 7) coarse-grained lake sediment, 8) alluvial sediment, 9) estuarine sediment, 10) artificial fill. Adapted from Need (1983).

a milky-white lake is probably an apt description.

Despite its apparent size, Lake Milwaukee appears to have had a relatively short life because stagnant ice masses of the Delavan Sublobe had not completely melted before being overrun during the first advance of the Lake Michigan Lobe to deposit fine-grained till of the Oak Creek Formation in the Valparaiso Moraine (Schneider, 1982, 1983). Much of the relief within the moraine reflects an older stagnant-ice topography that is veneered with an irregular blanket of younger till (Schneider, 1983, p. 78); it is highly probable that the lower part of the Oak Creek-Wadsworth complex was deposited atop masses of still stagnant ice that had not yet melted before being buried by ice that was rich in fine-grained lake deposits derived from glacial Lake Milwaukee.

We suggest that Lake Milwaukee occupied the Lake Michigan basin sometime between 14 500 and 15 500 radiocarbon years ago. No direct radiocarbon dates are available to verify its absolute age. Because the surface deposits of the Valparaiso Moraine consist of post-Lake Milwaukee Oak Creek and Wadsworth tills, however, radiocarbon dates related to the formation of the moraine should provide a minimum age for the lake. Unfortunately, only two such dates are available. Peat from the bottom of a kettle on an outwash apron deposited during construction of the Valparaiso Moraine in northeastern Illinois has yielded an age of 15 240 ± 120 B.P. (ISGS-465; Springer and Flemal, 1981). A mammoth bone from the same site was dated at 13 130 ± 350 B.P. (ISGS-485), a date which Springer and Flemal (1981) accepted as the more reasonable of the two dates for the age of the mammoth. The peat date is considered by them to be spuriously old. The bone date appears to be too young, however, for the age of the Valparaiso Moraine, which was probably constructed between 1000 and 1500 years earlier. If the West Chicago and Darien Moraines were built at about 15 500 B.P. (Fullerton, 1980, Plate 1), an incipient Lake Milwaukee might well have formed shortly thereafter. The lake probably existed for a few hundred years before the Lake Michigan Lobe readvanced to the Valparaiso Moraine, the lake having attained its maximum extent perhaps at about 15 000 B.P. (Fig. 8).

CONCLUSION

Lithologic and stratigraphic evidence indicate the presence of a sizable proglacial lake in the Lake Michigan basin just prior to the advance of the Lake Michigan Lobe to its Valparaiso position. If a proglacial lake (Early Lake Chicago) was present in the southern part of the basin between the Valparaiso and Tinley advances, as Bretz (1951, p. 404-406; 1955, p. 107) and especially Hough (1958, p. 164-165; 1963, p. 90) have postulated, then surely the more substantive evidence presented here indicates that a lake must have existed before the Valparaiso advance. Indeed, the fine-grained character of the basal Oak Creek and Wadsworth till units and their widespread distribution beyond the Tinley ice margin suggest that the pre-Valparaiso lake was probably much larger than Early Lake Chicago. We believe that the name "glacial Lake Milwaukee" is an appropriate designation for this lake and suggest that usage of this name be continued.

Lake Milwaukee apparently formed in the Lake Michigan basin between 15 500 and 15 000 years ago and existed for several hundred years thereafter. Definitive radiocarbon dates are needed to determine its age more precisely.

Although the regional lithologic and stratigraphic evidence from the Milwaukee area is substantial, Lake Milwaukee must be verified by further independent evidence, particularly from other parts of the lake basin before it can be firmly established as a significant phase in the late-glacial history of the Lake Michigan basin.

ACKNOWLEDGEMENTS

We express thanks to several of our colleagues who have commented on the evidence for glacial Lake Milwaukee, particularly that at the St. Francis bluff exposure. Consultations and field visits with David Mickelson, Ardith Hansel, and Mark Christensen have been particularly helpful. The Illinois State Geological Survey provided many of the grain-size analyses included in our data. We thank the Milwaukee Water Pollution Abatement Program and the Milwaukee Metropolitan Sewerage District for the opportunity to study the geotechnical borings and boring logs from the Milwaukee and Menomonee River valleys. Need's work on the subsurface materials was performed while he was employed by D'Appolonia Consulting Engineers, Inc. The manuscript was reviewed by Ned Bleuer, Ardith Hansel, David Mickelson, and Lawrence Taylor; we thank them all for their valuable suggestions.

REFERENCES

Alden, W.C., 1902, Description of the Chicago District, Illinois-Indiana: United States Geological Survey Atlas, Folio 81, 14 p.

_____, 1904, The Delavan Lobe of the Lake Michigan Glacier of the Wisconsin Stage of Glaciation: United States Geological Survey Professional Paper 34, 106 p.

_____, 1906, Description of the Milwaukee Quadrangle, Wisconsin: United States Geological Survey Atlas, Folio 140, 12 p.

_____, 1918, The Quaternary Geology of Southeastern Wisconsin: United States Geological Survey Professional Paper 106, 356 p.

Atwood, W.W., and Goldthwait, J.W., 1908, Physical Geography of the Evanston-Waukegan Region: Illinois State Geological Survey Bulletin 7, 102 p.

Bretz, JH., 1939, Geology of the Chicago Region, Part I-General: Illinois State Geological Survey Bulletin 65, Part I, 118 p.

_____, 1951, The Stages of Lake Chicago – Their Causes and Correlations: American Journal of Science, v. 249, p. 401-429.

_____, 1955, Geology of the Chicago Region, Part II – The Pleistocene: Illinois State Geological Survey Bulletin 65, Part II, 132 p.

Christensen, M.L., and Schneider, A.F., 1984, Stratigraphy of Quaternary Sediments in a Lake Michigan Bluff Exposure at St. Francis, Wisconsin: Geological Society of America Abstracts with Programs, v. 16, no. 3, p. 128.

Cressey, G.B., 1928, The Indiana Sand Dunes and Shore Lines of the Lake Michigan Basin: Geographic Society of Chicago Bulletin 8, 80 p.

Ekblaw, G.E., 1931, Some Evidences of Incipient Stages of Lake Chicago: Illinois Academy of Science Transactions, v. 23, p. 387-390.

Fullerton, D.S., 1980, Preliminary Correlation of Post-Erie Intersta-dial Events (16 000-10 000 Radiocarbon Years Before Present), Central and Eastern Great Lakes Region, and Hudson, Champlain, and St. Lawrence Lowlands, United States and Canada: United States Geological Survey Professional Paper 1089, 52 p.

Goldthwait, J.W., 1906, Correlation of the Raised Beaches on the West Side of Lake Michigan: Journal of Geology, v. 14, p. 411-424.

———, 1907, The Abandoned Shore Lines of Eastern Wisconsin: Wisconsin Geological and Natural History Survey Bulletin 17, 134 p.

———, 1908, A Reconstruction of Water Planes of the Extinct Glacial Lakes in the Lake Michigan Basin: Journal of Geology, v. 16, p. 459-476.

———, 1909, Physical Features of the Des Plaines Valley: Illinois State Geological Survey Bulletin 11, 103 p.

Hansel, A.K., 1983, The Wadsworth Till Member of Illinois and the Equivalent Oak Creek Formation of Wisconsin: in Mickelson, D.M., and Clayton, Lee, eds., Late Pleistocene History of Southeastern Wisconsin: Geoscience Wisconsin, v. 7, p. 1-16.

Hansel, A.K., Mickelson, D.M., Schneider, A.F., and Larsen, C.E., 1985, Late Wisconsinan and Holocene History of the Lake Michigan Basin: in Karrow, P.F., and Calkin, P.E., eds., Quaternary Evolution of the Great Lakes: Geological Associa-tion of Canada Special Paper 30.

Hough, J.L., 1958, Geology of the Great Lakes: Urbana, University of Illinois Press, 313 p.

———, 1963, The Prehistoric Great Lakes of North America: American Scientist, v. 51, p. 84-109.

Kelley, R.W., and Farrand, W.R., 1967, The Glacial Lakes Around Michigan: Michigan Geological Survey Bulletin 4, 23 p.

Klauk, R.H., 1978, Stratigraphic and Engineering Study of the Lake Michigan Shore Zone Bluffs in Milwaukee County, Wisconsin: M.S. Thesis, University of Wisconsin-Milwaukee, 67 p.

Leverett, Frank, 1897, The Pleistocene Features and Deposits of the Chicago Area: Chicago Academy of Sciences Bulletin 2, 86 p.

———, 1899, the Illinois Glacial Lobe: United States Geological Survey Monograph 38, 817 p.

Leverett, Frank, and Taylor, F.B., 1915, The Pleistocene of Indiana and Michigan and the History of the Great Lakes: United States Geological Survey Monograph 53, 529 p.

Martin, Lawrence, 1916, The Physical Geography of Wisconsin: Wisconsin Geological and Natural History Survey Bulletin 36, 608 p. (Second edition published in 1932, third edition in 1965.)

Mickelson, D.M., Schneider, A.F., Stanford, S.D., Follmer, L.R., and Lasca, N.P., 1983, Late Glacial History and Environmen-tal Geology of Southeastern Wisconsin: Wisconsin Geological and Natural History Survey Field Trip Guide Book 7, 39 p.

Mickelson, D.M., Clayton, Lee, Baker, R.W., Mode, W.N., and Schneider, A.F., 1984, Pleistocene Stratigraphic Units of Wis-consin: Wisconsin Geological and Natural History Survey Miscellaneous Paper 84-1, 97 p.

Need, E.A., 1983, Quaternary Stratigraphy of the Lower Milwaukee and Menomonee River Valleys, Milwaukee, Wisconsin: in Mickelson, D.M., and Clayton, Lee, eds., Late Pleistocene History of Southeastern Wisconsin: Geoscience Wisconsin, v. 7, p. 24-42.

Salisbury, R.D., and Alden, W.C., 1899, The Geography of Chicago and its Environs: Geographic Society of Chicago Bulletin 1, 64 p.

Schneider, A.F., 1968a, The Tinley Moraine in Indiana: Indiana Academy of Science Proceedings, v. 77, p. 271-278.

———, 1968b, History of a Morainal Gap at Valparaiso, Indiana: Geological Society of America Special Paper 115, p. 398-399.

———, 1982, Past and Current Viewpoints Concerning the Late Wisconsinan Delavan Sublobe of Southeastern Wisconsin: American Quaternary Association Program and Abstracts, Seventh Biennial Conference, Seattle, University of Washington, p. 159.

———, 1983, Wisconsinan Stratigraphy and Glacial Sequence in Southeastern Wisconsin: in Mickelson, D.M., and Clayton, Lee, eds., Late Pleistocene History of Southeastern Wisconsin: Geoscience Wisconsin, v. 7, p. 59-85.

Schneider, A.F., and Need, E.A., 1983, Lithologic and Stratigraphic Evidence for a Late mid-Woodfordian Proglacial Lake in the Lake Michigan Basin: Geological Society of America Abstracts with Programs, v. 15, no. 6, p. 680.

Springer, J.W., and Flemal, R.C., 1981, Paleontological and Geological Results from Two Fossil Proboscidean Finds in Northern Illinois: Illinois Academy of Science Transactions, v. 74, p. 87-99.

Thwaites, F.T., 1950, Outline of Glacial Geology: Ann Arbor, Michigan, Edwards Brothers, Inc., 129 p.

Thwaites, F.T., and Bertrand, Kenneth, 1957, Pleistocene Geology of the Door Peninsula, Wisconsin: Geological Society of America Bulletin, v. 68, p. 831-880.

Wayne, W.J., and Zumberge, J.H., 1965, Pleistocene Geology of Indiana and Michigan: in Wright, H.E., Jr., and Frey, D.G., eds., the Quaternary of the United States: Princeton, N.J., Princeton University Press, p. 63-84.

Wickham, S.S., 1975, The Tiskilwa Till Member, Wedron Forma-tion; A Regional Study in Northeastern Illinois: M.S. Thesis, University of Illinois, Urbana, Illinois, 229 p.

Willman, H.B., 1971, Summary of the Geology of the Chicago Area: Illinois State Geological Survey Circular 460, 77 p.

Willman, H.B., and Frye, J.C., 1970, Pleistocene Stratigraphy of Illinois: Illinois State Geological Survey Bulletin 94, 204 p.

Wright, G.F., 1918, Explanation of the Abandoned Beaches about the South End of Lake Michigan: Geological Society of America Bulletin, v. 29, p. 235-244.

Quaternary Evolution of the Great Lakes,
edited by P.F. Karrow and P.E. Calkin,
Geological Association of Canada Special Paper 30, 1985

LAKE LEVEL, UPLIFT, AND OUTLET INCISION,
THE NIPISSING AND ALGOMA GREAT LAKES

Curtis E. Larsen

U.S. Geological Survey, 954 National Center, Reston, Virginia 22092

ABSTRACT

The Nipissing (5500 to 3800 B.P.), Algoma (3800 to 2500 B.P.), and modern Lakes Michigan and Huron (2500 B.P. to the present) are Holocene lake level stands in the upper Great Lakes region. These resulted when post-glacial isostatic uplift raised late-glacial northern outlet channels, causing the upper lakes to rise to the altitude of pre-existing late-glacial outlets at Chicago, Illinois, and Port Huron, Michigan. The transgression reached a maximum defined as the Nipissing level (184.5 m). Incision of the outlet channel at Port Huron is the cause given for a fall from the Nipissing to the Algoma level (181.5 m), while further incision marked a fall to the level of modern Lakes Michigan and Huron (177 m).

Stratigraphic studies conducted near Chicago since 1970 present a different record. High levels also occurred between 1600 and 1200 B.P., 950 and 750 B.P., and 450 B.P. and A.D. 1800. These were fluctuations from 1 to 2 m above the historic mean of the lakes that lasted from 200 to 300 years. The Nipissing and Algoma levels also represent events in a fluctuating system. An early Nipissing I level attained an altitude of 183 m 4500 years ago, a lower Nipissing-II level reached an altitude of 180.5 m 4000 years ago, and an Algoma level reached a maximum at 179 m 3200 years ago. Neoglacial and pollen records suggest that changes in the levels of the lakes were climate-related.

The Nipissing-II and Algoma terraces around southern Lake Michigan occur at lower altitudes than near Port Huron. These differences suggest that differential vertical movement of the region continued through the Holocene and raised the level of the Port Huron outlet relative to the southern shore of Lake Michigan.

RÉSUMÉ

Pendant près d'un siècle, trois étapes holocènes lacustres ont été reconnues dans la région des Grands Lacs: les niveaux Nipissing (5500 à 3800 B.P.), Algoma (3800 à 2500 B.P.) et les lacs Michigan et Huron contemporains (à partir de 2500 B.P.). Ces niveaux lacustres ont été créés lorsque le soulèvement isostatique post-glaciaire éleva les lits des exutoires qui drainaient les lacs en traversant les régions isostatiquement déprimées du sud-ouest de l'Ontario. Le niveau des Grands Lacs supérieurs s'éleva, jusqu'à ce qu'il ait atteint l'altitude d'exutoires glaciaires tardifs préexistants à Chicago en Illinois et Port Huron, au Michigan (184.5 m). Le niveau maximum atteint par cette transgression post-glaciaire a été défini comme étant le niveau Nipissing. Le surcreusement du lit de l'exutoire à Port Huron, autour de 3800 B.P., est généralement considéré comme la cause d'une part de la baisse des eaux lacustres du niveau Nipissing jusqu'au niveau Algoma à 181.5 m, et d'autre part, de l'abandon de l'exutoire de Chicago. Un surcreusement plus profond à Port Huron, il y a environ 2500 ans marquerait la chute finale jusqu'au niveau actuel des lacs Michigan et Huron (177 m).

Les études stratigraphiques faites dans la région de Chicago au cours de la dernière décennie suggère une histoire différente: celle d'un niveau lacustre fluctuant. De hauts niveaux ont été atteints par le lac Michigan pour les périodes de 1600 et 1200 B.P., 950 et 750 B.P., et 450 B.P. à 1800 A.D. lors de périodes précédemment considérées de niveau relativement stable. Ces niveaux se sont élevés jusqu'à des altitudes de 1 à 2 m au-dessus du niveau historique moyen des lacs Michigan et Huron et ont duré de 200 à 300 ans. Les niveaux du Nipissing et de l'Algoma représentent aussi des événements hautement transgressifs dans un système fluctuant. Une étape Nipissing-inférieur (Nipissing I) atteignit l'altitude de 183 m il y a environ 4500 ans, tandis qu'un niveau plus tardif et plus bas (Nipissing II) atteignit l'altitude de 180.5 m, il y a environ 4000 ans. Une étape Algoma supérieur atteignit un maximum de 179 m autour de 3200 ans B.P. L'information néo-glaciaire et pollinique suggère que les variations du niveau des lacs étaient contrôlées climatiquement.

Les terrasses Nipissing et Algoma autour du lac Michigan méridional sont plus basses que celles près de Port Huron. Ces différences suggèrent que le soulèvement différentiel de la région continua au cours de l'Holocène et éleva le niveau de l'exutoire de Port Huron au-dessus de l'altitude du lac

Michigan méridional. Le surcreusement de l'exutoire de Port Huron semble avoir opéré au même rythme que le soulèvement isostatique laissant ainsi en témoignage une information stratigraphique et géomorphologique des fluctuations des niveaux lacustres surimposée au soulèvement différentiel des bassins méridionaux.

INTRODUCTION

The Quaternary geological evolution of the upper Great Lakes was originally interpreted in the late nineteenth and early twentieth centuries, before the advent of radiocarbon dating and prior to detailed research on postglacial crustal movements. The early research in the Lake Michigan and Huron basin began from two loci. Frank Leverett (1897) and William Alden (1902), working in the southern Lake Michigan basin, defined the geological history of glacial Lake Chicago on the basis of the surficial geology and coastal landforms of the Chicago area. Frank B. Taylor (1894, 1897) concentrated his efforts in the northern Lake Michigan and then the Lake Huron basin, similarly defining the glacial geology and proglacial lake history.

J.W. Goldthwait (1906, 1907, 1908a, 1908b) complemented the work of the others by mapping coastal terraces along the western shore of Lake Michigan. He also presented an early interpretation of the postglacial uplift history of the Great Lakes based upon warped coastal terraces in the northern parts of the lake basin. Late-glacial coastal terraces in the northern Lake Michigan and Huron basins had been raised above the altitudes of contemporary terraces in the south. When plotted along the north-south axes of the lakes, the terraces showed progressive curvilinear warping upward to the north. In the Lake Michigan basin, the warped terraces of the north converged at a "hinge line" near the latitude of Traverse Bay, Michigan. Terraces south of this area were apparently horizontal, implying crustal stability (or possible uniform movement) in the southern basin and active differential uplift and tilting in the north.

While nearly a century of later work (Stanley, 1936, 1938; Bretz, 1955; Hough, 1958, 1963; Lewis, 1969, 1970) added detail and a more absolute chronology to glacial and lake level events, the interpretation of the Quaternary history of the Michigan and Huron basins has remained much the same. More recent research causes reconsideration of the classical ideas on the evolution of the upper Great Lakes. Clark and Persoage (1970), refining ideas presented earlier by Gilbert (1898), Gutenberg (1933), and Moore (1948) have interpreted the entire Great Lakes basin to be undergoing active postglacial uplift. Differential movements in the northern portion of the region are consistent with the warped glacial and postglacial shorelines of Goldthwait (1908a) and Leverett and Taylor (1915), but the pattern of uplift extends south of the "hinge lines" they presented. Modern uplift approaches a minimum to the south rather than terminating abruptly at a hinge line.

In addition, an accepted formal correlation of terrace surfaces by altitude and position has been made more difficult in light of recent stratigraphic analyses of the underlying deposits (Larsen, 1974, 1985a). For example, low altitude terraces along the southern shore of Lake Michigan, once considered to be of Algoma age (3800 to 2500 B.P.), are dated to the late Nipissing Great Lakes (4000 to 3800 B.P.) and apparently correlate temporally with higher surfaces along the southern Lake Huron shore.

This study presents a summary of the middle and late Holocene lake level history for the southern Lake Michigan basin from Larsen (1974, 1985a) and attempts to reconcile some of the inconsistencies present in the current models of the postglacial upper Great Lakes. The outlet control and postglacial uplift models of Hough (1953, 1958, 1963) pertaining to the Holocene Great Lakes are reconsidered in light of the recent analyses and are reinterpreted to include continuing earth movements in the southern Lake Michigan basin. A record of climate-related fluctuation in the middle and late Holocene levels of Lake Michigan is summarized from earlier studies (Larsen, 1973, 1974, 1985a; Fraser *et al.*, 1975) to show the dynamic nature of the postglacial hydrological system.

LAKE ALGONQUIN AND THE NIPISSING GREAT LAKES

The retreat of Greatlakean ice from the Lake Michigan and Huron basins about 11 000 B.P. (Evenson and Dreimanis, 1976) created a single confluent lake, as first the Indian River Lowland across the lower peninsula of Michigan and then the Straits of Mackinac were opened. The water plane of this lake is represented by a high terrace identified by Spencer (1888, 1891), Taylor (1894), Goldthwait (1906, 1910) and Leverett and Taylor (1915) as the Algonquin or upper Algonquin shoreline. Leverett and Taylor (1915), and later Hough (1958), argued that Lake Algonquin stood at a level of 184.5 m, controlled by the altitudes of outlet channels at Kirkfield, Ontario, Port Huron, Michigan, and Chicago, Illinois. Between 10 000 and 10 500 B.P. (Karrow *et al.*, 1975), as the ice front retreated northward, a lower outlet was uncovered at North Bay, Ontario. The level of the lakes fell below the thresholds of the southern outlets as Lake Algonquin drained eastward to the St. Lawrence River valley via the Mattawa and Ottawa valleys (Stanley, 1937, 1938; Hough, 1958, 1963; Harrison, 1972). This period marks the transition from the glacial to the postglacial Great Lakes. Ice fronts ceased to be a factor for changing the levels of the lakes at this time as isostatic rebound, climatic change, and the altitudes of outlet channels became the dominant variables in the system.

Stanley (1936, 1937) inferred an extremely low post-Algonquin lake level in the Huron basin on the basis of warped terraces that projected below the modern level of the lakes. This low level was later referred to as the Stanley low stage by Hough (1962), who proposed a contemporary Chippewa low stage for the Lake Michigan basin (Hough, 1953, 1958). Based on a date for the deglaciation of the North Bay outlet at about 10 000 B.P. (Harrison, 1972), and a series of dates from the Winnetka Member of the Lake Michigan Formation (6900 to 7900 B.P., Lineback *et al.*, 1979, Buckley, 1974), the Chippewa low levels of Lake Michigan can be dated between 10 000 and 7500 B.P.

Uplift of the North Bay region progressively raised the altitude of the northern outlet. The lakes in the Lake Michi-

gan and Huron basins rose accordingly until their level returned to the altitude of the pre-existing outlets at Chicago
and Port Huron and stabilized temporarily at about 4500 B.P.
This event marked the establishment of the Nipissing Great
Lakes. Lakes Superior, Michigan and Huron were confluent
at this time. Initially the Nipissing level was controlled by
three outlets, but the North Bay outlet was soon abandoned
as it continued to rise above the altitude of the southern
outlets.

The Nipissing and post-Nipissing levels of the lakes were
originally discussed by Taylor (1894), Goldthwait (1906), and
Leverett and Taylor (1915), but the current interpretation is
the result of work by later researchers such as Bretz (1955),
Hough (1953, 1958), Prest (1970), and Lewis (1969, 1970).
These writers defined three middle and late Holocene lake
stages – the Nipissing (5500 to 3800 B.P.), the Algoma (3800
to 2500 B.P.) and modern lakes Michigan and Huron (2500 to
present). According to Hough (1953, 1958), the Nipissing
stage level stood at 184.5 m, governed by the altitude of the
southern outlets. Incision of the Port Huron outlet into unconsolidated glacial deposits caused the lakes to fall to their
Algoma level at 181.5 m and to abandon the bedrock-floored
Chicago outlet. This fall in level, as well as differential uplift
of the St. Mary's River, separated Lake Superior from the
lower lakes. A channel change and renewed incision of the
Port Huron outlet at about 2500 B.P. is generally accepted as
the cause for a subsequent drop to the modern lake level
(177 m) (Dorr and Eschman, 1970).

LIMITATIONS OF THE HOUGH MODEL

Hough's (1953, 1958) interpretation of the outlet control of
the Nipissing Great Lakes has affected subsequent work.
Relying on the assumed tectonic and isostatic stability of the
southern Lake Michigan basin, he attempted to reconcile
altitudinal differences between Nipissing and Algonquin terraces in the northern and southern extremes of the lake basins. Coastal landforms and terraces north of Traverse Bay,
Michigan, identified as Nipissing in age, had been progressively tilted to the north by postglacial isostatic uplift, while
those to the south were seemingly horizontal. Leverett and
Taylor's (1915) "hinge line", or isobase of zero uplift, tran-
sected the Lake Michigan basin at the latitude of Traverse
Bay, separating the stable south from the isostatically active
northern basin. Hough therefore considered the bedrock-
floored outlet at Chicago to have remained at its assumed
Algonquin altitude of 184.5 m since the Port Huron stade.
Thus, the Nipissing level in Lake Michigan reoccupied the
Algonquin-level outlet at Chicago, while simultaneously
draining through a contemporaneous outlet at a similar altitude at Port Huron.

Several inconsistencies affect Hough's interpretation.
First, the threshold altitude of the Chicago outlet as originally determined by Leverett (1897, p. 59) was 180 m.
Leverett (1897, p. 74) associated terraces and beach features
between 5.5 m and 7.6 m (18 and 25 ft) above modern lake
level with this threshold. The difference in depth between
the floor of this outlet channel and its contemporary water
surface is comparable with that of the late nineteenth century
St. Clair River at Port Huron prior to dredging where the

channel floor was 4.5 to 6 m lower than the mean level of
Lake Huron (Horton, 1927). Second, the base to the St. Clair
River delta, built into Lake St. Clair by overflow and sediment supplied from Lake Huron since Nipissing times, lies at
an altitude of 172.6 m, at the approximate altitude of the late
nineteenth century Port Huron sill (Raphael and Jaworski,
1982). The delta rests on lacustrine clays thought to have
been deposited in glacial lakes Whittlesey and Warren. Organics from the surface of the lacustrine clays range in age
from 9500 to 7300 B.P., showing that the delta is of middle
and late Holocene age. These data contradict Taylor
(Leverett and Taylor, 1915) who argued that the earliest St.
Clair delta was related to the Algonquin level, with only its
surface related to the Nipissing Great Lakes. The delta does
not preserve a record of this earlier discharge. In neither the
Chicago nor Port Huron areas is there a clear record of
Algonquin-age lacustrine, littoral, or deltaic sediments above
the present lake level (Hansel *et al.*, 1985; Karrow, 1980;
Raphael and Jaworski, 1982). Clearly there are unresolved
problems in the interpretation of the pre-Nipissing outlets to
the lakes.

A third inconsistency affecting Hough's (1953, 1958)
Holocene lake level interpretation is the assumed isostatic
and tectonic stability of the southern Lake Michigan and
Huron basins. A century ago Gilbert (1898) argued that ongoing differential vertical earth movements were influencing
the Great Lakes basin. He maintained that differential postglacial vertical movements had continued into modern times,
and could be monitored through a network of lake level
gauges placed about the Great Lakes. Taylor (Leverett and
Taylor,1915) put aside this dynamic concept by invoking the
more static hinge line model of Goldthwait (1908a). Thus,
active postglacial rebound was dismissed as a significant
factor in the southern basins.

Subsequent detailed and accurate historic measurements
(Fig. 1) were utilized by Clark and Persoage (1970) and the
Coordinating Committee on Great Lakes Basic Hydraulic
and Hydrologic Data (1977). Vertical movement has continued south of the hinge lines. In combination, these inconsistencies raise questions regarding Hough's (1953, 1958)
interpretation of the middle and late Holocene levels of
Lakes Michigan and Huron, and call for a reexamination of
the data.

MIDDLE AND LATE HOLOCENE
LAKE LEVEL CHANGES

Cooperative research programs between the Illinois
Geological Survey and the U.S. Geological Survey have
provided new perspectives on the lake level history of the
southern Lake Michigan basin. Ongoing studies of the
geomorphology and stratigraphy, supported by radiocarbon
dating, provide a chronological framework to the region not
available to the early researchers.

Rather than the static outlet-incision concept advanced by
Hough (1953, 1958, 1963) for control of the Nipissing and
Algoma levels of the lakes, Larsen (1974, 1985a) and Fraser
et al. (1975) have presented a detailed lake level history
marked by climate-related changes in level. A recent interpretation (Larsen 1985a) is shown in Figure 2, which

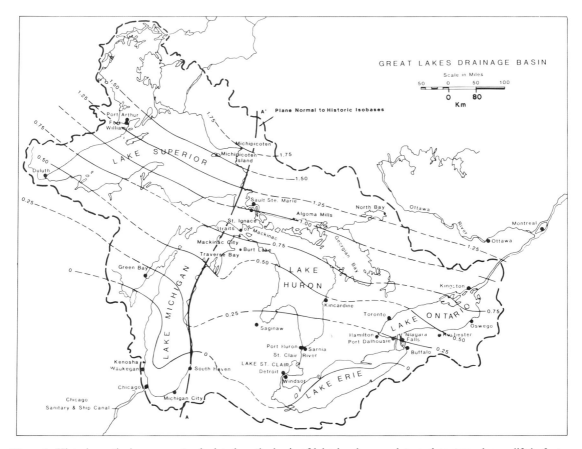

Figure 1. Historic vertical movement calculated on the basis of lake level gauge data and contoured as uplift in feet per century. Section A-A' represents a plane drawn normal to isobases along the eastern shore of Lake Michigan (see Fig. 5). Modified from Clark and Persoage (1970).

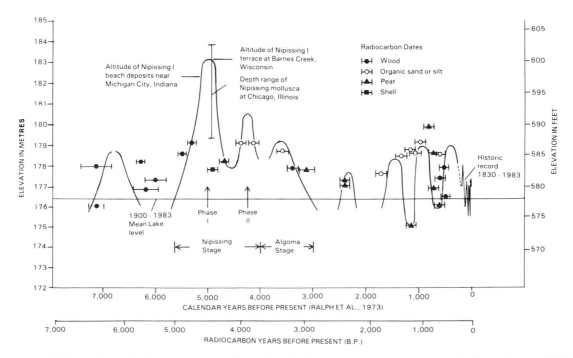

Figure 2. Middle and Late Holocene lake-level fluctuations in the southern Lake Michigan basin. From Larsen (1985a).

TABLE I
TENTATIVE CORRELATION OF CLIMATIC CHANGES DURING THE PAST 2000 YEARS
WITH SOUTHERN LAKE MICHIGAN LEVELS (FROM LARSEN, 1985a)

Years B.P.	Northwestern North America (glacial activity; Denton and Karlén, 1973)	Northern Midwest United States (pollen; Webb and Bryson, 1972)	Northern Wisconsin (pollen, seeds, charcoal; Swain, 1978)	Northern Lower Peninsula, Michigan (pollen; Bernabo, 1981)	Southern Lake Michigan levels (Larsen 1985a)
	Contraction		Historical disturbance		Low
200 -				Warm	
	Expansion		Moist		High
400 -					
		Cool		Cool	
600 -					
					Low
800 -	Contraction		Dry		
				Warm	
1000 -					High
	Expansion		Moist		
1200 -				Cool	Low
1400 -		Cool			
			Dry		High
1600 -					
	Contraction	Cool		Mild temperatures	
1800 -					
2000 -			Moist		Low
2200 -					
					High

shows a record defined by 30 radiocarbon dates. These are discussed here as uncalibrated ages although a calibrated time scale (Ralph *et al.*, 1973) is provided in Figure 2. The appropriate standard deviations are also shown. A record of the dates shown is compiled elsewhere (Larsen, 1985a). Fluctuations of 200 years to 300 years duration apparently took place about contemporary means that were graded to the outlets of the lakes. Of particular interest is the record for the past 2000 years which in Hough's interpretation, marked the inception of the hydrologically modern Lakes Michigan and Huron. These were characterized by relatively stable levels comparable to those of the historic record. Hough (1958, 1963) also considered Holocene climates to have been like those of the historic period.

Fluctuating Late Holocene Lake Levels in Southern Lake Michigan

Rather than showing stable levels, Figure 2 shows conspicuous fluctuations to have occurred about the modern mean level of the lake at 177 m. High levels of as much as 2 m above the present are recorded by incremental aggradational events totaling these heights in stream-mouth alluvial fills near Waukegan, Illinois. Comparable periods of lower lake level are marked by peat deposits from the bases of lakeshore marshes.

During the period 1600 to 1200 B.P., alluviation at stream mouths was common and terraces were built to at least 1.5 m above the present stream beds. A similar record of alluviation is recorded near Saginaw Bay, Michigan (Speth, 1972).

This event was followed by a period of low level when peat was deposited in marshes at a depth of 2 m below the present lake level near Waukegan. Flooding of the lakeshore marshes followed, accompanied by the deposition of silt. Renewed alluviation occurred near stream mouths between 950 and 700 B.P., indicating another transgressive event. A rise in lake level during this same interval was documented by Olson (1958) on the basis of dune morphology along the Indiana lakeshore. Other deposits related to this transgression are found as far north as the Straits of Mackinac in an archeological context (McPherron, 1967). Lake level fell below 177 m again between 700 and 450 B.P. as shown by renewed peat deposition and the development of regressional dunes in southern Indiana (Olson, 1958). A final period of transgression reached a maximum between 450 B.P. and the beginning of the last century. This most recent period of higher than normal lake level relates to the pre-1860 lake level record reconstructed by Horton (1927) from the Lake Huron and Lake Erie basins. Thus, a drop in lake level observed during historic times, followed by the rising levels of the past decades, shows continuity with a fluctuating hydrologic system.

This episodic pattern of lake level change points to an important linkage between past and present processes. Fraser *et al.* (1975) noted that the trends in Lake Michigan and Huron levels over the historic period varied with precipitation and temperature changes. This suggestion was expanded to include the late Holocene paleoclimatic record. Table I (Larsen, 1985a) shows a comparison of climate related changes recorded at various North American locations over the past 2000 years. Similar scale changes among lake levels, and temperature and moisture patterns in Wisconsin and Michigan (Swain, 1978; Bernabo, 1981) over the past 1200 years suggest a related variation in the water budget of the upper Great Lakes. Although the dating criteria used by these authors differs, there may be a correlation between the most recent episode of high lake level and cool, moist climate patterns in the northern portions of the Lake Michigan basin. Low lake level seems to have coincided with warm, dry periods. An earlier chronological agreement is not as secure. Between 600 and 1300 B.P., there is only a general association between high lake level and cool, moist climatic episodes. A better temporal correlation exists between high lake levels and Neoglacial expansion (Denton and Karlén, 1973), but this may be fortuitous. In summary, the evidence available at present suggests that late Holocene climates and lake levels seem to have fluctuated at a similar scale, if not synchronously.

A pattern of climate and lake-level change is found in late Holocene archeological data (Fig. 3; see Larsen, 1981; 1982; 1985b) where there appears to have been a time-latitudinal shift in the distribution of archaeological sites in relation to the modern transition zone between oak-hickory and northern deciduous forest associations in Michigan and Wisconsin. This zone falls at about latitude 44° N. Artifacts indicative of prehistoric Indian groups associated with northern, deciduous forests are found south of the forest transition zone during episodes when lake levels were high. Groups indicative of southern oak-hickory forest associations spread north of this latitude when levels were low. Thus, northern hunting groups apparently shifted southward during more extreme cool weather periods, and agriculturally oriented southern groups moved northward with rising temperatures and decreasing precipitation. Such human movements may be more sensitive indicators than the vegetation records of the region.

The hydrological cause for fluctuations in lake level is not yet firmly established. However, the range of the long-term fluctuations, which is in the order of 1 to 2 m about the historic mean level of Lake Michigan at 177 m, is comparable to the 2 m modern range between the extreme high and low monthly levels on Lakes Michigan and Huron (De-Cooke, 1967). Thus, the late Holocene fluctuations, like those observed over the past century, appear to relate to temperature and precipitation changes. This comparison furnishes a model that relates historic and prehistoric lake level changes with contemporary outlet flow.

A good contemporary example may be the St. Clair River at Port Huron. This was deepened from its natural sill altitude of 171.7 m to 170.6 m in 1893 and was dredged again to about 165 m to service modern shipping (Horton, 1927). It is now maintained at an altitude of about 169 m. Although the mean level of Lakes Michigan and Huron has fallen 0.12 m since 1900 due to dredging effects (Derecki, 1984), the channel accommodates a range of water level variations comparable to those of the late Holocene.

The Nipissing and Algoma Levels

The transgression from the Chippewa and Stanley low levels of Lakes Michigan and Huron to the high level of the Nipissing Great Lakes is recorded at three key locations along the southern Lake Michigan shore. Exposures provide well-dated stratigraphic sections along Barnes Creek south of Kenosha, Wisconsin, along the North Shore Channel to the Chicago River in metropolitan Chicago, and along the eroding shore west of Michigan City, Indiana. Altitudes of the pertinent deposits and terraces were determined by leveling from known benchmarks. These stratigraphic sections are compiled in Larsen (1985a, Appendix I).

The Chippewa low stage was ended in the southern Lake Michigan basin about 6350 ± 200 B.P. (ISGS-185) when water rose above the present level and drowned an oak-hickory forest south of Kenosha (Larsen, 1974, 1985a; Fraser et al., 1975; Schneider et al., 1979). Marsh deposits near the present level of Lake Michigan at each of the three locations above show that Lake Michigan was stable or slightly lower than the present between 5500 ± 75 and 4740 ± 75 B.P. (ISGS-313 and ISGS-259, respectively). After 4740 B.P., marshes at altitude 179 m at Barnes Creek were covered with nearshore and beach berm deposits of the Nipissing transgression. A maximum Nipissing level of about 183 m was attained which is recorded as an erosional terrace at Barnes Creek and by imbricated beach gravels between 182.5 and 183 m near Michigan City, Indiana (Larsen, 1974, 1985a; Gutschick and Gonsiewski, 1976).

During this time of maximum Nipissing level, the lake drained southward via the Chicago outlet. Nipissing-age lakeshore and riverine areas near the outlet contained a rich molluscan fauna consisting of the unioid mussels *Elliptio crassidens, Amblema peruviana,* and *Pleuroblema coccinea magnalacustris* dated by radiocarbon between 4300 ± 75 and 4690 ± 90 B.P. (ISGS-266 and ISGS-959 in Larsen, 1985a and Hansel et al., 1985). Baker (1920), who described the stratigraphic exposures and the molluscan fauna at the North Shore Channel, attributed these species to a fluvial environment with a hard rocky substrate. The suggested depth range for the molluscs was from 1.5 to 6 m of clear water. Associated with the mussels were various gastropods, including *Goniobasis livescens* which Miller et al. (1979) suggest as a Nipissing-age fossil in the Lake Huron basin. This interpretation is consistent with the dated stratigraphy at Chicago.

This environment at Chicago was superseded by further deposition of marsh silts and clays. An oxidized surface of the marsh at about altitude 178 m is marked by thin lenses of peat dated at 4185 ± 75 B.P. (ISGS-286, Larsen, 1974, 1985a), and indicates a drop from the high Nipissing level by this date. Therefore, the rise to the Nipissing maximum at Chicago represented a short-term transgressive event which reached a maximum (183 m) between 4740 and 4185 B.P. It is identified here as the Nipissing I phase of the Nipissing Great Lakes.

The lake subsequently rose from about 178 m during the Nipissing II phase to an altitude of 180.5 m between the deposition of the 4185-B.P. peat at Chicago and 3800 B.P. when a thin paleosol was formed beneath the surface of a terrace formed at this altitude at Barnes Creek. The 180.5-m terrace was formed by reworking of earlier Nipissing I nearshore sand deposits and was subsequently covered by relatively horizontal beach face and berm deposits. No further wave action disturbed this terrace surface, indicating that the level of the lake fell below 180.5 m prior to the development of the 3800-B.P. soil. Terrace surfaces found south of the "hinge line" running through Green Bay, Wisconsin and Traverse Bay, Michigan at this altitude are generally associated with the Algoma level of the lake in Hough's (1953, 1958) model. In southeastern Wisconsin, the 180.5-m terrace was exposed to subaerial weathering prior to the Algoma level. This terrace indicates that two discrete transgressive events occurred between 4740 and 3800 B.P. Following Lewis' (1970) and Prest's (1970) interpretations for a two-phase Nipissing, the lower level at Barnes Creek is related to the Nipissing-II phase. The threshold altitude of the Chicago outlet (180 m) corresponds with the Nipissing II terrace at Barnes Creek, therefore, the outlet was apparently abandoned or carried only sluggish local drainage at this time. Dated peat samples from the outlet show that marsh development began prior to 3390 ± 70 B.P. (ISGS-1240). Thus, the St. Clair River at Port Huron became the main outlet to the upper Great Lakes by

the end of Nipissing time, marking the inception of the Algoma level of the lake below the 180-m altitude.

In the southern Lake Michigan basin, the next successively lower coastal landform in relation to the Barnes Creek 180.5-m terrace, lies between altitudes of about 179 and 180 m near the Illinois-Wisconsin boundary. Here, the toe of an erosional bluff is bordered by beach ridges with crests near 180 m. Using Hough's (1953, 1958) sequencing of progressively lower and younger coastal landforms, these ridges are identified here as Algoma in age. Organic sands from the bases of inter-ridge marshes limit the age of the ridges to 3275 ± 75 B.P. (ISGS-265). This indicates that the lake had retreated, or that progradation of the beach ridge complex had occurred by that date. Still farther to the south, near Winthrop Harbor, Illinois, other beach deposits at 177.8 m are overlain by lakeshore marshes. Basal peat from the marshes is dated between 3130 ± 100 and 2980 ± 130 B.P. (ISGS-217 and ISGS-218) providing a limiting date for the fall from the Algoma level. This fall in level marks the end of

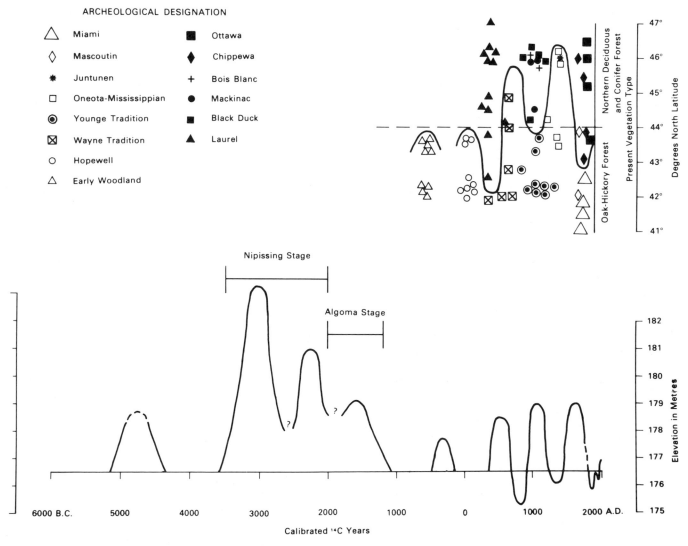

Figure 3. Time-latitudinal distribution of Woodland-stage archaeological sites in Michigan and northern Wisconsin compared with the Late Holocene levels of Lake Michigan and Lake Huron. From Larsen (1985b).

Hough's "Algoma stage" prior to about 3000 B.P. The level continued to fall below the modern mean for the lake and remained low for several hundred years (Larsen, 1974, 1985a). A regression below the modern lake level is evidenced by a broad series of beach ridges near Zion, Illinois with their crests buried beneath a marsh surface at an altitude of 178 m. Such marsh deposits are greater than 1 m in thickness (Fraser *et al.*, 1975, p. 62; Larsen, 1985a, Appendix I) and imply a mean water level below 177 m.

With the exception of an apparent brief 1-m rise in lake level about 2280 ± 75 B.P. (ISGS-225) that may have lasted for a few centuries (Larsen, 1974, 1985a; Fraser *et al.*, 1975), the lake seems to have remained low until a return to the higher late Holocene levels beginning about 1700 B.P. In summary, the pattern of middle Holocene lake level changes also includes a series of fluctuations on a scale similar to those of the late Holocene.

While the local paleoclimatic record for this time period is not well defined, the inception of the Nipissing Great Lakes follows the end of warmer and drier northern climates associated with the Altithermal or Hypsithermal episode in Holocene climatic history. After 6000 B.P., cooler and moister climates returned to the region as indicated by potentially related changes in forest composition in Michigan, Wisconsin, and Minnesota (Webb *et al.*, 1983, p. 163) and in the eastern United States (Davis, 1983, p. 179). With this knowledge, the Nipissing and Algoma levels may be viewed as partially related to paleoclimatic changes and hence to variations in precipitation and evaporation in the drainage basins. The range of variation observed in the middle and late Holocene fluctuations were governed by the contemporaneous altitudes and cross sections of the outlet channels.

POSTGLACIAL ISOSTATIC UPLIFT

The assumed isostatic stability of regions south of the "hinge line" has become an important concept for interpreting the Quaternary evolution of the Great Lakes basin. Hough's assumption of coincidence between the Algonquin and Nipissing levels of Lakes Michigan and Huron required crustal stability in the outlet regions for a period of 5000 years. Research on glacio-isostasy by Andrews (1970a, 1970b), Walcott (1970, 1972), Peltier (1981) and Clark *et al.* (1984) pertaining to Hudson Bay and Great Lakes regions makes a reexamination of the hinge line concept desirable.

Figure 1 maps uplift rates in feet per century over the Great Lakes drainage basin derived from historic lake level gauge data from the United States and Canada (Clark and Persoage, 1970). Isobases trend northwest-southeast across the basin and range from a high rate of 1.75 ft./century (0.53 m/century) at Michipicoten, Ontario to zero in the southern Lake Michigan basin. A 0.25 ft./century (0.07 m/century) isobase transects the basin at Green Bay in Lake Michigan and Saginaw Bay in Lake Huron, well south of the Nipissing hinge line at Traverse Bay, Michigan shown by Hough (1958, p. 256).

The historical vertical earth movements for the Great Lakes region appear to represent the southern margin of greater contemporary crustal movement with its maximum located near the former Laurentide ice centers near Hudson Bay (Farrand, 1962; Andrews, 1970a, 1970b; Walcott, 1970, 1972). The rate of historic uplift (0.05 to 0.07 m/century) measured from areas south of the Nipissing hinge line (Fig. 1) appears to be a continuation of postglacial crustal adjustment reflected in the middle and late Holocene raised beaches to the north.

This relationship is amplified by Andrews' (1970b, p. 709) studies in northern Canada where uplift rates, calculated from the altitudes of dated marine terraces, were plotted as functions of distance from the Laurentide ice centres. A least squares regression calculated from the altitudes of the various terraces showed uplift rates to follow an exponential function decreasing with distance from the former ice centers. Profiles plotted normal to isobases represent curvilinear traces rising towards the former ice centre and region of maximum isostatic depression. Historic vertical movement data summarized by Clark and Persoage (1970) for the upper Great Lakes region may be examined in a similar manner.

Figure 4 is a least squares regression calculated for the historic uplift rates. It is plotted on a plane erected normal to the isobases of Clark and Persoage (1970) and along the eastern shore of Lake Michigan, rather than the Pleistocene-Holocene isobases of Hough or Leverett and Taylor. Differential vertical movements presented by the Coordinating Committee for Basic Hydraulic and Hydrologic Data (1977) show comparable ongoing deformation, but relative to southern Lake Huron. Both data sets when viewed relative to the southern shore of Lake Michigan support the predicted exponential increase in the amount and rate of uplift with distance northward. The isobase passing through the vicinity of North Bay, Ontario marks the approximate location of the early postglacial through Nipissing-age outlet to the upper Great Lakes, and records the rate of uplift relative to the former outlet channel at Chicago. Clark and Persoage's interpretation of historic crustal movement, shown here as an exponential function of distance, provides a comparative model for examining the Nipissing- and Algoma-age uplift of the basin.

CORRELATION OF NIPISSING AND ALGOMA TERRACES

Terrace surfaces attributed to the Nipissing and Algoma levels of Lakes Michigan and Huron were originally defined by Leverett and Taylor (1915) on the basis of altitude and their succession above the modern level of the lakes. The Nipissing terrace was a well-defined surface, often bordered by an erosional bluff, that was considered the nearest prominent terrace above modern lake level. A successively lower, but less well-defined terrace was named the Algoma. Both terraces were noticeably uplifted north of the "hinge-line" near Traverse Bay. South of Traverse Bay, Leverett and Taylor correlated the Nipissing surface with a 181.7-m coastal terrace that was thought to extend southward at this altitude to the outlet at Chicago. To Leverett and Taylor (1915), the Algoma surface was obscured south of the "hinge line," while a 185-m terrace south of Grand Traverse Bay was considered to be of Algonquin age. This too was projected southward to correlate with coastal landforms at Chicago.

Hough (1953, 1958) revised the model of Leverett and Taylor south of the hinge line by making the Nipissing sur-

TABLE II

UPLIFTED SHORELINE FEATURES OF LAKES MICHIGAN AND HURON RELATIVE TO MODERN LAKE LEVEL (177 m)

Location	Distance from South Shore of Lake Michigan	Historic Uplift m/century	Relative Altitude of Algoma Terrace		Relative Altitude of Nipissing Terrace		Reference
			Sea Level	Lake Level	Sea Level	Lake Level	
Michigan City (Nipissing I)	10 km		—	—	182.5 m	5.5 m	Larsen (1974, 1985a) Gutschick and Gonsiewski (1976)
Kenosha (Nipissing I) (Nipissing II)	100 km 100 km 100 km	— — —	179 m — —	2 m — —	— 183 m 180.5 m	— 6 m 3.5 m	Larsen (1974, 1985a)
Port Huron/Sarnia	190 km	—	180.5 m	3.5 m	183.5 m	6.5 m	Lewis (1969, 1970), Papworth (1967), Karrow (1980)
Saginaw Bay	210 km	0.07 m	181 m	4.0 m	—	—	Clark and Persoage, 1970; Larsen and Demeter (1979)
Manistee	335 km	—	182.5 m	5.5 m	185.5 m	8.5 m	Leverett and Taylor (1915) Parkdale 7.5′ Quadrangle
Traverse Bay	385 km	0.15 m	—	—	—	—	(Carke and Persoage (1970)
Eastport	415 km		185.0 m	8.0 m	190.0 m	13.0 m	Central Lake 7.5′ Quadrangle
Charlevoix	440 km		185.0 m	8.0 m	188.0 m	11.0 m	Leverett and Taylor (1915) Forest Beach 7.5′ Quadrangle
Burt Lake, Michigan	450 km	—	184.5 m	7.5 m	—	—	Wm. Lovis (pers. commun., 1982)
Cross Village	480 km		183.0 m	6.0 m	188.8 m	11.8 m	Leverett and Taylor (1915)
Mackinac City	490 km	0.23 m	185.3 m	8.3 m	190.5 m	13.5 m	Leverett and Taylor (1915) Clark and Persoage (1970)
Mackinac Island	510 km	—	185.5 m	8.5 m	192.5 m	15.5 m	Leverett and Taylor (1915)
St. Ignace	510 km	—	—	—	191.5 m	14.5 m	Leverett and Taylor (1915)
Manitoulin Island	530 km	—	—	—	195.1 m	18.1 m	Lewis (1970)
Algoma Mills	570 km	—	189.1 m	12.1 m	196.7 m	19.7 m	Leverett and Taylor (1915)
Sault Ste. Marie	570 km	0.31 m	—	—	197 m	20.0 m	Clark and Persoage (1970)
Killarney Bay	590 km	—	—	—	199.6 m	22.6 m	Lewis (1970)
North Bay (Nipissing I) (Nipissing II)	630 km	0.38 m	— — —	— — —	— 212/213 m 202.0 m	— 35.0/36.0 25.0 m	Clark and Persoage (1970) Lewis (1969) Harrison (1972)
Michipicoten Island	700 km	0.45 m	—	—	—	—	Clark and Persoage (1970)
Michipicoten	700 km	0.53 m	—	—	—	—	Clark and Persoage (1970)

face coincident with the higher "Algonquin" terrace. The Algoma terrace was reassigned as the 181.7-m surface. Therefore, those terraces north of the "hinge" belong to the classification of Leverett and Taylor while to the south Hough's redefinition generally applies. The first 1:62 500-scale maps appeared in the 1950s while the first 1:25 000-scale maps of the hinge line area (used here in Table II) were published in the 1980s. Therefore, without clear chronological or topographic control, the correlation of terrace surfaces was often arbitrary.

Dreimanis (1958), Farrand and Miller (1968), Lewis (1969, 1970), Prest (1970), Cowan (1978), and Terasmae (1979) have added radiocarbon ages to certain of the Nipissing deposits in the Lake Huron basin. Similar control in the Lake Michigan basin was provided by Winkler (1962), Larsen (1974, 1985a), Fraser et al. (1975), and Gutschick and Gonsiewski (1976). In general these authors recognize a Nipissing trans-gression that rose above present lake level between 6000 and 5000 years B.P. and attained a maximum level between about 4700 and 3000 years B.P. Lewis (1969) presented evidence for two discrete Nipissing levels at the North Bay outlet to the lakes, while Larsen (1985a) defined two Nipissing-age terrace surfaces near the Chicago outlet to the lakes. Lewis (1969) limited the age of the two Nipissing levels between 5500 and 3800 B.P. and identified a 212-m Nipissing terrace at North Bay. He also limited the final use of the northern outlet channel to about 4400 B.P., on the basis of dated basal-gyttja deposits from lakes presently occupying the channel. The final Nipissing level must have slightly exceeded 202 m, the present altitude of Trout Lake immediately below the North Bay sill. Thus, two potential Nipissing-age water planes can be identified at North Bay; an upper surface at 212 m (Lewis, 1969; Harrison, 1972), and a lower at the approximate 202-m threshold to the outlet.

In comparison, the two Nipissing surfaces near the Chicago outlet are dated between 4740 and 3800 B.P. The higher and earlier Nipissing-I level occurs at 182.5 and 183 m at Michigan City and at 183 m near Kenosha. The lower Nipissing-II terrace at Kenosha is found at 180.5 m. The bedrock floor to the Chicago outlet at about 180 m is considered as a Nipissing-II surface in the south. This 180-m threshold and its 202-m counterpart at North Bay represent the terminal flow of outlets at opposite extremes of the lake system.

It is necessary to distinguish terrace surfaces by age and altitude for detailed study of lake levels and crustal deformation. This is particularly true in distinguishing the apparent differences in altitude among the Nipissing-age surfaces at the Chicago, Port Huron, and North Bay outlets. Correlation is made difficult by the uncertain connection between the "named-Nipissing" terraces of Leverett and Taylor (1915) and Hough (1953, 1958), and different Nipissing I and II levels indicated by Lewis (1969) in the Huron basin and Larsen (1985a) in the Michigan basin.

The exponential model derived from Clark and Persoage's (1970) data, coupled with Andrews' (1970a, 1970b) observations on the curvilinear deformation of marine terraces in central Canada, provide a useful mechanism for terrace cor-

relation. For example, if the observed historic vertical movement (Fig. 4) is considered to reflect an ongoing isostatic reponse to ice unloading north of the Great Lakes in the Hudson Bay region, then the deformed Nipissing and Algoma terrace surfaces should also reflect an exponential increase in altitude toward the former ice centres. The altitudes of Nipissing and Algoma terraces from the Lake Michigan and Huron basins can be compared by projecting them on to a common normal plane along the eastern shore of Lake Michigan along parallels to the isobases of historic vertical movement (Fig. 1). Least squares regressions calculated on the terrace altitudes as exponential functions of distance from the southernmost outlet should differentiate terraces of comparable age and deformation.

The altitudes of the Nipissing and Algoma terrace surfaces relative to sea level and the historic mean level of Lakes Michigan and Huron (177 m) are assembled in Table II. Least squares regressions of the function, log y = mx + b, are calculated for four theoretical Nipissing surfaces to test the closeness of fit between the "named-Nipissing" surfaces and the Nipissing I and II levels recognized at Chicago and North Bay. Table III shows the four theoretical combinations of terrace altitudes with correlation coefficients for these surfaces.

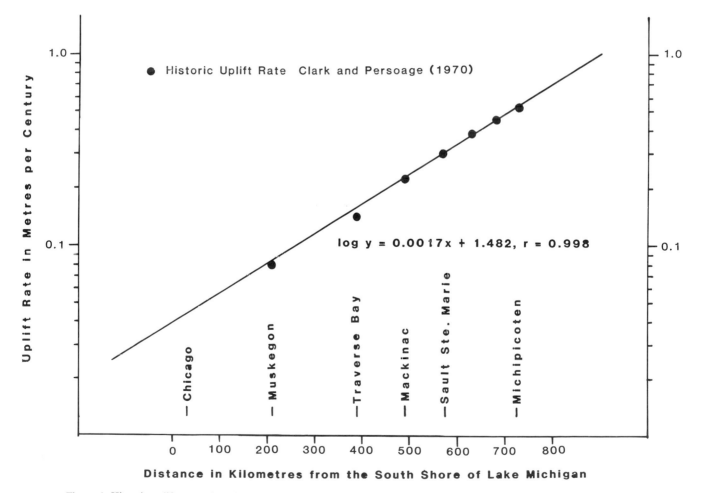

Figure 4. Historic uplift rates plotted on a plane normal to historic isobases (Fig. 1, A-A') along the eastern shore of Lake Michigan. Data derived from Clark and Persoage (1970).

TABLE III

THEORETICAL CORRELATION OF "NAMED-NIPISSING" AND NIPISSING I AND II SURFACES

	Case I	Case II
N = 14		
North Bay	212 m	212 m
Chicago	182.5 m	180 m
Kenosha	183 m	180.5 m
Best-fit Curve	log y = 0.000073x + 2.2510	log y = 0.000085x + 2.2459
Correlation	r = 0.828	r = 0.857
	Case III	**Case IV**
N = 14		
North Bay	202 m	202 m
Chicago	182.5 m	180 m
Kenosha	183 m	180.5 m
Best-fit Curve	log y = 0.000065x + 2.2532	log y = 0.000074x + 2.2485
Correlation	r = 0.888	r = 0.928

Case I, with a correlation coefficient r = 0.828, relates the North Bay Nipissing terrace at 212 m with the Nipissing I surfaces at Michigan City (representing the Chicago outlet) and Kenosha. Case II compares the 212-m North Bay surface with the Nipissing II surface at Kenosha and the sill of the southern outlet (180 m). In this case, the correlation coefficient r equals 0.856. When the floor of the North Bay channel at about 202 m is compared to the Nipissing I surfaces in southern Lake Michigan (Case III), a better correlation, r = 0.888, is found. Case IV, which combines the abandoned North Bay and Chicago channels at 202 m and 180 m with the Nipissing II surface identified at Kenosha, provides the best correlation to the 14 data points (r = 0.928). On the basis of these regression analyses, the altitudes of floors of the North Bay and Chicago outlet channels and the Nipissing-II surface appear to be the best correlates with the "named-Nipissing" terraces of Leverett and Taylor (1915) from the area north of the "hinge line."

The calculated curve for Case IV, with sea level as a datum, is not a close fit to the measured data points (Fig. 5). When the regression is recalculated with the historic mean lake level of 177 m as a datum, this fit is improved. The best-fit curve in this case is log y = 0.0015x + 0.4563, r = 0.986. The calculated curve for the Algoma surface relative to historic lake level is log y = 0.0014x + 0.2481, r = 0.956. The historic mean level at 177 m is controlled by the cross section and depth of the Port Huron outlet, the only outlet common to the modern and Nipissing-age Lakes Michigan and Huron. The use of an exponential least squares regression model imposes an arbitrary asymptotic limit at the datum altitude chosen. Thus the best-fit curves calculated relative to sea level have steeper slopes, while those related to the lowest contemporaneous outlet have a better fit to the data. This suggests that in the study of lake terraces, choice of datum for the calculation of terrace surfaces should consider the altitudes of the appropriate outlet channels in addition to sea level.

Figure 5 shows the curvilinear trends calculated for the Nipissing II and Algoma terrace surfaces, as well as an estimated Nipissing I surface. In each case the trends appear independent of the "hinge line" chosen as a structural control by Goldthwait (1908a), Leverett and Taylor (1915), and Hough (1958, 1963). It also suggests that the Nipissing I levels in evidence at Chicago may relate to the 212-m and 213-m Nipissing surfaces near North Bay (Lewis, 1969; Harrison 1972). Perhaps more significantly, the Nipissing I surfaces near Chicago occur at altitudes similar to the calculated Nipissing II surfaces near Port Huron. This condition may have influenced Hough (1953, 1958) to propose that a "named-Nipissing" terrace at 184.5 m was horizontal between the Chicago outlet and the "hinge line" south of Traverse Bay. Although Goldthwait (1908a) pointed out that erosion had apparently removed the evidence for terrace correlation at the hinge line, the paucity of identified terraces suggests that earlier researchers also had difficulty differentiating landforms on the basis of altitude in this critical area.

The Nipissing-age terrace surfaces near Port Huron described by Lewis (1969, 1970) and Karrow (1980) between 183 and 183.6 m are underlain by earlier Nipissing deposits, but are apparently related to the Nipissing II event in southern Lake Michigan that left a dated terrace surface at Barnes Creek, Wisconsin at an altitude of 180.5 m. The Nipissing I stratigraphy near Michigan City, Indiana that records a high level of the lake at 183 m has no certain dated correlate in southern Lake Huron. The Algoma terrace in southern Lake Michigan, on the other hand, is found at an altitude of 179 m, while it is reported to occur at a 180.5-m altitude along the shores of southern Lake Huron (Lewis, 1969; 1970; Papworth, 1967).

The Holocene and historic uplift curves indicate that movement suggestive of isostatic adjustment has occurred over the past 4000 to 5000 years. Rather than indicating crustal stability south of the hinge line, these data suggest that relative uplift, as measured from the position of deformed water planes, continued relative to the southern shores of Lakes Michigan and Huron. Deformation of the calculated Nipissing II and Algoma terraces south of Grand Traverse Bay is minimal in comparison with areas farther to the north. This gives rise to Leverett and Taylor's (1915) reference to a zone of horizontality within which the different terrace altitudes might be regarded as errors in measurement. Syntheses of historic vertical earth movements (Clark and Persoage, 1970; Coordinating Committee on Basic Hydraulic and Hydrologic Data, 1977) temper these early interpretations by showing that movement decreases southward and beyond the arbitrary limits imposed by hinge lines. This view is supported by Clark et al. (1984) who find no geophysical evidence for a hinge line in the southern Lake Michigan and Huron basins.

LAKE LEVEL, UPLIFT, AND OUTLET INCISION (SUMMARY AND CONCLUSION)

The incision of outlet channels into unconsolidated glacial deposits is the popularly cited mechanism for lowering the levels of the Great Lakes (Leverett, 1897; Leverett and Taylor, 1915; Bretz, 1955; Hough, 1958, 1963; Farrand,

1962). This is an important variable for interpreting the geological evolution of the lakes, but one which leads to an oversimplification of complex processes. Hough (1958, 1963) saw a step-like drop from the Nipissing level to the Algoma level, and finally to the modern level of Lakes Michigan and Huron. Each drop reflected a seemingly fortuitous episode of outlet incision at Port Huron to account for the change.

The recognition of a fluctuating Holocene lake level, coupled with an actively rebounding basin, including the regions of the outlets, presents a more dynamic perspective. Conspicuous high and low lake levels lasting on the order of 200 to 300 years fluctuated about the historic mean lake level at 177 m (Fig. 2). The mean, in turn, was controlled by the threshold altitude of the St. Clair River at about 172 m (Horton, 1927). The Nipissing and Algoma high lake levels represent similar scale fluctuations about an earlier mean lake level.

Climate-related episodic changes in lake level, fluctuating about means adjusted to outlet flow, explain the apparent fall from the Nipissing to the Algoma and then to the late Holocene levels. The Nipissing and Algoma terraces represent periods of coastal erosion and deposition during climatic episodes favouring rises in lake level. Evidence for intervening low lake levels has been masked by subsequent transgressive events. Thus, the Nipissing and Algoma landforms reflect variations in the volume of water entering the basin as runoff with a subdued loss to evaporation (Fraser et al., 1975). Low lake levels, by corollary, may represent periods of less runoff and increased evaporation from the lake surface. This model allows for more gradual erosional processes at the Port Huron outlet, while episodic changes in lake level account for the landforms.

By least squares regression analysis, the Nipissing I and II, and Algoma terraces occur at lower altitudes in the southern Lake Michigan basin than they do along the southern shore of Lake Huron. Figure 5 shows the calculated differences in the altitude of terraces between the southern shores of Lakes Michigan and Huron and suggests that deformation was related to differential isostatic uplift of the basins over the past 5000 years. We lack a clear understanding of the outlet control of the Nipissing- and Algoma-age outlet channels, therefore a reconstruction of the Holocene uplift history is still incomplete.

The apparent differential vertical movement of the Port Huron outlet relative to Chicago since Nipissing II times was in the order of 3 m. By comparing the different altitudes of the Algoma water plane between the two areas, the uplift since that time was 1.5 m. Assuming equal time increments for the measured uplift, it appears that the rate of uplift decreased through time at Port Huron, in keeping with the exponential uplift models of Washburn and Stuiver (1962), Andrews (1970a, 1970b) and Ten Brink (1974).

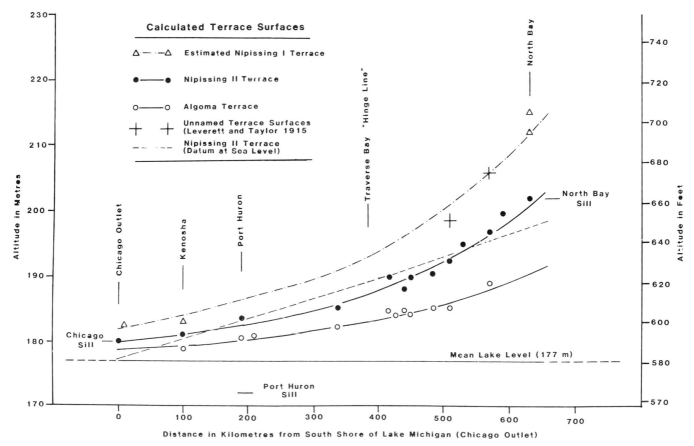

Figure 5. Terrace surfaces for the Nipissing and Algoma Great Lakes calculated on the basis of altitudes presented in Table II. Data are plotted on a plane normal to historic isobases (Fig. 1, A-A') along the eastern shore of Lake Michigan. Lake Huron and North Bay data are projected parallel to isobases of historic vertical movement shown in Figure 1.

It is not yet possible to provide a definitive interpretation of the Holocene outlet control to the lakes as more detailed information is needed on postglacial vertical earth movements. The Nipissing-I-phase level reached an altitude of 183 m between 4000 and 5000 years ago, exceeding the threshold of the Chicago outlet at 180 m. Thus, this lake drained southward from Chicago via the Des Plaines and Illinois River valleys at this time. By the Nipissing-II-phase high level at 180.5 m, between 4185 and 3800 years ago, drainage may have continued to the south through the Chicago outlet, but with less discharge. The altitude of the Algoma stage level at 179 m precludes effective use of the channel and clearly the drainage of both lakes was through the St. Clair River at Port Huron, Michigan.

The middle and late Holocene history of Lakes Michigan and Huron is a more complex interrelationship of variables than considered by Leverett and Taylor (1915) or Hough (1953, 1958, 1963). The Nipissing and Algoma levels of the lakes were not the results of a simple transgression that rose to the thresholds of earlier southern outlets and then fell in a step-like manner as episodic erosion took place at Port Huron. A revised interpretation places the episodic emphasis on climatic change in the drainage basin. Erosional and depositional terraces were left at progressively higher altitudes northward along the shores of Lakes Michigan and Huron, reflecting differences in the rates of rebound from south to north. Erosion and incision of the Port Huron outlet occurred as the land surface rose relative to the level of the lake.

ACKNOWLEDGEMENTS

I would like to express my appreciation to Charles Collinson and Ardith Hansel of the Illinois State Geological Survey for their encouragement and interest in my Lake Michigan research. William Farrand of the University of Michigan has been a mentor during the development of many of my theoretical views of Great Lakes level studies. I am grateful for this valuable interaction. John Peper and J.P. Schafer of the U.S. Geological Survey, P.F. Karrow of the University of Waterloo, Arthur Bloom of Cornell University, and C.F.M. Lewis of the Geological Survey of Canada provided critical reviews of this manuscript. Their comments and suggestions were helpful and aided in clarifying certain of the ideas presented here. All interpretations presented are the responsibility of the author.

REFERENCES

Alden, W.C., 1902, Description of the Chicago District, Illinois-Indiana: United States Geological Survey Geologic Atlas, Folio 81, 14. p.

Andrews, J.T., 1970a, Differential Crustal Recovery and Glacial Chronology (6700 to 0 B.P.), West Baffin Island, N.W.T., Canada: Arctic and Alpine Research, v. 2, p. 115-143.

———, 1970b, Present and Postglacial Rates of Uplift for Glaciated Northern and Eastern North America Derived from Postglacial Uplift Curves: Canadian Journal of Earth Sciences, v. 7, p. 703-715.

Baker, F.C., 1920, The Life of the Pleistocene or Glacial Period as Recorded in the Deposits Laid Down by the Great Ice Sheets: University of Illinois Bulletin, v. 17, no. 14, 476 p.

Bernabo, J.C., 1981, Quantitative Estimates of Temperature Changes Over the Last 2700 Years in Michigan Based on Pollen Data: Quaternary Research, v. 15, p. 143-159.

Bretz, JH., 1955, Geology of the Chicago Region, Part II: The Pleistocene: Illinois State Geological Survey Bulletin 65, 132 p.

Buckley, S.B., 1974, Study of Post-Pleistocene Ostracod Distribution in the Soft Sediments of Southern Lake Michigan: Ph.D. Thesis, University of Illinois, Urbana, Illinois, 189 p.

Clark, J.A., Pranger, H.S., Primms, J.A., and Walsh, J.K., 1984, Holocene Sea Level and Proglacial Lake Indicators of Vertical Crustal Movement: Program with Abstracts, American Geophysical Union Chapman Conference on Vertical Crustal Motion: Measurement and Modeling, October 22-26, 1984, Harpers Ferry, West Virginia.

Clark, R.H., and Persoage, N.P., 1970, Some Implications of Crustal Movement in Engineering Planning: Canadian Journal of Earth Sciences, v. 7, p. 628-633.

Coordinating Committee on Great Lakes Basic Hydraulic Data, 1977, Apparent Vertical Movement Over the Great Lakes: Detroit, Mich., Detroit District, United States Army Corps of Engineers, 70 p.

Cowan, W.R., 1978, Radiocarbon Dating of Nipissing Great Lakes Events Near Sault Ste. Marie, Ontario: Canadian Journal of Earth Sciences, v. 15, p. 2026-2030.

Davis, M.B., 1983, Holocene Vegetational History of the Eastern United States: in Wright, H.E., Jr. ed., Late-Quaternary Environments of the United States, Vol. 2: The Holocene: Minneapolis, University of Minnesota Press, p. 166-181.

DeCooke, B.G., 1967, Control of Great Lakes Water Levels: Journal of the American Water Works Association, v. 59, p. 684-698.

Denton, G.H., and Karlén, Wibjorn, 1973, Holocene Climatic Variations and Their Probable Cause: Quaternary Research, v. 3, p. 155-205.

Dorr, J.A., and Eschman, D.F., 1970, Geology of Michigan: Ann Arbor, University of Michigan Press, 476 p.

Derecki, J.A., 1984, Effect of Channel Changes in the St. Clair River During the Present Century: Great Lakes Environmental Research Laboratory Contribution No. 408, Ann Arbor, Michigan, 20 p.

Dreimanis, Aleksis, 1958, Beginning of the Nipissing Phase of Lake Huron: Journal of Geology, v. 66, p. 591-594.

Evenson, E.B., and Dreimanis, Aleksis, 1976, Late Glacial (14 000-10 000 B.P.) History of the Great Lakes Region and Possible Correlations: in Quaternary Glaciations in the Northern Hemisphere, UNESCO International Geology Correlation Program, Report No. 3, p. 217-239.

Farrand, W.R., 1962, Postglacial Uplift in North America: American Journal of Science, v. 260, p. 181-199.

Farrand, W.R., and Miller, B.B., 1968, Radiocarbon Dates on and Depositional Environment of the Wasaga Beach Marl Deposit: Ohio Journal of Science, v. 68, p. 235-239.

Fraser, G.S., Larsen, C.E., and Hester, N.C., 1975, Climatically Controlled High Lake Levels in the Lake Michigan and Huron Basins: Anais. Academia Brasileira Ciencias, v. 47, p. 51-66 (Suplemento).

Gilbert, G.K., 1898, Recent Earth Movements in the Great Lakes Region: United States Geological Survey, 18th Annual Report, Part 2, p. 601-647.

Goldthwait, J.W., 1906, Correlation of the Raised Beaches on the West Side of Lake Michigan: Journal of Geology, v. 14, p. 411-424.

————, 1907, Abandoned Shore-Lines of Eastern Wisconsin: Wisconsin Geological and Natural History Survey Bulletin 17.

————, 1908a, A Reconstruction of Water Planes of the Extinct Glacial Lakes in the Lake Michigan Basin: Journal of Geology, v. 16, p. 459-476.

————, 1908b, The Records of the Extinct Lakes: in Atwood, W.W., and Goldthwait, J.W., Physical Geography of the Evanston-Waukegan Region: Illinois State Geological Survey Bulletin 7, p. 54-68.

————, 1910, An Instrumental Survey of the Shorelines of Extinct Lakes in southwestern Ontario: Geological Survey of Canada Memoir 10, 57 p.

Gutenberg, B., 1933, Tilting Due to Glacial Melting: Journal of Geology, v. 41, p. 449-467.

Gutschick, R.C., and Gonsiewski, J., 1976, Coastal Geology of Mt. Baldy Indiana Dunes National Lakeshore, South End Lake Michigan: in Guidebook for Fieldtrips, North Central Section, Geological Society of America Meeting, Western Michigan University, Kalamazoo, p. 40-90.

Hansel, A.K., Mickelson, D.M., Schneider, A.F., and Larsen, C.E., 1985, Late Wisconsinan and Holocene History of the Lake Michigan Basin: in Karrow, P.F., and Calkin, P.F., eds., Quaternary Evolution of the Great Lakes: Geological Association of Canada Special Paper 30.

Harrison, J.E., 1972, Quaternary Geology of the North Bay-Mattawa Region: Geological Survey of Canada Paper 71-26, 37 p.

Horton, R.E., 1927, Hydrology of the Great Lakes: Chicago, Chicago Sanitary District, 432 p.

Hough, J.L., 1953, Revision of the Nipissing Stage of the Great Lakes: Illinois State Academy of Science Transactions, v. 46, p. 133-141.

————, 1958, Geology of the Great Lakes: Urbana, University of Illinois Press, 313 p.

————, 1962, Lake Stanley, a Low Stage of Lake Huron Indicated by Bottom Sediments: Geological Society of America Bulletin, v. 73, p. 613-620.

————, 1963, The Prehistoric Great Lakes of North America: American Scientist, v. 51, p. 84-109.

Karrow, P.F., 1980, The Nipissing Transgression Around Southern Lake Huron: Canadian Journal of Earth Sciences, v. 17, p. 1271-1274.

Karrow, P.F., Anderson, T.W., Clarke, A.H., Delorme, L.D., and Sreenivasa, M.R., 1975, Stratigraphy, Paleontology, and Age of Lake Algonquin Sediments in Southwestern Ontario, Canada: Quaternary Research, v. 5, p. 49-87.

Larsen, C.E., 1973, Prehistoric Levels of Lake Michigan-Huron: Their Potential in Shoreland Planning: in Botts, L. ed., Proceedings of the Shoreland Planning Conference, Chicago: Lake Michigan Federation, p. 169-195.

————, 1974, Late Holocene Lake Levels in Southern Lake Michigan: in Collinson, Charles, ed., Coastal Geology, Sedimentology and Management; Chicago and the Northshore: Illinois State Geological Survey Guidebook, Series 12, p. 39-49.

————, 1981, The Changing Levels of Lake Michigan-Huron: A Revised Framework for Great Lakes Prehistory: Program and Abstracts, 46th Annual Meeting, Society for American Archaeology, San Diego, California.

————, 1982, Geoarcheological Interpretation of Great Lakes Lakeshore Environments: Program and Abstracts, 47th Annual Meeting, Society for American Archaeology, Minneapolis, Minnesota.

————, 1985a, A stratigraphic Study of Beach Features on the Southwestern Shore of Lake Michigan: New Evidence of Holocene Lake Level Fluctuations: Illinois State Geological Survey Environmental Geology Notes 112, 31 p.

————, 1985b, Geoarchaeological Interpretation of Great Lakes Coastal Environments: in Stein, J.K., and Farrand, W.R., eds., Archaeological Sediments in Context: Peopling of the Americas Edited Series No. 1, Orono, Maine, University of Maine, Institute for Quaternary Studies, p. 99-110.

Larsen, C.E., and Demeter, C.S., 1979, Archeological Investigation of the Proposed West River Drive, Bay City, Michigan: Jackson, Michigan, Commonwealth Associates Inc., 108 p.

Leverett, Frank, 1897, The Pleistocene Features and Deposits of the Chicago Area: Geology and Natural History Survey Bulletin II, Chicago, Chicago Academy of Sciences, 86 p.

Leverett, Frank, and Taylor, F.B., 1915, The Pleistocene of Indiana and Michigan and the History of the Great Lakes: United States Geological Survey Monograph 53, 529 p.

Lewis, C.F.M., 1969, Late Quaternary History of Lake Levels in the Huron and Erie Basins: Proceedings 12th Conference on Great Lakes Research, International Association for Great Lakes Research, p. 250-270.

————, 1970, Recent Uplift of Manitoulin Island, Ontario: Canadian Journal of Earth Sciences, v. 7, p. 665-675.

Lineback, J.A., Dell, C.I., and Gross, D.L., 1979, Glacial and Postglacial Sediments in Lakes Superior and Michigan: Geological Society of America Bulletin, v. 90, p. 781-791.

McPherron, A., 1967, The Juntunen Site and the Late Woodland Prehistory of the Upper Great Lakes Area: Museum of Anthropology, Anthropological Paper No. 30, Ann Arbor, University of Michigan Press, 316 p.

Miller, B.B., Karrow, P.F., and Kalas, L.L., 1979, Late Quaternary Mollusks from Glacial Lake Algonquin, Nipissing, and Transitional Sediments from Southwestern Ontario, Canada: Quaternary Research, v. 11, p. 93-112.

Moore, Sherman, 1948, Crustal Movement in the Great Lakes Area: Geological Society of America Bulletin, v. 59, p. 699-709.

Olson, J.S., 1958, Lake Michigan Dune Development 3. Lake level, Beach and Dune Oscillation: Journal of Geology, v. 66, p. 473-483.

Papworth, M.L., 1967, Cultural Traditions in the Lake Forest Region during the High Water Stages of the Post-Glacial Great Lakes: Ph.D. Thesis, University of Michigan, Ann Arbor, Michigan, 276 p.

Peltier, W.R., 1981, Ice Age Geodynamics: Annual Review of Earth and Planetary Sciences, v. 9, p. 199-225.

Prest, V.K., 1970, Quaternary Geology of Canada: in Douglas, R.J.W., ed., Geology and Economic Minerals of Canada, Economic Geology Report No. 1: Department of Energy, Mines and Resources, Geological Survey of Canada, p. 676-764.

Ralph, E.K., Michael, H.N., and Han, M.C., 1973, Radiocarbon Dates and Reality: University of Pennsylvania MASCA Newsletter, v. 9, p. 1-20.

Raphael, C.N., and Jaworski, Eugene, 1982, The St. Clair River Delta, A Unique Lake Delta: The Geographical Bulletin, v. 21, p. 7-27.

Schneider, A.F., Sander, P., and Larsen, C.E., 1979, A Late Quaternary Buried Forest Bed in Southeastern Wisconsin: Geological Society of America Abstracts with Programs, v. 11, no. 5, p. 256.

Spencer, J.W., 1888, Notes on the Origin and History of the Great Lakes of North America: Proceedings of the American Association for the Advancement of Science, v. 37, p. 197-199.

_____, 1891, Deformation of the Algonquin Beach and Birth of Lake Huron: American Journal of Science, v. 41, p. 12-21.

Speth, J.D., 1972, Geology of the Schultz Site: *in* Fitting, J.E., ed., The Schultz Site, Museum of Anthropology Memoir 4, Ann Arbor, Michigan, University of Michigan Press, p. 53-75.

Stanley, G.M., 1936, Lower Algonquin Beaches of Pentanguishene Peninsula: Geological Society of America Bulletin, v. 47, p. 1933-1960.

_____, 1937, Lower Algonquin Beaches of Cape Rich, Georgian Bay: Geological Society of America Bulletin, v. 48, p. 1665-1686.

_____, 1938, The submerged valley through Mackinac Straits: Journal of Geology, v. 46, p. 966-974.

Swain, A.M., 1978, Environmental Changes During the Past 2000 Years in North Central Wisconsin: Analysis of Pollen, Charcoal, and Seeds from Varved Lake Sediments: Quaternary Research, v. 10, p. 55-68.

Taylor, F.B., 1894, A Reconnaissance of the Ancient Shore Lines of Green Bay: American Geologist, v. 13, p. 315-327.

_____, 1897, The Nipissing-Mattawa River, the Outlet of the Nipissing Great Lakes: American Geologist, v. 20, p. 65-66.

Ten Brink, N.W., 1974, Glacio-Isostasy: New data from West Greenland and its Geophysical Implications: Geological Society of America Bulletin, v. 85, p. 219-228.

Terasmae, J., 1979, Radiocarbon Dating and Palynology of Glacial Lake Nipissing deposits at Wasaga Beach, Ontario: Journal of Great Lakes Research, v. 5, p. 292-300.

Walcott, R.I., 1970, Isostatic Response to Loading of the Crust in Canada: Canadian Journal of Earth Sciences, v. 7, p. 716-727.

_____, 1972, Late Quaternary Vertical Movements in Eastern North America: Quantitative Evidence of Glacio-Isostatic Rebound: Reviews of Geophysics and Space Physics, v. 10, p. 849-884.

Washburn, A.L., and Stuiver, M., 1962, Radiocarbon-Dated Postglacial Delevelling in Northeast Greenland and its Implication: Arctic, v. 15, p. 66-73.

Webb, Thompson, and Bryson, R.A., 1972, Late and Postglacial Climatic Change in the Northern Midwest, U.S.A.: Quantitative Multivariate Statistical Analyses: Quaternary Research, v. 2, p. 70-115.

Webb, Thompson, Cushing, E.J., and Wright, H.E., Jr., 1983, Holocene Changes in the Vegetation of the Midwest: *in* Wright, H.E., Jr., ed., Late Quaternary Environments of the United States, Vol. 2: The Holocene: Minneapolis, University of Minnesota Press, p. 142-165.

Winkler, E.M., 1962, Radiocarbon ages of postglacial lake clays near Michigan City, Indiana: Science, v. 137, p. 528-529.

Quaternary Evolution of the Great Lakes,
edited by P.F. Karrow and P.E. Calkin,
Geological Association of Canada Special Paper 30, 1985

HURON BASIN GLACIAL LAKES: A REVIEW

Donald F. Eschman

Department of Geological Sciences, University of Michigan, Ann Arbor, Michigan 48109

Paul F. Karrow

Department of Earth Sciences, University of Waterloo, Waterloo, Ontario N2L 3G1

ABSTRACT

Lake Maumee, which existed about 14 000 B.P., was shared with the Erie basin and drained initially southwest into Indiana but later across Michigan via Early Lake Saginaw and the glacial Grand Valley. Ice-marginal retreat created the lower, Lake Arkona levels which, in turn, gave way to a low phase with further retreat during the Mackinaw Interstade and eastward drainage into New York. The Port Huron readvance created Lake Saginaw (Saginaw basin) and Lake Whittlesey (Huron-Erie basins) about 13 000 B.P. with westward outlets to Lake Chicago. Subsequent ice retreat allowed coalescence of Saginaw, Huron, and Erie waters as Lake Warren. An intra-Warren low stage, Lake Wayne, apparently drained eastward but with uncertain ice-marginal positions. Probably the last phases shared with the Erie basin were Grassmere and Lundy.

Hypothetical Early Algonquin remains unconfirmed but Lake Schomberg, in the southern Georgian Bay basin, preceded a Main Algonquin. This transgressed southward probably because of a rising low stage outlet into the Ontario basin through Fenelon Falls. Lake Algonquin was shared with the Lake Michigan basin and, because of uplift, developed the Upper Algonquin beaches converging to the southward outlet at Port Huron. Step-wise deglaciation of outlets at North Bay created the Lower Algonquin beaches around 10 000 B.P. Low-level Lake Stanley (Huron basin) drained into Lake Hough (Georgian Bay basin), which drained by North Bay to the Champlain Sea. North Bay uplift caused southward transgression to form the Nipissing phase with southward outlet at Port Huron by around 5000 B.P. A weak Algoma beach (3000 B.P.) was formed during the regression to present Lake Huron.

RÉSUMÉ

Le lac Maumee (environ 14 000 B.P.) était partagé entre les bassins Huron et Érié et se drainait au commencement vers le sud-ouest en Indiana, et plus tard, probablement à travers le Michigan via le jeune lac Saginaw et la vallée glaciaire nommée Grand Valley. La retraite glaciaire de l'interstade Mackinaw a permis le drainage vers l'est dans l'état de New York, et les niveaux inférieurs du lac Arkona furent établis. La réavancée de Port Huron a causé la formation des lacs Saginaw (bassin Saginaw) et Whittlesey (bassin Huron-Érié) il y a environ 13 000 ans. Ces lacs avaient des exutoires vers l'ouest au lac Chicago. Des retraites glaciaires subséquentes ont permis la fusion des eaux des lacs Saginaw, Huron et Érié pour former le lac Warren. Un niveau bas intra-Warren, le lac Wayne, se drainait apparemment vers l'est; cependant les positions des limites des glaces pour cet épisode sont peu définies. Il est probable que les dernières phases partagées entre les bassins Huron et Érié furent les lacs Grassmere, avec drainage vers l'est, et Lundy, avec drainage vers le bassin du Michigan.

L'existence de la phase initiale du lac Algonquin n'est pas confirmée; toutefois le lac Schomberg, dans la partie sud du bassin de la baie georgienne, a précédé la phase principale du lac Algonquin. Cette transgression vers le sud est probablement le résultat du relèvement de l'exutoire de Fenelon Falls dans le bassin du lac Ontario. Le lac Algonquin couvrait, en plus du bassin du lac Huron, le bassin du lac Michigan et à cause du relèvement isostatique, les rivages du lac Algonquin supérieur convergent vers l'exutoire méridional à Port Huron. La déglaciation successive des exutoires à North Bay a permis la formation de plages de l'Algonquin inférieur vers 10 000 B.P. Le lac Stanley, à bas niveau (bassin du lac Huron), se drainait vers le lac Hough (bassin de la baie georgienne). Ce dernier se drainait à travers North Bay vers la mer de Champlain. Le relèvement isostatique à North Bay a entraîné une transgression lacustre vers le sud créant ainsi la phase Nipissing. Ce lac se drainait vers le sud à Port Huron, il y a environ 5000 ans. Un faible niveau Algoma (3000 B.P.) a précédé l'actuel lac Huron.

INTRODUCTION

There are few detailed data concerning the lake phases that occupied the Lake Huron basin prior to the retreat of the Late Wisconsinan ice that began around 15 000 B.P. However, there is little doubt that the basin supported a sequence of lakes at differing levels each time the ice margin crossed the area following earliest glacial deepening of the preglacial valleys. For example, work in the southern end of the basin northwest of Port Huron shows that the oldest till recognized there (the Mill Creek Till, of Middle to Late Wisconsinan age) was deposited over lacustrine clayey silt. In addition, each of the subsequent Late Wisconsinan tills in the area is also separated from the next older till by lacustrine deposits (Eschman, 1978).

The several outlets utilized by discharge from the Lake Huron basin during the last ice retreat are shown on Figure 1. Bretz (1953) cites evidence that the glacial Grand Valley was largely developed prior to the last ice advance to cross the area; he states that the relatively broad, straight valley had perhaps served as an outlet prior to Late Wisconsinan time. The John Ball Park organics (Zumberge and Benninghoff, 1969) and a 33 000-year-old log in outwash (Eschman, 1980) support the idea that the Grand River valley largely was formed well before the Erie Interstade. Eschman's work suggests that the Huron basin was relatively ice free during much of the Middle Wisconsinan.

The trend of the axis of the Lake Huron basin is roughly parallel to the direction of upwarping due to glacial rebound. Thus the altitude of the strands of the lake phases within the basin increases northward of the zone of apparent horizontality, and at an increasing rate. No serious attempt to trace the various strands within the basin has been made since the work of Leverett and Taylor (1915), Leverett (1939), and MacLachlan (1939). As there is now topographic coverage of the entire basin, a restudy of the strand features and their isostatic rebound should be undertaken, particularly as recent work of Larsen (1985a, 1985b) and Clark *et al.* (1985) in the Lake Michigan basin raises questions about much of the earlier work.

LAKE PHASES RELATED TO PORT BRUCE ICE

Lake Maumee

Final deglaciation began in the Huron basin during the Port Bruce Stade and the first lake to occupy the Erie and Huron basins with retreat of the ice was Lake Maumee (Fig. 2). The name "Maumee" was first applied by Dryer (1888), who reported on beach ridges and an area of lake plain pointing to an outlet at the head of the drainage near Fort Wayne, Indiana (Fig. 1). These features represent the highest phase of Maumee. Lake Maumee is generally considered to have been marked by three different lake levels, with the first and highest phase at 244 m (800 ft.), a second, lowest phase at 232 m (760 ft.) and a still younger phase at an intermediate level of 238 m (780 ft.) respectively (Leverett and Taylor, 1915). The altitudes cited are all from the southern part of the Erie basin where the strand lines are nearly horizontal. During all three phases of Maumee, that part of the Huron basin that is now the site of Lake Huron was filled with ice.

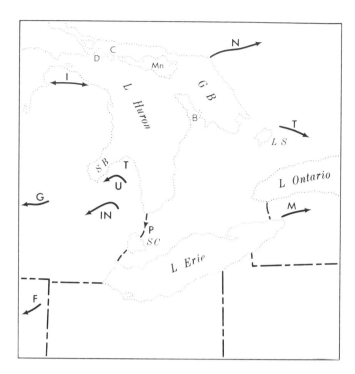

Figure 1. Outlets important to the Lake Huron sequence. Outlets: F – Ft. Wayne, G – glacial Grand River, I – Indian River lowland, IN – Imlay City-North Branch, M – Mohawk, N – North Bay, P – Port Huron, T – Trent lowland, U – Ubly. Other letter symbols: B – Bruce Peninsula, C – Cockburn Island, D – Drummond Island, GB – Georgian Bay, Mn – Manitoulin Island, SC – Lake St.Clair, LS – Lake Simcoe, T – Michigan's "Thumb".

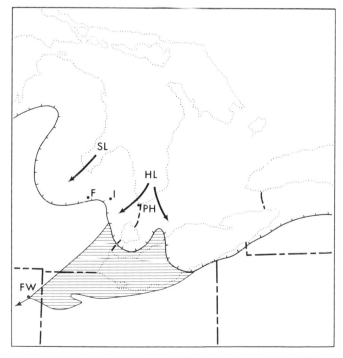

Figure 2. Highest Lake Maumee (244 m). Letter symbols: HL – Huron lobe, SL – Saginaw sublobe, F – Flint, FW – Fort Wayne, I – Imlay City, PH – Port Huron.

Bleuer and Moore (1972) questioned this order of occurrence and, more particularly, evidence in the literature for submergence of the beach of the lowest level. They also cited evidence from logs of borings suggesting that all levels of Lake Maumee drained through the Fort Wayne area. However, Bleuer (pers. commun., 1983) subsequently found evidence of a beach ridge modified by submergence at the 232 m level in the Maumee basin in northeastern Indiana.

Recent work in Indiana has yielded evidence of catastrophic drainage down the Wabash River valley. Vaughn and Ash (1983) recognized one such flood episode in the valley which they correlate with the 244-m level of Lake Maumee; according to them the discharge was sufficient to drain the lake in about three weeks. Fraser (1984) recognized two episodes of flood drainage in the valley during Late Wisconsinan time. However, he maintained that the earlier, higher one (Fraser and Bleuer, 1983) was related to outflow from temporary lakes in northern Indiana and northeastern Illinois, about 16 000 B.P., which joined the Wabash Valley at Delphi, and that the lower, later flood drainage is related to meltwater discharge (Fraser, 1983).

Lake Maumee finally expanded northward with retreat of the ice margin into the Lake Huron basin. When the ice front retreated well to the north of Imlay City (Fig. 2) it uncovered an outlet across the axis of Michigan's "Thumb". This lower outlet gave rise to the stable lake level at 232 m (Maumee II).

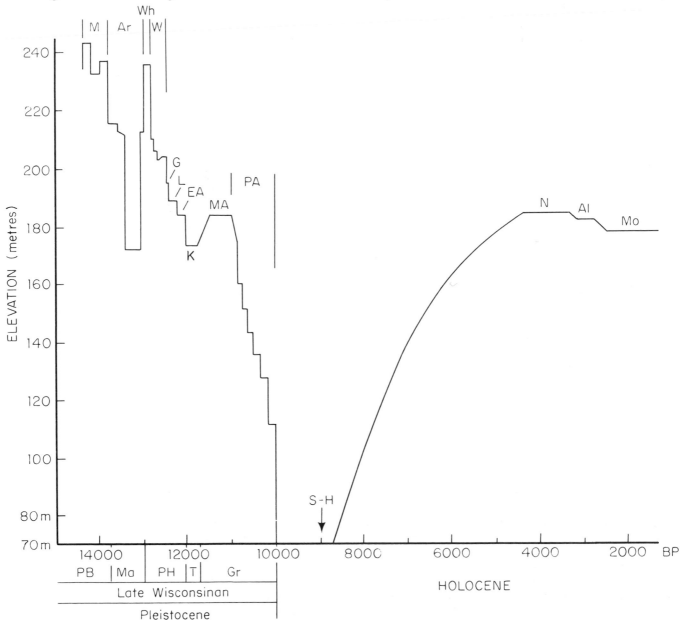

Figure 3. Lake phases in Lake Huron basin. Letter symbols: M – Maumee, Ar – Arkona, Wh – Whittlesey, W – Warren and Wayne, G – Grassmere, L – Lundy, EA – Early Algonquin, K – Kirkfield, MA – Main Algonquin, PA – Post-Algonquin, S-H – Stanley and Hough, N – Nipissing Great Lakes, Al – Algoma, Mo – Modern. Other letter symbols: Gr – Greatlakean Stade, Ma – Mackinaw Interstade, PB – Port Bruce Stade, PH – Port Huron Stade, T – Twocreekan Interstade.

The outlet used by the still later 238-m level of Maumee III, at Imlay City (Leverett and Taylor, 1915), may have been active for a short time as the surface of Maumee I dropped to that of Maumee II. On the other hand, that outlet may have remained blocked either by drift-buried ice in the channel or, farther downstream, by the Saginaw sublobe itself. No evidence has been found in the Huron basin for a lake at the intermediate level immediately following the highest phase.

There is little evidence of the lowest (232 m) level of Lake Maumee within the Huron basin itself. However, the glacial deposits exposed in the southern part of the basin suggest a pattern of glacial retreat and readvance that would explain a sequence of a low phase followed by an intermediate one. High stream cuts along the Black River, a south-flowing stream system that drains the eastern slope of Michigan's "Thumb", expose a lacustrine unit between two silty clay tills. Eschman (1978) interpreted the lacustrine deposits as representing the lowest phase of Lake Maumee. The overlying till unit, when traced to the northwest, can be correlated with Burgis' (1970) sandstone till of the Imlay City area. Eschman and Burgis (1980) maintained the sandstone till was deposited during a readvance of ice lobes on both sides of the interlobate area of Michigan's "Thumb", a

readvance that would cause the rise of the level of Lake Maumee from 232 m to 238 m and the development of drainage through the Imlay City-North Branch outlet, as proposed by Leverett and Taylor (1915).

An age of 13 770 ± 210 B.P. (I-4899), on fine-grained organic material exposed along Weaver Drain, within the Maumee Lake Plain about 20 km north of Imlay City, indicates the Imlay outlet was abandoned by about that time. Thus, all three phases of Lake Maumee span little more than 500 years (Fig. 3).

With continued retreat of the Huron lobe, the Imlay City-North Branch channel was abandoned and a series of outlet channels developed across the interlobate axis of the "Thumb" (Fig. 4). The lake level dropped intermittently as these channels were incised to bedrock one after another by relatively catastrophic drainage. These channels are described by Leverett and Taylor (1915), by Eschman (1978, 1982) and by Drake (1980).

Lake Saginaw

The term "Lake Saginaw" is used for a lake confined solely to the Saginaw basin. The name was first suggested by F. B. Taylor (Leverett and Taylor, 1915, p. 358). Lake

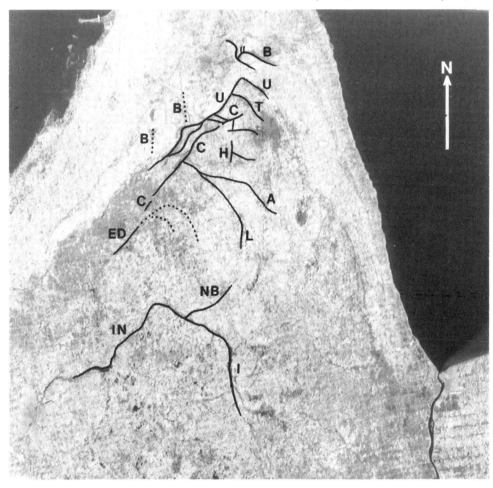

Figure 4. Outlet channels across Michigan's "Thumb". Landsat photo of 10 May 1975. Letter Symbols: A − Argyle, B − Bad Axe, C − Cumber, ED − East Dayton, H − Hay, I − Imlay, IN − Imlay City-North Branch, L − Lamotte, NB − North Branch Transverse, T − Tyre, U − Ubly.

Saginaw existed at two different times during the retreat of the Late Wisconsinan ice sheet from the Great Lakes region.

The earliest drainage from Lake Maumee across Michigan's "Thumb" flowed westward by various ice-marginal drainages to the glacial Grand Valley. It entered that valley at first just east of Grand Rapids, Michigan, and later via other drainages developed sequentially eastward as the margin of the Saginaw sublobe retreated. Finally, with retreat from the Flint moraine, near Flint, Michigan (Fig. 2), the earliest phase of Lake Saginaw formed.

This Early Lake Saginaw received drainage from the Imlay City-North Branch outlet during the later stages of Maumee III. The lake expanded as retreat continued until it became large enough for strand features to form. It continued as a separate lake through the interval of catastrophic drainage across Michigan's "Thumb" as ice retreat allowed for rapid draining of Maumee III. Early Lake Saginaw terminated when the ice margin finally retreated far enough to allow for the merging of water in the Huron and Erie basins with that in the Saginaw lowland.

Some time late in the history of Early Lake Saginaw, the head of the Grand Valley outlet was apparently incised to the level of the highest strand of Lake Arkona, although no clear evidence of a pre-Arkona lake at this level has been found within the Saginaw lowland. A common explanation for intermittent incision of an outlet such as the Grand Valley is that downcutting occurred as a result of greater discharge due to an increase in the amount of meltwater from a retreating ice front and that the level of the sill of the outlet was constant during periods of ice advance (Bretz, 1951). It seems probable that the great increase in discharge from Early Lake Saginaw caused by the addition of water by catastrophic draining of Maumee III was also an important factor in the lowering of the Grand Valley outlet to the level utilized by the highest phase of Lake Arkona.

A separate Lake Saginaw formed much later in time, when the advance of the ice during the Port Huron Stade once more resulted in the creation of separate lakes in the Saginaw and Huron-Erie basins around 13 000 B.P. This phase of Lake Saginaw is discussed below along with Lake Whittlesey.

Lake Arkona

The next proglacial lake stage represented by shoreline features in the Huron basin is Lake Arkona (Fig. 5). The lake was first named by Spencer (1891a) for a beach ridge at the main intersection in Arkona, Ontario. Much confusion has subsequently reigned over which lake phase is represented by this "type" Arkona beach. Leverett (1939) and Chapman and Putnam (1966) both maintained that the ridge in the center of Arkona is related to Lake Whittlesey. However, Cooper (1979) showed conclusively that Spencer's type beach is in fact related to Arkona, and that the Whittlesey beach in the area is some 0.7 km farther east. The confusion apparently arose from the fact that Spencer, in tracing the Arkona beach to the south and east, correlated it with several beach remnants that subsequently were proven to be related to Lake Whittlesey.

Lake Arkona is considered to represent several different low lake levels in the Huron and Erie basins that developed

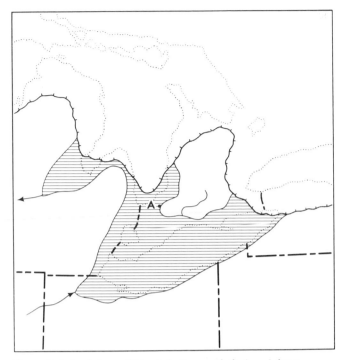

Figure 5. Lake Arkona (216 m). Letter symbol: A – Arkona.

just prior to and during the Mackinaw Interstade (Fullerton, 1980). At least three Arkona levels are recognized on the basis of strand features; these are at about 216 m (710 ft.), 213 m (700 ft.), and 212 m (695 ft.) respectively. All three Arkona strands are buried by deposits related to the later Port Huron advance on both sides of the northern part of Michigan's "Thumb".

There is increasing evidence that the Arkona levels do not represent the lowest lake levels within the basin during the Mackinaw Interstade (Dreimanis, 1969; Dreimanis and Goldthwait, 1973). Evenson and Dreimanis (1976, Fig. 2) in fact, postulate that the retreat of the Huron lobe was sufficient to allow drainage via the Trent Lowland to the Lake Ontario basin. Such an outlet would result in a lake level within the Huron basin at least as low as that of the much later Kirkfield phase, at about 172 m. In fact, taking into account that isostatic uplift of the outlet must have occurred in the approximately 1500-year interval between the Mackinaw Interstade and the later Kirkfield phase, the lowest lake level in the Huron basin during the Mackinaw Interstade was probably considerably less than 172 m. During the interstade the Lake Erie basin was the site of east-draining Lake Ypsilanti (Kunkle, 1963; Dreimanis, 1969). The surface of this lake was at least as low as 166 m, which fact also supports the concept of a relatively low level lake in the Huron basin at that time.

Within the Lake Huron basin in Ontario, the Arkona levels are not well defined. Cooper (1979) traced scattered remnants of shoreline features related to Arkona within the area he mapped and in several places identified lacustrine sediments at the appropriate elevation for Lake Arkona. The sediments are buried beneath till related to the advance of the Port Huron ice to its maximum position at the Wyoming moraine.

LAKE PHASES RELATED TO PORT HURON ICE

Lake Whittlesey and Saginaw

A readvance of the ice margin during the Port Huron stade around 13 000 B.P. closed off the low level Trent Lowland outlet, near Kirkfield, and the lake level within the southern end of the Huron basin rose to the level of Lake Whittlesey, 225 m (738 ft.) (Fig. 6). The name Lake Whittlesey was suggested by Taylor (1897) for the lake which formed what had previously been called the Belmore beach in the Huron and Erie basins. It was so named in recognition of Colonel Charles Whittlesey, the first person to explore the ancient shorelines, including the one related to this lake phase, in Ohio. Leverett (1939) gives a fuller account of the early work on the Whittlesey strand in Ohio and Michigan.

South of Port Huron, Lake Whittlesey extended as a broad lake east across southwestern Ontario and the Lake Erie basin to near Buffalo, New York (Barnett, 1979). It continued north of Port Huron as a narrow bay bordering the Huron lobe along the "Thumb". The outlet for Lake Whittlesey was the Ubly Channel located near the end of the "Thumb"; the lake drained through an outlet river into the eastern end of Lake Saginaw near Cass City, Michigan, where it built an extensive delta. At this time Lake Saginaw was at the lowest Arkona level, some 13 m lower than Lake Whittlesey. Lake Saginaw, in turn, drained west across Michigan via the Grand Valley to the Lake Michigan basin, which was then occupied by the Glenwood phase of Lake Chicago (Hansel *et al.*, 1985).

The Lake Whittlesey shoreline is readily traceable along the southern side of the Erie basin in Ohio and throughout southeastern Michigan. It is, in general, poorly developed in Ontario. However, Cooper (1979) traces remnants of it from a point east of Port Huron northeast for about 45 km; here it is located some 15 km southeast of the present lake shore.

Within Michigan, the prominent Whittlesey beach rises from 225 m in the "area of horizontality" south of Birmingham to the head of its outlet channel near Ubly, where it is at 246 m. The equivalent Lake Saginaw strand can be traced throughout the Saginaw basin from the delta built by the Ubly outlet river at Cass City to the head of the Grand Valley outlet and from there northeast for nearly another 100 km.

During the latter part of the Lake Whittlesey-Lake Saginaw interval, and with the beginning of ice retreat from the axis of the interlobate area north of Ubly, there developed a series of small short-lived proglacial lakes on both sides of the Michigan "Thumb". These lakes drained via several different channels, first across the Port Huron moraine into the Ubly channel and, subsequently, westward along the proximal edge of that moraine. Some of these channels are visible to the north of the Ubly channel on Figure 4. Just what the relationships of these several lakes and channels are to oscillation of the Port Huron ice, such as that which formed the prominent Outer and Inner Port Huron moraines found elsewhere in Michigan, has not been worked out. All evidence indicates Lake Whittlesey lasted only some 200 years.

With still further retreat of the ice margin from the Port Huron moraine a single lake level once more formed within

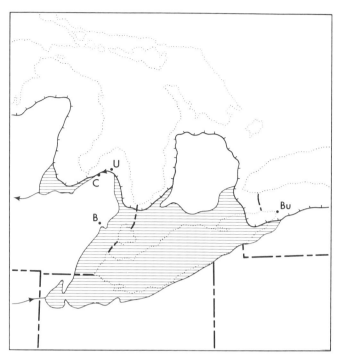

Figure 6. Lakes Whittlesey (225 m) and Saginaw (212 m). Letter symbols: B – Birmingham, Bu – Buffalo, C – Cass City, U – Ubly.

the Erie, Huron, and Saginaw basins. This lake, called Lake Warren, also drained westward down the Grand River valley. By the time the highest strand of Lake Warren was formed, the head of the outlet had apparently been lowered some 2 m.

Lake Warren

J.W. Spencer first used the term "Warren" in a paper delivered at the Cleveland meeting of the American Association for the Advancement of Science in 1888. He applied the term "Warren Water" to what he considered to be marine water that gave rise to all shoreline features at and above the level of Lake Iroquois within the Ontario basin (Spencer, 1888a). However, later the same year, Spencer (1888b) published a brief note in which he referred to that body of water as Lake Warren. The name "Warren" was chosen in honor of General G.K. Warren, whom Spencer considered to be the father of lacustrine geology. Taylor (1897) subsequently suggested restricting the term "Warren" to a particular lake level represented by the Forest beach in southern Ontario. Until reinterpreted by Hough (1958), Lake Warren was considered to be later than Lake Wayne (Leverett and Taylor, 1915; Leverett, 1939; Chapman and Putnam, 1966).

Nearly everywhere Lake Warren (Fig. 7) is represented by at least two shorelines some 4 to 7 m apart vertically. In some places there are three Warren strands, at about 210 m (690 ft.), 206 m (675 ft), and 203 m (665 ft.), respectively, in the area of apparent horizontality within the Erie basin. Various named glacial lake phases within the basin, such as Lake Warren, had several closely spaced levels (Leverett and Taylor, 1915; Hough, 1958, 1963). Since the work of Bretz (1951) these have generally been explained as resulting

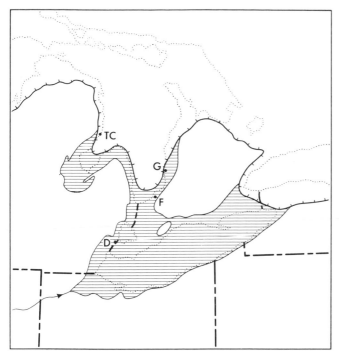

Figure 7. Highest Lake Warren (210 m). Letter symbols: D – Detroit, F – Forest, G – Goderich, TC – Tawas City.

from intermittent downcutting of the lake's outlet due to variations in discharge through the channel. In the case of lake levels only a few meters apart, it is entirely possible that the several levels are the result of normal climatic fluctuations, such as is proposed by Larsen (1985a). We would question, however, whether such climatic fluctuations can explain lake level variations of greater magnitude.

The Warren strands are difficult to trace within broad lowland areas such as southeastern Michigan and in the Saginaw lowland, in part because they commonly are covered with wind-blown sand. In areas of steeper slope, such as along the proximal slope of the Port Huron moraine in the "Thumb" of Michigan and on the east side of Lake Huron in Ontario, the Warren beaches and wave-cut cliffs are readily traceable. All levels of Lake Warren apparently drained westward via the Grand Valley outlet. Farrand and Eschman (1974) stated that Lake Chicago dropped from the Glenwood level (195 m) to that of the Calumet phase (189 m) by the end of highest Warren, probably by at least 12 700 B.P. On the other hand Hansel et al. (1985) maintain that the Glenwood level lasted in the Lake Michigan basin until the Twocreekan Interstade, around 11 850 B.P.

Lake Warren was held against the Michigan shore of the Huron basin by ice that stood just north of Saginaw Bay, at Tawas City (Burgis, 1977; Burgis and Eschman, 1981). The ice margin extended southward across Saginaw Bay and then, with lobate form, across the Lake Huron basin to the base of the Bruce Peninsula (Fig. 7). The margin then continued along the base of a topographic high south of Georgian Bay to the southeast to or beyond the Buffalo, New York area (Calkin, 1970; Calkin and Feenstra, 1985).

A large delta was built into Lake Warren by meltwater

drainage down the valley of the Au Sable River west of Tawas City, near the northernmost part of the lake (Burgis, 1977; Burgis and Eschman, 1981). The delta's surface is now at an average elevation of 245 m as a result of post-Warren rebound. A linear system of kettles traceable across its surface indicates the delta was prograded over blocks of stagnant ice. Burgis (1977) believed that these kettles marked the stand of the ice as it built the low Tawas moraine, and thus felt that lowest Lake Warren was present in the area until after retreat of the ice margin from that moraine.

Within southern Ontario the Warren beach was first recognized at the town of Forest, the type area of Spencer's Forest beach (Spencer, 1888a). MacLachlan (1939) reported on that general area, as well as the area west of the Wyoming moraine as far north as the base of the Bruce Peninsula. Still more recent work in Ontario, south of Lake Huron, includes that of Cooper (1979) and Fitzerald et al. (1979). Fragmental features related to Lake Warren are traceable from near the northern shore of Lake St. Clair to the northeast for some 200 km. Cooper found evidence of two Warren strands, separated vertically about 2 m, throughout much of the area he studied, but added that three Warren bluffs are present near Goderich, Ontario, about midway between the Bruce Peninsula and the southern end of Lake Huron. East of much of the Huron shore in Ontario the dissected flat west of the Wyoming moraine represents the Lake Warren plain.

Lake Wayne

Most present-day workers believe the Lake Warren sequence was interrupted by a short-lived lower lake phase with its surface at 201 m (660 ft.) named "Lake Wayne" for Wayne, Michigan (Leverett and Taylor, 1915). Much of the city of Wayne, some 28 km west of Detroit, is located on a broad, flat-topped, sandy ridge interpreted as a beach modified greatly both by submergence beneath a later lake and by a cover of wind-blown sand. In much of the earlier literature the strand representing this lake phase was referred to as "Lower Warren", and Gilbert (1873) referred to its strand in northwestern Ohio as the "Fourth Beach". The altitude of the Wayne shoreline in the area of apparent horizontality is such that the lake must have drained to the east.

Hough (1958) was the first to refer to Lake Wayne as a short-lived lake phase formed during the Lake Warren sequence as a result of relatively minor ice retreat. He, and most later workers, places Lake Wayne late in the Warren sequence, just prior to the lowest of the Warren phases. Muller and Prest (1985) also discuss the eastern drainage for Lake Wayne.

The Wayne strand is quite intermittent and difficult to follow except in a few areas, such as along the eastern slope of Michigan's "Thumb" where the slope is relatively steep. Features related to Lake Wayne can be traced, with some difficulty, on both the proximal and distal sides of the Port Huron morainic system along the western slope of the "Thumb". There is little evidence of Lake Wayne in southern Ontario.

The location of the Huron lobe ice that held in Lake Wayne is not entirely clear; taking into consideration the bathymetry of the Huron basin, the location of the margin may have been little different from that for Lake Warren (Fig. 7). On the other hand, only minor retreat of the ice margin near Buffalo would allow drainage eastward via the Mohawk outlet. The subsequent rise in lake level to that of the lowest strand of Lake Warren seems best explained by advance of the ice margin to close off this eastern outlet. Another explanation for the 2-m rise in lake level — that it resulted from normal fluctuations in climate (following Larsen, 1985a) — would require that the later phase of Lake Warren drained both east and west simultaneously. It should be clear to the reader that Lake Wayne is in need of further study with regards to its relationships to Lake Warren and, perhaps, even as to its validity as a separate lake phase. All of the lake phases assigned to Lake Warren and Lake Wayne occurred during a short time span of less than 400 years (Fig. 3).

Lake Grassmere

With retreat of the ice margin from its position during the lowest phase of Lake Warren, the water level dropped to 195 m (640 ft.); this drop in lake level resulted in the final abandonment of the Grand Valley as a lacustrine outlet. The lake at 195 m is referred to as Lake Grassmere, named by Lane (1900) for a small village near the end of Michigan's "Thumb". The outlet for Lake Grassmere is not definitely known. Hough (1966) speculated that the Grassmere and Glenwood phases in the Lake Huron and Lake Michigan basins, respectively, were continuous through the Indian River lowland across the northern part of the Southern Peninsula of Michigan. The Lake Michigan chronology of Hansel *et al.* (1985) would allow for such a connection. On the other hand, Eschman and Farrand (1970) maintained that the Glenwood phase came to an end during the existence of Lake Warren. The work of Burgis (1977), which clearly ruled out the possibility of a strait connecting Lake Grassmere to the Lake Michigan basin, required that Lake Grassmere drained to the east.

Throughout much of the area in which the Grassmere shore occurs it is difficult to trace, both because it generally is located well out on the flat, earlier-formed lake plain and because it is typically capped with wind-blown sand. There are few if any exposures in the ridges attributed to the lake. As F. B. Taylor traced the Lake Grassmere strand through southeastern Michigan, he found that it split into several levels beginning a short distance north of Port Huron (Leverett and Taylor, 1915, Chapter 20). Near the northern end of Michigan's "Thumb", elevations of the several strands he attributed to Lake Grassmere vary through some 6 m. While Taylor explained the several levels as indicating rebound during the Grassmere phase, the very short life for Grassmere seems to rule this out as an explanation. It is possible that some, if not most, of these "strands" assigned to Grassmere were formed as subaqueous bars and, thus, do not represent true shorelines.

Burgis (1977) showed that the ice which held in Lake Grassmere must have been only a short distance north of the main Port Huron moraine in the northeastern part of the Southern Peninsula of Michigan. There she found evidence for several interconnected small ice-marginal lakes that

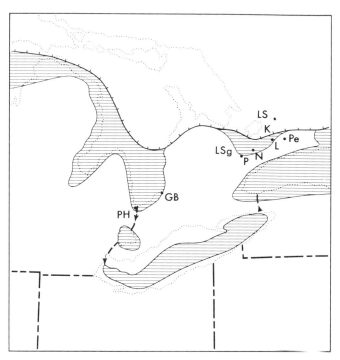

Figure 8. Early Lake Algonquin (184 m) and Lake Schomberg. Letter symbols: GB — Grand Bend, K — Kirkfield, LS — Lake Simcoe, LSg — Lake Schomberg, L — Lindsay, N — Newmarket, P — Palgrave, Pe — Peterborough, PH — Port Huron.

drained to the southeast between the ice front and the moraine. A relatively small delta was built into Lake Grassmere by the Au Sable River at the foot of the large delta built into Lake Warren west of Tawas City.

Cooper (1979) and Fitzgerald *et al.* (1979) identify Grassmere strand features in that part of Ontario south and east of Lake Huron and farther south along the St. Clair River. All available evidence suggests that Lake Grassmere was relatively short-lived, most likely lasting less than 100 years.

Lake Lundy

With still further retreat of the Huron lobe, the Indian River lowland, some 35 km south of the Strait of Mackinac, was freed of ice for the first time since the Port Huron maximum, around 13 000 B.P., and the level of the lake occupying the Lake Huron drainage dropped to 189 m (620 ft.) to form Lake Lundy. This lake was named by Spencer (1894) for Lundy(s) Lane, a road in the Niagara Falls, Ontario, area that follows the crest of a spit related to the Lundy phase. Other names previously applied to this lake phase include Dana (Fairchild, 1907) and Elkton (Lane, 1900); however, in some instances the supposedly correlative strand features cited have subsequently been shown to be unrelated to the Lundy phase (Leverett, 1939; Calkin and Feenstra, 1985).

In most places in the Lake Huron basin, the Lake Lundy shore is even more difficult to trace than is that of Lake Grassmere. Within lowland areas it is marked only by a low, linear ridge of wind-blown sand at about the appropriate elevation. F. B. Taylor included considerable detailed informa-

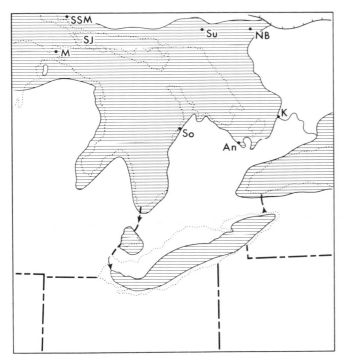

Figure 9. Main Lake Algonquin (184 m). Letter symbols: An − Alliston, K − Kirkfield, M − Mackinac Island, NB − North Bay, SJ − St. Joseph Island, So − Southampton, SSM − Sault Ste. Marie, Su − Sudbury.

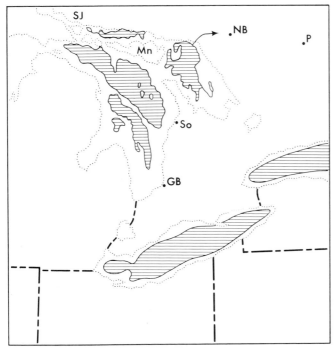

Figure 10. Lakes Stanley (approximately 45 m) and Hough. After Sly and Lewis (1972). Letter symbols: GB − Grand Bend, Mn − Manitoulin Island, NB − North Bay, P − Petawawa, SJ − St. Joseph Island, So − Southampton.

tion on the Lundy strand in Michigan in Monograph 53 (Leverett and Taylor, 1915, Chapter 20). Cooper (1979) found no evidence for Lake Lundy in the Grand Bend-Parkhill area of Ontario but Fitzgerald *et al.* (1979) mapped a Lundy strand along the southern end of Lake Huron. In places farther north along the Huron shore in Ontario, there is a weak, as yet unstudied shoreline feature well below the Warren strands that could represent either Grassmere or Lundy.

North of Saginaw Bay Burgis (1977) recognized a still smaller delta some 3 m below the level of the Grassmere delta as having been formed by the Au Sable River during the Lundy phase. All the evidence taken together suggests that Lake Lundy was also very short-lived; it apparently came to an end about 12 400 B.P. (Fig. 3).

LAKE ALGONQUIN

A single name, Lake Algonquin, is applied to several bodies of water which occupied parts or all of the Michigan, Huron, Superior, and Erie basins (Figs. 8, 9, and 10). The name was among the first applied to former Great Lakes water bodies and its early broad application has been retained to the present, even though it was realized subsequently that major changes in outlets and water levels took place. The Algonquin name was taken from a group of Indians who dwelt in the region.

The history of Lake Algonquin is generally considered to comprise four parts: 1) Early Lake Algonquin phase − a high-level, southward draining phase at about 184 m (605 ft.). A separate lake in the southern Georgian Bay basin, Lake Schomberg, is believed to be of equivalent age. 2) Kirkfield phase − a low-water phase draining east to the Ontario basin. 3) Late (or, more commonly, Main) Lake Algonquin − water level returned to 184 m. 4) Algonquin-Stanley phases − a transitional series of dropping water levels controlled by the opening of a succession of outlets in the northeast to the Ottawa River valley.

Early Lake Algonquin

Leverett and Taylor (1915, p. 328) postulated a very brief Early Lake Algonquin phase (Fig. 8) in the Lake Huron basin that preceded ice retreat to open Georgian Bay and the Trent lowland and had its outflow southward at Port Huron. Although they noted that no known shoreline features represent it, they inferred its existence on the ice-marginal position as indicated above, channels cut through the Port Huron moraine near Port Huron, and on five short supposedly postglacial channel segments cut into the Niagara Escarpment by the ancestral Niagara River. These latter may have been the first spillways of Lake Tonawanda, north of Buffalo, New York (Calkin and Feenstra, 1985). However, Hough (1958, 1963) clearly revealed the weakness of all the evidence for the south-draining Early Algonquin phase; he reasoned that the Port Huron outlet was cut to Algonquin level at the end of Lake Lundy time by north-flowing Erie basin drainage. In addition, Hough suggested that waters in the Huron and Michigan basins became confluent, with lake level control on bedrock at the Chicago outlet.

Lack of documented shore features continues to frustrate confirmation of such a lake phase. In southern Ontario, north of Grand Bend, high shorecliffs of the present lake generally preclude preservation of any former shorelines. In addition, because of the northwest trend of the "hinge line", most of the "Thumb" of Michigan is in the area of horizontality where Early and Main Algonquin and Nipissing would nearly coincide to the common outlet at Port Huron. The younger Nipissing waters largely erased or concealed features of earlier lakes (Karrow, 1980). If evidence exists anywhere, it seems necessary to search the area northwest of Saginaw Bay, in Michigan. Within the area worked, Burgis (1977) found no evidence for an early lake at the 184 m level.

Lake Schomberg

Lake Schomberg (Fig. 8) was named by Putnam and Chapman (1936, p. 466) for a village of that name southwest of Lake Simcoe. It is represented by lacustrine sand, silt, and clay deposits widely distributed on the north side of the Oak Ridges moraine, an interlobate complex between Georgian Bay and Lake Ontario. A high, early southward outlet to the Ontario basin over the moraine along a spillway by Palgrave, Ontario, was suggested by Putnam and Chapman (1936), and other outlets to the east to the Ontario basin and northwest to the Huron basin have been postulated, but never specifically identified. Most authors (Deane, 1950; Gravenor, 1957; Gwyn, 1972; White, 1975) stated that no shorelines have been recognized. However, Dreimanis (1954) and Chapman and Putnam (1966) recognized shorelines above 300 m elevation and at intervals down to the Algonquin shoreline near Newmarket, Ontario.

Lake Schomberg deposits drape over a very irregular surface of till and consist of up to 15 m of thick-varved silt and clay. The extent of the lake is ill-defined, but it is usually shown as extending from near the Niagara Escarpment on the west as a strip of variable width east to beyond Lindsay, Ontario.

Lake Schomberg existed while at least two tongues of fine-grained till and interfingering varved sediments were deposited by fluctuation of the Georgian Bay lobe ice north of the Oak Ridges moraine. The fine texture of this till (Kettleby Till) is believed to result from reworking of the lake sediments during ice readvances, as older tills are sandy.

Lake Schomberg is considered to be the age equivalent of Early Lake Algonquin in the Huron basin (Chapman and Putnam, 1966). Some lower "Schomberg" shorelines might belong to Early Algonquin, formed as the ice margin retreated off the Bruce Peninsula of Ontario and allowed waters to coalesce in the Huron and Georgian Bay basins before the opening of the Kirkfield outlet to the east. It is also possible that Schomberg drained eastward before being joined by Early Lake Algonquin.

Hoffman et al. (1962) and Gwyn (1972) noted the presence of molluscs in Schomberg deposits. These have received no systematic study and no other organic remains have been reported.

Kirkfield Phase

In following the course of the Main Algonquin beach southeast of Georgian Bay, Spencer (1889) recognized an eastward outlet in Ontario which has subsequently been referred to as the Kirkfield or Fenelon Falls outlet (Fig. 8). The outlet channel follows the Trent River valley (Fig. 1) eastward to beyond Peterborough, Ontario, near which it entered glacial Lake Iroquois in the Lake Ontario basin. There has been differing opinion as to whether the outlet sill was near Kirkfield or Fenelon Falls, Ontario. Finamore (1985), based on mapping in the outlet area, favored Fenelon Falls as the controlling sill. Because of long usage, however, the low-water phase will continue to be referred to as the Kirkfield phase. Johnston (1916), Stanley (1938a), and Deane (1950) provided geomorphic and stratigraphic evidence for the low-water phase around Lake Simcoe and southeastern Georgian Bay; however, the amount of drop in water level from Early Lake Algonquin remains uncertain. Chapman (1954) felt that the evidence for water-level drop could not be met by opening of the Fenelon Falls outlet and instead suggested deglaciation of a lower outlet near North Bay.

Both glacial readvance and uplift have been suggested as the cause of the closing of the Fenelon Falls outlet. Finamore's (1985) mapping of the outlet area revealed no positive evidence of readvance, nor can it be ruled out. The continuity of the Algonquin shoreline through the outlet area suggests that if ice readvance did close the outlet, it was reopened during ice retreat, only to finally close by uplift.

Four radiocarbon dates were obtained from wood in estuarine silts in valley terraces east of Lake Huron (Karrow et al., 1975; Miller et al., 1979). These are in logical sequence from 11 300 B.P. at the base to 10 500 B.P. higher in the sequence; they suggest the gradual rise of water level through a minimum range of about 10 m that would be predicted to result from uplift of the Fenelon Falls outlet in Ontario. It would be interesting to date wood from Stanley's (1938a) Sucker Creek locality; it could shed light on this interval, but the site is now within a military base and unavailable for further study. Stanley (1938a) reported buried plant material at this site which at least allows optimism about finding datable material elsewhere. Evidence of low-water levels at Two Creeks, Wisconsin, is dated at 11 850 B.P. (Broecker and Farrand, 1963) and is correlated with discharge through the Fenelon Falls outlet.

East of Fenelon Falls, the Trent River valley in Ontario contains evidence pertaining to the relationship between Lake Algonquin and Lake Iroquois. A delta in Rice Lake near the Lake Iroquois level of the Ontario basin suggests the Fenelon Falls outlet was open before Iroquois drained. Lake Algonquin drainage through Fenelon Falls continued into Post-Iroquois low stages (Gravenor, 1957).

LAKE PHASES RELATED TO GREATLAKEAN ICE

Main Lake Algonquin Phase

Spencer (1889) named the high-level prominent shoreline around Georgian Bay the "Algonquin Beach" and the associated water body "Algonquin Lake" (Spencer, 1891b). Spencer thought that the beach sloped south below present lake level near Sarnia, Ontario, however, Goldthwait concluded it was 8 m above present lake level and this has generally been accepted until recently. Kaszicki (1985) returned to Spencer's interpretation on the basis of re-examination of the possible effects of isostatic uplift on the Lake Algonquin shoreline. Leverett and Taylor (1915) showed the extent of this lake through the Michigan, Huron, and Georgian Bay basins, and Superior as well. Hough (1958) and Saarnisto (1975) felt that Main Lake Algonquin was excluded from the Lake Superior basin, but Cowan (1976, 1985) and Futyma (1981) indicated that it did extend into the southeastern Lake Superior basin.

The Main Algonquin shoreline is generally traceable through the Paleozoic terrain of southern Ontario and Michigan (Fig. 9); however, a short distance north of the Fenelon Falls outlet it passes onto the wooded and rocky terrain of the Precambrian Shield. This has frustrated attempts to trace it northward. Similar conditions prevail north of Lake Huron east of Sault Ste. Marie. Until recently, Mackinac Island (Stanley, 1945) and single survey profiles on Manitoulin Island and at Sault Ste. Marie (Hough, 1958) have been the only reference points for its occurrence in the northern part of the basin. Work by Futyma (1981), Karrow (1982), and by Cowan (1985) should help to clarify Lake Algonquin relationships in the northwestern Huron basin. Burwasser (1979) has described numerous shoreline features in the Sudbury basin of Ontario, but they have not been surveyed and the extent of the Main Algonquin shoreline there is uncertain. The Main Algonquin shoreline is believed to trend southeast from the Sudbury, Ontario, area and north from the Lake Simcoe area.

As shown by Spencer (1891b), Goldthwait (1910), and Leverett and Taylor (1915), the Algonquin Beach is tilted up to the north, and the rate of tilt increases northward. In the St. Joseph Island-Sault Ste. Marie district of Ontario and Michigan, the tilt reaches 1 m/km (Karrow, 1982). Goldthwait (1910) and Deane (1950) indicated a splitting and/or sharp increase in the tilt of the beach near Fenelon Falls, Ontario, an effect that would be expected to result from uplift while the Fenelon Falls outlet was being used. The Main Algonquin beach south of the outlet represents the maximum of a transgressing water level, whereas north of the outlet the early "Kirkfield beach" would diverge and rise above the later regressing Main Algonquin beach.

A variety of fossil remains (pollen, diatoms, plant macrofossils, molluscs, insects, ostracodes) have been recovered from Main Algonquin deposits in the southern part of the Georgian Bay and Lake Huron basins; these show that life was abundant in the lake at this time (Miller et al., 1979). Pollen correlation, supported by the first radiocarbon dates obtained for Lake Algonquin sediments, showed that the lake existed through the spruce-pine pollen transition and ended not much before 10 000 B.P. (Karrow et al., 1975). No fossil occurrences in Algonquin deposits have been found north of a line from Southampton to Alliston, and the exten-

sion of this line southeastward similarly delimits fossil occurrences in Lake Iroquois deposits of the Ontario basin (Karrow et al., 1972). This line is nearly parallel to the regional isobases and may be related to the position of the ice front to the northeast.

Algonquin-Stanley Phases

Numerous shorelines below the Main Algonquin beach record dropping water levels throughout the Huron basin. Leverett and Taylor (1915) believed these converged southward to the Port Huron outlet, but Stanley (1936) and Hough (1958) suggested that they were generally parallel and represented the opening of new outlets. Stanley (1938a, 1945) and Deane (1950) presented much new detail on Mackinac Island and southeastern Georgian Bay, but their work was concentrated in a relatively narrow zone along the isobase trend (about north 70° west). The question of parallelism or convergence of the shorelines will not be fully resolved until better data are available from a much wider spread of latitude.

Leverett and Taylor (1915) recognized an upper group of beaches, presently regarded as converging southwestward, and two lower groups, the Battlefield and Fort Brady beaches. Because of confusion in correlations at various sites, Stanley (1936) and Hough (1958) recommended discontinuance of the use of the Battlefield and Fort Brady names. Recent work on St. Joseph Island, Ontario, (Karrow, in press) reinforces the merit of this recommendation.

Of the lower beaches, Stanley (1936, p. 1948) named four, from highest to lowest: Wyebridge, Penetang, Cedar Point, and Payette. Deane (1950, p. 43) named three beaches within the upper group: the Ardtrea, Upper Orillia, and Lower Orillia. Hough (1958, p. 234, 235) named two beaches below the Payette: the Shequiandah and the Korah (the latter replacing Fort Brady from its type locality near Sault Ste. Marie).

As water levels dropped through successively lower phases, the Lake Simcoe and Minesing basins southeast of Georgian Bay became isolated from the main lake; this created the present Lake Simcoe after the abandonment of the Wyebridge beach (Deane, 1950) and a separate Lake Minesing in the Minesing basin (Fitzgerald, 1985). Lake Simcoe has been preserved because of its bedrock rim, but Lake Minesing drained by downcutting of its outlet.

Although no specific chronology is available for the post-Algonquin beaches, it is now generally accepted that each lake was quite brief and that the whole series probably took just a few centuries. Inasmuch as fossils are common in the Main Algonquin deposits in the south, the presence of life in the later and lower lakes can be assumed. A few occurrences have been noted by one of the authors, but are still undergoing analysis.

The Main Algonquin beach was traced by Spencer (1891b) to an elevation of 390 to 420 m near North Bay, Ontario. He considered the connection through a lowland eastward to be a strait of that lake. Furthermore, he inferred a later uplifting to turn drainage to the south, as at present, to Port Huron,

Michigan. The outlet at North Bay also attracted the attention of G.K. Gilbert (1889) who recognized its significance in ending the Algonquin lakes by drainage to a lower level.

As individual beaches of the Algonquin-Stanley transition became better known, named (1936-1958), and interpreted to be parallel, there evolved a need to identify a succession of lower outlets to account for them. The locations of the outlets remained unknown until Chapman (1954) described two near Fossmill, southeast of North Bay, Ontario. He suggested that these were the only ones between North Bay and Kirkfield, Ontario. More detailed mapping by Harrison (1972) led to his recognition of a series of linked sills and channels that can be correlated with most of the named beaches below the Lower Orillia of Deane (1950).

Lake Stanley and Lake Hough

The step-wise dropping of water levels in the Huron basin eventually reached its lowest level when outflow passed through North Bay eastward to the Ottawa River valley. Stanley (1936) inferred the existence of a very low lake phase in the Huron basin brought about by deglaciation of the isostatically downwarped North Bay area. He later described (1938b) a submerged channel in the bottom of the Mackinac Straits, between Lake Michigan and Lake Huron, which he attributed to a river joining low level lakes in these basins. Bottom coring in northwestern Lake Huron (Hough, 1962) suggested the existence of lake levels more than 100 m below the present (Fig. 3). Hough (1955, p. 965) formally named the low-water stage in the Huron basin Lake Stanley (Fig. 10). It was described (Hough, 1962) as initially draining north of Manitoulin Island, Ontario, into a yet lower-level lake in the Georgian Bay basin. This has been informally referred to as Lake Hough (Lewis, 1969; Prest, 1970); it now seems appropriate to formally name the Georgian Bay basin low water phase "Lake Hough". Because of the location of North Bay in the northeast part of the Huron basin, the lowest level beaches became submerged by the subsequently-rising water level through most of the basin and are not generally apparent today. Drainage to the east was via the Ottawa River valley and into the Champlain Sea at Petawawa, Ontario, where a delta was built (Prest, 1970).

The youngest ages for Main Algonquin deposits and basal dates from bogs on the Algonquin plain, together with numerous dates on submerged stumps and peat beds below Lake Huron, suggest that Lake Stanley began 10 000 B.P. or slightly later. During the next 5000 years, isostatic uplift of the North Bay outlet raised water level in the Huron basin above the present, high enough to drain south at Chicago and Port Huron. This period of rising water was termed Stanley-Nipissing transition by Hough (1958) and discussed by Prest (1970). The record of any phases or lake phenomena developed during this rise is either submerged below Lake Huron and Georgian Bay or was largely destroyed around the edges of the present water bodies by the strong and apparently continuous Nipissing transgression itself. During the lower water levels, streams on the adjacent land entrenched the lower reaches of their valleys and formed fossiliferous flood plain deposits farther upstream (Miller et al., 1979).

POSTGLACIAL LAKES

Nipissing Transgression and Beach

Taylor (1894) named the lowest major shoreline in the central Great Lakes the Nipissing beach after the existing Lake Nipissing and surrounding district. The related water body became known as the Nipissing Great Lakes (Leverett and Taylor, 1915). It is tempting to refer to the water body as Lake Nipissing, but this would cause confusion with modern Lake Nipissing at North Bay. The ice was long departed so it cannot be distinguished as a glacial lake. We are thus left with some verbal sidestepping, rather than attempting to substitute anything new for such a well-established name.

Opinions have differed over the years about the elevation of the Nipissing beach in the southern Lake Huron basin. High modern shore cliffs caused the same problem here as for the identification of the Algonquin beach in the same area. Leverett and Taylor (1915) showed the Algonquin level at 8 m above Lake Huron (at present 177 m, 581 ft.) and the Nipissing beach 5 m above Lake Huron. Hough (1953) argued for coincidence of the Algonquin and Nipissing levels at 184 m in the southern Huron basin. This correlation appeared to be confirmed by numerous radiocarbon dates in that area in both Ontario and Michigan (Karrow, 1980). However, Hansel et al. (1985) and Kaszicki (1985) regard the dates as only establishing the presence of the Nipissing water plane and do not believe Lake Algonquin reached a level high enough to drain southward.

The Nipissing transgression submerged, and concealed with sediment, broad areas that had been dry, vegetated land during the Stanley-Hough low lake phases. There is an abundance of dates on logs and smaller plant debris caught up by Nipissing waves and buried in the beach or in and under offshore sands. Buried peat bog and stream channel fills on St. Joseph Island in northwestern Lake Huron have ages around 7000 B.P. (Karrow, in press). Shallow buried soils underlie Lake Nipissing deposits near Grand Bend and Southampton, Ontario (Miller et al., 1979; Karrow, 1980) and the later part of the transgression is well-dated. Concurrently, a new lake, Lake Edenvale, was created in the Minesing basin, southeast of Georgian Bay (Fitzgerald, 1985), while the Nipissing phase existed in Georgian Bay.

Lewis (1969, 1970) provided many new dates related to Nipissing history and suggested a Nipissing I three-outlet phase (North Bay-Port Huron-Chicago) from 5500 to 4700 B.P., and a Nipissing II two-outlet phase from 4700 to 3700 B.P. Cowan (1978) and Larsen (1985a) suggest somewhat younger ages, with a Nipissing I culmination at 4500 B.P. and Nipissing II at 4000 B.P. However, it seems possible that lake phases Nipissing I and II may have been telescoped in time, since the tendency to downcut at Port Huron would increase as North Bay gradually rose. There would be a gradual transfer of water southward and a gradually increasing rate of erosion so that the Chicago outlet could have gone dry before, concurrently with, or after the emergence of North Bay, as a result of downcutting at Port Huron. Water level may have remained high only a short time. Larsen (1985a) suggests an oscillatory climatic control in fluctuating Nipissing water levels. In any case, the Chicago outlet was on bedrock and was abandoned as downcutting took place in the Port Huron outlet, bringing an end to the Nipissing phase.

Nipissing deposits are commonly fossiliferous (plants, molluscs). The molluscan assemblages differ markedly from those of Algonquin (Miller *et al.*, 1979; 1985), making it possible in many cases to distinguish sediments of the two lake phases.

Lake Algoma

The only notable shoreline among a profusion of features between the Lake Nipissing beach and Lake Huron level was named the Algoma Beach by Leverett and Tayor (1915, p. 464), after Algoma Mills, Ontario, on the north shore of Lake Huron. Deane (1950, p. 44) named the Waubaushene Beach in a similar position in southeastern Georgian Bay, but the relationship to the Lake Algoma level, as defined, is not known. Any outstanding shoreline features below the Nipissing are commonly referred to as Algoma by other workers. Algoma shore features have been identified at widely scattered locations around the Huron basin; the age of this phase is estimated at about 3000 B.P. (Lewis, 1969).

The Algoma level (about 3 m below the Nipissing, or 181 m, 594 ft.) is classically attributed to a pause in downcutting at Port Huron (Hough, 1958), perhaps related to the glacial stratigraphy in the outlet area. Following this pause, downcutting resumed, lowering water level in the Huron basin to the present 177 m (581 ft.). Larsen (1985a) explained the Algoma, and other strand features below those related to Nipissing, as merely representing particularly high-water levels due to normal climatic fluctuations during continuous donwcutting of the Port Huron outlet to its present elevation.

ACKNOWLEDGEMENTS

The authors much appreciated critical reading and comments on the manuscript by C.F.M. Lewis and W.N. Melhorn.

REFERENCES

Barnett, P.J., 1979, Glacial Lake Whittlesey: the Probable Ice Frontal Position in the Eastern End of the Erie Basin: Canadian Journal of Earth Sciences, v. 16, p. 568-574.

Bleuer, N.K., and Moore, M.C., 1972, Glacial Stratigraphy of the Fort Wayne Area and the Draining of Glacial Lake Maumee: Proceedings of the Indiana Academy of Science for 1971, v. 81, p. 195-209.

Bretz, J.H., 1951, Causes of the Glacial Lake Stages in Saginaw Basin: Journal of Geology, v. 59, p. 244-258.

_____, 1953, Glacial Grand River, Michigan: Michigan Academy of Science, Arts, and Letters, v. 38, p. 359-382.

Broecker, W.S., and Farrand, W.R., 1963, Radiocarbon Age of the Two Creeks Forest Bed, Wisconsin: Geological Society of America Bulletin, v. 74, p. 795-802.

Burgis, W.A., 1970, The Imlay Outlet of Glacial Lake Maumee, Imlay City, Michigan: M.S. Thesis, Ann Arbor, University of Michigan, 74 p.

_____, 1977, Late-Wisconsinan History of Northeastern Lower Michigan: Ph.D. Thesis, Ann Arbor, University of Michigan, 396 p.

Burgis, W.A., and Eschman, D.F., 1981, Late-Wisconsinan History of Northeastern Lower Michigan: 30th Annual Field Conference, Grayling, Michigan, Midwest Friends of the Pleistocene, 110 p.

Burwasser, G.J., 1979, Quaternary Geology of the Sudbury Basin Area, District of Sudbury: Ontario Geological Survey Report 181, 103 p.

Calkin, P.E., 1970, Strand Lines and Chronology of the Glacial Great Lakes in Northwestern New York: Ohio Journal of Science, v. 70, p. 78-96.

Calkin, P.E., and Feenstra, B.H., 1985, Evolution of the Erie-Basin Great Lakes: *in* Karrow, P.F., and Calkin, P.E., eds., Quaternary Evolution of the Great Lakes: Geological Association of Canada Special Paper 30.

Chapman, L.J., 1954, An Outlet of Lake Algonquin at Fossmill, Ontario: Proceedings Geological Association of Canada, v. 6, pt. II, p. 61-68.

Chapman, L.J., and Putnam, D.F., 1966, The Physiography of Southern Ontario: Second Edition, Ontario Research Foundation, Toronto, Ontario, University of Toronto Press, 386 p.

Clark, J.A., Walsh, J.K., Primus, J.A., and Pranger, H.S., 1985, A Model of Proglacial Lake Strandline Delevelling During the Past 18 000 Years: Stratigraphic Implications: Geological Society of America Abstracts with Program, v. 17, no. 5, p. 283.

Cooper, A.J., 1979, Quaternary Geology of the Grand Bend-Parkhill Area, Southern Ontario: Ontario Geological Survey Report 188, 70 p.

Cowan, W.R., 1976, Quaternary Geology of the Sault Ste. Marie Area, District of Algoma: Ontario Division of Mines Miscellaneous Paper 67, p. 134-136.

_____, 1978, Radiocarbon Dating of Nipissing Great Lakes Events Near Sault Ste. Marie, Ontario: Canadian Journal of Earth Sciences, v.15, p. 2026-2030.

_____, 1985, Deglacial Great Lakes Shorelines at Sault Ste. Marie, Ontario: *in* Karrow, P.F., and Calkin, P.E., Quaternary Evolution of the Great Lakes: Geological Association of Canada Special Paper 30.

Deane, R.E., 1950, Pleistocene Geology of the Lake Simcoe District, Ontario: Geological Survey of Canada Memoir 256, 108 p.

Drake, R.H., 1980, Lake Whittlesey Outlet Channels and the Late Wisconsinan History of the Michigan Thumb Region: Michigan Academician, v. 13, p. 181-197.

Dreimanis, Aleksis, 1954, Geology of the Upper Holland Watershed, Ontario: *in* Water, Part 4 of Upper Holland Valley Conservation Report, 1953: Ontario Department of Planning and Development, p. 6-22.

_____, 1969, Late-Pleistocene Lakes in the Ontario and Erie Basins: Proceedings 12th Conference on Great Lakes Research, International Association for Great Lakes Research, p. 170-180.

Dreimanis, Aleksis, and Golthwait, R.P., 1973, Wisconsin Glaciation in the Huron, Erie, and Ontario Lobes: *in* Black, R.F., Goldthwait, R.P., and Willman, H.B., eds., The Wisconsinan Stage: Geological Society of America Memoir 136, p. 71-106.

Dryer, C.R., 1888, Geology of Allen County, Indiana: Geological Survey of Indiana, 16th Annual Report, p. 107-126.

Eschman, D.F., 1978, Pleistocene Geology of the Thumb Area of Michigan: Guidebook, North Central Section, Geological Society of America Meeting, Ann Arbor, Michigan, p. 35-62.

———, 1980, Some Evidence of Mid-Wisconsinan Events in Michigan: Michigan Academician, v. 12, p. 423-436.

———, 1982, The Lake Maumee-Lake Whittlesey Interval in Michigan, Geological Society of America Abstracts with Programs, v. 14, no. 5, p. 259.

Eschman, D.F., and Burgis, W.A., 1980, The Imlay Channel and Glacial Lake Maumee: Geological Society of America Abstracts With Programs, v. 12, no. 5, p. 221.

Eschman, D.F., and Farrand, W.R., 1970, Glacial History of the Glacial Grand Valley: Guidebook, North Central Section, Geological Society of America Meeting, East Lansing, Michigan, p. 131-157.

Evenson, E.B., and Dreimanis, Aleksis, 1976, Late Glacial (14 000-10 000 years B.P.) History of the Great Lakes Region and its Possible Correlations: in Easterbrook, D.J., and Sibrava, Vladimir, eds., Quaternary Glaciations in the Northern Hemisphere, Project 73-1-24, Report no. 3 on the session in Bellingham Washington, USA, September 1975: UNESCO International Geological Correlation Program, p. 217-239.

Fairchild, H.L., 1907, Glacial Waters in the Lake Erie Basin: New York State Museum Bulletin 106, 86 p.

Farrand, W.R., and Eschman, D.F., 1974, Glaciation of the Southern Peninsula of Michigan: A Review: Michigan Academician, v. 7, p. 31-56.

Finamore, P.F., 1985, Glacial Lake Algonquin and the Fenelon Falls Outlet: in Karrow, P.F., and Calkin, P.E., eds., Quaternary Evolution of the Great Lakes: Geological Association of Canada Special Paper 30.

Fitzgerald, W.D., 1985, Postglacial History of the Minesing Basin, Ontario: in Karrow, P.F., and Calkin, P.E., eds., Quaternary Evolution of the Great Lakes: Geological Association of Canada Special Paper 30.

Fitzgerald, W.D., Janicki, E., and Storrison, D.J., 1979, Sarnia-Brights Grove Area, Southern Ontario: Ontario Geological Survey Preliminary Map P. 2222, Scale 1:50 000.

Fraser, G.S., 1983, Paleohydraulics of Meltwater Streams in North Central Indiana During the Late Woodfordian Subage: Geological Society of America Abstract with Programs, v. 15, no. 4, p. 226.

———, 1984. Flow Structure of a Late Wisconsinan Valley Jokulhlaup: Geological Society of America Abstracts with Programs, v. 16, no. 3, p. 138.

Fraser, G.S., and Bleuer, N.K., 1983, Late Wisconsinan Jokulhaup at Delphi, Indiana: Geological Society of America Abstract with Programs, v. 15, no. 4, p. 226.

Fullerton, D.S., 1980, Preliminary Correlation of Post-Erie Interstadial Events (16 000-10 000 Radiocarbon Years Before Present), Central and Eastern Great Lakes Region, and Hudson, Champlain, and St. Lawrence Lowlands, United States and Canada: United States Geological Survey Professional Paper 1089, 52 p.

Futyma, R.P., 1981, The Northern Limits of Glacial Lake Algonquin in Upper Michigan: Quaternary Research, v. 15, p. 291-310.

Gilbert, G.K., 1873, Surface Geology of the Maumee Valley: Report of the Geological Survey of Ohio, v. 1, pt. 1, p. 535-556.

———, 1889, The History of the Niagara River: New York Commissioners State Reservation, Niagara, 6th Annual Report, p. 61-84.

Goldthwait, J.W., 1910, An Instrumental Survey of the Shorelines of the Extinct Lakes Algonquin and Nipissing in Southwestern Ontario: Geological Survey of Canada Memoir 10, 57 p.

Gravenor, C.P., 1957, Surficial Geology of the Lindsay-Peterborough Area, Ontario, Victoria, Peterborough, Durham, and Northumberland Counties, Ontario: Geological Survey of Canada Memoir 288, 60 p.

Gwyn, Q.H.J., 1972, Quaternary Geology of the Alliston-Newmarket Area, Southern Ontario: Ontario Division of Mines Miscellaneous Paper 53, p. 144-147.

Hansel, A.K., Mickelson, D.M., Schneider, A.K., and Larsen, C.E., 1985, Late Wisconsinan and Holocene History of the Lake Michigan Basin: in Karrow, P.F., and Calkin, P.E., eds., Quaternary Evolution of the Great Lakes: Geological Association of Canada Special Paper 30.

Harrison, J.E., 1972, Quaternary Geology of the North Bay-Mattawa Region: Geological Survey of Canada Paper 71-26, 37 p.

Hoffman, D.W., Wicklund, R.E., and Richards, N.R., 1962, Soil Survey of Simcoe County, Ontario: Ontario Soil Survey Report Number 29, 109 p.

Hough, J.L., 1953, Revision of the Nipissing Stage of the Great Lakes: Illinois Academy of Science Transactions, v. 46, p. 133-141.

———, 1955, Lake Chippewa, A Low Stage of Lake Michigan Indicated by Bottom Sediments: Geological Society of America Bulletin, v. 66, p. 957-968.

———, 1958, Geology of the Great Lakes: Urbana, Illinois, University of Illinois Press, 313 p.

———, 1962, Lake Stanley, A Low Stage of Lake Huron Indicated by Bottom Sediments: Geological Society of America Bulletin, v. 73, p. 613-620.

———, 1963, The Prehistoric Great Lakes of North America: American Scientist, v. 51, p. 84-109.

———, 1966, Correlation of Glacial Lake Stages in the Huron-Erie and Michigan Basins: Journal of Geology, v. 74, p. 62-77.

Johnston, W.A., 1916, The Trent Valley Outlet of Lake Algonquin and the Deformation of the Algonquin Water-Plane in Lake Simcoe District, Ontario: Canada Geological Survey Museum Bulletin 23, 22 p.

Karrow, P.F., 1980, The Nipissing Transgression Around Southern Lake Huron: Canadian Journal of Earth Sciences, v. 17, p. 1271-1274.

———, 1982, Algonquin-Nipissing Glacial Lake Shorelines, St. Joseph Island, Ontario: Geological Society of America Abstracts with Programs, v. 14, no. 5, p. 264.

———, in press, Quaternary Geology of St. Joseph Island: Ontario Geological Survey.

Karrow, P.F., Anderson, T.W., Clarke, A.H., Delorme, L.D., and Srecnivasa, M.R., 1975, Stratigraphy, Paleontology, and Age of Lake Algonquin Sediments in Southwestern Ontario, Canada: Quaternary Research, v. 5, p. 49-87.

Karrow, P.F., Clarke, A.H., and Herrington, H.B., 1972, Pleistocene Molluscs from Lake Iroquois Deposits in Ontario: Canadian Journal of Earth Sciences, v. 9, p. 589-595.

Kaszicki, C.A., 1985, History of Lake Algonquin in the Haliburton Region, South Central Ontario: in Karrow, P.F., and Calkin, P.E., eds., Quaternary Evolution of the Great Lakes: Geological Association of Canada Special Paper 30.

Kunkle, G.R., 1963, Lake Ypsilanti: A Probable Late Pleistocene Low-Lake Stage in the Erie Basin: Journal of Geology, v. 71, p. 72-75.

Lane, A.C., 1900, Geological Report on Huron County, Michigan: Geological Survey of Michigan, v. 7, pt. 2, 329 p.

Larsen, C.E., 1985a, Lake Level, Uplift, and Outlet Incision, the Nipissing and Algoma Great Lakes: in Karrow, P.F., and Calkin, P.E., eds., Quaternary Evolution of the Great Lakes: Geological Association of Canada Special Paper 30.

_____, 1985b, Glacio-Isostasy — An Alternative to the Hinge-Line Model in the Southern Lake Michigan Basin: Geological Society of America Abstracts with Programs, v. 17, no. 5, p. 298.

Leverett, Frank, 1939, Correlation of Beaches with Moraines in the Huron and Erie Basins: American Journal of Science, v. 237, p.456-475.

Leverett, Frank, and Taylor, F.B., 1915, The Pleistocene of Indiana and Michigan and the History of the Great Lakes: United States Geological Survey Monograph 53, 529 p.

Lewis, C.F.M., 1969, Late Quaternary History of Lakes Levels in the Huron and Erie Basins: Proceedings 12th Conference on Great Lakes Research, International Association for Great Lakes Research, p. 250-270.

_____, 1970, Recent Uplift of Manitoulin Island: Canadian Journal of Earth Sciences, v. 7, p. 665-675.

MacLachlan, D.C., 1939, Warren Shoreline in Ontario and in the "Thumb" of Michigan and its Deformation: Ph.D. Thesis, Ann Arbor, University of Michigan, 89 p.

Miller, B.B., Karrow, P.F., and Kalas, L.L., 1979, Late Quaternary Mollusks from Glacial Lake Algonquin, Nipissing, and Transitional Sediments from Southwestern Ontario, Canada: Quaternary Research, v. 11, p. 93-112.

Miller, B.B., Karrow, P.F., and Mackie, G.L., 1985, Late Quaternary Molluscan Faunal Changes in the Huron Basin: in Karrow, P.F., and Calkin, P.E., eds., Quaternary Evolution of the Great Lakes: Geological Association of Canada Special Paper 30.

Muller, E.H., and Prest, V.K., 1985, Glacial Lakes in the Ontario Basin: in Karrow, P.F., and Calkin, P.E., eds., Quaternary Evolution of the Great Lakes: Geological Association of Canada Special Paper 30.

Prest, V.K., 1970, Quaternary Geology of Canada: in Douglas, R.J.W., ed., Geology and Economic Minerals of Canada: Geological Survey of Canada, Economic Geology Report No. 1, 5th ed., p. 676-764.

Putnam, D.F., and Chapman, L.J., 1936, The Physiography of South-Central Ontario: Scientific Agriculture, v. 16, p. 457-477.

Saarnisto, Matti, 1975, Stratigraphical Studies on the Shoreline Displacement of Lake Superior: Canadian Journal of Earth Sciences, v. 12, p. 300-319.

Sly, P.G., and Lewis, C.F.M., 1972, The Great Lakes of Canada — Quaternary Geology and Limnology: Guidebook for Field Excursion A43, 24th International Geological Congress, Montreal, 92 p.

Spencer, J.W., 1888a, The St. Lawrence Basin and the Great Lakes: Science, v. 12, p. 99-100.

_____, 1888b, The Iroquois Beach — A Chapter in the History of Lake Ontario: Science, v. 11, p. 49.

_____, 1889, Notes on the Origin and History of the Great Lakes of North America: Proceedings American Association for the Advancement of Science, v. 37, p. 197-199.

_____, 1891a, High Level Shores in the Region of the Great Lakes and Their Deformation: American Journal of Science, v. 41, p. 201-221.

_____, 1891b, Deformation of the Algonquin Beach, and Birth of Lake Huron: American Journal of Science, v. 41, p. 12-21.

_____, 1894, Deformation of the Lundy Beach and the Birth of Lake Erie: American Journal of Science, v. 48, p. 207-212.

Stanley, G.M., 1936, Lower Algonquin Beaches of Penetanguishene Peninsula; Geological Society of America Bulletin, v. 47, p. 1933-1960.

_____, 1938a, Impounded Early Algonquin Beaches at Sucker Creek, Grey County, Ontario: Michigan Academy of Science, Arts, and Letters Papers, v. 23, p. 477-495.

_____, 1938b, The Submerged Valley Through Mackinac Straits: Journal of Geology, v. 46, p. 966-974.

_____, 1945, Prehistoric Mackinac Island: Michigan Geological Survey Publication 43, 74 p.

Taylor, F.B., 1894, A Reconnaissance of the Abandoned Shore Lines of the South Coast of Lake Superior: American Geologist, v. 13, p. 365-383.

_____, 1897, Correlation of Erie-Huron Beaches With Outlets and Moraines in Southeastern Michigan: Geological Society of America Bulletin, v. 8, p. 313-317.

Vaughn, Danny, and Ash, D.W., 1983, Paleohydrology and Geomorphology of Selected Reaches of the Upper Wabash River, Indiana: Geological Society of America Abstracts With Programs, v. 15, no. 6, p. 711.

White, O.L., 1975, Quaternary Geology of the Bolton Area, Southern Ontario: Ontario Division of Mines Geological Report 117, 119 p.

Zumberge, J.H., and Benninghoff, W.S., 1969, A Mid-Wisconsin Peat in Michigan, U.S.A.: Pollen et Spores, v. 1, p. 585-601.

Quaternary Evolution of the Great Lakes,
edited by P.F. Karrow and P.E. Calkin,
Geological Association of Canada Special Paper 30, 1985

LATE QUATERNARY MOLLUSCAN FAUNAL CHANGES
IN THE HURON BASIN

Barry B. Miller

Department of Geology, Kent Sate University, Kent, Ohio 44242

Paul F. Karrow

Department of Earth Sciences, University of Waterloo, Waterloo, Ontario N2L 3G1

Gerald L. Mackie

Department of Zoology, University of Guelph, Guelph, Ontario N1G 2W1

ABSTRACT

Study of fossils from 52 sites in the Huron basin show that the Algonquin, transitional (Stanley) and Nipissing lake phases were characterized by distinctive molluscan assemblages. Eighteen of the sites are associated with Algonquin (12 000 to 10 000 B.P.), 25 with Nipissing (6000 to 4000 B.P.) and 9 with Lake Stanley transitional age sediments (10 000 to 6000 B.P.). One hundred and eight species, subspecies and "forms" (26 sphaeriid, 12 unionid and 70 gastropod taxa) have been identified from these sediments.

Most of the faunal differences that exist between these lake phases appear to be related to: 1) cool water temperatures during the Algonquin phase due to the pro-glacial position of that lake: these excluded some aquatic species, but permitted northern terrestrial species to occupy sites along the lake margin; and 2) drainage changes during the low-water Stanley phase; these isolated the Huron basin from the lower Great Lakes and the upper St. Lawrence but allowed terrestrial gastropods to migrate across the southern part of the basin. Sometime during the Nipissing phase, isostatic uplift changed the drainage pattern once again so that direct freshwater connections between the lower Great Lakes and Huron basin were re-established. This initiated another wave of immigrants into the basin from the south that consisted almost entirely of aquatic gastropods and unionid clams.

RÉSUMÉ

L'étude de 52 sites fossilifères dans le bassin du lac Huron indique que les lacs Algonquin, Nipissing et la phase transitoire du lac Stanley se caractérisaient par des assemblages distincts de mollusques. Dix-huit de ces sites sont associés au lac Algonquin (12 000 à 10 000 B.P.); vingt-cinq au lac Nipissing (6000 à 4000 B.P.); et neuf à la phase transitoire du lac Stanley (10 000 à 6000 B.P.). En tout cent-huit espèces, sous-espèces et "formes" ont été identifiées (26 sphaeriides, 12 unionides et 70 taxons de gastropodes).

Les différences faunales qui existent entre ces phases lacustres semblent être liées à: 1) des températures d'eau froides pendant la phase du lac Algonquin. Ces températures auraient favorisé le développement de certaines espèces terrestres nordiques principalement le long du rivage du lac tout en excluant certaines espèces aquatiques; et 2) des changements dans le drainage du lac lors de la phase de bas niveau du lac Stanley. Ces modifications ont eu pour effet d'isoler le bassin du lac Huron des autres Grands Lacs et de la vallée supérieure du Saint-Laurent tout en permettant à certains gastropodes terrestres de migrer vers la partie méridionale du bassin. Durant la phase du lac Nipissing le relèvement isostatique a entraîné un nouveau changement dans le système de drainage, rétablissant la liaison entre le bassin du lac Huron et les Grands Lacs inférieurs. Ce nouveau lien a favorisé l'immigration dans le bassin du lac Huron de nouvelles espèces dont des gastropodes aquatiques et des palourdes unionides.

INTRODUCTION

Within the past two decades, studies made of deposits associated with the lakes that occupied the Huron basin between 12 000 and 4000 B.P. have revealed a diverse fossil biota. Molluscs are among the most visible and ubiquitous of these fossils and, although their presence has long been recognized (Logan *et al.*, 1863; Spencer, 1891; Leverett and Taylor, 1915), they have remained essentially unstudied until the 1970s (Karrow *et al.*, 1972, 1975; Miller *et al.*, 1979; Miller and Karrow, 1981). These modern studies have had as one of their objectives the documentation of the times of entry and the routes followed by molluscan taxa as they migrated into the basin following retreat of the ice margin. It was hypothesized that climatic and geographic changes associated with deglaciation of the Huron basin might result in faunal changes that could serve as a basis for biostratigraphic zonation of Algonquin, Nipissing, and transitional (Stanley) age sediments (Miller *et al.*, 1979).

This report integrates new data acquired between 1979 and the present with the results of earlier published research (Miller *et al.*, 1979) on the molluscan faunas recovered from these deposits. Its purpose is to present the evidence for molluscan biostratigraphic zonation of these sediments and to account for the faunal changes that apparently occurred within the Huron basin between 12 000 and 4000 B.P. The data base for this report now consists of 52 molluscan assemblages representing 108 nominal forms, subspecies, and species of gastropods, and sphaeriid and unionid clams (Table I). With the few exceptions noted in Table I, the nomenclature in this paper follows the usage of Clarke (1981) for the aquatic and of Oughton (1948) for the terrestrial taxa. The collection sites extend from St. Joseph Island (Fig. 1, loc. 43) on the north, to Camlachie (Fig. 1, loc. 26) on the south, Victoria Harbor on the east (Fig. 1, loc. 44), and Harbor Beach and Port Sanilac, Michigan, (Fig. 1, loc. 39 and 40) on the west.

AGE OF MOLLUSCAN ASSEMBLAGES

At 21 of the 52 sites (Fig. 1, locs. 7, 8, 10, 12, 18, 19, 23 to 25, 29, 33, 35, 36, 38, 39, 40, 41, 44, 49 to 51), the molluscan assemblages occur in association with radiocarbon-dated materials that form the basis for their assignment to Main Algonquin, Stanley (transitional) or Nipissing lake phases. The interpreted age of some of the mollusc-bearing horizons was derived from their stratigraphic proximity to dated raised shoreline features, or to stream terraces that are graded to these features (Miller *et al.*, 1979, Fig. 2). At some sites the age was inferred from the stratigraphic position of the molluscs relative to radiocarbon-dated pollen zones. At localities where none of the previously mentioned techniques could be applied, "most probable" age assignments were made from probability tables that were developed from the number of molluscan species, their number of occurrences at localities of known age, and the total number of fossil bearing localities. On the basis of these assignments, 18 assemblages (Fig. 1, loc. 1 to 18) are considered related to Algonquin, nine to Stanley (Fig. 1, loc. 19 to 27) and 25 to Nipissing (Fig. 1, loc. 28 to 52) lake phases. All Algonquin localities referred to here belong to the late or Main Algonquin water level phase.

The distribution of sites is very uneven, and this can be attributed to several causes. Sites are most numerous in southern Ontario because of the better access and greater intensity of study in that area (including more people looking for sites). Known organic sites in northern Lake Huron were examined, but only one mollusc-bearing site was found on St. Joseph Island and one on Manitoulin Island; both of these are of Nipissing age. W. R. Cowan (pers. commun., 1981) found no shells in his mapping of the Sault Ste. Marie area. It is probable that shells have been leached from the acidic sands and gravels on the Shield, if they were present in the first place. Because Manitoulin Island has been given little attention thus far, it should be expected to yield more fossil sites as more detailed searches are carried out. St. Joseph

Island, on the other hand, has been given extensive recent study (Karrow, 1982), and more sites are unlikely to be discovered there. No sites are known from east of Georgian Bay, an area underlain by acidic Shield rocks.

Reconnaissance in Michigan failed to confirm the mollusc occurrence at Cheboygan reported by Leverett and Taylor (1915, p. 452); a dam has raised the water level in the river and the area is much affected by human disturbance. Abundant molluscs occur in Nipissing clay on the south bank of the Au Sable River west of Oscoda (Elias *et al.*, 1981); however, they have not been recovered in sufficient quantity and adequate degree of preservation to record here. Iosco County appears to be a relatively promising area for the discovery of additional sites.

It is also interesting that only Nipissing sites have been found outside southern Ontario. It seems likely that a retreating ice front inhibited the northward spread of molluscs in Lake Algonquin, just as it may have inhibited their eastward spread in Lake Iroquois (Karrow *et al.*, 1972).

Miller *et al.*, (1979) remarked on the meagre representation of the large unionid clams. These shells decompose readily and are difficult to recover for study. A more concerted effort to retrieve these shells has substantially extended their species list in Nipissing sites, and further extension of the list for transitional sites is potentially possible. Such is not the case for Algonquin deposits, in which large clams are not usually present, and all found so far belong to *Anodonta*. Thus, the unionid group also serves to differentiate between Algonquin and Nipissing deposits.

STRATIGRAPHIC DISTRIBUTION OF MOLLUSCS

Fifty-five nominal forms, subspecies and species, representing 18 aquatic and 20 terrestrial gastropods and one unionid and 17 sphaeriid clams, have been identified from sediments associated with the Main Lake Algonquin water level (Table I). Nineteen are limited to Algonquin-age sites and 9 additional taxa have stratigraphic ranges that extend into transitional-age deposits. Ten of the 19 taxa limited to Algonquin-age assemblages are known only from sites along the Nottawasaga River within the Alliston Embayment (Karrow *et al.*, 1975). Seven of this temporally restricted group of 19 occur only at sites near the Lake Huron shore, between the Maitland and Saugeen Rivers (Fig. 1). Only two taxa, *Fossaria modicella* and *Pisidium nitidum* form *pauperculanum*, occur at Algonquin-age sites in both areas. Twenty-five of the 55 molluscs present in Algonquin sites also occur in transitional and Nipissing stage deposits.

Fossils from transitional-age sites are believed to have lived during 10 000 to 6000 B.P. as the water rose from the Lake Stanley to the Nipissing level. Sixty-one taxa representing 19 aquatic and 29 terrestrial gastropods, one unionid clam and 12 sphaeriid clams occur in transitional-age sites. Thirty-four of these also occur in Algonquin-age sites and 27 represent new post-Algonquin migrants into the Huron basin. Nineteen of these new immigrants lived in the study area until at least the Nipissing phase (Table I). Eight of the new migrant species, *Gyraulus circumstriatus, Pomatiopsis lapidaria, Sphaerium (Musculium) rhomboideum, Pisidium walkeri, Vertigo gouldi, V. g. paradoxa, Punctum minutis-*

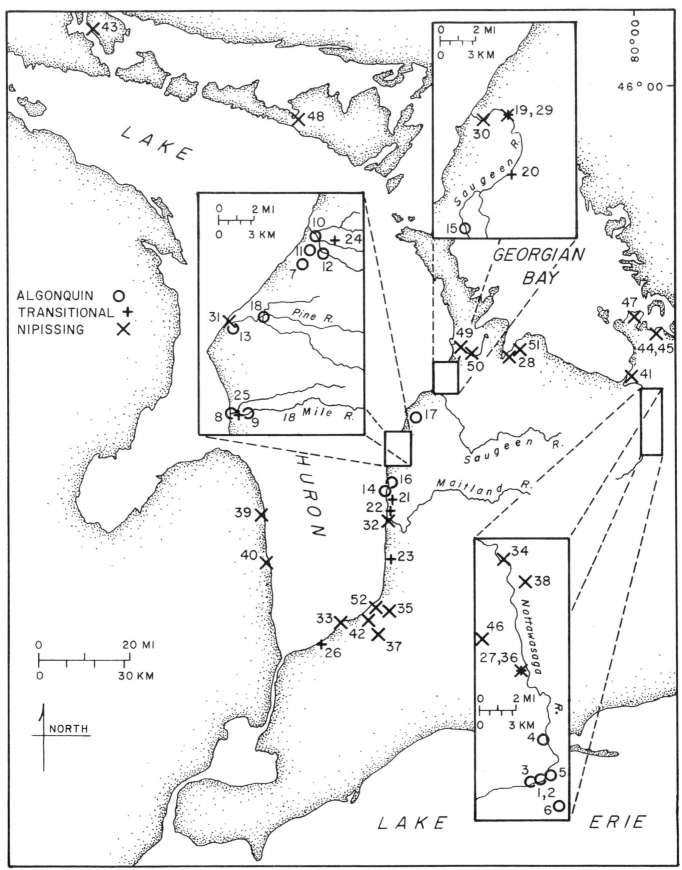

Figure 1. Locality map of fossil sites (indicated by numbers). Site information is provided in Appendix.

TABLE I
MOLLUSCAN FAUNA OF ALGONQUIN, TRANSITIONAL AND NIPISSING SITES

Taxon	Site Occurrences (Numbers refer to map locations in Figure 1)		
Aquatic or Terrestrial	Algonquin	Transitional	Nipissing
Aquatic Gastropods			
1. *Valvata sincera sincera*	1,3-7,10-13,15,17	19,20,22-25,27	28,30,34,36
2. *Valvata tricarinata*	1-15,17	19,20,23-27	28-30,32-35,37-51
3. *Amnicola limosa*	1,6-10,12-14,17cf.	20,21,23,25,26	28-30,32-35,37,39,41-51
4. *Cincinnatia cincinnatiensis*	13?	—	28,30,40,42,43
5. *Probythinella lacustris*	1cf,3-6,8,11,12,15,17	19,20,22-25,27	30,36,38,43
6. *Fossaria decampi*	1,3,5,7,8,10-17	19-25,27	29,30,33,34cf,35,37,40,42,43,45,46,50,52
7. *Fossaria parva*	7,18cf	—	—
8. *Fossaria humilis*	1,2	—	—
9. *Fossaria modicella*	6,7	—	—
10. *Lymnaea stagnalis*	1,5,10	19,20	33,41,43-46,51
11. *Stagnicola catascopium*	1,5	23cf,27	28cf,30,33,35,36,38-40,43,47cf,50
12. *Stagnicola elodes*	7,12cf,13cf,14,15cf	19,22	36cf,37cf,40cf,41,42,44cf,45
13. *Gyraulus sp. (arcticus?)*	1,5	—	—
14. *Gyraulus deflectus*	4,7,15-18	22,24	29,35,38,44,45,49,50
15. *Gyraulus parvus*	1,2,5-10,12-16	19-27	28-30,32-34,37,38,41,42,45-50
16. *Helisoma anceps*	1,4,7-10,12-17	19-27	28-30,32,34-38,40-43,46,48,49,51
17. *Physa sp.*	7,10,13,14,17,18	19,22-26	30,33,36-38,40-42,44-47,50,51
18. *Physa cf. heterostropha*	1	—	—
19. *Physa jennessi skinneri*	7	—	—
20. *Marstonia decepta*	—	21,26	29,30,32,34,35,38,41,42,44-47cf,48-51
21. *Pomatiopsis lapidaria*	—	26	—
22. *Fossaria obrussa*	—	25,26,27cf	32,33,36,38,51
23. *Ferrissia fragilis*	—	24,26	29
24. *Ferrissia parallela*	—	26	29,38,41
25. *Gyraulus circumstriatus?*	—	7	—
26. *Armiger crista*	—	24,26	29,30,50
27. *Physa gyrina*	—	20cf	29,32-34,42,43,48
28. *Valvata sincera helicoidea?*	—	—	29
29. *Goniobasis livescens*	—	—	28,30-40,42,43,48-52
30. *Campeloma sp.*	—	—	42
31. *Campeloma decisum*	—	—	35,37,38
32. *Fossaria dalli**	—	—	33,41
33. *Laevapex fuscus*	—	—	29,38
34. *Promenetus exacuous*	—	—	29,34,44,45,48,49,50
35. *Helisoma trivolvis*	—	—	41
36. *Helisoma campanulatum*	—	—	32,37,40,42,46,49,51
Sphaeriid Clams			
37. *Pisidium casertanum*	1,3-5,7-16	19-27	28-30,32-38,40-44,47,48,49,50
38. *Pisidium compressum*	1,3-10,12-17	19-26	28-30,33,34,37,41-46,48
39. *Pisidium conventus*	1,6	—	—
40. *Pisidium ferrugineum*	5,6,8	19	38,41,42,50
41. *Pisidium lilljeborgi*	1-6	—	38,42,50
42. *Pisidium milium?*	8	—	—
43. *Pisidium nitidum*	3,6-8,16	19,21,23	28,33,37,41,42,45,46
44. *Pisidium nitidum fm. contortum*	7,15	—	—
45. *Pisidium nitidum fm. pauperculanum*	1,3-5,7	—	—
46. *Pisidium subtruncatum*	1	21	—
47. *Pisidium variabile*	1,3,7,8	21-23,27	28,33,36,38,39,41,44,45,47,51
48. *Pisidium ventricosum*	6,7,15	25	—
49. *Pisidium walkeri fm. mainense*	4	—	—
50. *Sphaerium (Musculium) lacustre*	7,8	—	41
51. *Sphaerium (Musculium) partumeium*	10	—	—
52. *Sphaerium (Sphaerium) simile*	1,3	23,26	32,33,41,48,51
53. *Sphaerium (Sphaerium) striatinum*	1,4-6,11,12,14,15	19,20,22-24,27	28,33-36,38-46,48,50
54. *Pisidium adamsi*	—	24-26	41,44,45,56
55. *Pisidium walkeri*	—	24,26	—
56. *Sphaerium (Musculium) rhomboideum*	—	20cf.	—

Taxon	Site Occurrences (Numbers refer to map locations in Figure 1)		
Aquatic or Terrestrial	Algonquin	Transitional	Nipissing
57. *Pisidium dubium*	—	—	28cf., 33cf., 51
58. *Pisidium equilaterale*	—	—	36
59. *Pisidium fallax*	—	—	35,38,39,42,46
60. *Pisidium rotundatum*	—	—	50
61. *Sphaerium (Musculium) securis*	—	—	38,46,48
62. *Sphaerium (Sphaerium) corneum?*	—	—	36
Unionid Clams			
63. *Anodonta sp.*	8	—	—
64. *Anodonta grandis simpsoniana*	3	—	—
65. *Lampsilis radiata radiata*	—	21	33
66. *cf. Amblema plicata*	—	—	33
67. *Anodontoides ferrussacianus*	—	—	43
68. *Elliptio camplanata*	—	—	42
69. *Elliptio dilatata*	—	—	30
70. *Lampsilis radiata siliquoidea*	—	—	30,42cf.,43,44
71. *Lampsilis cf. L. ovata*	—	—	42
72. *Lasmigona complanata*	—	—	30
73. *Lasmigona costata*	—	—	30
74. *cf. Ligumia recta*	—	—	30,43
75. *Strophitus undulatus*	—	—	43
Terrestrial Gastropods			
1. *cf. Catinella "avara"*†	1,2,5,6,8	19,20,22-27	33-35,38,50
2. *Cionella lubrica*††	1,8	21,23-27	—
3. *Columella alticola*	1,5,18	19,25	—
4. *Columella edentula*	5,6	—	—
5. *Discus cronkhitei*	1,6,8,13,14	19,20-25,27	28-30,33,34,36,48,50
6. *Euconulus chersinus*	1	—	—
7. *Euconulus fulvus*	6,8,14	19,22-25,27	—
8. *Gastrocopta armifera*	16	22-25	29,33,34
9. *Nesovitrea electrina*†††	1,14,16,17	19,20-27	33,37,41
10. *Pupilla muscorum*	5,8,14,17	22,23,25	—
11. *Succinea ovalis*	7,16	—	—
12. *Vallonia "albula"*	8,14,16	19-27	30,33,34
13. *Vallonia costata*	1	—	—
14. *Vallonia pulchella*	1	—	—
15. *Vertigo ventricosa elatior*	1,5,16	23-27	33,51
16. *Vertigo gouldi hannai*	18	19	—
17. *Vertigo modesta*	7,8,14	22,24,25	—
18. *Vitrina limpida*	14,18	22	—
19. *Zonitoides arboreus*	1,6,9,16	19,23-25,27	30,33,41,50
20. *cf. Zoogenites harpa*	12	—	—
21. *Carychium exiguum*	—	21,23,24,26	28,30,34,50
22. *Gastrocopta contracta*	—	23	29,30,33
23. *Gastrocopta tappaniana*	—	19,21-27	28,29,30,33
24. *Hawaiia minuscula*	—	23	33
25. *Helicodiscus parallelus*	—	23	28-30,33,37,50
26. *cf. Oxyloma retusa*	—	21,26	—
27. *Punctum minutissimum*	—	22-25	—
28. *Striatura milium*	—	23,25	50
29. *Strobilops aenea*	—	23	33
30. *Strobilops labyrinthica*	—	23,24,26	28,30,33,34
31. *Strobilops sp.*	—	—	33
32. *Vertigo gouldi*	—	23,25,27	—
33. *v. g. paradoxa*	—	22,24	—
34. *Vertigo morsei*	—	24	33
35. *Vertigo ovata*	—	24	33
36. *Zonitoides nitidus*	—	26	29
37. *Pupoides albilabris*	—	—	30,33,41

†cf. *Catinella "avara"* = *Succinea avara*   ††*Cionella lubrica* = *Cochlicopa lubrica*
†††*Nesovitrea electrina* = *Retinella hammonis*   *Fossaria dalli* = *Bakerlymnaea dalli*

simum and cf. *Oxyloma retusa,* appear to be stratigraphically restricted to transitional-age sites (Table I).

The Nipissing fauna consists of 72 taxa and includes 26 aquatic and 19 terrestrial gastropods, 16 sphaeriid clams, and 11 unionid clams. Twenty-five members of this assemblage represent first stratigraphic occurrences within the study area (Table I).

CAUSES OF MOLLUSCAN ZONATION

Fifty-two (48%) of the taxa identified below the generic level appear to be temporally restricted to either Algonquin, transitional or Nipissing age deposits. Some of this stratigraphic "endemism" is probably an artifact resulting from: 1) taxonomists who have created the nomenclatural and taxonomic instabilities that seem to plague some nonmarine molluscan taxa (Miller, 1978); 2) the problems inherent in the identification of certain species from shell material; and 3) factors that have prevented sampling of similar habitats at each study site. However, we believe that most of the faunal differences between the three lake phases are real. In particular, we call attention to the relatively high percentages of taxa limited to Algonquin and Nipissing-age sites (Table I). These faunal changes are responses to a complex of climatic and environmental transformations that occurred between 12 000 and 4000 B.P. In the following sections we present data and arguments that we believe document and support this interpretation.

Algonquin Molluscan Assemblage

Although many of the fossil molluscan taxa can be found living in the study area (Clarke, 1981; Oughton, 1948), these fossil assemblages also include several significant geographic range extensions that have occurred within the past 12 000 years. Some of the terrestrial and aquatic molluscs found in Algonquin-age sediments clearly imply cooler temperatures at that time.

The close proximity of the ice-margin between 12 000 and 10 000 B.P. (Fig. 2a) may have kept the water temperature of Lake Algonquin low so that it was no higher than the present 3.6°C mean surface water temperature of Lake Superior (Bennett, 1978). This interpretation is based primarily on the present distribution and environmental conditions associated with *Pisidium conventus* and *Anodonta grandis simpsoniana. P. conventus,* a cold water species, is now rarely found at depths of less than 15 m within the temperate parts of its range (Clarke, 1981; Miller *et al.,* 1979). This species occurs as a fossil in shallow-water sediments (Fig. 1, locs. 1 and 6) representing the Alliston Embayment during the Main Algonquin phase; its occurrence implies much cooler water than the 5.2°C mean surface temperature (Bennett, 1978) that now characterizes Georgian Bay. *A. g. simpsoniana* also occurs in shallow water sediments associated with the Alliston Embayment (Fig. 1, loc. 3). Its modern range in Canada is the Interior Basin in the boreal forest from Quebec to central Alberta, northwest to the mouth of the Mackenzie River (Clarke, 1981). Commenting on its fossil occurrence in Lake Algonquin sediments, Clarke, (1973, p. 89) stated, "This is not surprising since one would expect that the first immigrants to a newly deglaciated

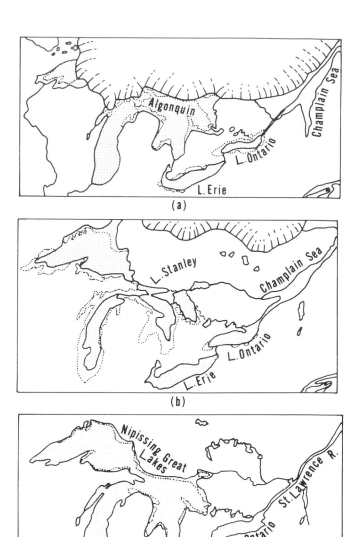

Figure 2. Map of (a) Main Lake Algonquin, (b) low water Lake Stanley and (c) Lake Nipissing. After Prest (1970).

area would be cold-tolerant, and by its present distribution in Canada *Anodonta grandis simpsoniana* is obviously cold-tolerant to a remarkable degree."

The presence of the terrestrial gastropods *Vertigo modesta, Columella alticola,* and *Zoogenites harpa* in Algonquin-age sediments of the study area represent geographic distributions well south of their present ranges in the Great Lakes region (Oughton, 1948). Two of these species, *Vertigo modesta* and *Columella alticola,* now have geographic ranges that extend much farther south at high elevations in the Rocky Mountains than in the Central Lowlands (Miller, in press), suggesting that high summer temperatures may be the limiting factor controlling their southern limits. Within the Great Lakes region, these species now reach the southern limits of their respective ranges near the 13°C summer mean isotherm along the north shore of Lake Superior (Oughton, 1948) and Mackinac Island (Miller, in

ALGONQUIN   **TRANSITIONAL**   **NIPISSING**

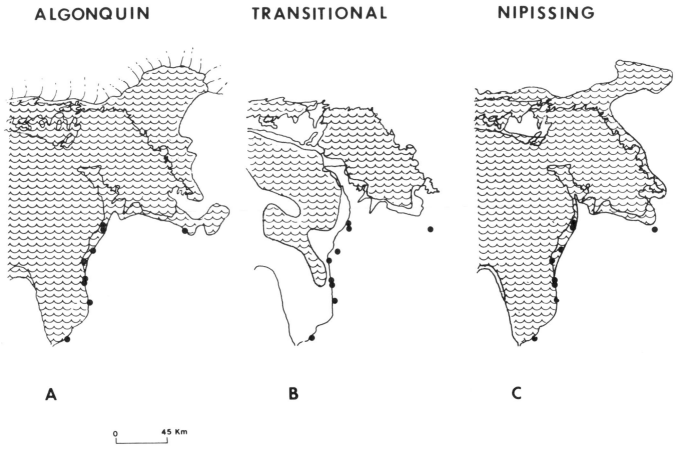

0   45 Km

Figure 3. Maps showing relative change in position of transitional age fossil sites (dots) as a result of lake level fluctuations.
After Prest (1970).

press). To account for the range extensions represented by these two species, requires the assumption that the mean summer temperatures, at least locally, may have been about 4°C lower than the present 17°C summer mean temperatures at the fossil sites.

Transitional Molluscan Assemblage

The sites associated with the rise in the water level from the low-water Lake Stanley phase to the Nipissing phase, (Fig 2b, 2c) between 10 000 and 6000 B.P. contain an assemblage that is transitional in the sense of both the age and the composition of the molluscan fauna. Sixty-two per cent of the aquatic taxa found in transitional-age sites had already entered the Huron basin during the Algonquin phase. Eight of the 12 aquatic molluscs that first appear in transitional-age deposits, continued in the basin at least through the Nipissing phase (Table I). Fourteen of the terrestrial gastropod taxa from transitional sites were already present in the area between 12 000 to 10 000 B.P. Seven of this number are restricted to pre-Nipissing-age sites (Table I).

At several of the transitional sites, there are species in association that are allopatric which now have geographic ranges in Ontario. At locality 25, for example, the northerly distributed species *V. modesta* and *C. alticola* occur with *Gastrocopta armifera* and *Vertigo morsei*. These latter two species now reach the northern limits of their respective

ranges in Ontario near Bayfield, Huron County and Hastings County (Oughton, 1948). A climate capable of sustaining both these northerly and southerly species would probably have to combine cooler summers with mean temperatures of about 13°C with a 215-day growing season, during which time the average temperature exceeds 4.6°C (Fremlin, 1974).

Most of the aquatic molluscs that first appear in the transitional-age deposits are taxa characteristic of small ponds, lakes or streams, with areas of relatively dense-rooted vegetation or of temporary bodies of water. This group of molluscs implies a different array and distribution of aquatic habitats in the transitional sites than were sampled from the Algonquin deposits. The possibility has been considered that both the changes in the aquatic molluscs and the relatively high percentage (56) of terrestrial taxa that first appear in the area between 10 000 and 6000 B.P. may be the result of a sampling bias. This may have been imposed by the lowering of the water in the basin to the Lake Stanley level when the ice-margin receded from the North Bay outlet. The estimated 61-m drop in the water level (Prest, 1970) had the effect of transforming localities that were littoral lacustrine and estuarine river environments during the Main Algonquin phase to positions that were tens of kilometres upstream from the shore of Lake Stanley (Fig. 3). Most of the transitional sediments represent riverine and floodplain environments. The dominance of these habitats may, in part, account for the change in environmental aspect implied by many of the aquatic gastropods that "first" appear in transitional-age deposits and for the apparent increase in terrestrial gastropods.

This explanation, however, does not entirely account for the increased representation of terrestrial species, many of which continued into the Nipissing phase but at relatively fewer localities. Isostatic uplift of the North Bay outlet resulted in the Nipissing level (ca. 186 m) and submerged the lower reaches of streams flowing into the basin.

Nipissing deposits, therefore, could be expected to include a greater representation of estuarine and lacustrine habitats than transitional-age deposits. They should represent essentially the same type of aquatic habitats that were available during the high water Main Algonquin phase (Fig. 3). The Nipissing molluscan fauna should also be much like that of the Algonquin phase, minus the cool water aquatic and boreal terrestrial elements that were probably extirpated during the "Climatic Optimum". The fact that the Nipissing assemblage includes many of the taxa that first appear in the transitional fauna implies that many of these taxa must have migrated into the basin between 10 000 to 6000 B.P. Many of these predominantly terrestrial taxa probably entered southwestern Ontario from Michigan during the low Lake Stanley phase when the southern Huron basin would have offered an easy migration route.

Nipissing Molluscan Assemblage

A second major wave of new migrants, represented by 24 aquatic and one terrestrial taxa, first appear in the basin in Nipissing-age deposits. Two of these aquatic forms, *V. sincera helicoidea?* and *Sphaerium corneum?*, are based on single specimens for which the identifications are equivocal and are not considered in the following discussion.

The specific pathways followed by these new migrants into the Huron basin is not clearly established for most of these taxa. However, published molluscan faunal lists from deposits 12 000 to 4000 B.P. within the Great Lakes and peripheral areas, and the present distribution of these taxa, provide insight into the probable migration routes followed by some of the aquatic molluscs.

Fossil occurrences of *Anodontoides ferrusacianus* and *Lasmigona complanata* in the Lake Agassiz basin (Ashworth and Cvancara, 1983), and of *Lampsilis radiata siliquoidea* in younger sediments from the Nipigon region (Zoltai and Herrington, 1966), predate the first appearance of these taxa in Nipissing-age deposits of the Lake Huron basin by thousands of years. A general west to east migration of these taxa is suggested by the fossil distributions.

P. exacuous and *F. dalli* occur to the west and east of the study area in deposits older than Nipissing age sediments of the Huron basin (Miller *et al.*, 1979). These may have either entered the basin through the Ottawa River, after the Champlain Sea regressed from the upper St. Lawrence, or they may have entered the upper Great Lakes earlier through a post-Emerson-phase outlet of Lake Agassiz. The chronology suggested by Clayton (1983) has water from the Superior basin draining eastward into Lake Stanley and out the Ottawa Valley by about 9000 B.P.

A second group of taxa that first appears in Nipissing-age sediments seems to have gained entry into the Huron basin from either the lower Great Lakes and/or through the St. Lawrence-Ottawa River system after withdrawal of the Champlain Sea. At least two of the unionid species from this group, *Amblema plicata* and *Lasmigona complanata*, are now absent from the St. Lawrence-Ottawa drainage (Fig. 4) and may have entered the Huron basin from Lake Erie through the Port Huron outlet. *Elliptio* cf. *E. complanata*, which now occurs in the St. Lawrence-Ottawa system but is absent from the Huron drainage south of Georgian Bay (Fig. 4) very probably migrated into the study area through the St. Lawrence-Ottawa drainage before the Port Huron outlet became re-established. Five other species from this second group, *Goniobasis livescens*, *Pisidium* cf. *dubium*, *Elliptio dilatata*, *Ligumia recta*, and *Lasmigona costata*, have modern distributions that include both the St. Lawrence-Ottawa drainage, and Lakes Huron, Erie, and Ontario and their tributaries (Fig. 4). None of these five species is now living in Lake Superior (Clarke, 1981); at least in the cases of *G. livescens*, *E. dilatata*, and *P. dubium*, their exclusion from Lake Superior may be related to cold water temperatures.

Radiocarbon dates from sites in the lower Cuyahoga River near Lake Erie (Miller, 1983) and from the Niagara River (Calkin and Brett, 1978) indicate that *Goniobasis livescens* and *Campeloma* (probably *C. decisum*) were living in the lower Great Lakes between 10 000 and 6000 B.P. These species, as well as many of the other aquatic taxa that first appear in the Huron basin in Nipissing-age sediments, may have been excluded from earlier entry by cold water in the basin during the Main Algonquin stage. This occurred because of the position of this proglacial lake relative to the ice margin (Fig. 2). Cold water continued discharging into the basin from the ice-margined Superior basin until about 9000 B.P. (Clayton, 1983). Glacial meltwater from Cochrane phase ice, draining through Lake Timiskaming (Prest, 1970, Fig. XII-6u), may have kept warm-water species from migrating up the Ottawa River until after ca. 8100 B.P. By about 8000 B.P., the Cochrane phase ice margin had retreated far enough north so meltwater no longer drained south and the Ottawa River became usable as a migration route into Lake Nipissing from the upper St. Lawrence.

Some of the faunal changes among the terrestrial gastropods between Nipissing and pre-Nipissing assemblages appear to be related to the climatic warming during the "Climatic Optimum". These changes include local extirpation of *Vertigo modesta* and *Columella alticola* from the study area, together with a modest range expansion of *Vertigo morsei* and *Pupoides albilabris* (Fig. 5).

SUMMARY

The Algonquin, transitional, and Nipissing lake stages of the Huron basin are characterized by distinctive assemblages of molluscs. Most of these faunal differences can be explained in terms of: 1) climatic changes; 2) retreat of ice margins; and, 3) isostatic rebound, which have changed the Huron basin drainage between 12 000 and 4000 B.P.

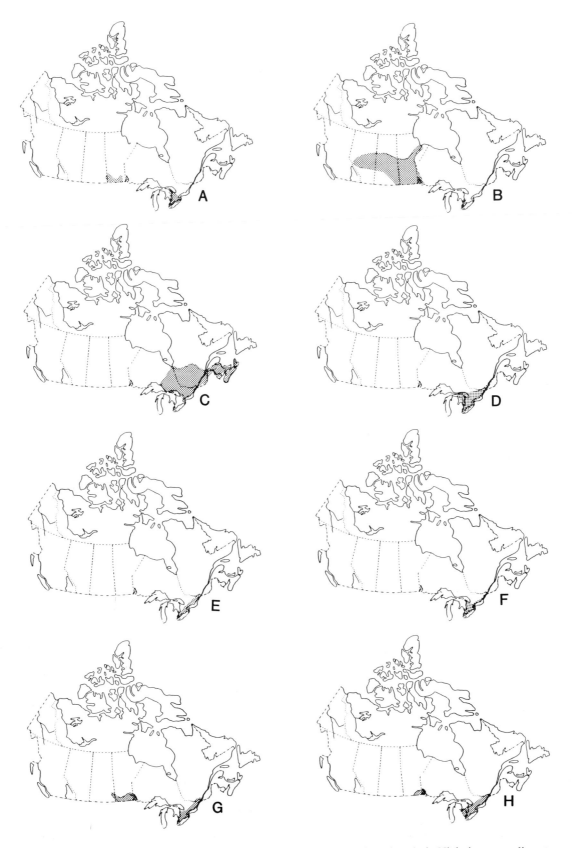

Figure 4. Present distribution maps of taxa that first appeared in the region of study in Nipissing age sediments: (A) *Amblema plicata*, (B) *Lasmigona complanata*, (C) *Elliptio complanata*, (D) *Goniobasis livescens*, (E) *Pisidium dubium*, (F) *Elliptio dilatata*, (G) *Ligumia recta*, and (H) *Lasmigona costata*. After Clarke (1981).

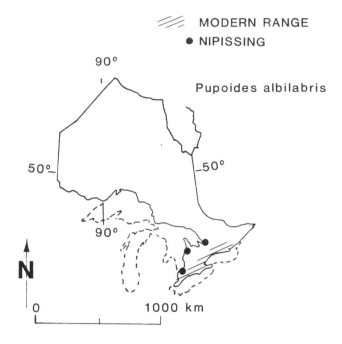

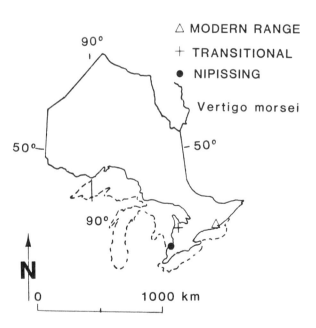

Figure 5. Distribution maps of *Vertigo morsei* and *Pupoides albilabris* in Ontario. After Oughton (1948).

The Lake Algonquin assemblage includes both cool water aquatic and boreal terrestrial molluscs that imply the presence of cooler water and ambient atmospheric temperatures. Some of these boreal terrestrial taxa continued in the area through the interval represented by the transitional-age sites, 10 000 to 6000 B.P., suggesting that cooler summer temperatures may have still characterized the study area. During this interval, geographic changes in the basin related to retreat of the ice margin from North Bay exposed a lower outlet that permitted the water level to drop about 61 m below the Main Algonquin level (Prest, 1970). During this low water phase, the Port Huron outlet was abandoned and discharge was through the Ottawa River into the Champlain Sea. After retreat of the Champlain Sea from the upper St. Lawrence, the Ottawa River may still have been carrying glacial meltwater from the Cochrane ice margin until about 8100 B.P. (Prest, 1970).

These changes probably effectively severed potential direct freshwater migration connections between the Huron basin and the upper St. Lawrence and the lower Great Lakes. During the low-water phase, terrestrial molluscs were able to migrate across the southern part of the Huron basin, thus accounting in part for the great increase in terrestrial taxa in transitional-age sites. During the Nipissing phase, isostatic uplift changed the drainage pattern once again so that direct freshwater connections between the Huron basin and lower Great Lakes became re-established. This initiated another wave of new immigrants into the basin from the south, which is represented almost entirely by aquatic taxa.

ACKNOWLEDGEMENTS

We thank W. D. Fitzgerald for drawing our attention to sites 35, 38, 44, 45 and 46; W. R. Cowan for bringing to our attention sites 18 and 24; D. R. Sharpe for sites 49 and 50; B. H. Feenstra for site 51; P. J. Barnett for site 48; J. Cronin for site 47; and D. F. Eschman for site 40. The illustrations were drafted by Bruce P. Metzger, Kent State University. The program for construction of the probability tables used in the study was written by Richard G. Craig, Department of Geology, Kent State University. Representatives of most of the fossil molluscs reported here will be stored at the Royal Ontario Museum. The critical reviews and comments make on this paper by A. M. Cvancara and J. B. Burch are gratefully acknowledged.

REFERENCES

Ashworth, A.C., and Cvancara, A.M., 1983, Paleoecology of the Southern Part of the Lake Agassiz Basin: *in* Teller, J.T. and Clayton, Lee, eds., Glacial Lake Agassiz: Geological Association of Canada Special Paper 26, p. 133-156.

Bennett, E.B., 1978, Characteristics of the Thermal Regime of Lake Superior: Journal of Great Lakes Research, v. 4, p. 310-319.

Calkin, P.E., and Brett, C.E., 1978, Ancestral Niagara River Drainage: Stratigraphic and Paleontologic Setting: Geological Society of America Bulletin, v. 89, p. 1140-1154.

Clarke, A.H., 1973, The Freshwater Molluscs of the Canadian Interior Basin: Malacologia, v. 13, p. 1-510.

―――, 1981, The Freshwater Molluscs of Canada: Ottawa, National Museums of Canada, 446 p.

Clayton, L., 1983, Chronology of Lake Agassiz Drainage to Lake Superior: *in* Teller, J.T. and Clayton, Lee, eds., Glacial Lake Agassiz: Geological Association of Canada Special Paper 26, p. 291-307.

Elias, S.A., Morgan, Anne and Morgan, A.V., 1981, Preliminary Note on a Fossil Insect Assemblage from the Au Sable River, Michigan: *in* Burgis, W.A. and Eschman, D.F., eds., Late Wisconsinan History of Northeastern Lower Michigan, Midwest Friends of the Pleistocene, 30th Annual Field Conference, p. 105-110.

Farrand, W.R., and Miller, B.B., 1968, Radiocarbon Dates on and Depositional Environment of the Wasaga Beach (Ontario) Marl Deposit: Ohio Journal of Science, v. 68, p. 235-239.

Fremlin, G., ed., 1974, The National Atlas of Canada: Ottawa, MacMillan, 254 p.

Karrow, P.F., 1980, The Nipissing Transgression Around Southern Lake Huron: Canadian Journal of Earth Sciences, v. 17, p. 1271-1274.

_____, 1982, Quaternary Geology of St. Joseph Island; Ontario Geological Survey Preliminary Map P. 2581, Scale 1:50 000.

Karrow, P.F., Anderson, T.W., Clarke, A.H., Delorme, L.D., and Sreenivasa, M.R., 1975, Stratigraphy, Paleontology and Age of Lake Algonquin Sediments in Southwestern Ontario: Quaternary Research, v. 5, p. 49-87.

Karrow, P.F., Clarke, A.H., and Herrington, H.B., 1972, Pleistocene Molluscs from Lake Iroquois Deposits in Ontario; Canadian Journal of Earth Sciences, v. 9, p. 589-595.

Leverett, F. and Taylor, F.B., 1915, The Pleistocene of Indiana and Michigan and the History of the Great Lakes: United States Geological Survey Monograph 53, 529 p.

Logan, W.M., Murray, A., Hunt, T.S., and Billings, E., 1863, Geological Survey of Canada Report of Progress from its Commencement to 1863: Montreal, Dawson Brothers, 983 p.

Miller, B.B., 1978, Nonmarine Molluscs in Quaternary Paleoecology: Malacological Review, v. 11, p. 27-38.

_____, 1983, Late Quaternary Fluvial History of the Lower Cuyahoga River in Northeastern Ohio: Journal of Great Lakes Research, v. 9, p. 97-105.

_____, (in press), Radiocarbon-Dated Molluscan Assemblages From Ohio-Indiana: Their Climatic Significance: National Geographic Society Research Reports.

Miller, B.B., and Karrow, P.F., 1981, Nonmarine Molluscan Biostratigraphic Zones in Late Quaternary Sediments (12 000 to 4000 years B.P.) From Southwestern Ontario: Geological Society of America Abstracts with Programs, v. 13, p. 310.

Miller, B.B., Karrow, P.F., and Kalas, L.L., 1979, Late Quaternary Molluscs from Glacial Lake Algonquin, Nipissing and Transitional Sediments in Southwestern Ontario: Quaternary Research, v. 11, p. 93-112.

Oughton, J., 1948, A Zoogeographical Study of the Land Snails of Ontario: University of Toronto Biological Series, No. 47, 128 p.

Prest, V.K., 1970, Quaternary Geology of Canada: in Douglas, R.J.W., ed., Geology and Economic Minerals of Canada: Geological Survey of Canada Economic Geology Report No. 1, 5th ed., p. 676-764.

Spencer, J.W., 1891, Deformation of the Algonquin Beach and the Birth of Lake Huron: American Journal of Science, v. 41, p. 12-21.

Zoltai, S.C., and Herrington, H.B., 1966, Late Glacial Molluscan Fauna North of Lake Superior, Ontario: Journal of Paleontology, v. 40, p. 439-446.

APPENDIX

NOTES ON LOCALITIES

1. I (Karrow *et al.*, 1975).
2. IL *ibid.*
3. II *ibid.*
4. IV *ibid.*
5. V *ibid.*
6. VI *ibid.*
* 7. Kincardine Bog (Karrow *et al.*, 1975).

* 8. K1 and 18 M (Karrow *et al.*, 1975, and Miller *et al.*, 1979).
9. K2 (Karrow *et al.*, 1975).
*10. K12 Miller *et al.*, 1979.
11. K4 *ibid.*
*12. K6 *ibid.*
13. K3 Miller *et al.*, 1979.
14. K17 *ibid.*
15. K21 North bank Mill Creek, east of township road, 1.6 km west of Saugeen River and 3 km south southeast of Port Elgin, Bruce County, Ontario. Bank exposes 9.7 m of mainly silt with molluscs scattered throughout. When surface is freshly eroded, thin laminae of plant debris are visible along bedding planes in the lower part.
16. K22 Near mouth of creek 3 km south of Kingsbridge, and 3 km north of Pt. Albert, Huron County, Ontario. Terrace (elev. 196 m) underlain by 1 m of sand and gravel with sparse molluscs.
17. K29 North bank Underwood Creek, 8 km north northeast of Tiverton, 3 km east of Lake Huron at Baie du Dore, Bruce County. Elevation, top of terrace, 210.5 m. Bank exposes this section:
    2.0 m rounded medium gravel
    0.7 m coarse reddish sand
    2.4 m buff silt with sand stringers and molluscs. Traces of plant debris.
    0.3 m angular gravel
    1.2 m brownish grey clayey silt till
    1.8 m grey varved clay with dropstones. Units 5 cm thick at top to 30 cm at base. Silt 80% of layers.
    0.7 m grey buff stony clayey sand to silt till
    0.3 m covered to creek
*18. K9205 North bank South Pine River, 4 km east of mouth of Pine River, and 1 km northwest of Highway 21, Bruce County. Molluscs collected from silt at junction of terrace and high scarp, which may be Algonquin. Main terrace sequence may be inset into this, consisting of 1.5 m of fining upward silt over sand over gravel with molluscs and wood dated 7580 ± 120 (BGS-535).
*19. K10 upper Miller *et al.*, 1979.
20. K9 *ibid.*
21. K5 *ibid.*
22. K7 *ibid.*
*23. GB44 *ibid.*
*24. K9003A North bank North Penetangore River, 5 km east of intersection of Highways 9 and 21, west of township road, Bruce County. Low stream bank exposes 1.3 m silt and sand, molluscs in lower part with wood at base dated 8000 ± 120 (BGS-534), over 0.2 m gravel to stream.
*25. K30 North bank Eighteen Mile River between localities 8 and 9 in lower terrace, 3 km south of Amberley, Bruce County. Elevation top of terrace about 187 m. Top of bank exposes 2 m of terrace sediment (weathered silt and sand over gravel) with molluscs and pieces of charcoal, over clay till. Charcoal dated 9960 ± 210

(WAT-848) indicating it is a terrace formed a little after Main Algonquin as water level began to drop to Stanley low stage.

26. K23 South bank of creek, 3 km south of Harris Point, 3 km north of Camlachie, 0.5 km upstream from Lake Huron, Lambton County. Bank exposes 1 m of soil and weathered silt over about 0.3 m of silty sand and gravel containing molluscs, including unionids, over 6.3 m of clay till to stream level.

27. K38B ANGUS B Angus south section. West bank Nottawasaga River, south edge of Angus, Simcoe County. Upland is stepped by Nipissing terrace cut into sand plain. South of Nipissing scarp is 2.4 m of foreset bedded coarse sand with mollusc concentrations along foresets (Sample B).

28. K15 Miller *et al.*, 1979.

*29. K10 lower Miller *et al.*, 1979.

30. K14 *ibid.*

31. K3b *ibid.*

32. K19 *ibid.*

*33. K16 *ibid.*

34. K37 East bank Nottawasaga River 19 km northwest of Barrie, where river cuts through Edenvale moraine. Intermittent exposure revealed:

    5.3 m covered

    3.9 m sandy, clayey silt till

    6.9 m covered

    1.8 m stratified silt over fine sand, stones, molluscs

    6.3 m grey, sandy, clayey, silt till

    3.7 m covered to river

Gullies to north confirm continuity of till and that fossiliferous sediments are the remnants of a terrace perched on the valley wall.

*35. GB-768 At Nipissing shoreline 5.5 km south of Grand Bend, 2 km west of Harpley on Highway 81, Huron County. Shells dated 4700 ± 100 (BGS-341).

*36. K38A ANGUS Fitz + ANGUS A Angus south section. West bank Nottawasaga River, south edge of Angus, Simcoe County. Upland is stepped by Nipissing terrace cut into sand plain. Bank exposes section below Nipissing terrace

    0.8 m soil over medium sand

    0.3 m light grey fine sand with molluscs (Sample A).

    3.5 m light grey sand with silty bands. Sparse molluscs.

    2.1 m covered

    1.5 m grey quicksand. Lens of plant debris dated 9950 ± 490 (WAT-788).

37. K25 South of Parkhill Creek, 7 km west of Parkhill, west of road in ploughed field with numerous shells on surface near Nipissing shoreline, Middlesex County. Dug down 0.4 m into gravelly brown sand with shells.

*38. K42 Ditch exposure 2 km west of Minesing, north side of road. Molluscs, including unionids, very abundant. Date on shells 4320 ± 70 (WAT-559). Elevation 189 m.

*39. MF1 (Karrow, 1980).

*40. MF2 *ibid.*

*41. Wasaga Beach (Farrand and Miller, 1968).

42. K28 East face gravel pit, south end of mid-bay bar of Thedford marsh, 4.5 km north of Thedford, Lambton County. Face exposes up to 1 m of stratified silty sand and gravel with abundant shells (many unionids) over 0.3 m paleosol with 2-8 cm of humus over leached brown stony sand, over 0.7 m buff calcareous medium sand with gravelly zones. Upper sand Nipissing, lower probably Algonquin.

43. SJ70 Gravel pit 1 km east of Richardson Point and 1 km west of Highway 548, St. Joseph Island, Algoma District. Face exposes 6 m stratified sand and gravel with abundant molluscs, including unionids.

*44. K41A Dorian gravel pits 2.5 km southwest of Victoria Harbour, Georgian Bay, east of Hog Creek and west of road south of Highway 12, Simcoe County. Exposure A at north side of pits shows 3 m steeply bedded medium gravel over sand and silt rich in molluscs and plant debris at the water table. Unionids present. Wood dated 6890 ± 140 (WAT-710).

45. K41B Dorian gravel pits 2.5 km southwest of Victoria Harbour, Georgian Bay, east of Hog Creek and west of road south of Highway 12, Simcoe County. Exposure B is east bank of Hog Creek which exposes 2.4 m of silts with molluscs and logs at the base over boulders.

46. K39 East bank Coates Creek 5 km east of New Lowell, Simcoe County. Bank exposes:

    0.7 m sod over marly silt rich in molluscs

    0.15 m humus and leached sand paleosol. Some charcoal but roots numerous.

    0.75 m buff medium sand

    1.5 m covered to creek

47. K40 Gravel pit 1 km south of Sawlog Point, Georgian Bay, west of road, Simcoe County. Face exposes 3 m medium sand and gravel, over 0.3 m grey silty sand with shells, over 0.9 m covered to pit floor.

48. K43 Gore Bay gravel pits in Nipissing bar, northwest edge of town, Manitoulin Island. Pit faces up to 12 m high. In upper 3 m there are lenses of sand overlain by clast-supported gravel with clay infills. Molluscs occur in clay infills. Pit floor shows patches of grey silt with plant matter.

*49. W336 North bank Sauble River, 5 km northeast of Sauble Beach, 2.2 km east of Lake Huron, Bruce County.

    5.2 m buff fine stratified sand with widely scattered molluscs.

    1.5 m grey stratified sand and silt with molluscs and concentration of pieces of wood 0.3 m from top, dated 4290 ± 125 (BGS-740).

    0.7 m fine to medium sand with silty zones. Some molluscs and wood.

    1.5 m covered to river.

*50. W347 North bank Sauble River, 5 km north-northeast of Sauble Beach, 3.5 km east-northeast of river mouth, Bruce County. Bank exposes section below duned Nipissing plane:

    3.9 m buff medium eolian sand

    0.7 m medium to fine olive buff sand with molluscs, including unionids.

0.3 m paleosol with 7 cm humus over buff over orange leached sand. Date on charcoal 5300 ± 130 (BGS-741).

1.2 m buff medium sand

2.4 m covered to river level

*51. 0-963 West bank Telfer Creek short distance upstream from location 28 south of Leith, Grey County. Bank exposes:

4 m fine to medium buff sand, with gravelly layers and mollusc concentrations at about 3 m. Basal gravel 20 cm thick.

2 m complex lacustrine clay and silt over clayey silt till to stream level. Lens 1.5 m of bedded woody peat inset into depression in till, all truncated by upper sand and gravel. Piece of wood from middle of peat section dated 6100 ± 110 (WAT-979).

52. K27 East face of gravel pit in mid-bay bar of Thedford marsh, 6 km south of Grand Bend, west of Ausable River, Lambton County. Face exposes 1.2 m fine gravel with shells in lower part (unionids present) over 0.3 m of paleosol with 2 to 3 cm humus over leached brown sand, over 0.3 m buff, stony, calcareous sand. Upper sand Nipissing, lower probably Algonquin.

---

* Denotes radiocarbon-dated localities

Quaternary Evolution of the Great Lakes,
edited by P.F. Karrow and P.E. Calkin,
Geological Association of Canada Special Paper 30, 1985

HISTORY OF GLACIAL LAKE ALGONQUIN IN THE HALIBURTON REGION, SOUTH CENTRAL ONTARIO

Christine A. Kaszycki
Geological Survey of Canada, 601 Booth Street, Ottawa, Ontario K1A 0E8

ABSTRACT

Elevations of shoreline features spanning a 50 km north-east/southwest-trending segment of the Gull River valley, in the Haliburton Highlands of south central Ontario, indicate that an arm of Main Lake Algonquin extended northward from the Kirkfield outlet area into the Haliburton region. Sedimentologic and morphologic evidence indicates that Main Lake Algonquin expanded northward against a retreating ice front in this region. It is proposed that Main Lake Algonquin evolved in response to deglaciation of the Kirkfield outlet, and that Main Algonquin beaches within this region represent a stable lake level draining eastward through the Trent River valley.

Exponential projection of the Main Algonquin water plane from the Kirkfield area indicates that water level in the vicinity of the Port Huron outlet was approximately 131 m (439 ft.) or about 45.7 m (150 ft.) below present lake level at this time. The highest beaches in the southern portion of the Huron basin are thought to represent transgressional shorelines associated with post-Main Algonquin and Nipissing transgression. Relationships between northern outlet elevations and the Ardtrea and Upper Orillia water planes suggest that eastward drainage through the Kirkfield outlet was terminated by deglaciation of the South River outlet and inception of the Upper Orillia phase of Lake Algonquin.

Deglaciation of the Kirkfield outlet is estimated to have occurred approximately 12 000 B.P. (Karrow et al., 1975; Mirynech, 1967; Gravenor, 1957), and was the sole point of discharge for Lake Algonquin until deglaciation of the South River outlet approximately 10 600 to 10 800 B.P. (Fullerton, 1980; Karrow et al., 1975).

RÉSUMÉ

Les auteurs ont cartographié de vastes dépôts de sédiments lacustres à grains fins, de même que les deltas et les plages qui leur sont associés, à l'intérieur de la vallée de la rivière Gull située dans les hautes-terres d'Haliburton dans le centre-sud de l'Ontario. La rivière Gull, qui a sa source dans les hautes-terres, s'écoule vers le sud et rejoint le réseau de la rivière Trent (partie du déversoir de Kirkfield) au lac Balsam, environ 6.5 km à l'est de la ville de Kirkfield. On a calculé les hauteurs de plusieurs deltas et fragments de plages qui couvrent une partie de la vallée longue de 50 km et orientée du nord-est au sud-ouest. On a ensuite comparé ces données avec celles de Harrison (1972), de Chapman (1954) et de Deane (1950), et on a conclu qu'un bras du grand lac Algonquin s'est étendu vers le nord, à partir du déversoir, jusque dans la région d'Haliburton.

D'après les données stratigraphiques, sédimentologiques et morphologiques recueuillies, le grand lac Algonquin a progressé vers le nord contre un front glaciaire en recul; il s'agissait donc d'un lac de front glaciaire, et non d'un lac de transgression. Les auteurs avancent l'hypothèse suivante: le mouvement du grand lac Algonquin a été déterminé par la déglaciation du déversoir de Kirkfield et, à l'intérieur de cette région, les plages du grand lac Algonquin correspondent à un lac de niveau stable qui s'est écoulé vers l'est par la vallée de la rivière Trent. Une projection exponentielle du plan d'eau du lac Algonquin dans cette région indique que le niveau de l'eau au voisinage du déversoir de Port Huron était d'environ 131 m (430 pieds), soit environ 45.7 m (150 pieds) sous le niveau actuel. En conséquence, on croit que les plus hautes plages de la partie sud du bassin du lac Huron sont des rivages transgressifs associés à une transgression postérieure au grand lac Algonquin et au Nipissing, plutôt que des rivages du grand lac Algonquin comme on l'avait cru auparavant.

En extrapolant vers le nord le plan d'eau du grand lac Algonquin, on constate qu'au nord et à l'ouest du lac Eagle, des éléments de rivages se rencontrent à des hauteurs successivement inférieures à celles qui avaient été établies par la projection du plan d'eau du grand lac Algonquin dans la région du lac Simcoe. Ces rivages plus bas sont provisoirement mis en relation avec les phases Ardtrea et Upper Orillia des lacs postérieurs au lac Algonquin. Il semble, d'après les relations observées entre les hauteurs des déversoirs et les plans d'eau des lacs Ardtrea et Upper Orillia, que l'écoulement vers l'est, par le déversoir de Kirkfield, a pris fin au moment de la déglaciation du déversoir de South River et de la naissance de la phase Upper Orillia du lac Algonquin.

La chronologie de ces événements n'est pas certaine. La déglaciation du déversoir de Kirkfield et la naissance du grand lac Algonquin se seraient produites, pense-t-on, il y a environ 12 000 ans (Karrow et al., 1975; Mirynech, 1967, Gravenor, 1957). Le déversoir de Kirkfield était l'unique point de sortie des eaux du lac Algonquin jusqu'à la déglaciation du déversoir de South River, il y a environ 10 600 à 10 800 ans (Fullerton, 1980; Karrow et al., 1975). Les données recueuillies dans le delta de la rivière St. Clair donnent à penser que le déversoir de Port Huron a été impraticable jusqu'à la fin de la transgression de Nipissing, il y a environ 5000 ans (Raphael et Jaworski, 1982).

INTRODUCTION

Glacial Lake Algonquin was the largest of the glacial Great Lakes; it is considered by some to have encompassed the Lake Huron, Lake Michigan, Lake Erie, and parts of the Lake Superior basins at various stages of its evolution. Prominent raised terraces and beaches along the shores of Lakes Michigan and Huron attracted the interest of early workers (Spencer, 1891; Goldthwait, 1910; Gilbert, 1896; Leverett and Taylor, 1915), and their work has provided a framework for modern interpretations.

Interpretation of the history of Algonquin and post-Algonquin lake phases is complicated by a number of factors:

1) The margin of several separate ice lobes formed its northern border during deglaciation. Oscillation of these ice margins occurred partly independently, obscuring correlation of lake stages.

2) Four major outlets have been identified: the Chicago outlet in the Lake Michigan basin, and the Port Huron, Kirkfield, and North Bay outlets in the Lake Huron basin. The timing, duration of activity, and influence of these outlets on water level have not been fully evaluated.

3) Raised shoreline features defining the Algonquin water plane are scattered and poorly defined in the northern Lake Huron basin, and have been completely removed by modern shoreline erosion throughout large portions of the southern Lake Huron basin. Water plane curves and position of the Algonquin hinge line in this region were based largely upon inference.

4) Activity of outlets and their control on water level is dependent not only upon retreat of the ice margin and isostatic uplift, but also upon the volume of water draining into the basin and the magnitude of discharge accommodated by outlet channels. At best, sill elevation during a discharge event provides a minimum estimate of water level in the drainage basin. Because the post-glacial uplift history of the Huron basin is poorly known, the problem of assessing sill elevation and corresponding lake levels is compounded.

5) The establishment of eastward drainage through both the Kirkfield and North Bay outlets was dependent on the timing of deglaciation in eastern Ontario. The chronology of these events has not been completely resolved.

TABLE I

CLASSICAL CONCEPT OF THE EVOLUTION OF LAKE ALGONQUIN

Lake Phase	Lake Level	Outlets	Mechanism
Early Lake Algonquin	184.4 m (605 ft)	Port Huron Chicago	outlet incision?
Kirkfield Low Phase	?152.4-176.8 m (580-500 ft)	Kirkfield	outlet deglaciation
Kirkfield/ Main Algonquin Transition	184.4 m (605 ft)	Kirkfield Port Huron Chicago	differential uplift
Main Lake Algonquin	184.4 m (605 ft)	Port Huron Chicago	differential uplift
Post-Algonquin Upper Group	184.4 m (605 ft)	Port Huron Chicago	differential uplift

After Leverett and Taylor (1915)

Recent study of the Chicago outlet (Hansel et al., 1985) has suggested that major revision of the extent of Algonquin lake phases in the Lake Michigan basin is needed. Similarly, evidence from the Gull River valley (Fig. 1), tributary to drainage through the Kirkfield outlet, indicates that traditional concepts of the inception and history of Lake Algonquin in the Huron basin should be re-evaluated. Classic interpretations are here reviewed and evaluated in the light of new evidence from the Gull River valley, and alternative interpretations are presented.

EVOLUTION OF GLACIAL LAKE ALGONQUIN

Spencer (1891) described deformation of the Algonquin water plane as a result of differential uplift. He projected a water plane which sloped from northeast to southwest, to lie 6.1 m (20 ft.) beneath modern water level in the southern Lake Huron basin, and 88.4 m (290 ft.) beneath present water level in the southern Lake Michigan basin. Goldthwait (1910) rejected Spencer's southward projection of the Algonquin water plane and hypothesized the existence of a hinge line, located in southern Lake Huron and central Lake Michigan, south of which no uplift and hence no deformation of the Algonquin strandline had occurred. Leverett and Taylor (1915) adopted Goldthwait's concept of an Algonquin hinge line and developed the classic model of a five stage evolution of Lake Algonquin, based on the assumption that the Algonquin water plane is undeformed southward of an isobase of elevation 184.4 m (605 ft.) (Table I). This sequence of events has come to be widely accepted with only slight modification. For example, Deane (1950) suggested the Kirkfield outlet was closed by ice readvance rather than by uplift, an hypothesis supported by Prest (1970), Hough (1958), and Harrison (1972).

At the close of the Algonquin phase, deglaciation of lower outlets to the north resulted in successively lower lake levels. This phase culminated with drainage into the Champlain Sea via the North Bay outlet (Leverett and Taylor, 1915; Stanley, 1936, 1937, 1938; Chapman, 1954),

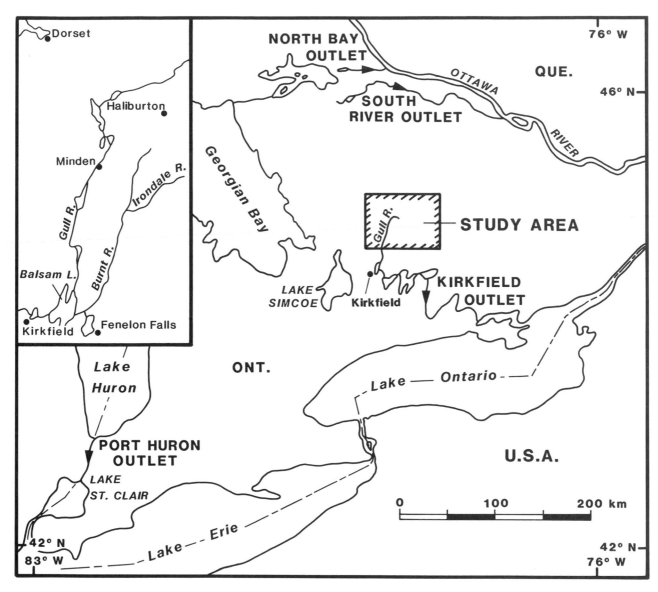

Figure 1. Location map of study area.

draining the Lake Huron basin to the low Lake Stanley level. Uplift of the North Bay outlet resulted in southward transgression, and the Nipissing phase was established when discharge was channelled once again through the Port Huron and Chicago outlets. Hough (1953) estimated the elevation of the Nipissing hinge line to be 184.4 m (605 ft.). Consequently, south of the Algonquin hinge line both the Nipissing and Algonquin beaches were inferred to have formed at the same elevation.

The Hinge Line Concept

A major constraint imposed upon previous interpretations of the history of Lake Algonquin is the concept that the Main Algonquin water plane achieves horizontality in the southern parts of the Lake Michigan and Lake Huron basins, at an elevation controlled by the Chicago and Port Huron outlets. Recent work on the Nipissing transgression in the southern

Lake Huron region (Karrow, 1980) suggests that shoreline features previously attributed to Lake Algonquin are Nipissing in age. In addition, all dated shoreline features at an elevation of approximately 184.4 m (605 ft.) in the southern Lake Michigan basin have been demonstrated to be of Nipissing rather than Algonquin age (Hansel et al., 1985). These re-interpretations suggest that the concept of an Algonquin hinge line at 184.4 m may have been based on erroneous interpretations.

Present uplift data and the configuration of projected isobases in the Great Lakes basins have been presented by Clark and Persoage (1970). Interpretation of these data indicates that the southern portions of the Huron and Michigan basins are presently undergoing isostatic adjustment in response to glacial unloading. Based on this work, Larsen (1985b) has suggested that the traditional concept of a Nipissing hinge line is no longer tenable. If glacio-isostatic adjustments are occurring today, and can be demonstrated to

TABLE II

SITE LOCATIONS AND ELEVATIONS OF UPPER AND LOWER SURFACES IN THE GULL RIVER VALLEY

Site	Location UTM Grid Zone 17t Eastings	Northings	*Elevation (m)	Site	Location UTM Grid Zone 17t Eastings	Northings	Elevation (m)
1	673188	4963950	286.7	21	686150	4999525	330.20 ± 2.02
2	677925	4972875	299.72	22	687688	4999688	329.77 ± 1.59
3	677660	4981075	308.24	23	688750	5000188	331.50 ± 1.88
4	678600	4979825	306.53	24	689625	5000588	332.37 ± 2.46
5	678575	4978650	307.7	25	690375	5001013	336.28 ± 1.16
6	680038	4979500	309.09	26	690781	5001375	337.60 ± 1.29
7	681725	4981050	309.66	27	690844	5001625	338.45 ± 0.72
8	683875	4983725	308.24	28	694675	4999700	335.24
9	681550	4988630	317.03	29	691750	4998925	337.1 ± ?
10	681855	4988900	319.1	30	694375	4999150	334.37
11	681825	4989725	317.37	31	677575	4973740	279.98
12	681260	4991060	321.38	32	676975	4974760	280.8
13	679600	4993475	321.67	33	678450	4975325	280.23
14	678563	4994725	321.43	34	678900	4976600	283.17
15	681400	4994413	321.52 ± 0.87	35	679025	4978150	285.52
16	685663	4997100	330.97 ± 1.33	36	678435	4979775	285.88
17	683313	4998313	326.58 ± 1.88	37	680350	4978850	283.03
18	685031	4998031	327.74 ± 1.30	38	679400	4977350	273.12
19	684625	4998688	330.78 ± 1.45	39	677600	4974575	269.47
20	685350	4999038	330.78 ± 1.74				

*Sites where plus or minus variation has been recorded are those at which only 2 altimeter readings were taken. Elsewhere, 3 or more measurements were taken at each site, enabling elevations to be more accurately determined.

have occurred throughout the Holocene, (Larsen, 1985b), it seems unreasonable to assume that the southern Lake Michigan and Huron basins were isostatically stable during Algonquin time. It is proposed, therefore, that the concept that the Main Algonquin water plane achieves horizontality at an elevation controlled by the Port Huron and Chicago outlets (184.4 m) can no longer be accepted, and that the Main Algonquin water plane is deformed throughout the entire Lake Huron basin.

Re-evaluation of the elevation of the Algonquin water plane in the southern Lake Huron basin necessitates re-examination of timing, duration of activity, and influence on water level of the Port Huron and Kirkfield outlets. This paper focuses on lake level fluctuations as recorded in the vicinity of the Kirkfield outlet. The head water of the Trent River is located at the head of the Gull River system in the Haliburton region. As a northern extension of the Trent River valley, sedimentation in the Gull River valley should reflect water level fluctuations at the outlet and elucidate the timing and duration of eastward drainage through the Trent River.

LACUSTRINE SEDIMENTATION IN THE HALIBURTON REGION

Complex patterns, of glaciofluvial, glaciolacustrine, and ice-marginal sedimentation in the Haliburton Region suggest that ice retreated by stagnation of debris-rich ice in the vicinity of a large proglacial lake. Chapman (1954) mapped a shoreline feature in the Gull River valley which he correlated with Main Lake Algonquin. This extension of Lake Algonquin has significant implications for chronologic interpretations of lacustrine events within the region.

Extent and Morphology of Lacustrine Sediment

Surficial features mapped in the Haliburton area include raised deltas, beach fragments, and terraces along the Gull River valley. Raised deltas and lacustrine terraces have also been mapped in the Dorset area, the Irondale River valley, and the Burnt River valley. Chapman (1954) depicted a continuous arm of Lake Algonquin extending northward through the Gull River valley into the Dorset area. Results of present mapping indicate that this link does not exist and that the two areas may represent separate arms of Lake Algonquin. Focus has been placed on features within the Gull River valley because of their proximity to the Kirkfield outlet, because sediment sequences are well exposed, and because the morphology of these deposits is well expressed. Within the Gull River valley three distinct surfaces have been identified.

Upper Surface. The upper surface is represented by several prominent deltas and poorly developed beach fragments. The altitude of these surfaces was determined by use of an aneroid barometer (altimeter) (Table II). All readings were taken at least twice during a given day and tied to two bench marks of differing elevation on each occasion. This enabled diurnal barometric pressure variations to be monitored and accounted for. To test the accuracy of this method, the elevation of the North Shore delta (site 13) was determined on several separate occasions. Measured altitudes varied from 321.4 m to 322 m, a degree of accuracy considered sufficient for the purposes of this investigation.

In order to establish the relationship between these surfaces and glacial Lake Algonquin, a water plane curve was constructed (Fig. 2) along an azimuth of 21°, corresponding to the regional ice flow trend and approximating the direction of maximum uplift (Deane, 1950). Data from Deane (1950), Harrison (1972), and Chapman (1954) were used as a basis for comparison. Data from the Haliburton region compare favourably with the Main Algonquin water plane constructed by previous workers within the Lake Simcoe area, and it is hypothesized that the upper surface represents an arm of Lake Algonquin which extended from the outlet valley northward into the Gull River valley. Shoreline configuration and isobase map are presented in Figure 3. The Algonquin shoreline rises from an elevation of approximately 286.5 m (940 ft.) in the southern portion of the valley, to approximately 335.3 m (1100 ft.) at its northeastern extremity.

Lower Surfaces. Two terraces below the upper surface have been identified and corresponding elevations are plotted on Figure 2. The higher of these two surfaces (terrace A) is restricted to the region north of Gull Lake (Fig. 4). The lower terrace (B) is fragmented and elevations have been determined at only two sites (sites 38 and 39, Fig. 2). The relationship among the two lower terraces, the Main Algonquin surface, and post-Algonquin lake levels in the Lake Huron basin is an important consideration in deciphering the post-glacial history of the region. The parallelism between terraces A and B, and slight convergence with the Main Algonquin surface suggests that the formation of these terraces is closely linked in time to the history of Lake Algonquin and post-Algonquin lakes.

Sedimentology of Lacustrine Deposits

Extensive lacustrine fine-grained sediment and associated deltaic, beach, and subaqueous fan deposits occur within the Gull River valley. Prominent lacustrine terraces, composed of highly faulted and contorted laminated silt, clay, and sand, have been mapped throughout the northeastern portion of the valley, from Boshkung Lake eastward to Eagle Lake (Fig. 3). Rhythmites occurring throughout the valley are composed of individual fining-upward sequences, commonly characterized by a thin (~ 1 mm) basal sand to granule layer, fining upward to a thick (1 to 4 mm) silt layer, which may or may not be capped by a thin (<1 mm) clay layer. In thin section, basal sands exhibit an erosional contact with underlying laminae and subjacent fine sediment is commonly brecciated, suggesting a turbidity current genesis. Thin diamiction layers (1 to 2 mm) are often interbedded with rhythmites indicating a near-ice sediment source. Sub-bottom seismic profiling, conducted on all major lakes within the Gull River valley, indicates that lakes are floored by intensely faulted laminated silt, sand, and clay. The occurrence of lacustrine terraces rimming modern lakes, coupled with faulted sediment within lake basins, suggest that remnant ice blocks were isolated in depressions in the Gull River valley during proglacial inundation (Shilts, 1983).

Deltaic deposits are characterized by coarsening-upward sequences composed predominantly of coarse, granular sand and gravel foreset bedding, overlain by cross-bedded and channellized coarse sand to cobbly gravel. Morphologically these deposits exhibit nearly horizontal planar surfaces and steeply dipping fore-slopes, typical of classic 'Gilbert type' deltas. Elevations of delta plain surfaces fall on the Main Algonquin water plane within the Gull River valley. Deltaic sediment is commonly faulted, exhibiting both high angle reverse and normal faulting. The presence of high angle reverse faults is thought to reflect deposition on ice and subsequent collapse during meltout (McDonald and Shilts,

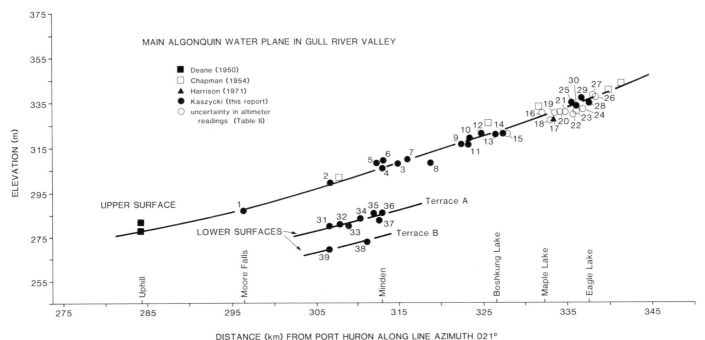

Figure 2. Water plane curves for upper and lower Algonquin surfaces in the Gull River valley. Some data points from Chapman (1954), Deane (1950), and Harrison (1971) have been included for comparison.

1975). This, coupled with the common occurrence of boulder gravel and diamicton lenses in the proximal facies of deltaic sequences supports an ice-contact or near-ice environment during lacustrine sedimentation. This interpretation suggests that Main Lake Algonquin was ice-marginal in this region.

Fining-upward sequences have been observed at several sites within the Gull valley. Section 1 (Figs. 4 and 5) illustrates a sequence which occurs in the lower portion of the valley. Lacustrine laminated silts and clays overlie well sorted, massive, medium-to-fine sand, in an abrupt but con-

formable contact. Farther north, near the town of Minden, a similar but much thicker sequence is exposed (section 2, Figs. 4 and 5). At this site, approximately 3 m of stratified medium-to-coarse granular sand is overlain by laminated silt and clay, approximately 2 m in thickness. The lower 50 cm of laminated sediment contains abundant thin (1 to 4 cm) diamicton lenses, indicating an ice-proximal position during deposition. At a third site, located in the northeastern region of the Gull River valley, the distal portion of the Eagle Lake delta exhibits well sorted and stratified fine-to-medium

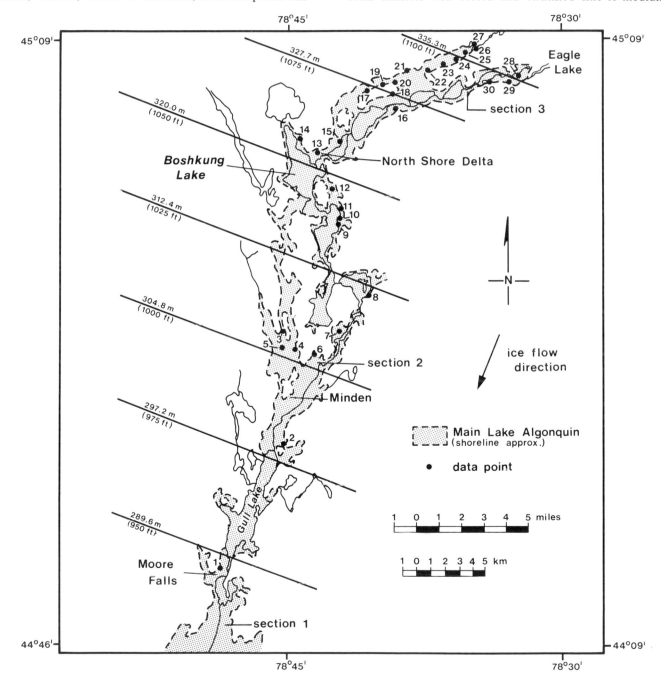

Figure 3. Main Lake Algonquin shoreline configuration and isobase map of the Gull valley. Numbers refer to site locations where elevation readings were obtained. See Table II and Figure 2.

grained sand overlain by laminated silts and clays. The laminated silts and clays are erosionally isolated, exposed only on a ridge at the distal end of the delta. Lower valley plain sediment at this location is predominantly sand and gravel, attesting to an erosional event following lacustrine deposition. The elevation of the Eagle Lake delta is 335.3 m (1100 ft.), an elevation which falls on the Main Algonquin water plane for this locality (site 28, Fig. 2, Table II).

The fining-upward sequences described above can be interpreted in two ways. In the first case, the occurrence of laminated silt and clay overlying basal sands can be interpreted in terms of a change in base level within the Gull River valley. The sequence of sedimentation would then suggest: 1) an initial low phase during which basal sands were deposited followed by 2) transgression to the Main Algonquin level, resulting in delta formation at Eagle Lake and

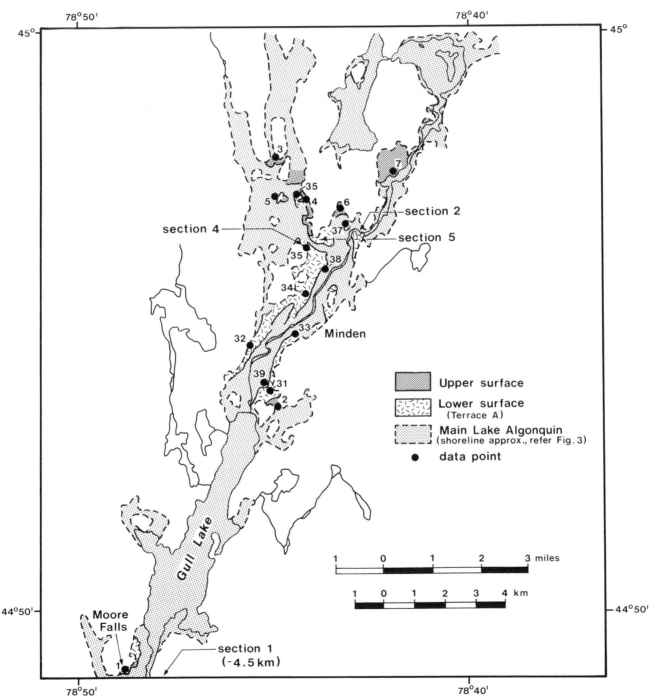

Figure 4. Map of upper Algonquin surface and lower terrace surfaces in the Gull River valley. Numbers refer to site locations where elevation readings were obtained. See Table II and Figure 2.

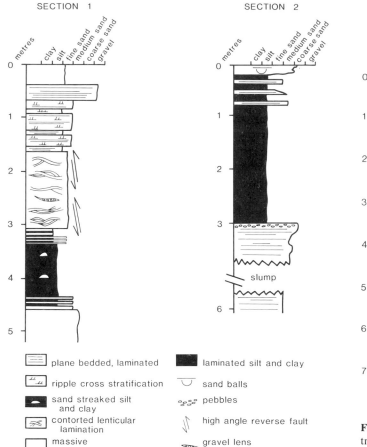

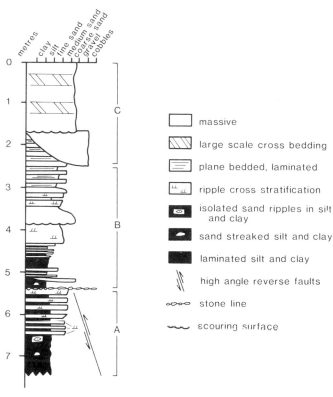

SECTION 1 SECTION 2 SECTION 3

Figure 5. Sedimentary sequences illustrating basal sand underlying lacustrine silt and clay observed at several sites in the Gull River valley. Section locations are plotted on Figures 3 and 4.

Figure 6. Sedimentary succession exhibiting two episodes of lacustrine sedimentation. Units A and B (section 3) are separated by an unconformity marked by a stoneline and gravel layer. Valley plain channellized sand and gravel (unit C) was deposited during post-Algonquin regression. Section location plotted on Figure 2.

elsewhere, and deposition of laminated silt and clay throughout the valley. Remnant ice blocks would have persisted within the valley during this interval, facilitating deposition of diamicton lenses in laminated silt and clay, and generating faulting observed within deltaic and laminated sediment.

Alternatively, fining upward sequences may represent a subaqueous fan environment. In this case, basal sand may represent an ice-proximal facies of subaqueous outwash. The sharp contact with overlying laminated sediment may reflect an abrupt change in sediment supply from the ice margin and/or a shift in position of the meltwater conduit (Rust and Romanelli, 1975; Cheel, 1982), rather than lacustrine transgression. These sequences are characteristic of proglacial lacustrine deposition near a receding ice margin. This interpretation is consistent with proglacial inundation of stagnant debris-rich ice during deglaciation and is favoured in this report.

Approximately 4.75 km downstream from the Eagle Lake delta, a river cut through the valley plain surface reveals a sediment sequence which represents two separate episodes of lacustrine sedimentation (section 3, Figs. 3 and 6). This section is characterized by two coarsening-upward se-

quences, capped by fluvial sand and gravel. The basal unit (unit A) is composed of laminated silt, clay, and sand (average thickness of laminae is 10 mm), which grades upward into rhythmically interbedded ripple and flaser cross-laminated fine sand with silt drapes. This unit is intensely faulted, exhibiting abundant high angle reverse faults, again indicating deposition on ice (McDonald and Shilts, 1975). The faulted sequence is truncated by a gravel layer and stone line of pebble to cobble sized clasts, which marks the top of unit A. Fine sand underlying cobbles is scoured indicating current activity during stone line formation. Unit B exhibits a second coarsening-upward sequence characterized by basal laminated silt, clay, and sand, grading upward into ripple cross-laminated medium-to-fine sand. The upper 2 m of the section, unit C, are composed of coarse sand and gravel channel deposits. Neither units B nor C exhibit faulting, suggesting that the time interval between deposition of units A and B was sufficient for buried ice to melt.

Similar sequences of lacustrine sedimentation have been observed in seismic profiles (Fig. 7). Preliminary interpretation of sonar records throughout the Gull River valley indicates the presence of a ubiquitous basal unit of highly faulted, laminated sediment, unconformably overlain by an undeformed unit of similar composition. Interpretation of these sequences is not clear. Again two possible scenarios can be projected. In the first case, two episodes of lacustrine sedimentation are proposed, separated by a hiatus reflecting an interval of low water level. The following sequence of events can be inferred:

1) Initial proglacial inundation while remnant ice remained in the valley resulted in deposition of unit A at section 3, and the basal faulted unit observed on sonar records.

2) A decrease in water level in the Gull River valley caused individual basins within the valley to become isolated, thereby substantially decreasing sediment input and causing erosion and stoneline formation at section 3. The duration of this hiatus in lacustrine sedimentation was sufficient for buried ice to melt (100s to 1000 years?).

3) Subsequent increase in water level renewed lacustrine sedimentation within the valley. These deposits drape the previously faulted sediment surface.

The low water phase proposed in this sequence of events does not appear to correlate with that inferred from the depositional sequences at sites 1 and 2, and the Eagle Lake delta. In this case low water levels associated with a hiatus in

lacustrine sedimentation would post-date ice-contact deposition associated with Main Lake Algonquin. In contrast, evidence from sites 1 and 2, and the Eagle Lake Delta, would suggest that a low lake level occurred prior to inundation by Main Lake Algonquin.

The second and preferred interpretation of the depositional sequence at site 3 involves one episode of lacustrine inundation characterized by two discrete intervals of clastic sedimentation, separated by an interval of nondeposition. The sequence of events is projected as follows:

1) Initial proglacial inundation as previously described.

2) Lacustrine sedimentation proceeded, but at a lessening rate as remnant ice within the region melted and the glacial sediment source retreated further north. During this time clastic sedimentation effectively ceased. Buried ice melted, resulting in faulting of unit A at section 3, and the basal unit on sonar profiles. The stone line and gravel marking the upper contact of unit A may reflect sediment flow activity associated with ice collapse.

3) Lacustrine sedimentation was renewed. Falling water level associated with regression of Main Lake Algon-

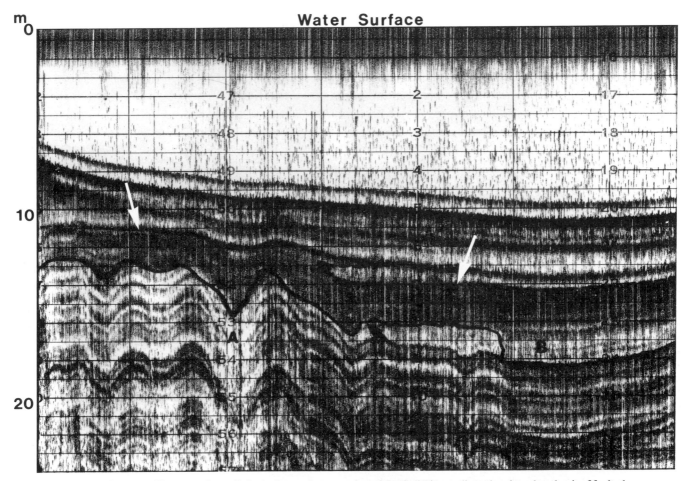

Water Surface

Figure 7. Sonar profile across Green Lake in the northeast portion of the Gull River valley, showing a basal unit of faulted, laminated clastic sediment (A), uncomformably overlain by an undeformed unit of similar composition (B). Dashed line marks a gradational boundary between unit B and overlying organic sediment. Arrows mark unit boundaries. Profiling was carried out using a Raytheon RTT-1000A-1 "Portable Survey System" with a dual low frequency (3.5 and 7.0 kHz) transducer coupled with a high frequency (200 kHz) transducer (Klassen and Shilts, 1982).

quin resulted in emergence and dissection of basin-fill sediment in topographically high positions within the valley, and resedimentation within the basins. This episode of dissection and clastic sedimentation is represented by units B and C at section 3, and the upper unfaulted sequence on seismic profiles. The sequence at section 3 reflects initial infilling of a small kettle on the sublacustrine surface (unit B) and subsequent dissection as regression proceeded (unit C). As water level decreased, individual basins became isolated and lacustrine sedimentation proceeded until dissection of upland areas was achieved.

This scenario suggests that the Main Algonquin inundation of the Gull River valley was long-lived, characterized initially by ice-proximal sedimentation. High lake levels persisted long enough for remnant ice blocks to melt (100s to 1000 years?) during which time sedimentation virtually ceased. Lacustrine sedimentation was renewed during emergence and dissection of basin-fill sediment associated with regressional phases of Main Lake Algonquin.

Evolution of the lower surfaces mapped in the southern portion of the Gull River valley (terraces A and B) is thought to be related to the second episode of lacustrine sedimentation discussed above. The sedimentology of terrace A has been studied at two sites (sites 4 and 5, Fig. 8). Sedimentary logging of stream cuts revealed an overall thickening and coarsening-upward trend attributed to decreasing water depth. Section 4 is interpreted as part of a prograding delta complex. Channel scour at the top of section 4 is ascribed to fluviatile sedimentation on the delta plain. These sediments overlie unfaulted delta-front deposits of rhythmically bedded sand and silt which in turn overlie basal pro-delta silt and clay. Section 5 depicts the upper 3 m of a terrace A sequence located approximately 1.2 km down-valley from section 4. At this site channel cut-and-fill structures were not observed. The sequence coarsens upward from medium-to-coarse sand at 3 m to sand and gravel at 1 m. Although mostly obscured by slump, the base of the section is composed of laminated silt and clay. The environment of deposition for this sequence is difficult to discern, but the sequence overall suggests decreasing water level. It is hypothesized that post-Main Algonquin regression initiated dissection of basin-fill sediment up-valley and resulted in delta progradation and deposition of rhythmically bedded ripple cross-laminated fine sand and silt as delta-front density flows. The absence of faulted sediment supports this interpretation. Terrace A sequences, therefore, may be related to a lower lake level associated with the drainage of Main Lake Algonquin, and inception of the upper group lakes.

Alternatively, terrace A may represent an erosional surface associated with regression of Main Lake Algonquin. Channelized sequences at the top of section 4 may represent erosion of pre-existing valley-fill sediment. In this case the slope of terrace A would represent a stream gradient rather than a temporary water plane.

In summary, lacustrine sedimentation within the Gull River valley is related to proglacial inundation by Main Lake Algonquin. Evidence for base level changes within the Gull River valley, prior to regression associated with drainage of

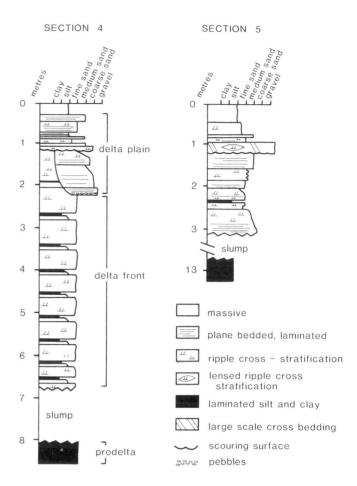

Figure 8. Sedimentary logs of terrace A sequences exhibiting coarsening and thickening upward trends. Section locations are plotted on Figure 3.

Main Algonquin, is equivocal, and observed depositional sequences can be reasonably explained without recourse to fluctuating water level. Two episodes of lacustrine sedimentation are recorded within the valley. These sequences may be interpreted in terms of base level change or prolonged lacustrine inundation and renewed sedimentation during emergence. At present, the latter explanation is preferred as it is consistent with terrace sequences observed in the southern part of the Gull River valley, and more completely describes the observed sediment assemblages. Likewise, sediment sequences exhibiting basal sand overlain by laminated silt and clay are thought to represent deposition within a proglacial subaqueous fan environment, rather than a change in base level. It is possible that sediment sequences elsewhere in the Lake Huron/Lake Simcoe region, previously interpreted to represent lacustrine transgression during the Kirkfield/Main Algonquin transition, may, in fact, be more readily explained as subaqueous ice-marginal deposits.

DISCUSSION

The influence of the Kirkfield outlet on water level within the Huron basin has been widely debated. Leverett and Taylor (1915) proposed that discharge through this outlet was ephemeral, resulting in a low lake level (the Kirkfield Phase), which was initiated by deglaciation of the Trent River valley, and terminated by uplift of this outlet relative to the Port Huron outlet. This caused drainage to be diverted southward and marked the inception of Main Lake Algonquin. Johnston (1916) interpreted an unconformity in Algonquin lake sediments at Jackson Point, Ontario, as marking the Kirkfield-Algonquin transition. He argued that the proximity of this site to the Kirkfield outlet precluded the possibility that uplift alone produced the Main Algonquin transgression, and he proposed a readvance of the Lake Simcoe lobe to form the Lake Simcoe moraine and block the Kirkfield outlet. Recent work by Finamore (1985), however, indicates that there is no evidence in support of a readvance in this region and that the Lake Simcoe moraine constitutes a recessional moraine formed during a single retreat phase.

The presence of Main Algonquin shoreline features in the Gull River valley east and north of the Lake Simcoe moraine also argues against the readvance hypothesis. More significantly, the ice-contact genesis of these features indicates that the transgression of Main Lake Algonquin in this vicinity occurred against a retreating ice front, rather than in response to uplift of the Kirkfield outlet as suggested by Leverett and Taylor (1915). It is proposed, therefore, that Main Lake Algonquin in the Lake Simcoe and Kirkfield districts evolved in response to deglaciation of the Kirkfield outlet, and that Main Algonquin beaches within this region represent a stable lake level draining eastward through the Trent River valley.

Using the method of Larsen (1985a, 1985b) and Andrews (1970), the Main Algonquin water plane in the Lake Simcoe and Kirkfield areas has been projected southward along an exponential profile. A semi-log plot of elevation of Main Algonquin shoreline features in this region vs. distance from Port Huron yields a straight line relationship with a correlation coefficient of $R = .996$. This relationship suggests that features attributed to Main Lake Algonquin in the Lake Simcoe area represent a single lake phase. Southward projection of this line should yield an estimate of the elevation of a correlative lake level in the southern Huron basin if this model is valid for the entire deformed water plane. Using this technique the elevation of Main Lake Algonquin in the vicinity of the Port Huron outlet has been estimated to be approximately 131 m (430 ft.) or approximately 45.7 m (150 ft.) *below* modern lake level. It is proposed, therefore, that the inception of eastward drainage through the Trent River valley generated a low level lake in the southern Lake Huron basin correlative with Main Algonquin beaches in the Kirkfield area (Fig. 9).

The highest Main Algonquin shoreline features north of Kirkfield are located within 50 km of the outlet, extending as far north as Eagle Lake in the Gull River valley (Fig. 9). Algonquin features within the Georgian Bay basin, west and north of the Gull River valley, are composed primarily of ice-contact deltas which occur at elevations successively lower than would be predicted by an exponential Main Algonquin profile in the Lake Simcoe area (Sharpe, 1978). A similar sequence of northward splitting water planes has been described by Mirynech (1967) in the Trent valley em-

bayment at the northeastern end of Lake Ontario, where an ice margin formed the northern shore of Lake Iroquois. Likewise, Main Lake Algonquin expanded northward against a retreating ice front, producing progressively younger shoreline features. Consequently, ice-contact deltas and associated lacustrine features developed successively later in the uplift history of the basin, at elevations below that projected for Main Lake Algonquin. Ice-contact deltas within the Georgian Bay basin (Sharpe, 1978) occur at elevations below the elevation of isobases projected westward from the Gull River valley, and indicate that retreat of ice from Georgian Bay post-dated deglaciation in the Gull River valley.

Northward extrapolation of Upper Group beaches from the Lake Simcoe district, although tenuous, enables tentative correlation with successively lower shoreline features observed further north. By this method, the Ardtrea and Upper Orillia water planes can be extended northward and their relationship to lower outlets explored (Fig. 9). The Ardtrea water plane can be extrapolated as far north as the town of Sundridge, approximately 15 km south of the South River outlet. Northward projection of the Upper Orillia water plane is highly speculative, but appears to correlate with a low shoreline feature in the Sundridge area, documented by Leverett and Taylor (1915), and a water surface elevation for the South River outlet recorded by Harrison (1972). Elevations of Upper Orillia beaches in the Lake Simcoe area fall approximately 9.14 m (30 ft.) below the elevation of the sill at Kirkfield, indicating that eastward drainage through the Trent River valley had ceased at this time. It is proposed that deglaciation of the South River outlet initiated a decrease in lake level to the Upper Orillia phase. At this time, drainage through the Kirkfield outlet ceased and eastward drainage of Lake Algonquin was re-routed via a series of outlets into the Ottawa valley and the Champlain Sea.

Concurrent with the development of lower shorelines to the north, successively higher transgressive lake phases evolved in the southern portion of the Lake Huron basin. If differential uplift was the only mechanism effecting lake level change within the basin, then the highest shoreline in the south might reasonably be correlated with the lowest shoreline to the north. The lowest northern shoreline developed prior to deglaciation of the South River outlet has been correlated with Ardtrea beaches in the Kirkfield area. It follows then, that the highest shoreline features in the southern Huron basin are related to the Ardtrea phase of Lake Algonquin, rather than Main Lake Algonquin, as previously interpreted. Figure 9 illustrates the southward projection of Algonquin Upper Group beaches above the Main Algonquin profile. The projected elevation of the Main Algonquin water plane in this region corresponds roughly to the elevation of lower shoreline features mapped by previous workers. It is concluded, therefore, that north of Grand Bend and south of a zone of convergence along an isobase through Alliston, the highest shorelines represent transgressional beaches of the Ardtrea phase of the Algonquin Upper Group Lakes.

From the foregoing discussion, it is evident that shoreline features throughout the Lake Huron basin, previously attributed to Main Lake Algonquin probably represent a number of different lake phases. The Main Algonquin water plane as projected by Leverett and Taylor (1915), Chapman (1954), and Harrison (1972), among others, is a composite of Nipissing beaches south of the so-called Algonquin Hinge line at Grand Bend, transgressional Upper Group beaches between Port Elgin and Grand Bend, pro-glacial and ice-contact Main Algonquin shorelines in the Lake Simcoe-Kirkfield area, and ice-contact post-Algonquin Upper Group shorelines to the north (Fig. 9).

Acceptance of this model requires re-evaluation of evidence for a Kirkfield low phase in the Lake Huron basin. Sediment sequences in the Lake Simcoe area (Deane, 1950; Johnston, 1916) and paleoecologic evidence in the Kincardine district (Karrow et al., 1975) have been interpreted to represent a Kirkfield-Main Algonquin transgression. In the Lake Simcoe area, sediment sequences comprising barren sand overlain by fossiliferous lacustrine silts may be reasonably explained as a product of pro-glacial deposition in an ice-marginal lake, and do not necessarily reflect a change in base level within the basin. Similar sediment sequences occur within the Gull River valley and have been interpreted

as subaqueous fan deposits. Secondly, the stratigraphy observed at the Kincardine Bog site and Eighteen Mile River sections (Karrow et al., 1975), although correctly interpreted as reflecting transgressional sequences, does not necessarily reflect a Kirkfield-Main Algonquin transition; but, rather, may represent the Main Algonquin-Upper Group transgression as depicted in Figure 9.

Minor fluctuations in water level within the Lake Huron basin may have occurred during the existence of Main Lake Algonquin, in response to glacial events in the Lake Michigan basin. The Two Rivers advance approximately 11 800 years ago (Hansel et al., 1985) would have effectively cut off eastward drainage from the western Great Lakes, thereby substantially decreasing the area of the drainage basin discharging through the Kirkfield outlet. Deglaciation of the Straits of Mackinac shortly before 11 000 yrs B.P. (Hansel et al., 1985) re-established eastward drainage from the Lake Michigan basin and may have affected base level in the Lake Huron basin (A.K. Hansel, pers. commun., 1984). However, the magnitude of the effects of these events, if any, is not known.

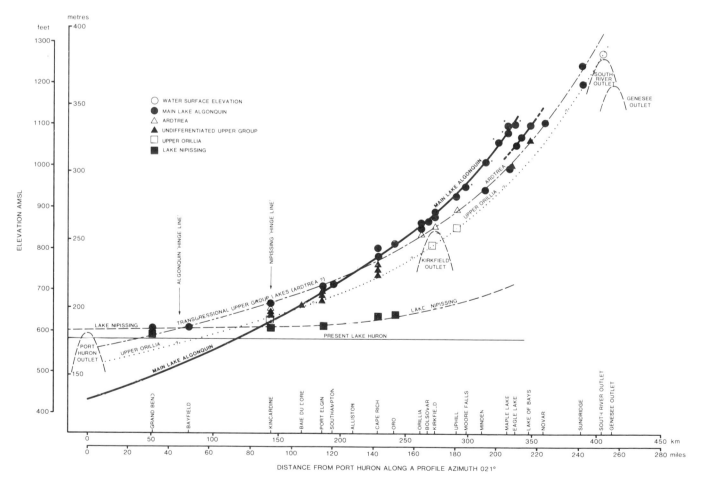

Figure 9. Re-interpreted water plane curves for Main Algonquin and post-Algonquin Upper Group Lakes in the Huron Basin. The Main Lake Algonquin profile has been extended southward from the Lake Simcoe area by means of an exponential projection after Larsen (1985a, 1985b), and Andrews (1970). Symbols identify water planes as interpreted by various workers (Goldthwait, 1910; Leverett and Taylor, 1915; Stanley, 1938; Deane, 1950; Chapman, 1954; Harrison, 1972; Sharpe, 1978; Finamore, 1985; Kaszycki, this paper).

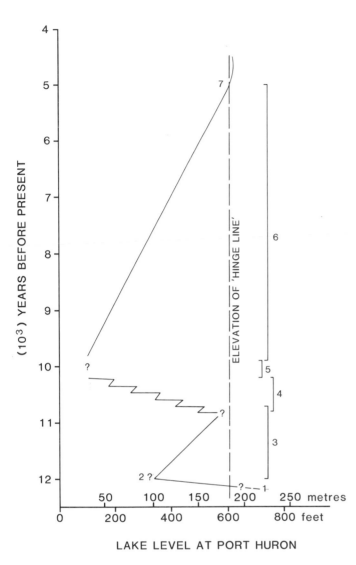

Figure 10. Highly schematic representation of lake level fluctuation during Algonquin and pre-Nipissing time, in the vicinity of the Port Huron Outlet. Timing of events is not precisely known and the chronology presented here is also schematic; 1) Early Lake Algonquin − confluent with lakes in the Lake Erie basin?; 2) Main Lake Algonquin − deglaciation of the Kirkfield outlet and inception of eastward drainage through the Trent River valley into Lake Iroquois; 3) Post-Algonquin Upper Group lakes − the Ardtrea phase is transgressional, Upper and Lower Orillia phases are related to deglaciation of the South River outlet; 4) Post-Algonquin Lower Group lakes − deglaciation of successively lower outlets between South River and North Bay; 5) Lake Stanley − deglaciation of the North Bay outlet; 6) Nipissing Transgression; 7) Lake Nipissing − pre-modern delta formation, St. Clair river delta, Port Huron.

Chronology

The timing of post-glacial lacustrine events within the Lake Huron basin has not been established unequivocally. A schematic chronology for water-level fluctuation within the southern Lake Huron basin is presented in Figure 10. Drainage through the Trent River valley into Lake Iroquois has been documented by Gravenor (1957). Channellization near

the mouth of the Trent River in the Lake Ontario basin supports this interpretation, suggesting that the Kirkfield outlet was open at the time Lake Iroquois drained to post-Iroquois low phases (Mirynech, 1967; Johnston, 1916). The inception of Lake Iroquois in the western Lake Ontario basin has been dated at approximately 12 300 B.P. (Fullerton, 1980), and drainage to the post-Iroquois low phases is thought to have occurred shortly after 12 000 B.P. (Karrow *et al.*, 1975). These dates bracket the timing of deglaciation of the Kirkfield outlet, which initiated eastward drainage and the inception of Main Lake Algonquin. This timing is supported by a date of 11600 ± 140 (GSC-4019) on basal organics from Plastic Lake, on upland north of the Gull River valley and about 70 km north of Kirkfield. Karrow *et al.* (1975) proposed a *minimum* estimate of 11 500 B.P. for inception of the "Kirkfield low phase". They also suggested that "Main Lake Algonquin" drained shortly after 10 600 B.P. Reinterpretation of these data within the framework proposed in this study suggests that Main Lake Algonquin existed in the southern Huron basin prior to 11 500 B.P., a date not inconsistent with deglaciation of the Kirkfield outlet approximately 12 000 B.P. Transgressional phases of the post-Algonquin Upper Group lakes culminated approximately 10 600 B.P. with deglaciation of the South River outlet, at which time the Kirkfield outlet was abandonned. Fullerton (1980) correlated this event with formation of the Petawawa delta, dated at 10 870 B.P. In contrast, Harrison (1972) estimated deglaciation of the South River outlet at approximately 12 500 B.P., and correlated this event with the inception of Lake Wyebridge (Algonquin Lower Group lakes). This chronology is considered to be too old in relation to the timing of events in adjacent basins. Allowing 500 to 1000 years for ice retreat between Kirkfield and South River, deglaciation of the Trent River valley would have occurred approximately 13 000 to 13 500 B.P., prior to deglaciation of the Lake Ontario basin, and precluding the possibility of eastward drainage through the Kirkfield outlet.

Recent study of the St. Clair River delta (Raphael and Jaworski, 1982) indicates that pre-modern delta formation occurred at some time after 7300 B.P., and is most likely related to Nipissing transgression and inundation of the Port Huron outlet approximately 5000 B.P. They found no evidence to indicate that active delta formation took place during Algonquin time. This suggests that the Port Huron outlet was not utilized after deglaciation of the Trent River Valley and that the Kirkfield outlet acted as the sole point of discharge for Main Lake Algonquin, from approximately 12 000 B.P. to approximately 10 800 to 10 600 B.P.

CONCLUSION

The history of glacial Lake Algonquin and post-Algonquin Upper Group lakes in the Huron basin is complicated by a number of factors. A major constraint imposed upon previous interpretations of lake-level fluctuations is the concept that the Main Algonquin water plane achieves horizontality in the southern parts of the Lake Michigan and Huron basins, at an elevation controlled by the Port Huron and Chicago outlets. Studies of historic uplift (Clark and Persoage, 1970) indicate that the Lake Michigan and Lake Huron basins are presently undergoing vertical adjustment. The configuration of historic isobases suggests that modern tilt rates are a function of glacial unloading, contrary to the supposition that these areas have been isostatically stable since Main Algonquin time. This necessitates a re-examination of sill elevation and outlet control on water level in the Huron and Michigan basins (Larsen, 1985a).

Classic interpretations of lake level fluctuation during the evolution of Main Lake Algonquin (Leverett and Taylor, 1915) emphasize the ephemeral nature of eastward drainage through the Kirkfield outlet, resulting in a low level lake (the Kirkfield phase). Stratigraphic, sedimentologic, and morphologic evidence from the Gull River valley, a northern tributary to drainage through the Kirkfield outlet, suggests that Main Lake Algonquin expanded northward against a retreating ice front. This interpretation contradicts that of Leverett and Taylor (1915) who suggested that trangression to the Main Algonquin level in this region resulted from uplift of the Kirkfield outlet. It is concluded, therefore, that deglaciation of the Kirkfield outlet marked the inception of Main Lake Algonquin in the Lake Simcoe district, rather than the Kirkfield low phase as proposed by Leverett and Taylor (1915).

Exponential extrapolation of the Main Algonquin water plane (after Larsen, 1985a) in the Kirkfield area, indicates that the elevation of Main Lake Algonquin in the vicinity of the Port Huron outlet was approximately 131 m (430 ft.), approximately 45.7 m (150 ft.) below modern lake level. It is proposed that the inception of eastward drainage through the Trent River valley generated a low level lake in the southern Lake Huron basin correlative with Main Algonquin beaches in the Kirkfield area. The highest beaches in the southern portion of the Huron basin represent transgressional shorelines associated with post-Main Algonquin and Nipissing transgression, rather than Main Algonquin shorelines as previously interpreted.

Northward extrapolation of the Main Algonquin water plane indicates that north and west of Eagle Lake, shoreline features occur at elevations successively lower than that projected from the Kirkfield area (Sharpe, 1978). Northward splitting shorelines developed successively later in the uplift history of the basin, and reflect lacustrine inundation against a retreating ice front. These lower shorelines are tentatively correlated with the Ardtrea and Upper Orillia phases of Lake Algonquin in the Kirkfield area. Relationships between projected water plane elevations and outlet elevations suggest that the Kirkfield outlet was operative throughout the existence of Main Lake Algonquin and the Ardtrea phase of the Upper Group lakes, and ended with deglaciation of the South River outlet and the inception of the Upper Orillia phase of Lake Algonquin.

It is concluded that shoreline features throughout the Lake Huron basin, previously attributed to Main Lake Algonquin, are a composite of different lake phases comprising Nipissing beaches south of Grand Bend, transgressional Upper Group beaches between Port Elgin and Grand Bend, proglacial and ice-contact Main Algonquin shorelines in the Lake Simcoe area, and ice-contact post-Algonquin Upper Group shorelines to the north. Evidence for a Kirkfield low phase in the Lake Huron basin is equivocal and observed depositional sequences can be explained without recourse to fluctuating water level.

The timing of lacustrine events within the Huron basin is not certain. Deglaciation of the Kirkfield outlet and the inception of Main Lake Algonquin is estimated to have occurred approximately 12 000 B.P. (Karrow et al., 1975; Mirynech, 1967; Gravenor, 1957). The Kirkfield outlet was the sole point of discharge for Lake Algonquin until deglaciation of the South River outlet approximately 10 800 to 10 600 B.P. (Fullerton, 1980; Karrow et al., 1975). Evidence from the St. Clair River delta suggests that the Port Huron outlet was inoperative until the end of the Nipissing transgression approximately 5000 B.P. (Raphael and Jaworski, 1982).

ACKNOWLEDGEMENTS

Financial support for this research was received from the Geological Survey of Canada while the author was undertaking graduate study at the University of Illinois. Thanks are owed to W. Hilton Johnson, Ardith K. Hansel, and Curtis E. Larsen for enlightening discussions on related topics. W.H. Johnson, W.W. Shilts, D.R. Sharpe, W.A. Gorman, and P.F. Karrow reviewed the manuscript and provided valuable suggestions for revision.

REFERENCES

Andrews, J.T., 1970, A Geomorphological Study of Post-glacial Uplift with Particular Reference to Arctic Canada: Institute of British Geographers Special Publications 2, 156 p.

Chapman, L.J., 1954, An outlet of Lake Algonquin at Fossmill, Ontario: Geological Association of Canada, Proceedings, v. 6, p. 61-68.

Cheel, R.J., 1982, The Depositional History of an Esker near Ottawa, Canada: Canadian Journal of Earth Sciences, v. 19, p. 1417-1427.

Clark, R.H., and Persoage, N.P., 1970, Some Implications of Crustal Movement in Engineering Planning: Canadian Journal of Earth Sciences, v. 7, p. 628-633.

Deane, R.E., 1950, Pleistocene Geology of the Lake Simcoe District, Ontario: Geological Survey of Canada Memoir 256, 108 p.

Finamore, Paul, F., 1985, Glacial Lake Algonquin and the Fenelon Falls Outlet: in Karrow, P.F., and Calkin, P.E., eds., Quaternary Evolution of the Great Lakes: Geological Association of Canada Special Paper 30.

Fullerton, D.S., 1980, Preliminary Correlation of Post-Erie Interstadial Events (16 000 − 10 000 Radiocarbon Years Before Present), Central and Eastern Great Lakes Region and Hudson, Champlain, and St. Lawrence Lowlands, United States and Canada: United States Geological Survey Professional Paper 1089, 52 p.

Gravenor, C.P., 1957, Surficial Geology of the Lindsay-Peterborough Area, Ontario, Victoria, Peterborough, Durham, and Northumberland Counties, Ontario: Geological Survey of Canada Memoir 288, 60 p.

Gilbert, G.K., 1896, The Algonquin River: American Geologist (Abs.), v. 18, p. 231.

Goldthwait, J.W., 1910, An Instrumental Survey of the Shorelines of the Extinct Lakes Algonquin and Nipissing in Southwestern Ontario: Geological Survey of Canada Memoir 10, 57 p.

Hansel, A.K., Mickelson, D.M., Schneider, A.F., Larsen, Curtis, E., 1985, Late Wisconsinan and Early Holocene History of the Lake Michigan Basin: in Karrow, P.F., and Calkin, P.E., eds., Quaternary Evolution of the Great Lakes: Geological Association of Canada Special Paper 30.

Harrison, J.E., 1972, Quaternary Geology of the North Bay – Mattawa Region: Geological Survey of Canada Paper 71-26, 37 p.

Hough, J.L., 1953, Revision of the Nipissing Stage of the Great Lakes: Illinois Academy of Sciences Transactions, v. 46, p. 957-969.

———, 1958, Geology of the Great Lakes: Urbana, Illinois, University of Illinois Press, 313 p.

Johnston, W.A., 1916, The Trent Valley Outlet of Lake Algonquin and the Deformation of the Algonquin Water Plane in the Lake Simcoe District, Ontario: Geological Survey of Canada Museum Bulletin, no. 23, 27 p.

Karrow, P. F., 1980, The Nipissing Transgression around Southern Lake Huron: Canadain Jounal of Earth Sciences, v. 17, p. 1271-1274.

Karrow, P.F., Anderson, T.W., Clarke, A.H., Delorme, L.D., and Sreenivasa, M.R., 1975, Stratigraphy, Paleontology, and Age of Lake Algonquin Sediments in Southwestern Ontario, Canada: Quaternary Research, v. 5, p. 49-87.

Klassen, R.A. and Shilts, W.W., 1982, iSubbottom Profiling of Lakes of the Canadian Shield: in Current Research, Part A, Geological Survey of Canada Paper 82-1A, p. 375-384.

Larsen, Curtis, E., 1985a, Glacio-isostasy – An Alternative to the Hinge-line Model in the Southern Lake Michigan Basin: Geological Society of America Abstracts with Programs, v. 17, no. 5, p. 298.

———, 1985b, Lake Level, Uplift, and Outlet Incision, a New Perspective on the Nipissing- and Algoma-Stage Great Lakes: in Karrow, P.F., and Calkin, P.E., eds., Quaternary Evolution of the Great Lakes: Geological Association of Canada Special Paper 30.

Leverett, F., and Taylor, F.B., 1915, The Pleistocene of Indiana and Michigan and the History of the Great Lakes: United States Geological Survey Monograph 53, 529 p.

McDonald, B.C., and Shilts, W.W., 1975, Interpretation of Faults in Glaciofluvial Sediments: in Jopling, A.V., and McDonald, B.C., eds., Glaciofluvial and Glaciolacustrine Sedimentation: Society of Economic Paleontologists and Mineralogists Special Publication 23, p. 123-131.

Mirynech, E., 1967, Pleistocene and Surficial Geology of the Kingston-Cobourg-Tweed Area, Ontario: in Jenness, S.E., ed., Geology of Parts of Eastern Ontario and Western Quebec, Geological Association of Canada Guidebook, p. 183-198.

Prest, V.K., 1970, Quaternary Geology in Canada: in Douglas, R.J.E., ed., Geology and Economic Minerals of Canada: Geological Survey of Canada, 5th ed. Economic Geology Report 1, p. 675-764.

Raphael, C.N., and Jaworski, E., 1982, The St. Clair Delta, A Unique Lake Delta: The Geographical Bulletin, v. 21, p. 7-27.

Rust, B.R., and Romanelli, R., 1975, Late Quaternary Subaqueous Outwash Deposits near Ottawa, Canada: in Jopling, A.V., and McDonald, B.C., eds., Glaciofluvial and Glaciolacustrine Sedimentation: Society of Economic Paleontologists and Mineralogists Special Publication 23, p. 177-192.

Sharpe, D.R., 1978, Quaternary Geology in the Gravenhurst, Bracebridge and Huntsville areas, District Municipality of Muskoka: Ontario Geological Survey Miscellaneous Paper 82, p. 152-154.

Shilts, W.W., 1983, Sonar Studies of Late and Postglacial Sediments in Canadian Lakes: Geological Society of America Annual Meeting, Abstracts with Program, v. 15, no. 6, p. 686.

Spencer, J.W., 1891, Deformation of the Algonquin Beach and Birth of Lake Huron: American Journal of Science 3rd Series, v. 41, p. 12-21.

Stanley, G.M., 1936, Lower Algonquin Beaches of Penetanguishene Peninsula: Geological Society of America Bulletin, v. 47, p. 1933-1960.

———, 1937, Lower Algonquin Beaches of Cape Rich, Georgian Bay: Geological Society of America Bulletin, v. 48, p. 1665-1686.

———, 1938, Impounded Early Algonquin Beaches at Sucker Creek, Grey County, Ontario: Michigan Academy of Science, Arts, and Letters, Papers, v. 23, p. 477-495.

Quaternary Evolution of the Great Lakes,
edited by P.F. Karrow and P.E. Calkin,
Geological Association of Canada Special Paper 30, 1985

GLACIAL LAKE ALGONQUIN AND THE FENELON FALLS OUTLET

P.F. Finamore

Ontario Geological Survey, 77 Grenville Street, Toronto, Ontario M5S 1B3

ABSTRACT

Certain revisions regarding the level and deformation of the Main Algonquin water plane and use of the Fenelon Falls outlet in the Kawartha Lakes region of south-central Ontario have been made. Evidence obtained from Quaternary geological mapping and shoreline studies in this region suggests the following. 1) The water plane representing the main level of glacial Lake Algonquin was between 3.0 and 4.5 m (10 and 15 feet) higher than previous studies suggested. 2) The slope of the Main Algonquin shoreline in the Kawartha Lakes region is about 0.7 m/km (3.8 ft./mi). Irregularities in the Main Algonquin water plane formerly attributed to local faulting appear to be minimal. 3) Port Huron has long been recognized as the primary outlet of the Main Algonquin lake phase. The difference in elevation between the bedrock sill at Fenelon Falls and the Main Algonquin shoreline suggests that the Fenelon Falls outlet continued in use during the early part of the Main Algonquin lake phase. 4) Uplift rather than an ice readvance (between Early and Main Algonquin time) is presently believed to have closed the Fenelon Falls outlet.

RÉSUMÉ

Certaines modifications concernant le niveau d'eau et la déformation du plan d'eau de la phase principale du lac Algonquin de même que l'utilisation de l'exutoire à Fenelon Falls dans la région des lacs Kawartha (centre-sud de l'Ontario) ont été apportées. Les informations tirées de la cartographie des dépôts quaternaires ainsi que de l'étude des lignes de rivages suggèrent que. 1) Le plan d'eau correspondant au niveau principal du lac glaciaire Algonquin se trouve à une altitude de 3 à 4.5 m (10 à 15 pieds) plus élevée que ce qui était mentionné dans les études antérieures. 2) Dans la région des lacs Kawartha, la pente du rivage de la phase principale du lac Algonquin est d'environ 0.7 m/km (3.8 pieds au mille). Les irrégularités du plan d'eau de la phase principale du lac Algonquin, autrefois attribuées au système de failles locales, sont en fait minimes. 3) Quoique Port Huron soit reconnu depuis longtemps comme l'exutoire dominant de la phase principale du lac Algonquin, la

différence d'élévation entre le seuil de la roche de fond à Fenelon Falls et la ligne de rivage de la phase principale du lac Algonquin semble indiquer que l'exutoire de Fenelon Falls a continué d'être utilisé pendant la première partie de la phase principale du lac Algonquin. 4) La fermeture de l'exutoire de Fenelon Falls résulterait d'un soulèvement plutôt que d'une nouvelle avancée glaciaire entre les périodes ancienne et principale du lac Algonquin.

INTRODUCTION

Glacial Lake Algonquin has been studied for more than 100 years and, although it is relatively well understood in general terms, it is poorly known in detail. For example, the Fenelon Falls (or Kirkfield) outlet, often referred to as a temporary outlet of glacial Lake Algonquin, has long been the subject of uncertainty and controversy in the literature. The number of times that the outlet was in use and the length of time involved during each use have never been firmly established. Thus, the glacial deposits and raised shoreline record near the Fenelon Falls outlet of glacial Lake Algonquin were examined in order to gain a better understanding of the relationships between the history of ice retreat and the timing and manner of operation of the outlet.

The area investigated includes the National Topographic Series Orillia (31D/11) and Fenelon Falls (31D/10) mapsheets (Fig. 1). Quaternary geological mapping was completed for the entire study area. Shoreline studies were conducted primarily in the Fenelon Falls map area.

PREVIOUS WORK

History of Glacial Lake Algonquin

The Kawartha Lakes region has received considerable attention regarding the history of glacial Lake Algonquin and use of the Fenelon Falls outlet. Regional studies that pertain to the history of the Great Lakes, including Lake Algonquin, were presented by Leverett and Taylor (1915, with extensive reference to earlier literature), Hough (1958, 1963, 1968), Chapman and Putnam (1951, 1966), Prest (1970), and Fullerton (1980).

Studies that specifically relate to the shoreline record, and to the outlet of glacial Lake Algonquin in the Kawartha Lakes region have been carried out by several workers. Spencer (1891) and Gilbert (1896) were among the first to describe the Trent Valley outlet channel of glacial Lake Algonquin. Goldthwait (1910), Johnston (1916), Stanley (1936, 1937, 1938), and Deane (1950) have all dealt with the shoreline record and history of glacial Lake Algonquin for southern Georgian Bay and Lake Simcoe in considerable detail. Chapman (1954), Anderson (1971), and Karrow *et al.*, (1975) also discuss the history of Lake Algonquin and the possible use of the "Kirkfield outlet" during the low-water phase that preceded Main Lake Algonquin. Kaszycki (1985), who also discusses the history of glacial Lake Algonquin, suggests that "Kirkfield" was the sole outlet for Main Lake Algonquin. Other significant studies that deal with the history and age of glacial Lake Algonquin include those by Lewis (1969), Harrison (1970, 1972), Saarnisto (1974, 1975), Cowan (1976), Terasmae (1980), Futyma (1981), and Karrow (1982).

The above studies suggest that three events best describe the history of glacial Lake Algonquin: 1) Early Algonquin lake phase, 2) Kirkfield low-level phase, and 3) Main Algonquin lake phase, including the Post-Main Algonquin glacial lakes.

The Kawartha Lakes region was apparently ice covered when Early Lake Algonquin formed in the Huron basin and subsequently coalesced with waters in the Michigan basin at 184 m (605 ft.) above sea level. Once ice retreated far enough to uncover the Fenelon Falls outlet, the Kirkfield low-level phase began and water levels dropped an estimated 15 to 30 m (50 to 100 ft.). The sequence of events after the Kirkfield low-level phase is uncertain. Isostatic uplift and an ice readvance have both been proposed as mechanisms that closed the Fenelon Falls outlet, initiating the Main Algonquin lake phase. Whether Fenelon Falls was in use during the Main Algonquin lake phase is also uncertain. In any case, Main Algonquin was established with its outlet at 184 m (605 ft.) above sea level at Port Huron (see Karrow *et al.*, 1975).

Once the ice margin retreated to the North Bay region, a series of lower glacial lakes formed in response to the uncovering of successively lower outlets. These lakes are referred to as the Post-Main Algonquin glacial lakes, several of which have been identified by Deane (1950) and Stanley (1936, 1937) in the Lake Simcoe and Georgian Bay areas, respectively. Lake Algonquin came to an end when the ice margin withdrew and exposed outlets between Fossmill and North

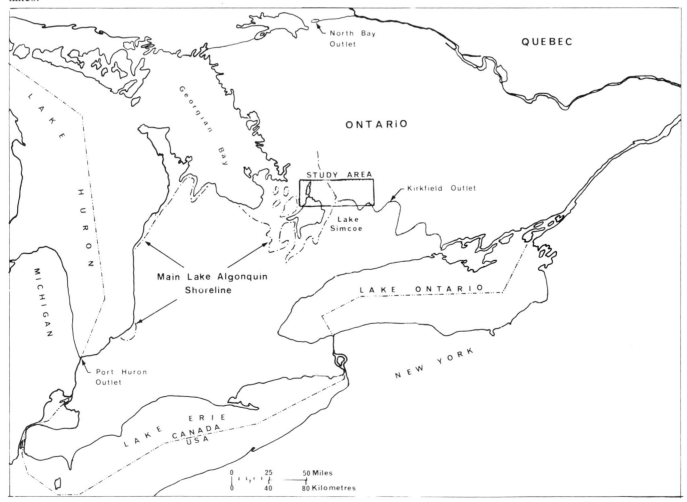

Figure 1. Location Map.

Bay, providing access to the Ottawa valley and the Champlain Sea (Harrison, 1970, 1972; Prest, 1970).

Age of Glacial Lake Algonquin

Glaciolacustrine varves and radiocarbon dating have both been used to estimate the time span of glacial Lake Algonquin.

Glaciolacustrine varves provide evidence as to the minimum duration of glacial Lake Algonquin. Varves are repeated couplets of silt and clay and they represent, by definition, annual lake sedimentation (Jamieson, 1979). There are at least 560 couplets of silt and clay (varves) exposed in a river bank near the community of Burnt River (Finamore and Bajc, 1983). North of the study area, Antevs (1925) reported 784 varves in a clay pit near Bracebridge and Jamieson (1979) counted 652 varves in a house excavation near Huntsville. Similarly, Fitzgerald (1985) attributes more than 650 varves to Lake Algonquin in the Minesing Basin, west of Lake Simcoe. If the sediments at the above localities represent single events, a substantial lake history can be inferred.

The time span of glacial Lake Algonquin also has, to a large degree, been inferred from radiocarbon dates of related events. As noted by Karrow *et al.* (1975), relatively few of the many lake phases of the Great Lakes have been dated directly. The following list demonstrates that estimates of the time span of glacial Lake Algonquin are not in strict agreement, although the discrepancies may not be detectable using the radiocarbon method of dating.

Years BP	
Wayne and Zumberge (1965)	12 200 to 10 500
Hough (1968)	12 000 to 11 000
Lewis (1969)	11 300 (end)
Prest (1970)	12 500 to 11 200
Harrison (1972)	13 000 to well before 12 000 (Main Algonquin)
Saarnisto (1974)	11 000 (end)
Karrow *et al.* (1975)	12 500 to 10 400
Fullerton (1980)	12 400 to 11 000
Futyma (1981)	10 600 (end)

From the above data, it is suggested that glacial Lake Algonquin began about 12 500 B.P. The most recent studies suggested that it ended about 10 500 B.P. (Karrow *et al.*, 1975; Futyma, 1981).

Previous Shoreline Studies

The most notable shoreline studies of glacial Lake Algonquin in the Lake Simcoe district were those by Deane (1950) and Goldthwait (1910). As well, Johnston (1916) studied the Algonquin shoreline in the Kawartha Lake District. All of the above studies differ in various respects.

In the Lake Simcoe district, isobase maps and water plane profiles of glacial Lake Algonquin that were prepared by

TABLE I

SELECTED DESCRIPTIONS OF MAIN LAKE ALGONQUIN SHORELINE FEATURES (AFTER DEANE, 1950)

Location	Description of Algonquin Beaches	Elevation
Ardtrea Island	Altitudes varying between 261.5 and 267.0 m (858 and 876 ft.). – Strong southeast-facing bluff. Beach not well defined as slopes off gently in places. Evidence of two terraces here, indicating different lake levels at 266.7, 263.3, and 261.5 m (875, 864, and 858 ft.; Deane, 1950, p. 57).	263.3 m (864 ft.)
Ardtrea Island	Altitudes varying between 262.7 and 268.2 m (862 and 880 ft.). – Strong 10.7 m (35 ft.) bluff somewhat weaker to the north where it forms the northern extremity of Ardtrea Island. Terrace narrow with gravel ridge associated. Altitude of 265.8 m (872 ft.). – Gravel spit extending northward from tip of Island. Altitude of 264.9 m (869 ft.). – A gravel ridge east of spit above. Beaches on the north side of the Island are 1.5 to 3.0 m (5 to 10 ft.) lower than beaches on the east side (Deane, 1950, p. 58).	265.2 m (870 ft.)
Uphill	Altitudes of 281.6, 281.3, 280.1, 279.8, and 279.2 m (924, 923, 919, 918, and 916 ft.). – A group of beach ridges 0.8 km (1/2 mile) north of Uphill. Bedrock close to surface. Ridges 0.6 to 1.8 m (2 to 6 ft.) high and mainly of cobbles. May be ice shoved. Altitude of 277.0 m (909 ft.). – Moderate 2.4 m (8 ft.) bluff and boulder strewn terrace below cobble ridges (Deane, 1950, p. 71).	277.4 m (910 ft.)

Deane (1950) and Goldthwait (1910) are very similar below 250 m (820 ft.) a.s.l. However, above this elevation, they differ considerably (Fig. 2). Some isobases differ by as much as 4.6 m (15 ft.).

Shoreline descriptions by Deane (1950) at several sites above the 250-m (820-ft.) isobase suggest that the Main Algonquin water plane is difficult to define precisely in this region. For example, near Bolsover (Fig. 2), Deane (1950) indicates a baymouth bar varying between 263.0 and 264.2 m (863 and 867 ft.) a.s.l., but his 262-m (860-ft.) isobase lies about 5.5 km northeast of this locality. Deane (1950) also describes a strong gravel beach ridge 2 km northwest of Kirkfield (Fig. 3) as being 4.6 to 5.5 m (15 to 18 ft.) too high for Lake Algonquin. Descriptions of other ambiguous sites are listed below in Table I and the locations are indicated in Figure 2. The elevations chosen by Deane (1950) to represent the Main Algonquin shoreline are also given in Table I.

The above localities indicate that there is considerable uncertainty regarding the elevation of the Main Algonquin shoreline north of the 250-m (820-ft.) isobase in the Lake Simcoe district.

Johnston (1916) provided the only comprehensive study of shoreline features in the Kawartha Lakes district. By assigning only the highest, well defined shoreline features as belonging to the Main Algonquin water plane, Johnston suggested that Main Algonquin isobases are quite irregular (Fig. 3). He also suggested that local faulting may have contributed to these irregularities. The fault indicated by Johnston (1916) near Kirkfield was examined by the author and it is now interpreted to be a surface stress release feature or "pop-up" (White and Russell, 1982). These features indicate the presence of high horizontal stresses at very shallow depths in the Paleozoic bedrock (White *et al.*, 1973), but do not suggest any tectonic disturbance.

While the Main Algonquin beach is displaced vertically about 0.5 m by the pop-up in this locality, the displacement occurs only immediately above the pop-up. Beyond the intersection of the pop-up and beach ridge, no lateral or vertical displacement of the beach ridge was observed.

It seems unlikely, therefore, that faulting contributed to the irregular isobases proposed by Johnston (1916). Also, the irregularities previously described in the Lake Simcoe district combined with those described by Johnston (1916) in the Kawartha Lakes district, suggest a more regional rather than local "irregularity" of the Main Algonquin shoreline.

PRESENT STUDY

Field Procedures

After shoreline features were identified and delineated during field mapping, they were levelled using a telescopic alidade and self-reading stadia rod. Wave-cut bluffs were the most desirable shoreline features to measure because they tend to be more reliable water level indicators. However, in the Kawartha Lakes region, beach ridges and bars dominate in a relatively shallow drift-covered region of low relief. The crests of these features were usually measured unless a related wave-cut bluff could be identified and measured. Although the crests of beach ridges, bars, and spits do not define water levels as precisely as do wave-cuts bluffs, they have been used in order to facilitate the comparison of data with previous studies.

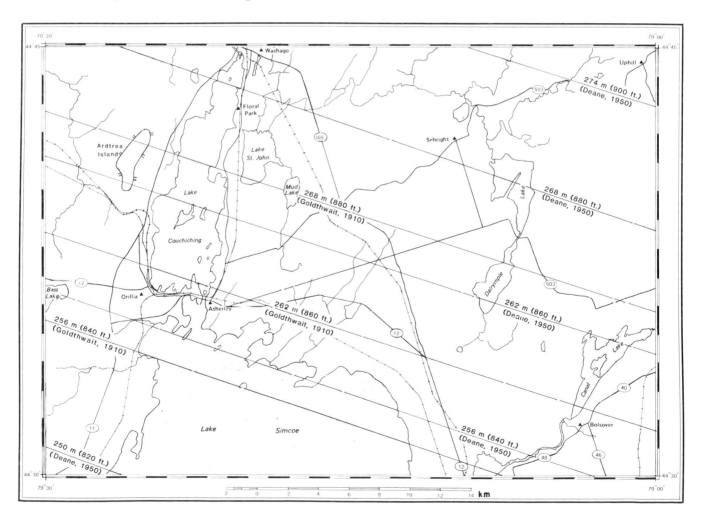

Figure 2. Isobase map of Main Lake Algonquin, Orillia area. After Deane (1950) and Goldthwait (1910).

Results

In the Lake Simcoe district, Main Algonquin shoreline features are usually well defined and continuous. However, in the study area, they become infrequent and discontinuous. In many places, they are not discernable.

The irregularities of the Main Algonquin shoreline in the Kawartha Lakes district suggested by Johnston (1916, Fig. 3) were based on the assumption that only the highest, well defined shoreline features belonged to the Main Algonquin water plane. However, in each respective lake basin in the study area, there are well-developed shoreline features that occur at elevations comparable to those of the Main Algonquin level established by Goldthwait (1910) in the adjacent Lake Simcoe district. Therefore, it is suggested that the Main Algonquin isobases are a concordant set which do not require the bends that Johnston (1916) suggested.

A regular and continuous Main Algonquin water plane in the study area also suggests that Fenelon Falls, rather than Kirkfield, was the actual outlet. Work by Johnston (1916) and the results of this study suggest that the Main Algonquin shoreline continues east of Kirkfield, in the Balsam and Cameron Lake basins, and ends at Fenelon Falls. The pre-

sence of spillway terraces and well-developed shoreline features below the Main Algonquin level southeast of Fenelon Falls, also suggests that Fenelon Falls was the controlling sill.

Figure 4 is a proposed water plane profile for the Main Algonquin shoreline in the Kawartha Lakes district. Also, profiles of the Main Algonquin and Ardtrea water planes that were constructed by Deane (1950) in the Lake Simcoe district have been extrapolated onto this diagram for comparison and discussion.

The profile for this study was constructed along line A-B (Fig. 3) and N 21° E was chosen as the direction of maximum inclination, based on studies by Goldthwait (1910), Deane (1950), and others. An uplift rate of about 0.7 m/km (3.8 ft./mi.) has been calculated.

This study suggests that the Main Algonquin water plane in the study area is between 3.0 and 4.6 m (10 and 15 ft.) higher than Deane's Main Algonquin water plane in the adjacent Lake Simcoe district (Fig. 4). Similar differences were noted between Main Algonquin isobases proposed by Goldthwait (1910) and Deane (1950) in the Lake Simcoe district (Fig. 2). Thus, Goldthwait's (1910) interpretations are in

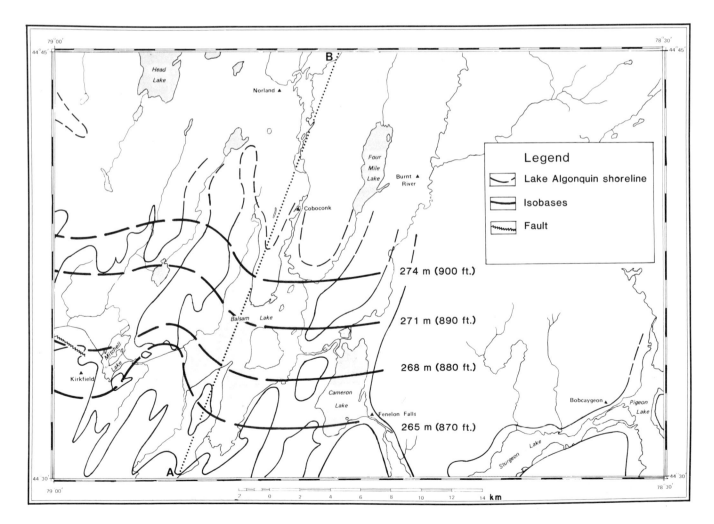

Figure 3. Isobase map and shoreline of Main Lake Algonquin in the Kawartha Lakes District. After Johnston (1916).

close agreement with those suggested from this study. Also, shoreline data presented by Deane (1950) in the Lake Simcoe district indicate that a higher Main Algonquin level may be more appropriate. (See, for example, Table I and Deane, 1950, Fig. 7)

As indicated in Figure 4, there are beaches both above and below the Main Algonquin shoreline. Beaches lying well above the Main Algonquin shoreline presumably represent earlier events because no cross-cutting relationships with below the Main Algonquin shoreline in the Kawartha Lakes district probably represent a series of lower lake levels that may have been controlled by both the Fenelon Falls and Port Huron outlets.

Studies by Deane (1950) suggested that an ice readvance closed the Fenelon Falls outlet, initiating the Main Algonquin lake phase. Field mapping in the Orillia-Fenelon Falls area indicates that there are a few localities where an ice readvance can be inferred. For example, till disconformably overlies horizontally cross-stratified sand in the Talbot River valley. Unfortunately, the age and continuity of these "older" sediments at this locality (and others) is not known. Also, pre-Main Algonquin shoreline features that have been identified in the study area would have been destroyed north of the margin of any ice readvance. It seems unlikely, therefore, that a readvance occurred between Early and Main Algonquin time.

DISCUSSION

Figure 5 is a hypothetical representation of water plane profiles for Glacial Lakes Algonquin and Nipissing, based on assumed history. Evidence to support each of the events indicated in Figure 5 is discussed below.

1) Early Lake Algonquin and the Fenelon Falls-Main Lake Algonquin Transition

As indicated in Figure 5, hypothetical Early Algonquin shorelines should be above the Main Algonquin water plane but they would have terminated at the isobase that passes through Fenelon Falls, once that outlet became open. They would supposedly converge south to Port Huron and they would have been destroyed north of the margin of any ice readvance.

A few pre-Main Algonquin shoreline features south of the "outlet isobase" have been identified by the author in two principal areas: south of Orillia near Lake Simcoe; and near Kirkfield. Pre-Main Algonquin shoreline features have also been identified by Chapman and Putnam (1966) near Barrie, west of Lake Simcoe, and by Sharpe and Jamieson (1982) in the Wiarton area. Both Chapman and Putnam (1966) and Sharpe and Jamieson (1982) suggested that their pre-Main Algonquin shoreline features may be related to other glacial lakes. However, considering the degree of uncertainty of pre-Main Algonquin shoreline features, Early Lake Algonquin remains a possibility.

Shoreline features north of the outlet isobase have also been identified in the study area (Fig. 4). Previous investigators suggested that "pre-Main Algonquin" shoreline features were a result of irregular uplift during Main Algonquin time (Johnston, 1916; Deane, 1950). In light of the evidence already presented to suggest a concordant set of Main Algonquin isobases in the study area, an alternative explanation is proposed. It is suggested that pre-Main Algonquin shoreline features north of the outlet isobase may have formed during the Fenelon Falls to Main Lake Algonquin transition (i.e., the Kirkfield low-level phase). Unfortu-

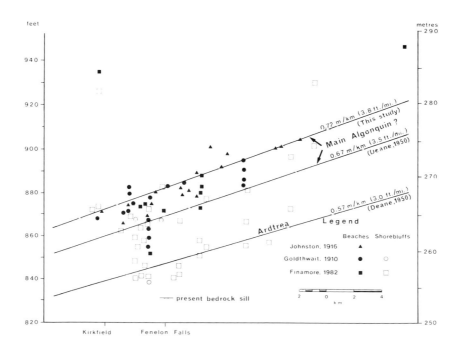

Figure 4. Algonquin water plane profiles and other shoreline features in the vicinity of the Fenelon Falls outlet.

nately, there are not enough of these high shoreline features to trace particular water planes and establish convergence to a particular outlet.

2) Transgressional Shorelines and Main Lake Algonquin

The sediment sequence of fossiliferous silt over nearly barren sand, described by Johnston (1916), Deane (1950), and Karrow *et al.* (1975), and impounded shore features, described by Stanley (1938) and Deane (1950), probably relate to transgressional shoreline(s) submerged by the Main Algonquin lake phase. This interpretation is compatible with all of the above studies.

Most studies suggested that the Main Algonquin shoreline formed when the Port Huron outlet was in use. If the interpretations of this study are correct, Fenelon Falls may have also been in use, based on the difference in elevation between the bedrock sill at Fenelon Falls and the Main Algonquin shoreline.

3) Main Algonquin Upper Group

Harrison (1972) suggested that the Main Algonquin Upper Group of beaches (namely the Ardtrea, Upper Orillia and Lower Orillia; Deane, 1950) all converge southward to Port Huron and are therefore uplift controlled. If Harrison's interpretations are correct, it is possible to estimate when the Fenelon Falls outlet was abandoned.

Based on the difference in elevation between the present bedrock sill at Fenelon Falls (253.3 m, 830.7 ft.) and the Main Algonquin shoreline near Fenelon Falls (approximately 268 m, 880 ft.), it is suggested that both Fenelon Falls and Port Huron were in use during Ardtrea time and that some time shortly before Upper Orillia time, the rising Fenelon Falls outlet was abandoned and Port Huron controlled Algonquin drainage.

4) Post-Main Algonquin Glacial Lakes

Most studies suggest that post-Main Algonquin (Lower Group) beaches are parallel and therefore outlet controlled (e.g., Harrison, 1972). Several outlets in the North Bay area are believed to have drained the post-Main Algonquin glacial lakes (see Prest, 1970; Harrison, 1970, 1972).

CONCLUSIONS

The interpretations of this study are based on the premise that there was no readvance of ice to block the Fenelon Falls outlet. The author feels that the age of sediments that may indicate a readvance is unknown, and because there are abandoned shoreline features well above the Main Algonquin shoreline, the Fenelon Falls outlet was probably abandoned by isostatic uplift. Thus, shoreline features above the Main Algonquin shoreline north of the isobase that passes through the Fenelon Falls outlet may be associated with the transition between the Kirkfield low-water phase and the Main Algonquin lake phase. South of the outlet isobase, pre-Main Algonquin shoreline features may be Early Algonquin correlatives.

ACKNOWLEDGEMENTS

Mapping of the study area and shoreline studies were undertaken by the author while employed with the Ontario Geological Survey. The University of Waterloo also provided financial assistance to complete the shoreline studies.

To the above institutions and to the many individuals who provided valuable technical assistance, particularly P.F. Karrow (University of Waterloo), through whom research funds were provided, and P.J. Barnett (Ontario Geological Survey), I extend my sincere gratitude.

I am also grateful to V.K. Prest and D.R. Sharpe for critical review of the manuscript.

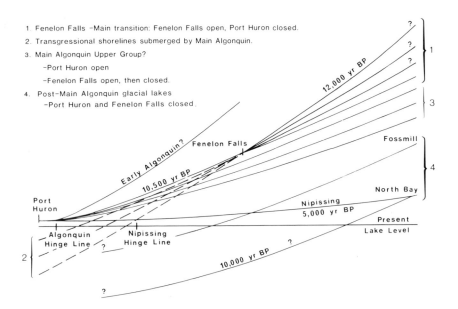

Figure 5. Diagrammatic representation of water-plane profiles for Glacial Lakes Algonquin and Nipissing.

REFERENCES

Anderson, T.W., 1971, Postglacial Vegetative Changes in the Lake Huron-Lake Simcoe District, Ontario, with Special Reference to Glacial Lake Algonquin: Ph.D. Thesis, Waterloo, Ontario, University of Waterloo, 246 p.

Antevs, E., 1925, Retreat of the Last Ice-sheet in Eastern Canada: Geological Survey of Canada Memoir 146, 141 p.

Chapman, L.J., 1954, An Outlet of Lake Algonquin at Fossmill, Ontario: Geological Association of Canada, Proceedings, v. 6, p. 61-68.

Chapman, L.J., and Putnam, D.F., 1951, The Physiography of Southern Ontario: Toronto, Ontario, University of Toronto Press, 284 p.

_____, 1966, The Physiography of Southern Ontario 2nd Edition: Toronto, Ontario, University of Toronto Press, 386 p.

Cowan, W.R., 1976, Quaternary Geology of the Sault Ste. Marie Area, District of Algoma: in Milne, V.G., Cowan, W.R., Card, K.D., and Robertson, J.A., eds., Summary of Field Work, 1976: Geological Branch, Ontario Division of Mines Miscellaneous Paper 67, p. 134-136.

Deane, R.E., 1950, Pleistocene Geology of the Lake Simcoe District, Ontario: Geological Survey of Canada Memoir 256, 108 p.

Finamore, P.F., and Bajc, A.F., 1983, Quaternary Geology of the Fenelon Falls Area, Southern Ontario: Ontario Geological Survey, Preliminary Map P.2596, Scale 1:50 000.

Fitzgerald, W.D., 1985, Postglacial History of the Minesing Basin, Ontario: in Karrow, P.F., and Calkin, P.E., eds., Quaternary Evolution of the Great Lakes: Geological Association of Canada Special Paper 30.

Fullerton, D.S., 1980, Preliminary Correlation of Post-Erie Interstadial Events (16 000-10 000 Radiocarbon Years Before Present), Central and Eastern Great Lakes Region, and Hudson, Champlain, and St. Lawrence Lowlands, United States and Canada: United States Geological Survey Professional Paper 1089, 51 p.

Futyma, R.P., 1981, The Northern Limits of Glacial Lake Algonquin in Upper Michigan: Quaternary Research, v. 15, p. 291-310.

Gilbert, G.K., 1896, The Algonquin River (Abst.): American Geologist, v. 18, p. 23.

Goldthwait, J.W., 1910, An Instrumental Survey of the Shorelines of the Extinct Lakes Algonquin and Nipissing in Southwestern Ontario: Geological Survey of Canada Memoir 10, 57 p.

Harrison, J.E., 1970, Deglaciation and Proglacial Drainage Evolution: North Bay-Mattawa Region, Ontario: Proceedings of the 13th Conference on Great Lakes Research, p. 756-767.

_____, 1972, Quaternary Geology of the North Bay-Mattawa Region: Geological Survey of Canada Paper 71-26, 37 p.

Hough, J.L., 1958, Geology of the Great Lakes: Urbana, Illinois, University of Illinois Press, 313 p.

_____, 1963, The Prehistoric Great Lakes of North America: American Scientist, v. 51, p. 84-109.

_____, 1968, Great Lakes (North America): in Fairbridge, R.W., ed., The Encyclopedia of Geomorphology: New York, Reinhold Book Corporation, p. 499-506.

Jamieson, G.R., 1979, Correlation, Sedimentology, and Nature of Grain-size Distribution of Pleistocene Glacial Varves of the Bracebridge-Huntsville Area, Ontario, Canada: B.Sc. Thesis, Waterloo, Ontario, University of Waterloo, 80 p.

Johnston, W.A., 1916, The Trent Valley Outlet of Lake Algonquin and the Deformation of the Algonquin Water-plane in the Lake Simcoe District, Ontario: Geological Survey of Canada Museum Bulletin 23, 27 p.

Karrow, P.F., 1982, Quaternary Geology of St. Joseph Island, Algoma District: Ontario Geological Survey, Preliminary Map P.2581, Scale 1:50 000.

Karrow, P.F., Anderson, T.W., Clarke, A.H., Delorme, L.D., and Sreenivasa, M.R., 1975, Stratigraphy, Paleontology, and Age of Lake Algonquin Sediments in Southwestern Ontario, Canada: Quaternary Research, v. 5, p. 49-87.

Kaszycki, C.A., 1985, History of Glacial Lake Algonquin in the Haliburton Region, South Central Ontario: in Karrow, P.F., and Calkin, P.E., eds., Quaternary Evolution of the Great Lakes: Geological Association of Canada Special Paper 30.

Leverett, F., and Taylor, F.B., 1915, The Pleistocene of Indiana and Michigan and the History of the Great Lakes: United States Geological Survey Monograph 53, 529 p.

Lewis, C.F.M., 1969, Late Quaternary History of Lake Levels in the Huron and Erie Basins: Proceedings of the 12th Conference on Great Lakes Research, p. 250-270.

Prest, V.K., 1970, Quaternary Geology of Canada: in Douglas, R.J.W., ed., Geology and Economic Minerals of Canada, 5th Edition: Geological Survey of Canada, Economic Geology Report 1, p. 676-764.

Saarnisto, M., 1974, The Deglaciation History of the Lake Superior Region and its Climatic Implications: Quaternary Research, v. 4, p. 316-339.

_____, 1975, Stratigraphic Studies on the Shoreline Displacement of Lake Superior: Canadian Journal of Earth Sciences, v. 12, p. 300-319.

Sharpe, D.R., and Jamieson, G.R., 1982, Quaternary Geology of the Wiarton Area, Southern Ontario: Ontario Geological Survey Preliminary Map P.2559, Scale 1:50 000.

Spencer, J.W., 1891, Deformation of the Algonquin Beach and Birth of Lake Huron: American Journal of Science, Third Series, v. 41, p. 12-21.

Stanley, G.M., 1936, Lower Algonquin Beaches of Penetanguishene Peninsula: Geological Society of America Bulletin, v. 47, p. 1933-1960.

_____, 1937, Lower Algonquin Beaches of Cape Rich, Georgian Bay: Geological Society of America Bulletin, v. 48, p. 1665-1686.

_____, 1938, Impounded Early Algonquin Beaches at Sucker Creek, Grey County, Ontario: Papers, Michigan Academy of Science, Arts, and Letters, v. 23, p. 477-495.

Terasmae, J., 1980, Some Problems of Late Wisconsinan History and Geochronology in Southeastern Ontario: Canadian Journal of Earth Sciences, v. 17, p. 361-381.

Wayne, W.J., and Zumberge, J.H., 1965, Pleistocene Geology of Indiana and Michigan: in Wright, H.E., and Frey, D.G., eds., The Quaternary of the United States: Princeton, New Jersey, Princeton University Press, p. 63-84.

White, O.L., Karrow, P.F., and Macdonald, J.R., 1973, Residual Stress Relief Phenomena in Southern Ontario: Proceedings of the 9th Canadian Rock Mechanics Symposium, Montreal, Quebec, December 1973, p. 323-348.

White, O.L., and Russell, D.J., 1982, High Horizontal Stresses in Southern Ontario — Their Orientation and their Magnitude: Proceedings, 4th Congress of the International Association of Engineering Geologists, New Delhi, India, 1982, p. 323-348.

Quaternary Evolution of the Great Lakes,
edited by P.F. Karrow and P.E. Calkin,
Geological Association of Canada Special Paper 30, 1985

POSTGLACIAL HISTORY OF THE MINESING BASIN, ONTARIO

W.D. Fitzgerald

Ontario Ministry of Natural Resources, Huronia District Midhurst, Ontario L0L 1X0

ABSTRACT

The Minesing Basin is located west of Barrie and north of Alliston, Ontario. Quaternary drift thickness generally exceeds 30 m and bedrock does not outcrop.

A study of the Minesing Basin was conducted to enable the postglacial history of the Basin to be interpreted. This study included: a survey of abandoned shorelines, identifying two new and distinct lakes, Minesing and Edenvale, restricted by the Edenvale Moraine to the Minesing Basin; an analysis of pollen assemblages from surface exposures and two deep cores in Minesing Swamp, which correlated well with previous studies in the vicinity of the Minesing Basin; and a study of mollusc assemblages, which provided additional environmental information.

The Minesing Basin underwent deglaciation some 12 000 B.P. The Basin was submerged by glacial Lake Algonquin and its immediate successors between 10 000 and 12 000 years ago and became emergent during the low water Lake Hough phase in Georgian Bay. The Basin again was submerged during the occupation of Georgian Bay by the Nipissing phase, about 5000 B.P.

RÉSUMÉ

La région de Minesing est située à l'ouest de Barrie et au nord d'Alliston. L'épaisseur des dépôts quaternaires dépasse généralement les 30 mètres et la roche de fond n'émerge pas.

Une étude du bassin de Minesing a été entreprise dans le but d'interpréter l'histoire post-glaciaire du bassin. Cette étude comprend: une reconnaissance des anciens rivages permettant l'identification de deux nouveaux lacs, le Minesing et l'Edenvale, tous deux restreints par la moraine d'Edenvale au bassin de Minesing; une analyse des assemblages polliniques, laquelle corrèle bien avec les études précédentes faites dans les environs du bassin de Minesing; et une étude sur les assemblages de mollusques qui fournit des informations additionnelles sur l'environnement.

Le bassin de Minesing a été déglacé il y a environ 12 000 ans. Le bassin a été inondé par les eaux du lac glaciaire Algonquin et par ses successeurs immédiats entre 10 000 et 12 000 ans B.P. Puis, il a émergé pendant la période de bas niveau du lac Hough dans la baie georgienne. Par la suite, le bassin a de nouveau été inondé lors de l'occupation de la baie georgienne par les eaux de lac Nipissing.

INTRODUCTION

The Great Lakes Basins were occupied by numerous glacial and postglacial lakes during the Late Wisconsinan and Holocene. Shoreline features and deposits developed by these ancient lakes can be seen throughout the Great Lakes Region. In particular, these features are well developed throughout the Georgian Bay-Lake Simcoe area. The most prominent of these are associated with glacial Lake Algonquin and the early transitional phases to the low level Lake Hough.

The Minesing Basin (Fig. 1) is located west of Barrie, some 100 km north of Toronto, Ontario. The Basin is located entirely within the glacial Lake Algonquin lake plain and comprises part of the present watershed of the Nottawasaga River.

The Minesing Basin is situated between the areas of Stanley's (1936, 1937, 1938) investigations of glacial Lake Algonquin in the Georgian Bay area and those of Deane (1946, 1950) in the Lake Simcoe District. Their work established a sequence of lake levels, but was carried out before the availability of radiocarbon dating and without the benefit of palynological and paleontological study. This study includes a survey of shoreline features found within the Minesing Basin and the extrapolation of these data for comparison with the studies of Deane (1950) and Stanley (1936, 1937, 1938). The postglacial vegetational history has been interpreted based on the palynological analysis of two long cores obtained from the Minesing Swamp (P$_3$, P$_4$, Fig. 2) and two additonal cores taken near Barclay and Everett. Additional paleo-environmental data have been obtained from the study of molluscs contained in one core and from several sections along the Nottawasaga River.

DESCRIPTION OF SAMPLE SITES

Raised Shoreline Survey

A raised shoreline survey was conducted throughout the

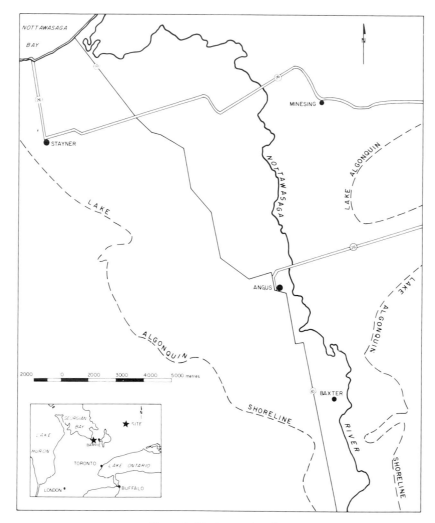

Figure 1. Study area location.

Minesing Basin using a self-reading alidade and stadia rod. All measurements were made to the nearest tenth of a foot and converted to metres. The locations surveyed (Fig. 2) were limited by the lack of benchmarks, the great distances between benchmarks and shoreline features, and the time available.

Barclay Site

This site (P₁, Fig. 2) is located 12.5 km south of Barrie within the northern extension of the Cookstown bog (Anderson, 1971). This site is approximately 250 m a.s.l., 15 m above the interpreted level of Lake Algonquin in this area (Deane, 1950). A Hiller peat sampler was used to obtain a 2.5 m core of black to brown, very woody peat. All samples collected for palynological study were prepared using methods described by Faegri and Iversen (1964).

Wales Site

This site (P₂, Fig. 2) is located 1.5 km north of Everett, in a small gravel pit on the property of Mr. James Wales. A drainage ditch had exposed a 3.5-m section of alluvial sands overlying approximately 1.0 m of woody peat, which in turn was overlying 1.5 m of sandy gravel. The sandy gravel contained numerous logs and sandy peat lenses. The sandy gravel was observed to overlie contorted, laminated (varved), silty clay and clay, approximately 100 m to the north. The peat deposit has a maximum thickness of 0.95 m and thins rapidly to either side. Samples were taken at 0.05 m intervals at the point of maximum thickness. The overlying sandy alluvium was also sampled for pollen analysis.

U.W.B.H. 128-78, Minesing Swamp Site

This site (P₃, Fig. 2) is located near the geographic centre of the Minesing Swamp and was accessible to sampling by a truck-mounted drill rig. The sample site is located 23 m south of a bridge spanning the Nottawasaga River. A continuous core to a depth of 34.14 m was obtained using 0.61 m Shelby tubes. The following log summarizes the sequence.

Stratigraphy:

0.00 − 0.73 m medium to coarse sandy alluvium.
0.73 − 3.07 m black to brown, clayey silt to clay-rich peat.
3.07 − 4.80 m clayey silt to clay, lacustrine, with molluscs.

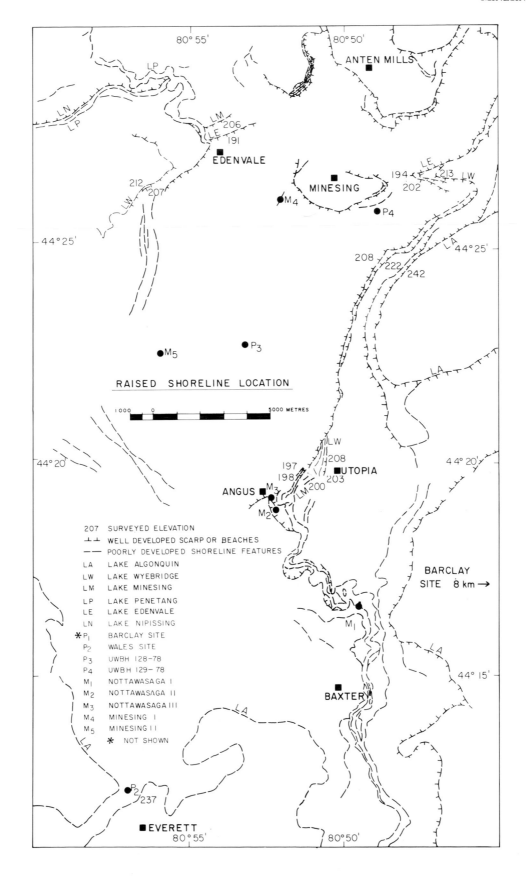

Figure 2. Sample site locations and abandoned shoreline features.

4.80 − 9.75 m medium to fine sand, some clayey sections, paleosol at 5.80 to 5.88 m.

9.75 − 33.20 m clayey silt to sandy silt, laminated (varved), lacustrine.

33.20 − 34.14 m hard, pebbly, medium to coarse, silty sand till.

U.W.B.H. 129-78 Minesing Swamp Site

This site (P_4, Fig. 2) is located in a northeast-trending extension of the Minesing Swamp, southeast of Minesing, and was accessible to sampling using a truck-mounted drill rig. A continuous core to a depth of 10.98 m was obtained using 0.61 m Shelby tubes.

Stratigraphy:

0.00 − 1.30 m fine sand to silt; oxidized alluvium.

1.30 − 1.58 m brown to black peat.

1.58 − 1.93 m silty peat.

1.93 − 3.40 m clayey silt with peaty sections, molluscs.

3.40 − 3.51 m solid wood.

3.51 − 3.79 m clayey silt to sand, mixed with woody peat.

3.79 − 4.54 m grey, clayey silt to clay.

4.54 − 4.67 m brown sandy silt.

4.67 − 10.98 m laminated (varved) clayey silt to silty clay, some silty and sandy layers.

Nottawasaga I Site

This site (M_1, Fig. 2) is situated along the Nottawasaga River approximately 3 km downstream from Baxter. A 27-m section of Quaternary deposits was exposed by the Nottawasaga River. The approximate elevation of the top of this section is 213 m a.s.l. Bulk samples at 2.13, 4.88, and 5.18 m from the top of the section were taken for mollusc analysis.

Stratigraphy:

0.00 − 1.22 m fine sand, eolian.

1.22 − 5.18 m medium to coarse, pebbly, fluvial sand, becoming coarser with depth, molluscs.

5.18 − 19.51 m clayey silt, laminated (varved), becoming coarser with depth, glaciolacustrine.

19.51 − 22.56 m very hard, pebbly silty sand till (Newmarket Till).

22.56 − 23.47 m clayey silt, contorted laminations, glaciolacustrine.

23.47 − 26.52 m medium to fine sand, ripple marks, loose to compact, glaciofluvial.

26.52 − 27.00 m slump to river level.

Nottawasaga II Site

This site (M_2, Fig. 2) is located along the Nottawasaga River approximately 1 km upstream from Angus. A long river section has exposed approximately 10 m of nearshore and/or fluvial, medium to fine sands. The base of an abandoned scarp, cut at right angles to the river, was approximately 189 m a.s.l. while the top of the scarp was approximately 197 m a.s.l. A second abandoned scarp was located approximately 300 m to the southwest at 197 m a.s.l.

The upper 2.5 to 3.0 m of the section behind (south of) the lower scarp consisted of steeply dipping foreset beds of medium to fine sand. Abundant molluscs were found along the bedding planes of the foreset beds. Bulk samples for molluscan study were taken at 1.52 and 1.83 m from the top of the section. The lower part of the section consisted of horizontally bedded fine sand with molluscs found along the bedding planes. Plant debris found in the lowest part of the downstream end of the section has been radiocarbon dated at 9950 ± 490 B.P. (WAT-788) (P.F. Karrow, peru. commun., 1981). A bulk sample for molluscan analysis was taken 3.66 m from the top of the section.

Nottawasaga III Site

This site (M_3, Fig. 2) is located along the Nottawasaga River in the southeast corner of Angus. The upper 2 m of a 7-m section exposed oxidized, medium to fine sand with molluscs. The remainder of the section had slumped. Since molluscs were not overly abundant, considerable time was taken to obtain sufficient numbers for study. The top of the section was approximately 189 m a.s.l.

Minesing I Site

This site (M_4, Fig. 2) is located 2.3 km southwest of Minesing. A low rise trending north to south at 189 m a.s.l. was cut by a drainage ditch exposing 2 m of silty clay to silt. The upper 1 m contained very abundant molluscs, including unionid clams. Bulk samples for radiocarbon dating and molluscan study were obtained from the 1-m level.

Minesing II Site

This site (M_5, Fig. 2) is located 5.5 km north-northwest of Angus at an elevation of 188 m a.s.l. A 2.5 m section along Coates Creek exposed 0.7 m of marly, silty clay with molluscs, overlying 1.7 m of oxidized medium to fine sand. A 0.1 m layer of peaty, medium sand was found at the contact of the upper and lower units, and a sample was collected for pollen analysis. Although these samples were not analyzed, they are mentioned here as a possible future site for further study in this area.

RAISED SHORELINE INTERPRETATION

Figures 3 to 6 represent the interpreted location and configuration of lakes present in the Minesing Basin using isobase elevations from Goldthwait (1910), Stanley (1936, 1937, 1938) and Deane (1950). The isobase elevations were transferred to 1:50 000 topographic maps with 25-foot contour lines to enable the interpretations of lake configurations to be made. Only four of the many lakes that have existed in the Basin are shown here. Figure 2 illustrates all shoreline features found in the Minesing Basin.

Lake Algonquin (Fig. 3), occupied the Minesing Basin approximately 10 600 to 11 000 years B.P. and produced well-developed scarps, beaches, spits, and bars throughout the Basin. Isostatic rebound has tilted the lake plain of Algonquin up to the northeast causing a change in elevation of 18 m from the southwest to the northeast within the Basin. During the Algonquin occupation of the Minesing Basin, only the Barclay and Wales sites were not submerged. Lakes

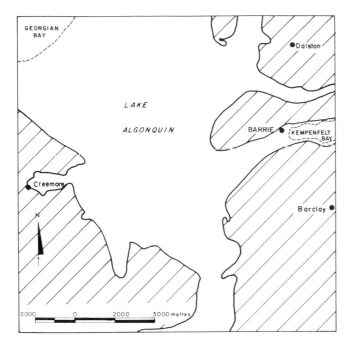

Figure 3. Lake Algonquin, shoreline interpretation.

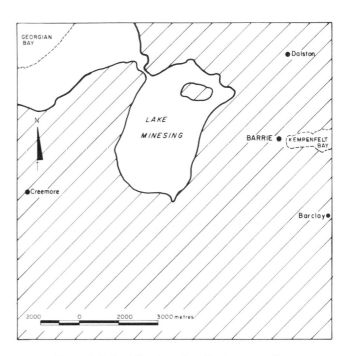

Figure 5. Lake Minesing, shoreline interpretation.

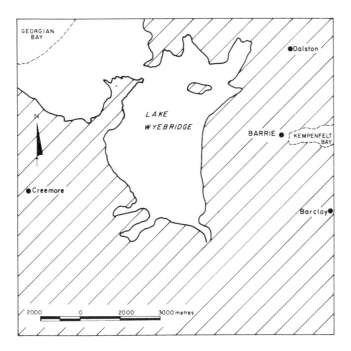

Figure 4. Lake Wyebridge, shoreline interpretation.

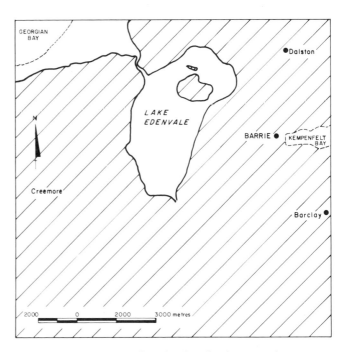

Figure 6. Lake Edenvale, shoreline interpretation.

Ardtrea, and Upper and Lower Orillia (Deane, 1946, 1950) were not identified, although they are most certainly included in those illustrated in Figure 2.

Lake Wyebridge (Fig. 4) (Stanley 1936, 1937, 1938) occupied the Minesing Basin, producing well-developed shoreline features. Isostatic rebound has tilted the lake plain of Wyebridge to the northeast causing a change in elevation of 12 m from southeast to northeast within the Minesing Basin. Nottawasaga I became emergent prior to the occupation of the Minesing Basin by Lake Wyebridge.

The Edenvale Moraine (Chapman and Putnam, 1966) became emergent during the lowering of the level of Lake Wyebridge to Lake Penetang (Stanley, 1936, 1937, 1938), which created a separate lake in the Minesing Basin (Fig. 5). This lake is named Lake Minesing (Fitzgerald, 1982) and its limits are recognized by a series of poorly developed shorelines. As the lake level dropped below that of the Penetang phase, the level of Lake Minesing lagged behind long enough to allow the river (which connected the lakes) to downcut through the Edenvale Moraine. The level of Lake

Minesing lowered as the river continued to downcut, creating a series of shorelines. Isostatic rebound has tilted the lake plain of Minesing to the northeast causing a change in elevation of 10 m from the southwest to the northeast within the Basin. The scarp located 300 m southwest of Nottawasaga II was cut by Lake Minesing.

The lake level in the Georgian Bay Basin continued to drop through the Cedar Point and Payette phases (Stanley 1936, 1937, 1938) to the low-level Lake Hough. The level of Lake Minesing lagged behind during the downcutting of its outlet through the Edenvale Moraine. Lake Minesing eventually drained, leaving isolated pondings or swamps in the Minesing Basin, much the same as today. All the sample sites in this study were dry and the paleosol found in U.W.B.H. 128-78 was probably developed at this time.

The river gradient through the Edenvale Moraine was reduced during the rise of the Nipissing phase in the Georgian Bay Basin. This caused the Minesing Basin to flood, creating Lake Edenvale (Fig. 6) (Fitzgerald, 1982). Lake Edenvale occupied the Minesing Basin at a slightly higher level than Lake Nipissing throughout Nipissing time. Isostatic rebound has only slightly affected the lake plain of Lake Edenvale. Sample sites U.W.B.H. 128-78 and 129-78, Minesing I and II, and Nottawasaga III were again submerged and the scarp at Nottawasaga II (elevation 189 m a.s.l.) was cut. A radiocarbon date on shells (*Goniobasis livescens*) from Minesing I dates Lake Edenvale (Nipissing phase) at 4320 ± 70 B.P. (WAT-559).

The level of the Nipissing phase dropped to the present level of Georgian Bay, increasing the gradient of the Nottawasaga River through the Edenvale Moraine and draining the Minesing Basin. Sections of the Basin (Minesing Swamp) remain wet today and during the spring runoff, a temporary lake forms when ice dams restrict flow through the narrows in the Edenvale Moraine.

POLLEN INTERPRETATION

Barclay Site

Pine- (*Pinus*) dominated pollen assemblages, similar to that of the lower part of the Barclay Site (Fig. 7), have commonly been interpreted as representing pine forests with scattered spruce (*Picea*) and oak (*Quercus*), (Bernabo and Webb, 1977; Anderson, 1971; Karrow et al., 1975; McAndrews, 1972, 1973). The low non-arboreal pollen (NAP) percentage indicates that the forest was essentially closed with few open areas. Local conditions were probably quite wet, as suggested by the high percentages of tamarack (*Larix*), cedar/juniper (*Cupressineae*), and red and black ash (*Fraxinus*), (Bobbette and Maycock, 1975; Hosie, 1969).

In the upper metre, the dominance of pine has been reduced by increased hemlock (*Tsuga*), oak, birch (*Betula*) and maple (*Acer*). The replacement of pine, is interpreted as indicating the northward migration of deciduous forest species in response to the warming of the climate. Bernabo and Webb (1977) illustrate this migration for birch, maple, beech (*Fagus*) and hemlock in the northeastern part of North America. Local conditions remained rather wet as suggested by the high percentages of tamarack, cedar/juniper, and red and black ash (Bobbette and Maycock, 1975; Hosie, 1969).

Wales Site

The domination of the lower half of the Wales Site pollen profile (Fig. 8) by spruce indicates it is within the Spruce Zone. Similar assemblages have commonly been interpreted as representing a spruce boreal forest (Bernabo and Webb, 1977; Anderson, 1971; Karrow et al., 1975, McAndrews, 1972; 1973). A radiocarbon date of 10 280 ± 100 B.P. (WAT-493) was obtained from a log found within the sandy gravel. The low NAP values suggest that there were few open areas within the spruce forest. High values of tamarack, cedar-juniper, and poplar (*Populus*) along with the dominating spruce indicate that the environment was cool and wet.

The partial replacement of spruce by pine represents the northward migration of pine into the area. The high values of spruce, tamarack, cedar/juniper, and red and black ash indicate that the environment continued to be wet.

The partial replacement of pine by hemlock and several deciduous species represents the continued northward migration of southern species in response to a warming and possible drying of the climate. NAP values increased slightly, indicating a more open forest while the local conditions remained relatively stable with wet low areas.

U.W.B.H. 129-78 and U.W.B.H. 129-78 Sites

Deposition of the lowermost lacustrine sediments (Fig. 9, 10), occurred during the occupation of the Minesing Basin by Lake Algonquin, 12 000 to 10 000 B.P. During Algonquin time these sites were submerged by 75 m of water. Palynomorph deposition in large bodies of water is greatly affected by differential floatation and sedimentation, and the strength and direction of wind and water currents (Davis and Brubaker, 1973; Hopkins, 1950; Brush and Brush, 1972). In addition, rivers entering a lake can bias the pollen assemblage towards the vegetation types present in the drainage basin of the river (McAndrews and Power, 1973; McAtee, 1977). Despite these factors it is considered that assemblages from large water bodies do represent the regional vegetation (Anderson and Terasmae, 1966; Davis et al., 1969; McAndrews, 1972, 1973; McAndrews and Power, 1973).

The vegetational history of the Minesing Swamp, as recorded by palynomorphs preserved, begins in the pre-Spruce/Pine Zone (present only in U.W.B.H. 128-78). Pine dominates this zone along with high percentages of spruce. Anderson's (1971) unit 2B closely resembles the pre-Spruce/Pine Zone and is interpreted as older than 11 000 B.P. Anderson (1971) considered the high pine percentage as representing windbown jackpine (*Pinus banksiana*), which originated further south. Bernabo and Webb (1977) suggest that less than 10% pine with high spruce can be expected in the Lake Simcoe Region prior to 11 000 B.P. Long-range transport of pine pollen from the south may explain the early high values.

Low pollen concentrations in the pre-Spruce-Pine Zone reflect the high sedimentation rate indicated by the thick rhythmites (varves) (2.03 cm average, 5 cm maximum) and the low pollen influx which may accompany an open pre-Boreal environment. The regional vegetation probably con-

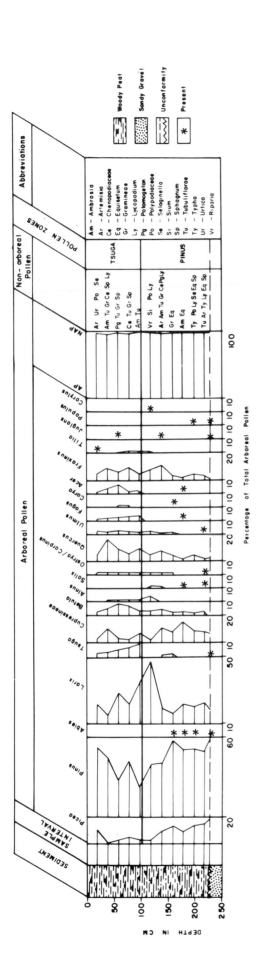

BARCLAY ONTARIO
RELATIVE POLLEN DIAGRAM

Figure 7. Barclay Site, pollen diagram.

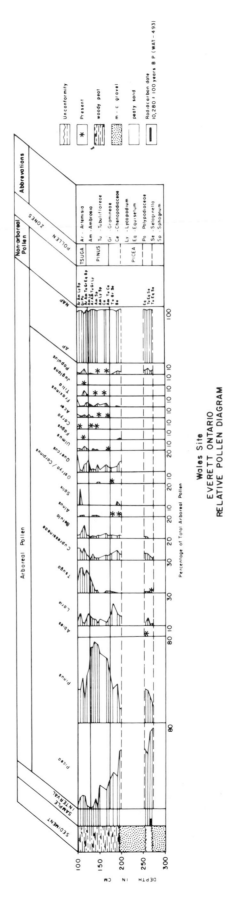

Wales Site
EVERETT ONTARIO
RELATIVE POLLEN DIAGRAM

Figure 8. Everett Site, pollen diagram.

sisted of a few scattered spruce, some shrubs, and grasses along with cedar/juniper and tamarack in the low wetland.

The Minesing Basin continued to be occupied by part of Lake Algonquin during the Spruce Zone. Varve counts indicate 654 years of deposition during the Spruce Zone in U.W.B.H. 128-78 and 688 years in U.W.B.H. 129-78. The spruce values are variable, with two maxima of 65% in U.W.B.H. 128-78 and one of 50% in 129-78. Pine appears stable, with variations reflecting those of spruce.

The Minesing Basin was still submerged by the waters of Lake Algonquin, the Upper Group of Algonquin beaches (Deane, 1950), the Lower Algonquin beaches (Stanley, 1936, 1937, 1938), and Lake Minesing (Fitzgerald, 1982) throughout the lower half of the Pine Zone. An unconformity within the Pine Zone, in both cores, marks the first time the sites

became emergent. Karrow *et al.* (1975) state that Lake Algonquin drained from the Cookstown site (Anderson, 1971) as late as 10 400 B.P. and from the Nicolston cut close to 10 600 B.P. (Anderson, 1971; Karrow *et al.*, 1975). Due to their elevation, they became emergent during the fall of Lake Algonquin and were probably not submerged by any of the post Lake Algonquin lake levels. The Minesing Basin, because of its lower elevation, continued to be submerged for some time after the above sites became dry. The environment of deposition within the Pine Zone above the unconformity had changed from a large lake to that of a quiet shallow lake, which occasionally became dry.

The regional vegetation throughout the Pine Zone consisted of a pine forest with declining amounts of spruce. During deposition of the varved sediment the local condi-

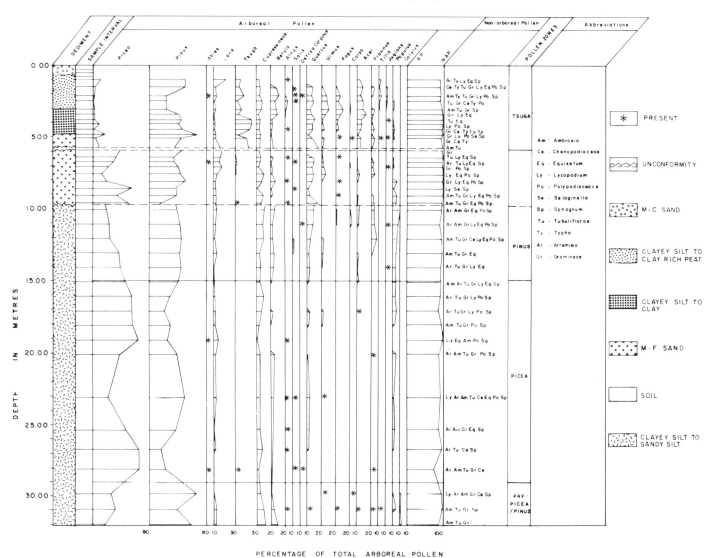

PERCENTAGE OF TOTAL ARBOREAL POLLEN

UWBH 128-78
MINESING SWAMP
RELATIVE POLLEN DIAGRAM

Figure 9. U.W.B.H. 128-78, pollen diagram.

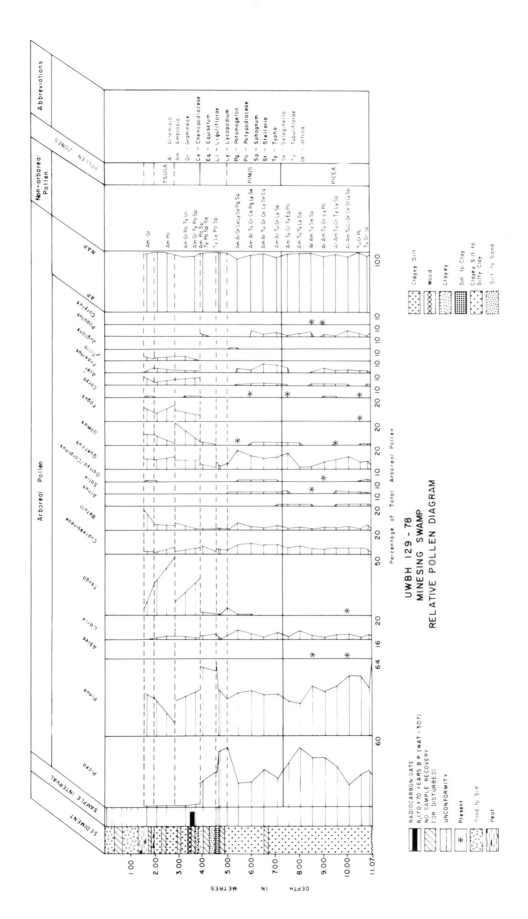

UWBH 129-78
MINESING SWAMP
RELATIVE POLLEN DIAGRAM

Figure 10. U.W.B.H. 129-78, pollen diagram.

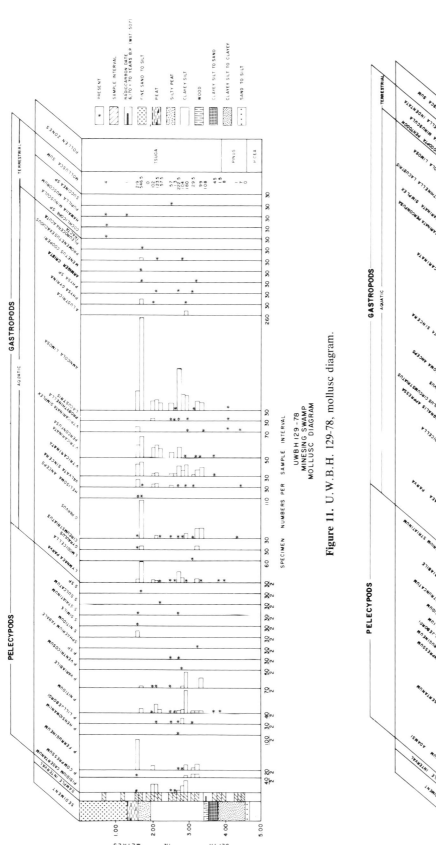

Figure 11. U.W.B.H. 129-78, mollusc diagram.

Figure 12. Nottawasaga I, mollusc diagram.

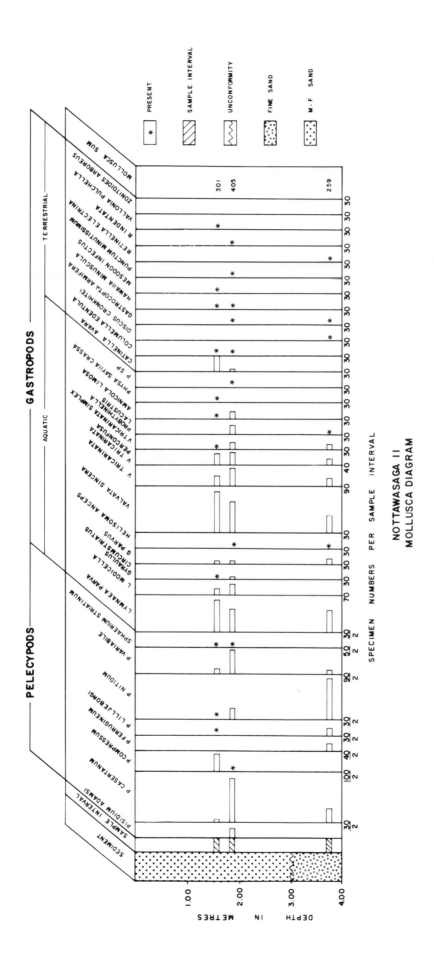

Figure 13. Nottawasaga II, mollusc diagram.

tions were much the same as during the Spruce Zone. During deposition of non-varved sediment, the upper Pine Zone, the sites were periodically dry and vegetated by black spruce (*Picea mariana*), tamarack, and cedar/juniper, while the surrounding uplands consisted of a forest dominated by pine.

The top of the Pine Zone is truncated in both cores, marking the boundary between the Pine/Hemlock Zones. This boundary in U.W.B.H. 128-78 is marked by a poorly developed soil horizon. A significant hiatus is suggested by the major changes in the pine, spruce, and hemlock percentages.

The Minesing Basin was flooded by Lake Edenvale during part of the Hemlock Zone. The instability of the Lake Edenvale water level is reflected by the number of unconformities present in U.W.B.H. 129-78 and the sediment changes in both cores. The unconformities at 3.88 m and 2.79 m represent significant lengths of time as reflected by major changes in a number of species, for example, pine, spruce, hemlock and grass. The unconformities at 1.93 m and 1.57 m in U.W.B.H. 129-78 represent shorter time intervals, since the vegetation appears relatively stable.

A bimodal hemlock maximum has been observed in several pollen assemblages in Southern Ontario and is present in both Minesing cores. The first peak occurred approximately 7500 B.P. and was followed by peaks in white pine (*Pinus strobus*) and hardwoods approximately 3500 B.P., (Anderson, 1971; Terasmae and Anderson, 1970). The interval between the hemlock peaks has been interpreted as the "Hypsithermal", a time of possibly warmer and/or drier conditions (Deevey and Flint, 1957; Terasmae, 1973; Wright 1972; Emiliani, 1972). A radiocarbon analysis of wood from the 3.40 m to 3.51 m interval in U.W.B.H. 129-78 yielded an age of 6170 ± 100 B.P. (WAT-507).

During the Hemlock Zone the pine was partially replaced by deciduous hardwoods. The local vegetation probably underwent sudden changes because of the fluctuating lake levels in the Minesing Basin. Black spruce (*Picea mariana*), tamarack, and cedar/juniper dominated the local low wetlands, as they do today.

INTERPRETATION OF MOLLUSCAN ASSEMBLAGES

U.W.B.H. 129-78, Minesing Swamp Site

The lower 1.22 m (Fig. 11) of the section analyzed for molluscs lies within the Pine Zone (Fig. 10). Three unconformities are present representing periods of non-deposition, while fine-grained sediments were deposited at other times. Few molluscs were found in this interval, possibly due to the instability of the water levels. It is doubtful that the migration of molluscs into the area had not yet occurred because Algonquin sites in the Alliston Basin contain abundant molluscs (Miller *et al.*, 1979), as do sites along the Nottawasaga River (Fitzgerald, 1982).

The few species present indicate a quiet or sheltered, littoral environment (Larocque, 1966, 1967, 1968, 1970; Harman, 1968; Clarke, 1973; Miller *et al.*, 1979). This is supported by the sediment type in which the molluscs are found and the intermittent nature of the lake occupation at this site.

In the Hemlock Zone, *Amnicola limosa* was by far the most abundant mollusc present, with a number of other

species being common (Fig. 11). The molluscs present indicate a quiet, open, lacustrine environment (Larocque, 1966, 1967, 1968, 1970; Harman, 1968; Clarke, 1973; Miller *et al.*, 1979). During times of higher abundance of *Gyraulus parvus*, and *Valvata tricarinata*, the lacustrine environment may have been substantially more permanent, cool, and silt free (Miller *et al.*, 1979).

The Minesing Basin was occupied by Lake Edenvale during this time period. *Goniobasis livescens*, which has been considered a "Zone" fossil for Nipissing deposits (Miller *et al.*, 1979), is absent from this assemblage. This species is a shallow-water inhabitant, therefore, it would not be expected to occur at deep-water sites, although it might have been present temporarily during the rising-water stage.

The upper part of the Hemlock Zone contained only a few terrestrial gastropods. The upper part of this zone has been interpreted to be alluvial in nature, and therefore, the absence of aquatic molluscs and the presence of only a few terrestrial gastropods is to be expected. The area had drained and the few molluscs present were probably washed into the site.

NOTTAWASAGA I SITE

The lowest point at which molluscs were observed in this river section was at the unconformity between laminated clayey silt and the overlying deposit of medium to coarse, pebbly sand. The mollusc assemblage obtained from this level (Fig. 12) contained abundant *Lymnaea parva* and *L. modicella*, indicating shallow water with moderate current such as a slow-flowing river (Harman, 1968; Larocque, 1968; Clarke, 1973; Karrow *et al.*, 1975; Miller *et al.*, 1979). The presence of a large, quiet lake is also indicated by the presence of *Valvata tricarinata* and *V. sincera*. A transitional environment between deep water lacustrine and a shallow, slow-moving river is probable.

In the second assemblage, 0.30 m above the first, *Valvata tricarinata*, *V. sincera*, and *Valvata tricarinata perconfusa* are much more abundant; *Amnicola limosa* and *Probythinella lacustris* also become more abundant. These indicate deeper, quieter water, with *Lymnaea parva* and *L. modicella* slightly more common and abundant *Gyraulus parvus* present, suggesting a shallow slow-moving water environment (Harman, 1968; Larocque, 1968; Clarke, 1973; Karrow *et al.*, 1975; Miller *et al.*, 1979). The environment of deposition was probably still transitional between an open deep lake and that of a slow-moving river.

The third level sampled, 3.05 m above the first, also in medium to coarse sands, was dominated by *Lymnaea parva*, *L. modicella*, *Probythinella lacustris*, and *Amnicola limosa*. *Pisidium casertanum*, *P. variabile*, *P. adamsi*, and *P. nitidum* also became abundant. The presence of these molluscs in large numbers indicates that the environment of deposition had become a shallow lacustrine one. The shoreline was definitely closer to this site than during the period of deposition of previous samples.

The location and elevation of this site indicates deposition within glacial Lake Algonquin and several of the lower phases. The presence of *Lymnaea modicella* within these sediments supports an Algonquin age because Miller *et al.*

(1979) state that this species is restricted to Algonquin deposits within the Alliston Basin.

NOTTAWASAGA II

The lowest sample taken at this site (Fig. 13), 3.66 m below the top of the section, was within horizontally bedded, fine sands. *Pisidium nitidum, P. casertanum, P. lilljeborgi,* and *P. ferrugineum* indicate a shallow water environment with a moderate current and possibly some vegetation present (Harman, 1968; Larocque, 1968; Clarke, 1973; Karrow *et al.*, 1975; Miller *et al.*, 1979). *Lymnaea parva, Valvata sincera,* and *V. tricarinata* indicate a shallow, nearshore, well-vegetated environment. The environment during deposition was probably near a river entering a large, quiet water body.

The second sample, taken from 1.83 m above the first, was from steeply dipping foreset beds of medium to fine sands. The aquatic gastropods present in the first sample were still abundant while *Lymnaea modicella* and *Valvata tricarinata perconfusa* became more common. This indicates shallower water, possibly closer to shore with increased vegetation (Harman, 1968; Larocque, 1968; Clarke, 1973; Karrow *et al.*, 1975; Miller *et al.*, 1979). *Pisidium lilljeborgi* and *P. ferrugineum* were less abundant, whereas *P. variabile* and *P. adamsi* were more abundant, indicating a shallower, vegetated environment with moderate current (Harman, 1968; Larocque, 1968; Clarke, 1973; Karrow *et al.*, 1975; Miller *et al.*, 1979).

The uppermost sample, taken from 2.14 m above the first, was from sands similar to those of the second sample. *Pisidium compressum* was the only pelecypod commonly found, but aquatic gastropods previously found were still common. *Catinella avara* had become abundant, indicating a nearby terrestrial environment. This assemblage of molluscs suggests a continued trend toward shallower water conditions, increased vegetation, and close proximity with the lakeshore (Harman, 1968; Larocque, 1968; Clarke, 1973; Karrow *et al.*, 1975; Miller *et al.*, 1979).

SUMMARY

During the final deglaciation of the Minesing Basin, approximately 12 000 B.P., glacial lakes occupied lowland areas adjacent to the ice-front. Shoreline features of the earliest lakes are poorly developed and have not been positively identified within the area.

During Algonquin time, 12 000 to 10 000 B.P., the Wales and Barclay sites were above the level of glacial Lake Algonquin. Organic accumulation began at the Barclay site during the latter part of the Pine Zone, less than 9500 B.P., and therefore the organics post-date the occupation of the surrounding lowlands by glacial Lake Algonquin. Deposition of fluvial sands and gravels at the Wales Site occurred during the Spruce Zone, 10 280 ± 100 B.P. (WAT-493). This corresponds to the later phases of glacial Lake Algonquin, possibly during Upper or Lower Orillia phases.

The Nottawasaga I site continued to be submerged until the lake level dropped below 213 m a.s.l., possibly the Lower Orillia phase. This interpretation is consistent with molluscs found which indicate an Algonquin age, i.e., *Lymnaea modicella* (Miller *et al.*, 1979).

The Nottawasaga II site became emergent when the lake level dropped below 192 m a.s.l., probably during Lake Minesing time (post-Wyebridge). A radiocarbon date obtained from organics found within the lower sediments gave an age of 9950 ± 490 B.P. (WAT-788), consistent with an acceptable minimum age for the draining of Lake Algonquin. The presence of *Lymnaea modicella* is suggestive of glacial Lake Algonquin deposit (Miller *et al.*, 1979).

The Minesing Basin became emergent some time after the Nottawasaga II site emerged, approximately 8000 years ago. Both U.W.B.H. 128-78 and U.W.B.H. 129-78 exhibit evidence of this, with U.W.B.H. 128-78 having a poorly developed paleosol horizon. The Basin probably resembled the Minesing Swamp as it is today.

Parts of the Minesing Basin became submerged once more due to the rise of Nipissing waters in the Georgian Bay Basin, creating Lake Edenvale. Two radiocarbon dates, one on wood from U.W.B.H. 129-78 (6170 ± 100 B.P., WAT-559), and one from shells found at the Minesing I site (4230 ± 70 B.P., WAT-559), indicate the existence of Lake Edenvale between 6000 and 4000 B.P.

Eventually the level of Lake Nipissing lowered to that of present-day Georgian Bay, causing Lake Edenvale to be drained.

ACKNOWLEDGEMENTS

The author thanks P.F. Karrow of the University of Waterloo for his guidance and encouragement, also Gail Jones, Cathy Martin and Raffaella Mooney for their assistance in the manuscript preparation. Randy Miller provided field assistance. Special thanks is given to my wife Kathy for her assistance and patience while preparing this paper.

REFERENCES

Anderson, T.W., 1971, Postglacial Vegetative Changes in the Lake Huron-Lake Simcoe District, Ontario, with Special Reference to Glacial Lake Algonquin: Ph.D. Thesis, Waterloo, Ontario, University of Waterloo, 246 p.

Anderson, T.W., and Terasmae, J., 1966, Palynological Study of the Bottom Sediments in Georgian Bay, Lake Huron: Great Lakes Research Division, University of Michigan Publication 15, p. 164-168.

Bernabo, J.C. and Webb, T. III, 1977, Changing Patterns in the Holocene Pollen Record of Northeastern North America: A Mapped Summary: Quaternary Research, v. 8, no. 1, p. 64-96.

Bobbette, R.S.W., and Maycock, P.F., 1975, Minesing Swamp Survey, General Description, Materials and Methods, and Ordinations: Prepared for the Minesing Swamp Technical Committee, P. Harvie, Chairman (unpublished), 172 p.

Brush, G.A., and Brush, L.M. Jr., 1972, Transport of Pollen in a Sediment-laden Channel: A Laboratory Study: American Journal of Science, v. 272, p. 359-381.

Chapman, L.J., and Putnam, D.F., 1966, Physiography of Southern Ontario: Ontario Research Foundation, Toronto, University of Toronto Press, 386 p.

Clarke, A.H., 1973, The Freshwater Molluscs of the Canadian Interior Basin: Malacologia, v. 13 (1-2), 509 p.

Davis, R.B., Brewster, L.A., and Sutherland, J., 1969, Variation in Pollen Spectra Within Lakes: Pollen et Spores, v. 11, p. 557-572.

Davis, M.B., and Brubaker, L.B., 1973, Differential Sedimentation of Pollen Grains in Lakes: Limnology and Oceanography, v. 18, no. 4, p. 635-646.

Deane, R.E., 1946, Pleistocene Deposits and Beaches of Orillia Map Area, Simcoe and Ontario Counties, Ontario (Preliminary Account): Geological Survey of Canada Paper 46-20, 29 p.

———, 1950, Pleistocene Geology of the Lake Simcoe District Ontario: Geological Survey of Canada Memoir 256, 108 p.

Deevey, E.S., and Flint, R.F., 1957, Postglacial Hypsithermal Interval: Science, v. 125, p. 182-184.

Emiliani, C., 1972, Quaternary Hypsithermals: Quaternary Research, v. 2, p. 270-273.

Faegri, K, and Iversen, J., 1964, Textbook of Modern Pollen Analysis: 2nd ed., Oxford, England, Blackwell, 295 p.

Fitzgerald, W.D., 1982, Post Glacial History of the Minesing Basin, Ontario: M.Sc. Thesis, Waterloo, Ontario, University of Waterloo, 93 p.

Goldthwait, J.W., 1910, An Instrumental Survey of the Shorelines of the Extinct Lakes Algonquin and Nipissing in Southwestern Ontario: Canada Department of Mines, Geological Survey Branch Memoir No. 10, 57 p.

Harman, W.N., 1968, The Distribution and Ecology of the Aquatic Gastropods of Central New York with Illustrated Keys to the Genera and Species: Ph.D. Thesis, Ithaca, New York, Cornell University, 398 p.

Hopkins, J.S., 1950, Differential Floatation and Deposition of Coniferous and Deciduous Tree Pollen: Ecology, v. 31, p. 633-641.

Hosie, R.C., 1969, Native Trees of Canada: Canadian Forestry Service, Department of Fisheries and Forestry, Ottawa, Ontario, Queen's Printer of Canada, 380 p.

Karrow, P.F., Anderson, T.W., Clarke, A.H., Delorme, L.D., and Sreenivasa, M.R., 1975, Stratigraphy, Paleontology, and Age of Lake Algonquin Sediments in Southwestern Ontario, Canada: Quaternary Research, v. 5, No. 1, p. 49-87.

LaRocque, A., 1966, Pleistocene Mollusca of Ohio Part 1: State of Ohio Geological Survey Bulletin 62, p. 1-111.

———, 1967, Pleistocene Mollusca of Ohio Part 2: State of Ohio Geological Survey Bulletin 62, p. 113-356.

———, 1968, Pleistocene Mollusca of Ohio Part 3: State of Ohio Geological Survey Bulletin 62, p. 357-553.

———, 1970, Pleistocene Mollusca of Ohio Part 4: State of Ohio Geological Survey Bulletin 62, p. 555-800.

McAndrews, J.H., 1972, Pollen Analysis of the Sediments of Lake Ontario: International Geological Congress — 24th, Section 8, p. 223-227.

———, 1973, Pollen Analysis of the Sediments of the Great Lakes of North America: Proceedings of the III International Palynological Conference, p. 76-80.

McAndrews, J.H., and Power, D.M., 1973, Palynology of the Great Lakes: The Surface Sediments of Lake Ontario: Canadian Journal Earth Sciences, v. 10, p. 777-792.

McAtee, C.L., 1977, Palynology of Late-Glacial and Postglacial Sediments in Georgian Bay, Ontario, Canada, as Related to the Great Lakes History: M.Sc. Thesis, St. Catharines, Ontario, Brock University, 153 p.

Miller, B.B., Karrow, P.F., and Kalas, L.L., 1979, Late Quaternary Mollusks from Glacial Lake Algonquin, Nipissing, and Transitional Sediments from Southwestern Ontario, Canada: Quaternary Research, v. 11, p. 93-112.

Stanley, G.M., 1936, Lower Algonquin Beaches of Penetanguishene Peninsula: Geological Society of American Bulletin, v. 47, p. 1933-1960.

———, 1937, Lower Algonquin Beaches of Cape Rich, Georgian Bay: Geological Society of America Bulletin v. 48, p. 1665-1686.

———, 1938, Impounded Early Algonquin Beaches at Sucker Creek, Grey County, Ontario: Papers, Michigan Academy of Science, Arts, and Letters. v. 23, p. 477-495.

Terasmae, J., 1973, Notes on Late Wisconsinan and Early Holocene History of Vegetation in Canada: Arctic and Alpine Research. v. 5, No. 3, Pt. 1, p. 201-222.

Terasmae, J., and Anderson, T.W., 1970, Hypsithermal Range Extension of White Pine (*Pinus strobus L.*) in Quebec, Canada: Canadian Jounal of Earth Sciences, v. 7, p. 406-413.

Wright, H.E., Jr., 1972, Interglacial and Postglacial Climate: The Pollen Record; Quaternary Research. v. 2, p. 274-282.

Quaternary Evolution of the Great Lakes,
edited by P.F. Karrow and P.E. Calkin,
Geological Association of Canada Special Paper 30, 1985

POSTGLACIAL LAKE LEVELS IN THE HURON BASIN: COMPARATIVE UPLIFT HISTORIES OF BASINS AND SILLS IN A REBOUNDING GLACIAL MARGINAL DEPRESSION

C.F.M. Lewis
Geological Survey of Canada, Box 1006, Dartmouth, Nova Scotia B2Y 4A2

T.W. Anderson
Geological Survey of Canada, 601 Booth Street, Ottawa, Ontario K1A 0E8

ABSTRACT

The postglacial rebound of Huron and adjacent basins is documented by the regional occurrence of the prominent upwarped Algonquin and Nipissing shorelines, approximately dated 10 500 and 4700 B.P. respectively. An exponential uplift history function, $E(t) = E_p - U_a e^{k(T_a - t)}$ where $E(t)$ is elevation at variable time t ka B.P., E_p is the present elevation, and U_a and T_a are the magnitude and age (ka B.P.) of the post Algonquin uplift respectively, was formulated to describe the kinematic rebound of any site relative to the southernmost defined (and least deformed) Algonquin and Nipissing isobases. At any site the uplift and age values for these two shorelines permit evaluation of the parameters and use of the uplift history function for predicting site elevation vs. time. The uplift histories and elevations of all potential drainage control sills were compared. The lake-level history was deduced by selecting the route of lowest control sills from eastern Superior and northern Michigan basins through all sub-basins of Huron and Georgian Bay areas to the outlet at North Bay. This computed history, outlined below, agrees with the available ^{14}C datings of sediments related to former water-planes.

Following drainage of the post-Algonquin glacial lakes, low-level Lake Stanley was isolated in northern Lake Huron basin (about 10 200 B.P. at about 50 m asl) and received runoff from higher ground in southern Lake Huron, Lakes Michigan and Superior basins. Lake Stanley drained north of Manitoulin Island into Lake Hough in Georgian Bay, leaving sills between Bruce Peninsula and Manitoulin Island dry. Lake Hough discharged northeastward via French River and North Bay outlet to Ottawa Valley. Stratigraphic evidence indicates a superimposed hydrological rise in lake levels in the order of 10 m or greater from about 9500 to 8500 B.P. This rise is correlated tentatively with glacial Lake Agassiz (Nipigon phase) discharge through Huron and Georgian Bay basins. By about 8200 B.P. the Lake Hough sill had backflooded upstream sills to create a confluent waterbody throughout Georgian Bay, Lake Huron and Lake Michigan basins. The North Bay outlet emerged in control of Georgian Bay, Huron and Michigan waters about 7800 B.P. and of Superior waters about 6400 B.P. Lake levels culminated in the Nipissing Great Lakes phase (184 m asl) which began to regress about 4700 B.P. as southern outlets from Huron and Michigan basins came into operation. Subsequent downward adjustment of the Huron outlet caused regression of the Michigan-Huron lakes to their present mean level (176.2 m asl).

RÉSUMÉ

Le relèvement isostatique postglaciaire du bassin du lac Huron et de ses bassins adjacents est enregistré par la présence des limites de rivage fossiles des lacs Algonquin et Nipissing, limites datées respectivement à 10 500 et 4700 B.P. La fonction décrivant le relèvement, $E(t) = E_p - U_a e^{k(T_a - t)}$ est une exponentielle, où $E(t)$ est l'élévation pour un temps variable t en ka B.P., E_p est l'élévation actuelle, U_a et T_a sont respectivement l'ampleur et l'âge en ka B.P. du relèvement post-Algonquin. Cette fonction a été formulée pour décrire le relèvement de tout site relié aux isobases les plus au sud (et les moins déformées) des lacs Algonquin et Nipissing. A n'importe quel site, les valeurs de relèvement et l'âge des deux limites de rivages permettent l'évaluation des paramètres nécessaires pour utiliser la fonction de relèvement et calculer l'élévation du site en fonction du temps. Par la suite, on compara l'histoire du relèvement et l'élévation de tous les seuils susceptibles de contrôler le drainage. L'histoire des niveaux des lacs a été déduite en choisissant le passage par les plus bas seuils de contrôle à partir de l'est du bassin du lac Supérieur et du nord du bassin du lac Michigan jusqu'à l'exutoire situé à North Bay, en passant par les sous-bassins de la région du lac Huron et de la Baie Georgienne. Cette histoire, résumée dans le paragraphe suivant, est en accord avec les datations au ^{14}C de sédiments associés aux plans d'eau antérieurs.

A la suite du drainage des lacs glaciaires post-Algonquin, le lac Stanley, d'un bas niveau d'eau, fut isolé dans le bassin nord du lac Huron (à environ 10 200 B.P. et 50m d'alt.) et reçut le déversement des bassins des lacs Huron, Michigan et Supérieur, de niveau plus élevé. Le lac Stanley se déversa dans le lac Hough, situé dans la Baie Georgienne, laissant des seuils secs entre la péninsule Bruce et l'île Manitoulin. Le lac Hough se déversa vers le nord en utilisant la rivière French et l'exutoire de North Bay jusqu'à la vallée de la rivière Outaouais. Des évidences stratigraphiques démontrent qu'il y a eu une hausse hydrologique des niveaux des lacs vers 9500 à 8500 B.P. Cette hausse atteignait un ordre de grandeur de 10 mètres ou même plus, et on lu relie à la décharge du lac glaciaire Agassiz (stade Nipigon) à travers les bassins du lac Huron et de la Baie Georgienne. Vers 8200 B.P., le seuil du lac Hough se déplaça vers l'amont, ce qui entraîna le passage de l'eau à travers les bassins de la Baie Georgienne, du lac Huron et du lac Michigan. L'exutoire de North Bay commença à contrôler les eaux des bassins de la Baie Georgienne, du lac Huron et du lac Michigan vers 7800 B.P. et du bassin du lac Supérieur vers 6400 B.P. Les niveaux des lacs atteignirent leurs maximums au stade "Grand Lacs Nipissing" (184m d'alt.) lequel commença à régresser vers 4700 B.P., alors que les exutoires sud des bassins des lacs Huron et Michigan commencèrent à fonctionner. Par la suite, le creusement de l'exutoire du bassin du lac Huron entraîna la baisse des lacs Michigan-Huron jusqu'à leur moyenne actuelle (176.2m d'alt.)

Quaternary Evolution of the Great Lakes,
edited by P.F. Karrow and P.E. Calkin,
Geological Association of Canada Special Paper 30, 1985

EVOLUTION OF THE ERIE-BASIN GREAT LAKES

Parker E. Calkin

Department of Geological Sciences, State University of New York, Buffalo, New York 14226

Bern H. Feenstra

Ministry of Natural Resources, 458 Central Avenue, London, Ontario N6B 2E5

ABSTRACT

The Erie basin had the earliest completed and one of the most complex successions of deglacial Great Lakes. It began 14 500 B.P. in northeastern Indiana and northwestern Ohio as Lake Maumee evolved with northward ice margin retreat. Lake Maumee, with 244-m, 238-m, and 232-m phases, drained westward through several different outlets before expansion resulted in a lower set of levels at 216, 213, and 212 m, designated as phases of Lake Arkona.

Subsequent ice-marginal retreat into the Lake Ontario basin during the Mackinaw Interstade about 13 300 B.P. caused reversal of drainage and Erie basin water levels dropped to the low, nonglacial Lake Ypsilanti. The subsequent Port Huron readvance reestablished westward drainage (through Ubly, Michigan) about 13 000 B.P. to form Lake Whittlesey, at 225 m. Following this, outlet deepening on the west, first rapidly, then more slowly, resulted in lower levels assigned to Lake Warren at 210, 207, and 206 m. Lowest Warren, which terminated at about 12 600 B.P., may have followed a drop to the 201-m Wayne level.

Ephemeral glacial lakes Grassmere, at 195 m, and Lundy, at 189 m, may have preceded a transient west-draining Early Lake Algonquin at 184 m, but subsiding waters in the northeastern Lake Erie basin drained eastward, lowering lake levels below the Niagara Escarpment about 12 400 B.P. This marked the nearly simultaneous formation of nonglacial Early Lake Erie, at 40 m below present level, Lake Iroquois in the Ontario basin, the intervening Lake Tonowanda, and initiation of the Niagara Falls and Gorge. Glacioisostatic uplift, with the modulating effect of changes of inflow discharge from the upper Great Lakes, raised lake levels from an initial two- or three-basin Early Lake Erie phase to an integrated lake within 4 m of the present level by 3400 B.P.

RÉSUMÉ

La plus ancienne des successions de déglaciation des Grands Lacs, et une des plus complexes, commença 14 500 ans B.P. dans le nord-ouest de l'Ohio avec la formation du lac Maumee lors du retrait de la glace vers le nord à travers la moraine Defiance. Le lac Maumee se drainait vers l'ouest lors des phases 244, 238 et 232 m. L'expansion du lac permit une seconde série de pauses aux niveaux 216, 213 et 212 m, appelée lac Arkona.

Le retrait ultérieur de la glace dans le bassin du lac Ontario au cours de l'interstade Mackinaw, 13 300 ans B.P. inversa le drainage et fit baisser le niveau du lac Érié jusqu'au lac non-glaciaire Ypsilanti. Toutefois, l'avancée de Port Huron rétablit le drainage vers l'ouest (par Ubly, au Michigan) 13 000 ans B.P. pour former le lac Whittlesey au niveau 225 m. Puis, l'oscillation glaciaire approfondit l'exutoire vers l'ouest, rapidement d'abord, puis plus lentement avec des pauses aux niveaux 210, 207 et 206 m. Ces phases du lac Warren se terminent 12 600 ans B.P. Le lac Warren inférieur a pu s'être formé après une baisse du niveau lacustre jusqu'à la cote 201 m correspondant au lac Wayne.

Les lacs glaciaires Grassmere au niveau 195 m et Lundy au niveau 189 m peuvent avoir précédé une période transitoire de drainage vers l'ouest appartenant à la phase initiale du lac Algonquin (184 m). Cependant, la baisse des eaux au nord-est du bassin du lac Érié permit un déversement vers l'est portant ainsi les niveaux lacustres en-dessous de l'escarpement du Niagara 12 400 ans B.P. Ceci marque la formation presque simultanée de la phase initiale du lac nonglaciaire Érié à 40 m au-dessous de son niveau actuel, du lac Iroquois dans le bassin de l'Ontario, du lac nonglaciaire Tonawanda, de même que de la gorge et des chutes du Niagara.

Sous l'influence du relèvement isostatique combiné aux variations d'écoulement des bassins supérieurs des Grands Lacs, le niveau d'eau lors de la phase initiale du lac Érié s'est progressivement élevé pour se retrouver, il y a 3400 ans à 4 m au-dessous du niveau actuel.

INTRODUCTION

Lake Erie, the southernmost and shallowest of the Laurentian Great Lakes (Fig. 1; Sly and Lewis, 1972), is the present-day result of the earliest completed, yet one of the more complicated of the deglacial Great Lakes successions. These lakes developed following thinning of the Laurentide ice sheet and final ice-marginal retreat into the Lake Erie and Lake Michigan basins about 14 500 years B.P. (Leverett and Taylor, 1915; Prest, 1970; Fullerton, 1980; Mickelson *et al.*, 1983). A series of proglacial (ice-dammed) and nonglacial low lake phases was initiated at this time as a result of repeated ice-marginal readvances, crustal warping due to glacial unloading and reloading, and downcutting of lake outlets during the overall ice-sheet dissipation. Only fragmentary evidence remains of earlier lake successions in the Lake Erie basin, and these features are largely buried (Dreimanis, 1969; also see Totten, 1982, 1985). However, such lakes must have formed during each Quaternary glaciation (Wayne and Zumberge, 1965).

The types of evidence used to define the now-classic deglacial Great Lakes succession considered in this paper have been recognized and described for many years. The earliest description of the lake plain rimming Lake Erie may be that by Dewey (1818) in Ohio. Whittlesey (1838, p. 55) described beach ridges in Ohio, including some that he recognized as being tilted. Later, Whittlesey (1850) examined wave-cut cliffs and terraces which occurred at altitudes lower than the beach ridges. Definition of water planes on the basis of altitudes of Great Lakes outlets may have begun with the recognition by Hubbard (1840) of the Fort Wayne, Indiana, outlet of Lake Maumee. These observations all came before the link between the lakes and a former ice sheet was conceived (Leverett, 1902).

Within the Lake Erie basin, shore features that record successively younger levels of Lake Maumee through Lake Lundy all have been differentially upwarped north of Cleveland, Ohio, and Detroit, Michigan, by glacial isostatic adjustment along an apparent maximum uplift trend of 020° to 030°. Unless otherwise indicated, altitudes given in this paper that represent former water surfaces are averages. They are derived from the measured altitudes of beach crests, or less commonly from other strand features, south of the so-called "zero isobase" for each reconstructed surface in the areas of apparent "horizontality" (Leverett and Taylor, 1915; Hough, 1963; see Deformation of the Shore Features).

Both the process of testing the glacial theory championed by Louis Agassiz, and the correlation of strand features and glacial advances in the Lake Erie Basin evolved concurrently during the latter half of the 19th Century through the efforts of many workers (see Leverett, 1902, for a review). However, the sequence of late Quaternary Great Lakes was reconstructed at the turn of the century principally by F. B. Taylor, Frank Leverett, and others as cited on the following pages. The general lake succession of Leverett and Taylor (1915), including the concept that some of the abandoned beaches (e.g., Lowest Maumee, Arkona, and Wayne) had been submerged by each of the repectively succeeding higher water phases, has been followed with some important

changes by Hough (1958, 1963, 1966), Wayne and Zumberge (1965), Chapman and Putnam (1966), Dorr and Eschman (1970), and Prest (1970).

Like many of our predecessors in Great Lakes reviews, we attempt to reconstruct the evolution of the Lake Erie-basin Great Lakes succession through an integration of the more relevant older literature and more recent research. This mixture of sources leaves room for alternative interpretations and conflicting chronologies in some cases; however, it also may encourage more critical field studies in the future. Our preferred chronology of the lake succession is shown in Figure 2.

LAKE MAUMEE

Evolution of the deglacial Great Lakes in the Lake Erie basin began in northwestern Ohio and northeastern Indiana following culmination of the Hiram glacial readvance during the Late Wisconsin, Port Bruce Stade (Fullerton 1980; Mickelson *et al.*, 1983). The margin of the ice lobe, formed of confluent Ontario-Erie and Huron-Erie ice flow, then retreated northeastward from the Wabash Moraine and subsequently from the succeeding Fort Wayne Moraine to a position farther east in the north-trending Maumee River valley (Figs. 1 and 3). Minimum ages for recession from the Hiram advance limit in Ohio are 14 500 ± 150 B.P. (ISGS-402; White, 1982) in northeastern Ohio to 14 300 ± 50 B.P. (W-198; Goldthwait, 1958) on the Wabash Moraine near Fort Wayne, Indiana (also see Mickelson *et al.*, 1983).

The earliest deglacial lakes in the Lake Erie basin may have been narrow ice marginal ones in northern Ohio, such as those that initially drained southward from the Cuyahoga and Black River valleys (Leverett, 1902; White, 1982). Others formed on the proximal side of the Fort Wayne Moraine near Lima, Ohio (Forsyth, 1973).

Continued ice-margin recession from the Fort Wayne Moraine soon initiated Highest Lake Maumee (Maumee I). This lake phase stabilized at about 244 m (800 ft.), with drainage westward at Fort Wayne (Fig. 3). At least two subsequent phases later were distinguished from the multiple Maumee strands: Middle Maumee (Maumee III) at 238 m (780 ft.) and Lowest Maumee (Maumee II) at 232 m (760 ft.). The lowest phase was believed to have preceded and to have been submerged by the Middle Maumee phase (Leverett and Taylor, 1915). More recent mapping suggests that the Lowest Maumee level was either reoccupied after the Middle phase or may actually have been third rather than second in the sequence.

The name "Maumee" was first applied to this glacial lake by Dryer (1888). Recognition of the lake waters' initial draining at Fort Wayne extended back through work of Gilbert (1871) to that of Hubbard (1840).

Highest Lake Maumee

Highest Lake Maumee beaches are well developed in western Ohio, as described by Leverett (1902, p. 714-740). Leverett and Taylor (1915) traced them northward into Michigan to a point 10 km north of Imlay (Fig. 1). At, or just south of Imlay, Michigan, an important outlet channel for Lake Maumee led westward to the Grand Valley and the

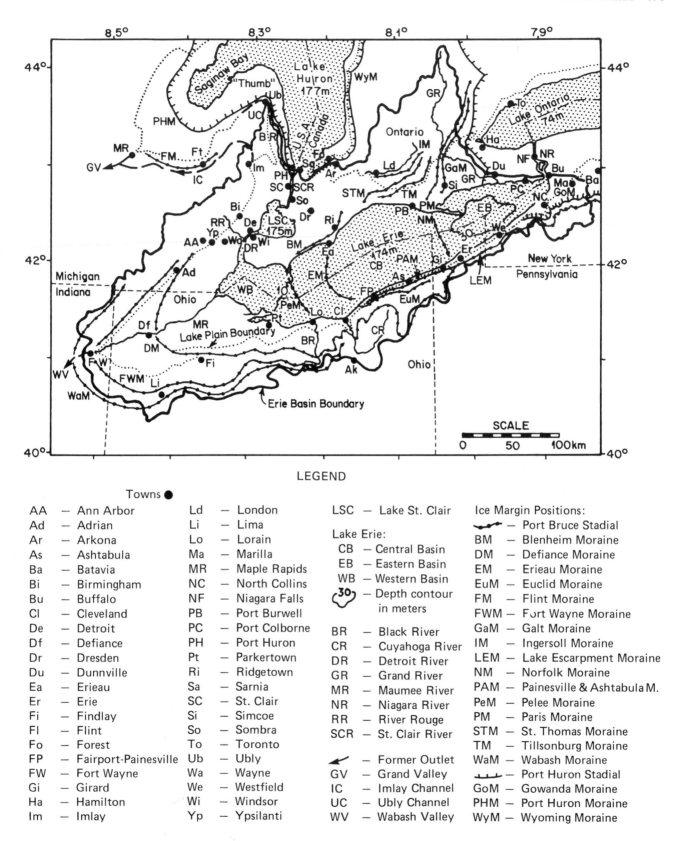

LEGEND

Towns ●

AA	— Ann Arbor	Ld	— London	LSC	— Lake St. Clair
Ad	— Adrian	Li	— Lima		
Ar	— Arkona	Lo	— Lorain	Lake Erie:	
As	— Ashtabula	Ma	— Marilla	CB	— Central Basin
Ba	— Batavia	MR	— Maple Rapids	EB	— Eastern Basin
Bi	— Birmingham	NC	— North Collins	WB	— Western Basin
Bu	— Buffalo	NF	— Niagara Falls	30	— Depth contour in meters
Cl	— Cleveland	PB	— Port Burwell		
De	— Detroit	PC	— Port Colborne	BR	— Black River
Df	— Defiance	PH	— Port Huron	CR	— Cuyahoga River
Dr	— Dresden	Pt	— Parkertown	DR	— Detroit River
Du	— Dunnville	Ri	— Ridgetown	GR	— Grand River
Ea	— Erieau	Sa	— Sarnia	MR	— Maumee River
Er	— Erie	SC	— St. Clair	NR	— Niagara River
Fi	— Findlay	Si	— Simcoe	RR	— River Rouge
Fl	— Flint	So	— Sombra	SCR	— St. Clair River
Fo	— Forest	To	— Toronto		
FP	— Fairport-Painesville	Ub	— Ubly	←	— Former Outlet
FW	— Fort Wayne	Wa	— Wayne	GV	— Grand Valley
Gi	— Girard	We	— Westfield	IC	— Imlay Channel
Ha	— Hamilton	Wi	— Windsor	UC	— Ubly Channel
Im	— Imlay	Yp	— Ypsilanti	WV	— Wabash Valley

Ice Margin Positions:

◄►—	— Port Bruce Stadial
BM	— Blenheim Moraine
DM	— Defiance Moraine
EM	— Erieau Moraine
EuM	— Euclid Moraine
FM	— Flint Moraine
FWM	— Fort Wayne Moraine
GaM	— Galt Moraine
IM	— Ingersoll Moraine
LEM	— Lake Escarpment Moraine
NM	— Norfolk Moraine
PAM	— Painesville & Ashtabula M.
PeM	— Pelee Moraine
PM	— Paris Moraine
STM	— St. Thomas Moraine
TM	— Tillsonburg Moraine
WaM	— Wabash Moraine
┴┴┴	— Port Huron Stadial
GoM	— Gowanda Moraine
PHM	— Port Huron Moraine
WyM	— Wyoming Moraine

Figure 1. Features of the Erie Basin. See Figures 7 and 8 for detail in the northeastern (Niagara) area.

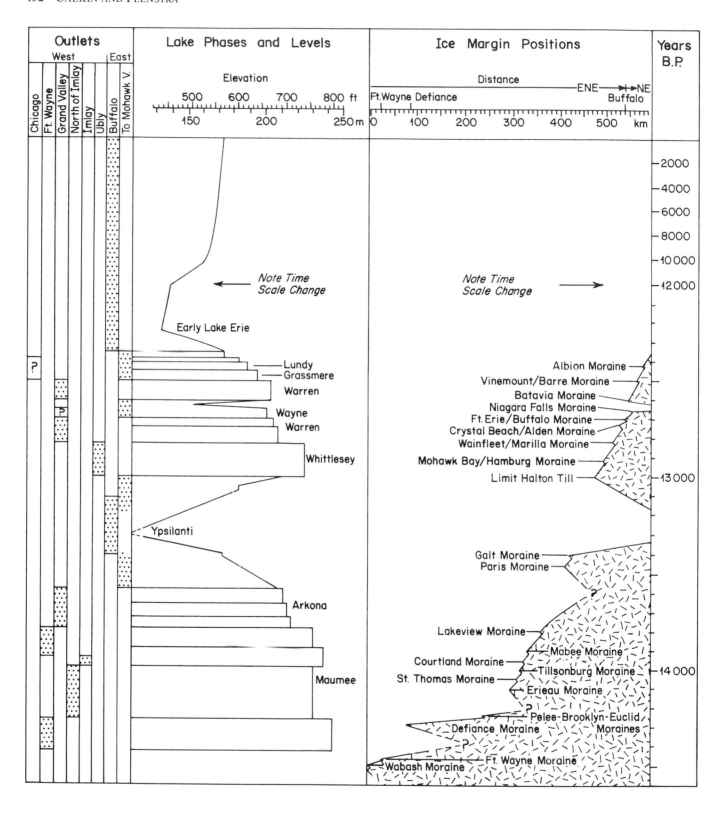

Figure 2. Correlation of lake phases and ice barriers in the Lake Erie basin. Four phases of Lake Maumee and three each of Lake Arkona and Warren are indicated. Two lake phases are indicated between Lake Lundy and Early Lake Erie; these are strands that have been tentatively assigned to respectively, Early Lake Algonquin and the lake formerly named "Lake Dana".

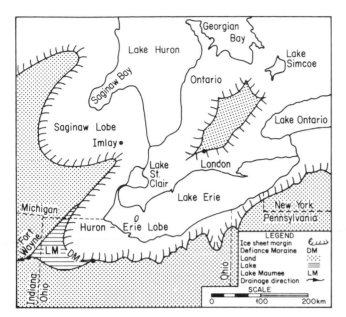

Figure 3. Highest Lake Maumee (Maumee I) at culmination of a glacial readvance to the Defiance Moraine.

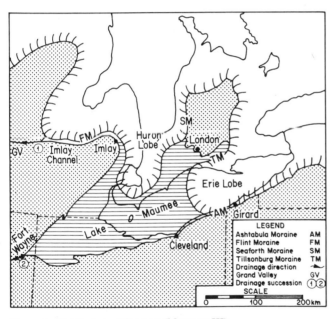

Figure 4. Middle Lake Maumee (Maumee III)

Lake Michigan basin. However, the Highest Lake Maumee phase is considered to have drained primarily through the Fort Wayne and adjacent Six Mile Creek outlets through the Fort Wayne Moraine and then down the Wabash and Ohio Rivers (Leverett, 1902; Bleuer and Moore, 1972).

The expansion of Highest Lake Maumee northward toward Imlay with ice-marginal retreat apparently was interrupted by a glacial readvance to the position of the Defiance Moraine (Fig. 3; Leverett, 1902; Fullerton, 1980). Although the magnitude of the readvance is uncertain, this moraine overlies clayey lake deposits in the Maumee River basin (Forsyth, 1959, 1973) and the "Lake" till of this readvance is

also more clayey than earlier tills (Mickelson *et al.*, 1983, p. 21). This indicates the intervening period and the distance of ice margin recession prior to the readvance must have been considerable (Leverett and Taylor, 1915; Fullerton, 1980). The Defiance ice margin truncated the Highest Maumee strand at Findlay, Ohio, and/or ice remained here long enough to prevent all but narrow arms of the lake from expanding farther eastward during most of the subsequent existence of this earliest lake phase (White, 1982, p. 68; Forsyth, 1959; Fig. 1). East of Findlay, strands labeled "highest" and "lowest" Maumee by Leverett (1902) or as "Maumee I" and "Maumee II" or "Maumee III" by Totten (1982, 1985) are believed to mark the Middle and Lowest phases, respectively, of Leverett and Taylor's (1915, p. 334) Maumee succession (Leverett, 1939; Forsyth, 1959).

Lower and Middle Lakes Maumee

General Sequence. The Lowest Lake Maumee beaches are faint and fragmentary. They were first recognized by Leverett (Russell and Leverett, 1908) in the Ann Arbor area of Michigan. Lowest Maumee originally was placed third in the Maumee sequence, although Leverett recognized that the feature had a "somewhat washed-down appearance". Leverett and Taylor (1915, p. 335) and Leverett (1931, p. 69) also described the nature of the beaches as "washed-down" or "broadened", and noted the presence of an apparent mantle of finer lake deposit on Lowest Maumee beaches and deltas in Michigan and Ohio. For this reason [and perhaps because of the lack of a known outlet, as suggested by Bleuer and Moore (1971, p. 207)], Leverett and Taylor (1915) assigned the Lowest Maumee strand features to the second Maumee phase, and they considered them to have been submerged by the rise of the lake level to the Middle Maumee phase. The Fort Wayne outlet in Indiana and the Imlay outlet for Lake Maumee in Michigan at this time were considered to have been too high for this Lowest Maumee phase (Leverett and Taylor, 1915, p. 322), so they suggested the chronology outlined in the following paragraph.

As the ice margin retreated northward along the "thumb" of Michigan during Highest Maumee time, a broad westward outlet was opened somewhat north of the present Imlay channel (Fig. 4). Thus the Fort Wayne outlet was abandoned and Lowest Lake Maumee was established. Subsequently, a glacial readvance (probably to form the Flint Moraine) shifted the outlet upslope to the position of the present, more narrow, Imlay outlet to the Grand Valley (Leverett and Taylor, 1915, p. 348). This hypothetical sequence of events accounted for a rise in lake level of 6 m, the closing of the Lowest Maumee phase, and establishment of the Middle Lake Maumee phase at 238 m (780 ft.).

The locations of the Maumee ice barriers following the Defiance readvance into Highest Maumee are not firmly established. However, the northern margin of the Erie lobe ice, during late Highest Maumee time and/or through the following Maumee phase, was retreating eastward from the Ingersoll and Westminster Moraines probably to the St. Thomas Moraine (Dreimanis, 1963; Fullerton, 1980; Barnett, 1982, 1985). To the southwest, the ice margin extended from the Blenheim and Pelee Moraines across the Erie basin by

Middle Lake Maumee time (Fig. 1). It had withdrawn to the Brooklyn and Euclid Moraines in northeastern Ohio prior to Middle Maumee time, as indicated by beaches on those moraines. Similarly, studies in Ohio have indicated that the Ashtabula advance, on the south side of the Lake Erie basin, occurred prior to termination of the Middle Lake Maumee phase (Fullerton, 1980; Totten, 1982).

Discussion of the Lake Maumee Succession. Several studies question the "Highest-Lowest-Middle" Maumee succession. Bleuer and Moore (1972) suggested that all three levels could have discharged at Fort Wayne; their work showed that "at least 10 feet of water from a 760-foot lake could have passed through the Fort Wayne outlet, and concurrently 5 feet through the Six Mile Creek Channel" (Bleuer and Moore, 1972, p. 207). They also questioned the "washed" appearance and the significance of the few, faint, Lowest Maumee beaches in the Fort Wayne area, noting that many may simply be offshore deposits (also see Leverett, 1931, p. 69). They observed (1972, p. 208) no evidence for other than the simplest sequence of descending phases, viz. Highest-Middle-Lowest Lake Maumee in the Fort Wayne area. However, they also presented no evidence that precluded the Highest-Lowest-Middle Maumee succession of Leverett and Taylor (1915). Totten (1982, 1985) also supports a descending sequence of the Maumee levels and also a descending sequence of the younger Lake Erie-basin lake phases, based on his mapping and sedimentologic studies. Totten (1985) notes, for example, that if submerged beaches did survive wave erosion, they should now be associated with lake silts on their landward sides and a silty cover, neither of which occurs in northeastern Ohio. Farrand and Eschman (1974, p. 50) indicated that evidence supporting submergence of the Lowest Maumee strand appears to be lacking in the Ann Arbor and Adrian areas of Michigan, but also that "there are few, if any, beach ridges at the 760-foot elevation in Michigan."

The distribution of Lake Maumee beaches in the Lake Erie basin also is compatible with the simple descending sequence. Beaches correlative with Middle Lake Maumee (the purported third lake phase) have been traced 40 km northeast of Cleveland (Leverett and Taylor, 1915; Totten, 1982). Those of the supposedly preceding Lowest Lake Maumee, though commonly poorly exposed, extend farther northward to Girard, Pennsylvania (Fig. 4; Leverett, 1939; Forsyth, 1959; Schooler, 1974). Leverett and Taylor (1915, p. 337) suggested that this strand geometry was a result of the readvance that brought Lowest Maumee to a close and caused the rise of Middle Lake Maumee. However, Leverett (1939) reconciled this apparent but anomalous pattern of beaches by assuming that there was a short-lived reoccupation of Lowest Lake Maumee prior to the formation of Lake Arkona. As noted by Fullerton (1980, p. 21), the downcutting below 232 m (760 ft.) at Fort Wayne reported by Bleuer and Moore (1972), could have occurred during reoccupation of the Lowest Maumee level, after extinction of Middle Lake Maumee.

Stratigraphic work at the head of the Imlay channel by Burgis (Farrand and Eschman, 1974; Burgis and Eschman, 1980) supports the concept of a readvance to Imlay during the latter part of Lowest Lake Maumee time; field data from southern Ontario also support the Leverett and Taylor (1915) history. Nevertheless, the simple descending sequence is not precluded by stratigraphic data, and the Leverett and Taylor succession (Fig. 2) is unconfirmed.

Middle Maumee and Reoccupied "?" Lowest Lake Maumee. Middle Lake Maumee, at 238 m (780 ft.), initially drained through the Imlay outlet, but the Fort Wayne outlet must have prevailed later as a result of differential isostatic uplift (Fig. 4; Hough, 1958, 1963; Fullerton, 1980). Middle Lake Maumee persisted until the ice margin had retreated to the northeast of Cleveland, Ohio. At this time the ice margin may have been at the position of the submerged Erieau Moraine across Lake Erie and perhaps east of the Tillsonburg, Courtland, or Maybee Moraines in southern Ontario (Figs. 1 and 2). With further ice margin retreat and probable downcutting at Fort Wayne, the lake level was lowered, resulting in a brief (reoccupied ?) phase of Lowest Lake Maumee. This sequence of events accounts for the Lowest Maumee beaches in northeastern Ohio and northwestern Pennsylvania if not also the Lowest Maumee beaches elsewhere. During this lowest lake phase, the ice margin retreated northward and the lake expanded at least to positions marked by the Girard Moraine and correlative positions south of the submerged Norfolk (Long Point-Erie) Moraine across the Lake Erie basin (see Williams and Meisburger, 1982, p. 20).

The last position of the ice-marginal Lake Maumee in Ontario may have been just southwest of the Lakeview Moraine near Port Burwell or even at the more easterly position of the Paris or Galt Moraines (Fig. 1). Subsequent retreat of the Huron and Saginaw lobe ice margin in Michigan caused lowering of waters to the succeeding Arkona lake phases. The third and/or last phase of Lake Maumee (Middle Maumee) occurred before 13 700 ± 220 B.P. (I-4899) in the Lake Huron basin (Farrand and Eschman, 1974, p. 42).

LAKE ARKONA

Origin and Sequence

Beaches of glacial Lake Arkona in the Lake Erie basin occur at 216 m (710 ft.) or as much as 9 m below those of Lake Whittlesey. Nevertheless, Lake Maumee generally is believed to have given way to the lower levels of Lake Arkona rather than to Lake Whittlesey (see the following section). This occurred as the ice margin that extended across the Erie-Huron basins and Saginaw Bay retreated sufficiently far northward (downslope) in Michigan to allow lakes in the southern parts of the Lake Erie and Lake Huron basins to join with each other (Fig. 5; Leverett and Taylor, 1915). Incipient Arkona waters merged with Early Lake Saginaw, and the combined Lake Arkona drained westward from the Saginaw Bay outlet and through the glacial Grand Valley to Glenwood I phase, Lake Chicago (Bretz, 1951; Hough, 1958; Hansel *et al.*, 1985). The main Arkona sequence was followed by an eastward-draining low-lake phase of the Mackinaw Interstade (Dreimanis and Karrow, 1972; Fullerton, 1980).

Drainage of Lake Arkona may have been marked by dis-

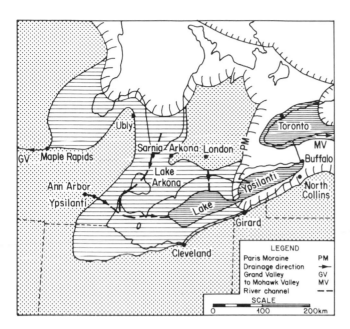

Figure 5. Early Lake Arkona and possible limit of succeeding, low-water, Lake Ypsilanti. After Dreimanis (1969).

tinct intervals of outlet erosion (Hough, 1958, p. 146), or isostatic and climatic events combined during more uniform downcutting of the outlet to produce three lake levels. Three beaches are distinguished locally along the lake plain between the "thumb" of Michigan and northwestern Pennsylvania. They are considered to represent the Highest Lake Arkona (I), at 216 m (710 ft.), Middle Lake Arkona (II), at 213 m (700 ft.), and Lowest Lake Arkona (III), at 212 m (695 ft.) (Taylor, 1905, p. 31; Leverett and Taylor, 1915).

Bretz (1951) argued that outlet elevations were important controls of lake levels, and particularly that glacial retreats were associated with increased delivery of meltwater and outlet deepening at the head of the Grand Valley; static lake intervals were associated with glacial readvances. He thus accounted for the three Arkona levels in the Huron basin during readvances, including the correlation of Lowest Arkona with the main Port Huron advance. Although Bretz's outlet-control concept is persuasive and it was adopted with modification by Hough (1958), subsequent field studies have indicated that it was not the controlling factor of many lake level changes (Farrand and Eschman, 1974; also see Hansel *et al.*, 1985). The work of Larsen (1985b) suggests that climate-related changes in the water budget may be a contributing factor in the Arkona and subsequent lake level changes of low magnitude.

It is considered probable that the Lowest Lake Arkona level existed prior to the change from westward to eastward drainage and prior to the early Port Huron readvance. However, a rejuvenated Lake Arkona may have formed briefly following the blocking of the eastward outlet in early Port Huron time (Hough, 1958; Wall, 1968; Dreimanis, 1969; Fullerton, 1980).

Early Investigations

The name "Arkona" was derived from the Ontario village of that name in the Huron basin (Fig. 1) where Spencer (1891) named a beach at 239 m (785 ft.). The name subsequently was applied by Taylor (1905) to the lake in which the beach was formed. Both Taylor (1839) and Leverett (1939) noted that that particular stretch of beach has since been assigned to Lake Whittlesey; however, more recent mapping by Cooper (1979, p. 28) indicates that both Whittlesey and Arkona strands are represented in Arkona, Ontario (also see Eschman and Karrow, 1985).

Work by Taylor (1905) in Michigan, and also by Taylor and Spencer (Leverett and Taylor, 1915, p. 362) in Ontario, first indicated that Lake Arkona followed Lake Maumee and was associated with an ice-marginal retreat some distance north of the "thumb" of Michigan. A subsequent glacial readvance blocked drainage between Saginaw Bay and the Lake Huron basin, caused the rise to the Whittlesey level in the Lake Erie basin, resulted in submergence of the Arkona strandlines, and also resulted in formation of the outer Port Huron Moraine in Michigan. Leverett and Taylor (1915, p. 362-374) developed this sequence on the basis of the observations outlined below.

Lake Arkona beaches in the Saginaw Bay area showed no evidence of submergence; strand features on the "thumb" of Michigan were presumed to have been overridden by ice during the early Port Huron advance. The strong development of Arkona beaches on the west side of main Lake Huron, where they now face nearby high ridges of the Port Huron Moraine, indicated that these shoreline deposits were formed before the readvance closed off the open water to the northeast. Some of these beaches appeared to have been buried by outwash associated with the Port Huron Moraine. The narrow Lake Whittlesey bays formed behind the Port Huron ice margin, both in Michigan and in the Ausable River valley near Arkona, Ontario, protected the submerged Arkona beaches from modification by waves (fetch was minimal in the narrow bays). However, those strands south of the Port Huron area in Michigan were unprotected from open water and they showed evidence of erosion and modification by Whittlesey waters. Here, the highest of the Arkona strands was noted to be gravelly and barely recognizable; the lowest beach and associated deltas were formed of gravel "stiffened by a moderate admixture of clay" (Leverett and Taylor, 1915, p. 373).

Nature of and Evidence for Lake Arkona East of Michigan

Evidence of modification and/or submergence of Arkona shore features may be inferred from exposures other than those just south of Lake Huron. In Ontario, the Arkona beach "has not been and to a large extent cannot be traced continuously" (Cooper, 1979, p. 26) and, although locally gravelly, the ridges in many areas lack good beach form (Chapman and Putnam, 1966, p. 88). Many features referred to Arkona by Spencer (1891) and by Leverett and Taylor (1915) are now reassigned. However, Arkona shore features have been traced "as discontinuous exposures" northward as far as Nairn, Ontario, where Arkona beach gravel is buried by 1.5 m of laminated silt and clay assigned to Lake Whittlesey (Cooper, 1979, p. 26 and Photo 8). Arkona beach gravel also has been identified tentatively below Port Huron-age till in some areas.

In Ohio, Arkona beaches are similarly described as being poorly developed and discontinuous, except where locally associated with deltaic material (Leverett, 1931, p. 79; Forsyth, 1959; Totten, 1982, 1985). Totten (1982, p. 58) reported the occurrence of Lake Arkona deposits "as extensive sheets of sand rather than distinct ridges" in northeastern Ohio "midway on the broad, gently sloping Middle (Whittlesey) Terrace surface." However, he interpreted the broad, washed appearance of the Arkona beaches (like those of Lowest Lake Maumee) as a consequence of the lack of association with any shore cliffs, and also of a slight lowering of lake level during deposition of the gravel. Furthermore, Totten (1985) suggested that the clay matrix, referred to by Taylor (1905; Leverett and Taylor, 1915), was most likely part of the beach sediment and a result of weathering of the shale clasts in the beach gravel.

Lake Arkona beaches have also been identified farther east, in Pennsylvania. Totten (1982; 1985) traced the upper two of three ridges identified as Arkona in northeastern Ohio up to a position 13 km east of the Ohio-Pennsylvania border. Leverett (1902) indicated that Arkona beaches extended to Girard, Pennsylvania, somewhat farther northeast (Fig. 5). However, tracing of raised beaches is difficult owing to the narrowness of the lake plain in Pennsylvania (Schooler, 1974). Beach ridges that were attributed to Lake Arkona and traced northeast of Girard in western Pennsylvania and into western New York by Taylor (Leverett and Taylor, 1915), previously had been correctly assigned by Leverett (1902) and by Fairchild (1907) to glacial Lake Warren (see Taylor, 1939; Leverett, 1939; Calkin, 1970).

Gravelly beach ridge segments at the projected Arkona level have been mapped as far northeast as the village of North Collins in western New York (Fig. 1); however, these show no clear evidence of submergence (Calkin, 1970, p. 88). These and some other "Arkona" strand features in the basin may represent a brief lake level essentially at the Lowest Arkona level (reoccupied) during lowering from Lake Whittlesey, prior to downcutting of the Lake Saginaw outlet to the Grand Valley. Nevertheless, there appears to be good evidence for pre-Whittlesey Lake Arkona phases in the Erie basin.

An age of 13 600 ± 500 B.P. (W-33; Hough, 1958), from a lagoon deposit near Cleveland, Ohio, at 210 m (690 ft.) may date Lowest Lake Arkona. The lagoon deposits are overlain by probable deeper water sediments assigned to Lake Whittlesey (see Goldthwait, 1958).

EASTWARD DRAINAGE DURING THE MACKINAW INTERSTADIAL AND LAKE YPSILANTI

That Lake Arkona (probably the Lowest Arkona phase) expanded with the retreating ice margin northeastward beyond Buffalo, New York, and drained across the Niagara Escarpment, is inferred largely on the basis of evidence that succeeding, post-Arkona, pre-Whittlesey low-water lake phases drained eastward (Fig. 5). These low phases occurred during the Mackinaw Interstade (Dreimanis and Karrow, 1972) and required eastward drainage from the Lake Michigan, Lake Huron, and Lake Erie basins via an independent low lake in the Lake Ontario basin. The low lake in the Ontario basin drained eastward through the Mohawk River valley to the Hudson River valley (Fullerton, 1980). In the Lake Erie basin, thick deposits of oxidized shallow-water or shore sand south of Cleveland at 201 m to 206 m (658 ft. to 677 ft.), were described by G. W. White (cited in Hough, 1958, p. 147). These deposits are overlain by a thick sequence of silt and clay that was deposited in Lake Whittlesey. Gravel underlying the bed of the Huron River near Ann Arbor and Ypsilanti, Michigan, was considered by Kunkle (1963) to have been deposited by a river that was graded to a lake phase in the Erie basin from about 166 m (543 ft.) to about 122 m (400 ft.) or less above sea level. The overlying deposits primarily were assigned to Lakes Whittlesey and Warren (Russell and Leverett, 1908, p. 9). Kunkle named this nonglacial low phase in the Erie basin Lake Ypsilanti (Fig. 5).

Additional evidence of a low lake phase in the Erie basin was revealed by sub-bottom seismic reflection surveys made by Wall (1968) in the central basin of Lake Erie north of Fairport, Ohio (Fig. 1). These show that a probable channel was cut into till to an altitude of about 91 m (300 ft.) and the channel was buried by compact glacial lake clay. The till is interpreted to be Port Stanley Till deposited during formation of Middle Lake Maumee; the clay over this till, filling the channel, was probably laid down in Lake Whittlesey or a later lake phase.

On the north side of Lake Erie, Barnett (1979, 1985) described deltaic deposits in the Simcoe, Ontario area (Fig. 1) which were overlain by Lake Whittlesey sediments. He suggested that these deltaic deposits were laid down in a lake about 26 m lower than the Lowest Lake Arkona. A buried channel cut into these appears to be graded to a level in the Lake Erie basin of less than 161 m (528 ft.), near that of Lake Ypsilanti (Barnett, 1985). Organic-bearing deltaic deposits (the Jacksonburg delta, Barnett, 1985) exposed beneath Wentworth "flow till" in the shore bluffs east of Port Burwell, Ontario (Fig. 1), may define a former lake between 175 and 185 m (573 and 598 ft.). Barnett indicated that this Jacksonburg delta level, and the Simcoe delta lake level, probably occurred just following Lowest Lake Arkona. Both deposits were also closely related to formation of the Paris and Galt Moraines (Figs. 1 and 2). The interpretations above are based on correlations of the Wentworth Till with pre-Port Huron readvance; this correlation has not been accepted by all workers (Fullerton, 1980; Mickelson et al., 1983).

Corroborating evidence of low levels or ice-margin retreat in the Lake Michigan and Lake Huron basins has been published by several authors (Farrand et al., 1969; Dreimanis and Goldthwait, 1973, p. 95; Farrand and Eschman, 1974; Fullerton, 1980; Hansel et al., 1985). In the Lake Ontario basin, data in the Toronto area indicate lake levels as low as 37 m (120 ft.) above Lake Iroquois (Dreimanis, 1969). These low lakes have drained eastward through central New York (see Fairchild, 1909; Fullerton, 1980). Current evidence suggests that the ice margin retreated north of Toronto and

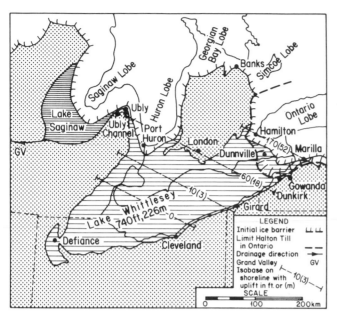

Figure 6. Lakes Whittlesey and Saginaw, and the Port Huron Stade ice barriers. Isobases on Whittlesey shoreline features tilted in N 27° E direction. After Barnett (1979). The true isobases may bow southwestward more nearly parallel to former ice margins as they cross the basin.

possibly north of the Trent River lowland in Ontario during the Mackinaw Interstade (Evenson and Dreimanis, 1976, Fig. 2; Eschman and Karrow, 1985, Fig. 5).

The Arkona-Whittlesey transition is inferred to have occurred about 13 000 B.P. (Dreimanis and Goldthwait, 1973). An age of 12 920 ± 400 B.P. (W-430), from wood beneath Whittlesey gravel at Parkertown, Ohio, and a minimum age of 12 600 ± 440 B.P. (S-31), from algae-contaminated wood in gravel near Ridgetown, Ontario (Fig. 1; Dreimanis, 1966; Calkin, 1970) are the only available age controls from post-Arkona and pre-Whittlesey deposits in the Lake Erie basin (Fullerton, 1980). Barnett (1985) reports an age of 13 360 ± 440 B.P. (BGS-929) from delicate leaf matter, believed to occur in place, from the buried Jacksonburg delta near Port Burwell. Stratigraphic relations indicate that the leaves were deposited shortly prior to inception of the Lake Ypsilanti low phase. This age measurement is similar to the age of 13 300 B.P. that was assigned to the Cheboygan bryophyte beds in Michigan by Farrand et al. (1969). The Cheboygan bed was attributed to the Mackinaw Interstade (Farrand and Eschman, 1974); however, it may be much younger (Fullerton, 1980; Hansel et al., 1985).

LAKE WHITTLESEY

General

Lake Whittlesey strands are among the strongest and best-developed in the Great Lakes region (Leverett and Taylor, 1915, p. 377). The lake also may be the best-dated of the Great Lakes phases in the Erie basin; a number of radiocarbon ages closely bracket the inception of Lake Whittlesey at about 13 000 B.P. (Goldthwait, 1958;

Dreimanis, 1966; Calkin, 1970; Barnett, 1978; Fullerton, 1980; Totten, 1982).

Lake Whittlesey formed in the Lake Erie basin during the Port Huron readvance, following the post-Arkona low lake phase (Lake Ypsilanti) at the end of the Mackinaw Interstade. The readvancing Ontario-Erie lobe ice margin obstructed eastward drainage through New York and the readvancing Huron lobe ice margin separated the lake in Saginaw Bay from the lake on the east (Fig. 6). The readvance in Michigan resulted in formation of the outer (early) Port Huron Moraine. Lake Saginaw was created at the Lowest Arkona level of 212 m (695 ft.). Waters in the Erie basin rose to form Lake Whittlesey at about 226 m (740 ft.), submerging the Arkona strands by about 9 m. Drainage was westward through a spillway at Ubly, Michigan, to Lake Saginaw (Fig. 6). From here, the drainage passed through the glacial Grand River valley to the reoccupied Glenwood (II) level of Lake Chicago (Leverett and Taylor, 1915; Hough, 1958; Hansel et al., 1985).

Definition and Nature of the Whittlesey Shore

Lake Whittlesey beaches were among the first noted by Charles Whittlesey (1838) in Ohio, and at about the same time Hubbard (1840) recorded them in southern Michigan. The Whittlesey strand was Winchell's (1872) "Belmore Ridge" and Gilbert's (1871) "third beach" in western Ohio, the "Ridgeway Beach" of Spencer (1891) in Michigan, and Leverett's (1895) "Sheridan Beach" in New York. Belmore was the name originally used until Taylor (1897) suggested that the name "Whittlesey" be used for the lake and its beach in honor of Charles Whittlesey. Taylor also identified the "Tyre-Ubly" (now Ubly) outlet and the contemporary position of the ice margin at the Port Huron-Saginaw Moraine.

By 1900, the Whittlesey shore had been mapped from the northwestern terminus just south of Ubly, Michigan, south and east through Ohio and Pennsylvania to its northeastern limit on the proximal side of the Hamburg Moraine near Marilla, New York (Figs. 1 and 7; Leverett, 1902; Calkin, 1970). The beach is discontinuous adjacent to Lake Huron, but southward in the Michigan portion of the Lake Erie basin it is nearly continuous, and it is the most prominent strand in Ohio, Pennsylvania, and southwestern New York (Forsyth, 1959; Calkin, 1970; Schooler, 1974).

This strength in part may have been a consequence of its formation by rising waters that countered the accelerated rebound in the northern part of the basin. Evidence of the transgressive nature of the shoreline west of Buffalo, New York, is noted by Muller and Prest (1985). The beach commonly has 3 to 5 m of relief in western Ohio and this increases eastward where the fetch was greater and the gravel supply more plentiful. The Whittlesey strand occurs nearly everywhere as a strong single ridge or bluff; however, Totten (1982, 1985) mapped a weak "Whittlesey I" beach 3 m above the main one in widely scattered areas of northeastern Ohio. Dual ridges also occur near Defiance, Ohio (Leverett and Taylor, 1915).

Totten (1982, 1985) attributed much of the prominence of the Whittlesey beach in northeastern Ohio to "its position at the brow of the prominent Middle (Whittlesey) Cliff'' (1982, p. 58). Cliffs and terraces cut into both drift and bedrock are conspicuous on the lake plain extending from Cleveland, Ohio, northeastward through western New York, where lake floor slopes were steep. Those identified with the Lake Whittlesey strand generally are the most imposing. Totten (1982, 1985) singled out the ''Whittlesey'' features cut into drift and also two other major wave-cut cliff/terrace sets that are generally attributed to Lakes Warren and Maumee. He argued that those three features are largely drift-mantled artifacts of high, ice-marginal lake phases that formed prior to the Late Wisconsin glaciation and the ''deglacial'' Great Lakes; he suggested that a yet older set of buried cliffs and terraces that are cut into bedrock in northeastern Ohio are pre-Wisconsin in age.

We believe that some segments of the deglacial Great Lakes shore features may be associated with relic or re-excavated wave-cut terraces and bluffs as Totten suggests.

However, at least in New York, Whittlesey beach gravel consisting of greater than 95% subrounded shale slabs, is quarried away in some areas to reveal sharp, unglaciated scarps and terraces that were formed in the same soft shale bedrock. The close association of raised wave-cut terraces in bedrock and drift, 5 to 8 m below Whittlesey storm beach crests from Ohio through western New York, strongly implies that the entire set of features is related to this single lake phase. Bedrock bluffs and terraces are being eroded today along broad reaches of the Lake Erie coast at rates up to 46 m/century (Geier and Calkin, 1983). In New York, Pennsylvania, and Ohio, bluffs are being cut in drift at more than three times these rates (Carter, 1977). However, these rates are too slow to explain the very wide, buried terraces described by Totten (1982, 1985) and further work to verify these subsurface features in Pennsylvania and New York is warranted.

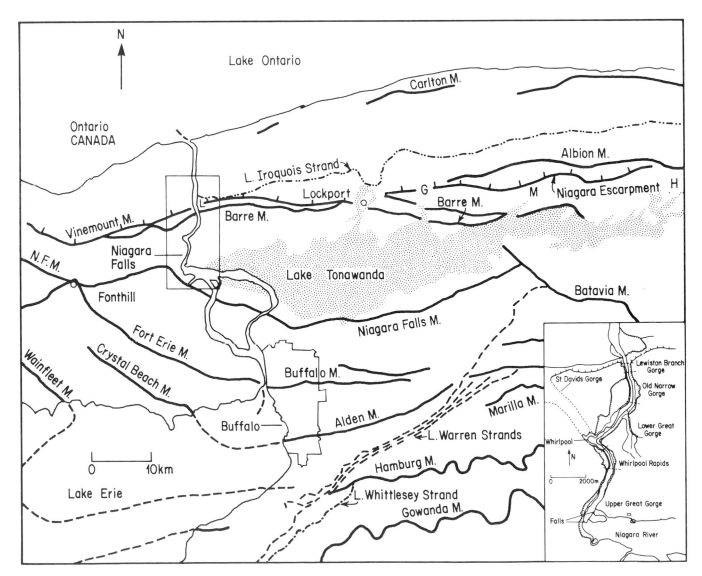

Figure 7. End moraines and glacial lake strands in the Niagara area. Lake Tonawanda is shown at its highest level, draining into glacial Lake Iroquois. Inset enlarges Niagara Gorge area.

Ice Barriers of Lake Whittlesey

The ice barrier of earliest Lake Whittlesey in the Lake Erie basin, contemporaneous with formation of the outer Port Huron Moraine in Michigan, was at least as far south as the Hamburg Moraine in New York. This is shown by ice contact features that are tied to the Whittlesey level at the location (Calkin, 1970; also see Muller and Prest, 1985). However, both Leverett (1902) and Taylor (1939) correlated the earliest ice barriers with the Gowanda Moraine (Figs. 6 and 7) based on an apparent weakening of the Whittlesey beach northeast of that moraine. On the basis of meltwater drainage features, Fairchild (1907, p. 74) concluded that the ice barrier was south of the New York/Pennsylvania border. Fullerton (1980; in Mickelson et al., 1983) correlated the earliest Port Huron readvance limit with the Girard Moraine in Pennsylvania and the submerged Norfolk Moraine farther north (Fig. 1). However, arguments for placing the early Port Huron readvance limit very far south of the Hamburg Moraine may be weakened by the occurrence of possible Arkona strands in southern New York (Calkin, 1970; Calkin and McAndrews, 1980), by geomagnetic evidence from the Genesee River valley (Brennan et al., 1984), and by new evidence for Lake Whittlesey in southern Ontario that is reviewed below.

The Paris Moraine in Ontario (Fig. 1) was correlated by Taylor (1939) with the Gowanda Moraine, based on the supposed limit of Whittlesey shore features. Karrow (1963) also related Lake Whittlesey to the Wentworth Till and the early Port Huron advance. Whittlesey shore features extend east of the Galt Moraine in Ontario (Fig. 1; Karrow, 1963). On the basis of mapped distribution of Lake Whittlesey strands, as well as the Summit delta and the buried Simcoe delta features in Ontario, Barnett (1979, 1985) concluded that the limit of the early Port Huron advance may be represented by the southern limit of the Halton Till near the Wainfleet Moraine in Ontario (Figs. 6 and 7). Continuous tracing of till sheets from the Port Huron and Wyoming Moraines in the Lake Huron basin is compatible with this correlation (Cowan et al., 1978 and references therein).

It is reasonably well established that Lake Whittlesey was followed by Highest Lake Warren, as a result of ice-marginal retreat and consequent westward drainage along the ice margin at the "thumb" of Michigan. At the time of extinction of Lake Whittlesey, the Ontario-Erie lobe margin had retreated from the position of the Marilla Moraine in New York (Calkin, 1970) and from the Wainfleet Moraine in Ontario (Feenstra, 1974, 1981).

LAKES WARREN AND WAYNE

Glacial Lake Warren developed in the Lake Erie and Lake Huron basins as the ice margin retreated from the outermost Port Huron Moraine north of Ubly, Michigan, allowing Lake Whittlesey to drain along the ice margin into the Saginaw Bay area of the Lake Huron basin (Fig. 6). Any increased discharge that may have accompanied ice margin retreat would have speeded down-cutting of the Lake Saginaw outlet, causing confluence of water in the Saginaw basin and the Lake Erie basin and formation of a confluent Highest Lake Warren (Warren I) at about 209 m (685 ft.). Lowest Warren (Warren III) existed at about 204 m (670 ft.) and, like Highest Warren, drained westward to a lower phase of Lake Chicago in the Michigan basin (see Hansel et al., 1985). This represented the last and most extensive of the major glacial Great Lake phases to occupy the Erie basin. An intermediate level (Middle Warren or Warren II) at about 206 m (675 ft.), which is commonly weaker, is represented locally. It is generally believed that a low lake phase at 201 m (660 ft.), called Lake Wayne, with drainage eastward through the Mohawk River valley in New York, immediately preceded the Lowest Warren level (Hough, 1966; Fullerton, 1980).

Totten (1982, p. 60) reports an age of 13 050 ± 100 B.P. (ISGS-437) for wood collected from an organic horizon beneath basal Warren I (of Totten, 1982, 1985) (Middle Warren) beach gravel in northeastern Ohio. Several dates between about 12 000 and 12 100 B.P., from Post-Warren sediments in the Lake Erie basin and adjacent parts of the Lake Ontario basin, yield minimum ages for this lake. These and other ages for Lake Warren are summarized by Dreimanis (1966), Calkin (1970), and Fullerton (1980).

Nature of the Shore Features

Lake Warren. Beaches of Lake Warren were among those identified by Hubbard (1840) in Michigan and also those traced by Whittlesey (1850) along the south shore in Ohio (Leverett, 1939). Gilbert mapped Warren beaches in Ohio, Pennsylvania, and western New York; the name "Crittenden beach" was derived from the latter area (Leverett and Taylor, 1915). In Ontario, Spencer (1888) named it the "Forest beach" after a village of that name. Spencer named both the water body associated with the Forest beach and also the older Arkona and Ridgeway (Whittlesey) beaches after General G. K. Warren, whom he regarded as the "father of lacustrine geology" in America (Leverett, 1902, p. 758). Spencer (1888) inferred that the "Warren Waters" were marine; however, Taylor (1897) restricted the name to the Forest (Warren) beaches and concluded that the beaches were glaciolacustrine in origin.

The Lake Warren beaches contrast with those of Lake Whittlesey in that they are more sandy and less gravelly, being associated with windblown deposits (Leverett, 1902, p. 764; Forsyth, 1959; Schooler, 1974; Totten 1982). The beaches also occur as multiple ridges. Less commonly, Warren strands are represented by wave-cut landforms. As a group, the Warren strands are strongly developed. They are easily traced throughout the basin. Most workers have generally distinguished a Highest Warren and a Lowest Warren shore, neither of which is consistently better developed than the other (Spencer, 1881; Leverett, 1902, 1939; Leverett and Taylor, 1915; MacLachlan, 1939; Chapman and Putnam, 1966). An intermediate ridge or group of ridges has been separated locally on sandy delta plains and elsewhere in the Lake Erie and Lake Huron basins (Calkin, 1970; Feenstra, 1981; Totten, 1982, 1985; Eschman and Karrow, 1985).

The distribution of the Lake Warren beaches in New York is important for the definition of the ice-marginal positions during the Warren phases and lake drainage. The Highest Lake Warren strands, together with some slightly lower ones that may correlate with a Middle Warren phase, terminate to the northeast at a point 6 km west of Alden, New York and south of the Alden Moraine (Figs. 7 and 8). Lowest Warren beaches continue northward past the village of Crittenden, west of Buffalo (Fairchild, 1907; Calkin, 1970); from there a very weak and discontinuous strand has been traced eastward through the Genesee Valley to Skaneateles, just west of Syracuse, New York, (Fairchild, 1897; also see Muller and Prest, 1985).

Lake Wayne. The Lake Wayne beach, occurring at about 183 m (660 ft.), about 3 m below the Lowest Warren beach, was named for the village of that name in Wayne County, Michigan, where its strong development was first noted by Hubbard (1840). It was first called lower Forest (Lowest Warren beach) but was separated after work north of the Black River, Michigan, showed that it displayed "clear evidence of having been submerged and greatly modified" (Leverett and Taylor, 1915, p. 389). In this area it resembled the broad discontinuous gravelly ridges of Lowest Maumee farther south in Michigan. The Wayne ridges in southeastern Michigan did not show "clear evidence" of submergence (Leverett and Taylor, 1915, p. 389). However, because of the modified appearance of the beaches in some other areas, Leverett and Taylor (1915) considered Lake Wayne to antedate a higher lake, which they interpreted to be the earliest (Highest) Lake Warren phase in the Lake Huron and Lake Erie basins. The outlet could not be determined by continuous tracing of the strands, but Taylor (*in* Leverett and Taylor, 1915, p. 336) considered the Saginaw Bay outlet to the glacial Grand Valley to be barely too high. Therefore, he assumed that drainage was eastward through central New York.

Lake Wayne beaches have not been systematically traced and they are recognized only rarely in Ontario (Chapman and Putnam, 1966). They are discontinuous in western Ohio (Forsyth, 1959). In the Cleveland area in northeastern Ohio, Wayne shore features were described by Leverett (1931) as wave-cut surfaces below the Lowest Warren beach crest. Totten (1982) recognized Wayne beaches with certainty in northeastern Ohio only near the Pennsylvania border and he did not consider them to show evidence of submergence. Wayne strands were not distinguished in western Pennsylvania by Schooler (1974) or in New York by Fairchild (1897, 1907). Several segments of apparently submerged or washed ridges occur in western New York 3 to 8 m below Lowest Warren. This places them at the projected Wayne level (Leverett and Taylor, 1915, p. 389; Calkin, 1970, p. 85); however, many of the Wayne features (both here and elsewhere in the basin) may be offshore bars of Lake Warren.

Development of the Lake Warren and Wayne Chronology

Leverett and Taylor (1915) assumed that Lake Wayne was a pre-Warren low lake that endured only during the maximum of a Whittlesey-Warren retreatal phase that was marked by a brief interval of eastward drainage. Fairchild (1909, 1932) also described such an episode of deglaciation, but placed it between Highest Warren and Lowest Warren

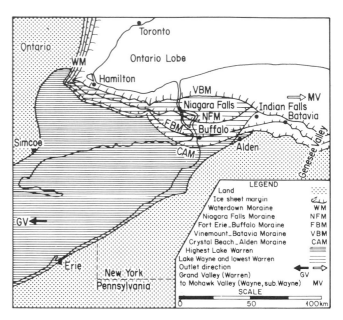

Figure 8. Ice barriers of Lake Warren in the Niagara area. The initial barrier may have been at the Marilla Moraine (Fig. 7).

(between Warren I and III) (Fairchild, 1932, p. 64). During the "intra-Warren" interval, lakes drained eastward through the Syracuse region to the Mohawk River valley (Fullerton, 1980; Muller and Prest, 1985).

Bretz (1951) correlated three consecutive Lake Warren phases following the Wayne phase with periods of stabilization of the Grand Valley outlet, and in turn, correlated the lake phases with three glacial readvances. Hough (1958) adopted Bretz's Warren history, including the correlation of the Lake Wayne time interval with the Two Creeks Interstade in the Lake Michigan basin. However, he placed the Wayne and Two Creeks interval phases between the Middle Warren and Lowest Warren periods (Bretz, 1959, 1964; Hough, 1966).

Subsequently, Karrow *et al.* (1961) inferred that final retreat of the Ontario-Erie lobe ice margin from the Niagara area in Ontario and New York occurred as early as 12 600 B.P., during the Port Huron event and prior to the Two Creeks Interstade. This forced the entire succession of glacial lakes Whittlesey through Lundy into an interval as short as 400 to 600 radiocarbon years. In a revised chronology, Hough (1963) proposed that Lake Wayne was a very short-lived low phase that followed Middle Lake Warren and discharged westward through the Saginaw Bay outlet or through another outlet (Hough, 1966, p. 67).

Eastward Drainage of Lake Wayne and Ice Barriers of Lake Warren

The inception of Highest Lake Warren occurred when the ice margin was at the Marilla Moraine in western New York (Leverett, 1902; Calkin, 1970) and probably just northeast (inside) of the Halton Till boundary on the Niagara Peninsula in Ontario (Figs. 2 and 6; Feenstra, 1981). According to field relations outlined by Calkin (1970) and Feenstra (1981) in the

Niagara area, Highest Warren lowered through a possible Middle Lake Warren level as the ice margin retreated northward from the Alden-Crystal Beach and Buffalo-Erie Moraines (Fig. 7). During the late Highest Warren and Middle Warren phases, drainage continued westward into a high level of Lake Chicago (Figs. 7 and 8; see Hansel *et al.*, 1985). Highest and/or Middle Lake Warren received outflow from Lake Hall in central New York (Fullerton, 1980; Muller and Prest, 1985).

Both Fullerton (1980) and Muller and Prest (1985) support the concept of an intra-Warren deglaciation interval with eastward drainage as suggested by Fairchild, rather than the westward-draining scenario of Hough (1963). According to the present interpretation, during Highest Lake Warren or perhaps during the Middle Warren phase, ice margin retreat caused coalescence of Lake Warren and high-level lakes in north-central New York. The opening of channels between the Genesee Valley and Syracuse, New York, then provided eastward drainage for Lake Wayne (Fullerton, 1980; Muller and Prest, 1985). The Wayne phase may have been followed by a brief period of even lower lake level when waters in the Lake Erie basin were lowered to levels below the Niagara Escarpment (Fairchild, 1932; Fullerton, 1980).

The latest, lowest level of Lake Warren and westward drainage via the glacial Grand Valley were re-established when the ice margin in New York readvanced to a position at least as far south as the Batavia Moraine (Figs. 7 and 8; Fullerton, 1980; Muller and Prest, 1985). Fullerton (1980) has suggested that the Alden Moraine was formed as a result of this readvance (also see Calkin, 1982). Subsequent recession allowed eastward expansion of Lowest Warren and eastward drainage was renewed with retreat from the Batavia Moraine (Calkin, 1970; Muller, 1977a, 1977b; Fullerton, 1980; Muller and Prest, 1985).

LAKES GRASSMERE, LUNDY, AND SUBSEQUENT LOWER GLACIAL LAKE PHASES

The drop in the lake level from Lowest Warren to nonglacial Early Lake Erie was marked by only brief pauses that are in turn now represented by generally weak and very discontinuous shore features. In the past, these features have been assigned, on the basis of their relative positions below Lake Warren strands, to the following lake phases of successively younger age in the Lakes Erie and Huron basins: Lake Grassmere at 195 m (640 ft.), Lake Lundy at 189 m (620 ft.), and a hypothetical Early Lake Algonquin level at 184 m (605 ft.). A still younger and lower lake phase in the Lake Erie and Lake Ontario basins, at about 180 m (590 ft.), was termed Lake Dana. Neither the direction of drainage nor the outlets of Lakes Grassmere and Lundy have been established with certainty, the existence of an Early Lake Algonquin phase in the Lake Erie basin has not been clearly documented by strand features, and the name "Dana" now appears inappropriate.

Beaches that are projected to the Lake Grassmere and Lake Lundy levels generally are sandy; they have a relief of less than 1 m to 2 m and they are discontinuous. Therefore, they have been mapped only locally (Leverett and Taylor, 1915; Forsyth, 1959; Chapman and Putnam, 1966; Calkin, 1970; Totten 1982, 1985). Some of the beaches probably are offshore bars formed in earlier lakes and some may be wind-blown sand. Strands below the Lowest Warren beaches have not been recognized in Pennsylvania (Schooler, 1974). Continuous tracing of Grassmere and Lundy strands in the Lake Erie or Lake Huron basins is virtually impossible, therefore, and correlations are tenuous.

Definition of Lakes Grassmere and Lundy

Lane (1900) first described a "Grassmere beach" and a more weakly developed "Elkton beach" about 6 to 9 m lower; both were named for villages on the "thumb" of Michigan. Leverett and Taylor (1915) subsequently applied the name "Glacial Lake Lundy" to the lake in which the Grassmere and Elkton beaches were formed. The Lake Dana beaches of Fairchild (1907) in New York, and apparently also the Lundy Lane beaches of Spencer (1894a) in Ontario, were attributed to Lake Lundy. Both of the latter were correlated with the Elkton level of Lake Lundy. The name "Lundy" was derived from Lundy(s) Lane near Niagara Falls, Ontario, where Lundy beaches at 32 m (144 ft.) above the level at Lake Erie were described as "extending westward from the Niagara River for two or three miles" (Spencer, 1894a, p. 209). Spencer correlated these with lower ridges at Sheridan, Ebenezer, and Akron, New York (Fig. 1); all these strands later were assigned to Fairchild's (1907) Lake Dana (Calkin, 1970). Spencer (1894a) suggested that "Lundy Lake" extended from Pelee Point, Ontario, to Niagara Falls.

According to generalized projections of uplift, the Elkton level is about 9 m higher than the theoretically computed "untilted level" of strands that were attributed by Fairchild (1907) to Lake Dana in western New York; they are also higher than the Lake Dana outlet he identified near Syracuse, New York. Therefore, the Elkton and Dana levels generally have been considered to have been different lakes (see Leverett, 1902, p. 772; 1939, p. 472; Fairchild, 1932, p. 620; Hough, 1958, p. 154; Calkin, 1970, p. 91). The Elkton level of Michigan is also about 5 m above the Lundy Lane strands in Ontario (Feenstra, 1981). Despite these disparities, the name "Lundy" has been retained by many workers to indicate the Elkton level at 189 m (620 ft.) (Hough, 1958, 1963; Wayne and Zumberge, 1965; Calkin, 1970). The Grassmere level, distinctly higher at 195 m (640 ft.) here is considered to represent a distinct lake phase although it may have had the same outlet as Lake Lundy (Elkton).

During the existence of Lake Grassmere, the Lake Huron and Lake Erie basins were believed to have been connected by a shallow strait near Port Huron (Leverett and Taylor, 1915). A subsequent drop to the Lundy (Elkton) level would have caused down-cutting through the Port Huron Moraine a few kilometres north of St. Clair, Michigan, to maintain concordance of water levels in the two basins (Leverett and Taylor, 1915). Based on an apparent southward trend of these Lake Lundy channels (above) and probably also based on his Elkton-Dana correlation, Taylor (Leverett and Taylor, 1915) suggested that drainage of both Lakes Grassmere and Lundy was eastward via the Marcellus-Cedarvale channels near Syracuse, New York, to the

Mohawk River valley. These channels were designated by Fairchild (1897, 1907) as the probable outlet of Lake Dana and later (Fairchild, 1932) as the probable outlet of Lake Lundy. The possibility of eastern outlets for these post-Warren lakes is considered in additional paragraphs below.

A Postulated Early Lake Algonquin Phase and Westward Drainage

Nonglacial Early Lake Erie, which drained through "early Niagara outlets" (Lake Tonawanda spillways?) to the Lake Ontario basin, was considered to have followed eastward-draining Lake Lundy. Leverett and Taylor (1915, p. 328) inferred that Early Lake Erie received drainage from a short-lived, Early Algonquin phase of the Lake Huron basin via distributaries of the St. Clair River that were cut to just below 184 m (605 ft.) into the Port Huron Moraine. Hough (1958, p. 153-156) pointed out the lack of unequivocal evidence of eastward drainage of either Lakes Grassmere or Lundy in the Lake Erie basin and Lake Huron basin or an early phase of Lake Algonquin in the Huron basin (also see Eschman and Karrow, 1985). He invoked (Hough, 1958, p. 157) a very brief, west-draining Early Algonquin lake interval following Lake Lundy to explain an apparent coincidence in level of the Lake Huron basin Early Algonquin outlet cut into drift near Port Huron, and an apparently correlative (Leverett and Taylor, 1915) outlet of the Toleston phase of Lake Chicago cut to bedrock at the same elevation at Chicago. In addition, Hough (1958) called attention to the coincidence of altitudes of the southward-draining Glenwood and Calumet phases of Lake Chicago with, respectively, Lakes Grassmere and Lundy of the combined Lake Erie-Huron basin. He proposed that Lakes Grassmere, Lundy, and Early Algonquin drained westward through the Chicago outlet. This sequence was later assigned a "pre-Valders" (pre-Two Creeks) age (Hough, 1963, 1966).

The simple westward sequence of Hough (1963) has been challenged by work in the southern peninsula of Michigan (Eschman and Farrand, 1970; Evenson, 1973) which has resulted in an interpretation that the Calumet phase of Lake Chicago, at 189 m (620 ft.), which followed the Glenwood phase at 195 m (640 ft.), was initiated prior to extinction of Highest Lake Warren (Fullerton, 1980). If true, this would preclude a Grassmere-Glenwood confluence. Hansel et al. (1985) note that the existence of a pre-Two Creeks Calumet phase remains unconfirmed in the Lake Michigan basin, and that Lake Chicago may have been at the Glenwood (195 m) level throughout Port Huron time. In this case, it is possible that the 195-m levels (Glenwood phase of Lake Chicago and Lake Grassmere) are causally related and confluent with drainage at Chicago (see Eschman and Karrow, 1985). In addition, the work of Hansel et al. does not document a Toleston level of Lake Chicago (184 m) until post-Two Creeks time, although the altitude of the outlet may have been cut to this level during Port Huron time.

Evidence for Lake Phases Below the Lundy (Elkton) Level

The Early Algonquin lake level in the Lake Huron and Lake Erie basins was assigned an altitude of about 184 m (605 ft.) although shore features at that level were not documented (Leverett and Taylor, 1915, p. 328; Hough, 1958, p. 157). Small, discontinuous, and weak beaches in the Lake Erie basin have since been assigned to this lake level (e.g., Chapman and Putnam, 1966; Calkin, 1970; Feenstra, 1981). The most prominent strand is the Dresden shoreline that is marked by scattered gravel and sand ridges that extend south from Sombra, Ontario, around the east side of Lake St. Clair to the west end of Lake Erie (Fig. 1; Chapman and Putnam 1966, p. 97). However, these strands, like a parallel set somewhat lower in the Dresden area (see Fitzgerald and Hradsky, 1980), may have been formed in an Early Lake St. Clair (Dreimanis, 1964; Fullerton, 1980), which drained into Early Lake Erie.

Leverett (1902, p. 771), Fairchild (1907, p. 74-76), and Spencer (1894a; also see Calkin, 1970) mapped a spectrum of short, sandy beach ridge segments in the Lake Erie basin of western New York that have less than 2 m of relief and that fall locally within a short vertical range of altitudes. The southernmost of this set of beaches occur at about 178 m (585 ft.) near the Lake Erie shore northwest of Westfield, New York (Fig. 1); they are at altitudes between 201 m (660 ft.) and 205 m (673 ft.) in Buffalo, New York, and between 198 and 204 m on the Niagara Peninsula of Ontario (Feenstra, 1981). The individual beaches themselves show no tilt, but if a water plane defined by the ridges is projected southward parallel to the lower level of Lake Warren, it intersects Lake Erie (at 174 m, 570 ft.) near Westfield, New York (Fairchild, 1907, p. 76; 1932, p. 611). The "untilted" water plane of the former lake was at or below the present Lake Erie level.

These low-level strands appear to represent an extremely brief interval of slowly subsiding lake levels in the northeastern part of the Lake Erie basin and the southwestern part of the Lake Ontario basin following extinction of Lake Lundy. Fairchild (1907) assigned them to Lake Dana, named after the eminent geologist and a leader in acceptance of the glacial theory, James Dana. The name "Dana" was originally applied by Fairchild (1899, p. 57) to the Geneva beach in north-central New York. He suggested at that time, and maintained in later publications (1907, 1909) that this lake drained to the Mohawk River valley via the Marcellus-Cedarvale outlet channel, now at 213 m (700 ft.) near Syracuse, New York. With assignment of the beaches in the Lake Erie basin to Lake Dana, the lake was assumed to extend along the ice margin between Toronto, Ontario, and Syracuse at a level about 55 m below the Highest Warren strands. Fieldwork by Muller and others (see summary below) now indicates that Lake Dana drained eastward through other channels in New York that are west of Syracuse. Therefore the name "Dana" is restricted to whatever lake in central New York drained through the Marcellus-Cedarvale channel; it is no longer appropriate for the lowering lake levels in western New York and adjacent Ontario area.

On the Niagara Peninsula of Ontario, Feenstra (1981, p. 33) has also recognized both a number of small sand and gravel bars and a very prominent delta at Dunnville, Ontario. Together these appear to represent a lake level approximately 4 m below the level that formerly was referred to as

"Lake Dana". The lake is named Lake Dunnville after the town at the mouth of the Grand River (Ontario) (Fig. 1).

The lake formerly named "Dana" and Lake Dunville immediately preceded separation of the proglacial waters over the Niagara Escarpment. They may have received drainage from Early Lake Algonquin in the Lake Huron basin.

Control of Eastward Drainage Discharge and Ice-Marginal Positions

Although the strands of Lakes Grassmere and Lundy cannot be traced to either an east or west outlet, events outlined below may account for abandonment of the glacial Grand River valley (Michigan) outlet and subsequent eastward drainage. Ice margin retreat from the Batavia Moraine and possibly from the Barre-Vinemont Moraine in the Niagara area (Fig. 7; Calkin, 1970; Feenstra, 1981) was followed by the confluence of waters in the Lake Ontario basin with those of Lowest Lake Warren. Nearly contemporaneous ice-marginal retreat in central New York and opening of the Guppy Gulf Channel just west of Syracuse, New York, (now at about 274 m, 900 ft.) may have resulted in the lowering from Lowest Warren to the Grassmere level (Fullerton, 1980; Muller and Prest, 1985).

The Lake Grassmere level may have then been controlled by the interrelationships of lakes in the Lakes Michigan and Huron basins. Mapping by Muller (1977b; Muller et al., 1981; see Muller and Prest, 1985) indicates that post-Warren levels of lakes draining east to the Mohawk River valley from the Lake Erie basin and western Lake Ontario basin, were controlled by a complex of channels just east of Batavia (near LeRoy), New York (Figs. 1 and 8). Drainage through the LeRoy channels (Fairchild, 1909) entered lakes in the Genesee Valley, New York (Fig. 8) and into an early phase of Lake Iroquois in the southeastern end of the Lake Ontario basin. The Taylor Channel, southeast of LeRoy, New York, may have been cut during the lowering from Grassmere to Lundy and/or carried drainage of the latter lake. However, outflow of the very brief post-Lundy glacial lake of the northern Lake Erie and Lake Ontario basins probably passed through one of the series of lower channels nearby.

The ice margin in the Lake Erie basin may have been near the Albion-Rochester Moraine at the time of the down-draining of Lake Lundy (Kindle and Taylor, 1913; Fairchild, 1932; Muller and Prest, 1985). Separation of lakes in the Erie basin from those in the Ontario basin occurred soon after ice-marginal retreat from this position (Fullerton, 1980; Muller and Prest, 1985).

EARLY LAKE ERIE AND THE ANCESTRAL NIAGARA

The post-Lake Lundy, proglacial lakes that may have existed in the Lake Erie basin must have existed only very briefly as northward retreat of the ice margin caused lake surfaces to fall below the level of the Niagara Escarpment for the last time. This removed the direct glacial influence in the Lake Erie basin and initiated the phase of the present lake, called Early Lake Erie by Hough (1958). The swift-moving, catastrophic flood waters (Forsyth, 1973) of final lowering must have first incised a channel across the Buffalo-Fort

Erie and Niagara Falls Moraines; however, this incipient Niagara River may have quickly cut down to the underlying resistant Onondaga Limestone surface at Buffalo (also see Barnett, 1985). This surface now forms the lake's threshold. Flow from the Buffalo outlet spilled northward into the Tonawanda lowland, over the emergent Niagara Escarpment beyond, and into proglacial lake waters of the Ontario basin (Fig. 7). With further ice retreat, these waters, in turn, soon merged eastward with those of glacial Lake Iroquois (Fairchild, 1932; Muller and Prest, 1985).

The earliest radiocarbon age for inception of nonglacial waters (Early Lake Erie) in the Erie basin may be 12 650 ± 170 B.P. (I-4040; Lewis, 1969), although pollen data suggest the dated sediments are younger (T. W. Anderson cited in Coakley and Lewis, 1985). The earliest age for proglacial waters occurring only north of the Niagara Escarpment in the Ontario basin is 12 660 ± 400 B.P. (W-861) from wood rerun as 12 080 ± 300 B.P. (W-883; Muller, 1965; Muller and Prest, 1985). A number of other ages from the Niagara area, together with the need to allow time for formation of the post-Whittlesey lakes in the Erie basin, suggest neither event occurred much before 12 400 B.P. (see Fullerton, 1980).

The evolution of Early Lake Erie to the present lake has been one of fluctuating levels which were controlled largely by varying inflow via Port Huron and the effects of decelerating rebound of the threshold at Buffalo. Complete severance of water flow from the upper Great Lakes may have reduced the Erie water supply by up to 90% (Lewis, 1969). However, changes in outlet shape and climate have also affected lake volume (Leverett and Taylor, 1915, p. 462; Coakley and Lewis, 1985; Larsen, 1985b).

At its initiation, Early Lake Erie received discharge from an early phase of Lake Algonquin of the Lake Huron basin via the newly formed St. Clair River, Early Lake St. Clair, and the Detroit River-Lake Rouge system (Fig. 1; Leverett and Taylor, 1915; Dreimanis, 1964; Vagners, 1972; Fitzgerald and Hradsky, 1980). The Buffalo threshold, still depressed by glacial loading, was as much as 40 m below present lake datum (Lewis, 1969; Coakley and Lewis, 1985). Because of this depression, Early Lake Erie may have initially consisted of an eastward descending and deepening series of up to three sub-lakes. These were connected by channels cut across the Pelee and Norfolk morainal ridges that separate the large central basin of Lake Erie from the broad, shallow western and much deeper eastern basins (Fig. 1). The analysis of Coakley and Lewis (1985) suggests that these Early Erie sub-lakes were initially at about 15, 30, and 40 m respectively below present Lake Erie datum (174 m, 570 ft.) or possibly the central and eastern sub-lakes were confluent.

A southward-declining beach, and wave-cut scarps 4 to 5 m above present lake level at Fort Erie, Ontario, have been assigned to this first phase of Early Erie (Leverett and Taylor, 1915, p. 463; Feenstra, 1981, p. 34). The height of the beach suggests that the water surface over the threshold at Buffalo may have been lowered very little since inception of the lake (Leverett and Taylor, 1915, p. 465).

The rapid rise in Lake Erie level, related to the differential glacioisostatic uplift of the Buffalo sill, may have been interrupted for the first time as Lake Algonquin outflow from the Huron basin by-passed Lake Erie and drained via the Kirkfield, Ontario, outlet to the Ontario basin for a brief interval. This may have occurred after about 11 800 B.P. (Coakley and Lewis, 1985; Eschman and Karrow, 1985). Dreimanis (1964) has described stratigraphic evidence for two phases of Early Lake St. Clair. The respective deposits are divided by an unconformity that he tentatively correlated with the diversion to this Kirkfield Algonquin-phase drainage. Wood from just below this unconformity was dated at 12 000 ± 200 B.P. (S-172).

Despite this interruption, uplift at Buffalo brought lake levels to −20 m or even −10 m in all sub-lakes by 10 500 B.P. (Lewis, 1969; also see Williams and Meisburger, 1982; Coakley and Lewis, 1985). At about this time, rising Erie levels must again have been slowed and/or the water surface was lowered as ice retreat opened direct eastward discharge to the St. Lawrence basin for the upper Great Lakes, terminating the Lake Algonquin phase in the Lake Huron basin (Eschman and Karrow, 1985). The return of drainage from the upper Great Lakes corresponding to the Lake Nipissing phase in the Lakes Michigan and Huron basins at about 5000 B.P., may once again have accelerated the general rise in Lake Erie. The level was −4 m by about 3500 B.P. or soon after initiation of the Lake Algoma phase in the Michigan and Huron basins (Lewis, 1969; Calkin and Brett, 1978; Barnett, 1985; Coakley and Lewis, 1985; Hansel et al., 1985). Dated alluvial deposits in the Port Burwell, Ontario, area suggest that lake level may have risen to 5 m above that of the present about 2000 years ago (Barnett, 1985) or possibly even earlier during the Nipissing incursion of the Lake Huron basin (Coakley and Lewis, 1985). Lake Erie waters have now reached near-stable levels, although very minor crustal warping appears to have continued to the present.

Ancestral Niagara Drainage

The geology and evolution of the Niagara River drainage have been presented and updated successively by a number of authors since early work by Charles Lyell (1842) and James Hall (1842). Calkin and Brett (1978) and Calkin and Wilkinson (1982) give some of the significant references and present some new data to help define the chronology of the Niagara outlet.

Lake Tonawanda. During initiation of Early Lake Erie, former outlets through the Niagara Escarpment west of the Falls (Karrow, 1973; Flint and Lolcama, in press) or the St. Davids Gorge (Fig. 7) were drift-filled. Therefore the Erie outflow past Buffalo flooded the lowland south of the Niagara Escarpment, forming a shallow river-lake called Lake Tonawanda (Kindle and Taylor, 1913). This extended 93 km eastward at its high level (178.3 m) and discharged Niagara waters to Lake Iroquois via spillways at Lewiston and farther eastward at Lockport, Gasport, Medina, and Holly, New York (Fig. 7). Leverett and Taylor (1915, p. 328) cited the cutting of these outlets as support for their Early Algonquin phase in the Lake Huron basin; however, at least partial cutting of one of these, the Lockport spillway, had occurred prior to the last ice margin advance (Calkin and Brett, 1978).

The main channel of the Lewiston spillway, heading 1200 to 2000 m north of the American Falls, became the principal Niagara River, as differential uplift progressively raised eastern outlets, so that by 10 920 ± 160 B.P. (I-5841), all outflow was shifted westward from the Lockport spillway (Calkin and Brett, 1978). An age of 10 450 ± 400 B.P. (W-1038) (Muller, 1977b) for wood on scoured clay near a southeastern outflow area of Lake Tonawanda may reflect water-level lowering corresponding to final cessation of Lake Algonquin inflow into Lake Erie. The return to full discharge at the end of Lake Nipissing time appears to be recorded by a mollusc assemblage dated 3780 ± 90 B.P. (BGS-273) overlying scoured glacial lake clays at 170 m (560 ft.) at the western edge of Lake Tonawanda (Fig. 7; Calkin and Brett, 1978).

Niagara Gorge. Taylor (Kindle and Taylor, 1913) proposed a correlation of Niagara Gorge sections (Fig. 7) with the lake history based on physical dimensions of the Gorge and variations in Niagara River discharge. However, recent dating of Gorge deposits and extrapolation of historic recession rates (Calkin and Brett, 1978; Fullerton, 1980) may yield less speculative correlations. Radiocarbon ages, averaging 9800 B.P. for mollusc shells within Niagara River terrace gravels above the Whirlpool, suggest that the cataract itself was about 800 m downstream at that time. The overall rate of recession to this point (Whirlpool) may have been on the order of 1.6 m/yr if cutting began at Lewiston, New York, about 12 400 B.P.

The Upper Great Gorge (Fig. 7) is 3700 m long and, as suggested by Kindle and Taylor (1915), appears to be the product of the full post-Nipissing cutting. This is supported at least in part by comparison of its mean rate of cutting with that of historic data. The mean recession rate must have been on the order of 0.8 to 1.0 m/yr for the historic period 1842 through 1905 (International Joint Commission, 1953, p. 14), before major man-made water diversions were begun. An average recession rate of 1.1 m/yr has been determined for the total years of record 1670 through 1969 (American Falls International Board, 1974).

DEFORMATION OF THE SHORE FEATURES

Spencer (1849b, p. 492), in an often-quoted passage, suggested "if the rate of terrestrial deformation continues as it appears to have done, then in about 5000 years the life of the Niagara Falls will cease by the turning of the waters into the Mississippi." Thus, the study of strand deformation was already well underway by 1900. The first systematic study of Great Lakes area uplift that used "modern" observations was undertaken by Gilbert (1898). It showed that deglacial tilting processes had slowed from earlier rates but could still be detected in the present lakes.

The possible causes and controls of shoreline deformation were examined carefully several years later by Leverett and Taylor (1915, p. 518) who concluded that "ice weight" was the principal mechanism. Walcott (1972) gathered together quantitative evidence for glacioisostatic uplift in the Great Lakes. However, the probable influence of buried tectonic structures has also been noted by MacLachlan (1939).

TABLE 1

MEASURED UPLIFT OF CLEVELAND, OHIO, RELATIVE TO PORT COLBORNE, ONTARIO*

Author – Date –	Gilbert 1896	Freeman 1926	Gutenberg 1933 or 1941	Moore 1947	Coordinating Committee	
					1957	1977
Relative Uplift mm/century	−216	−149	−204	−101	−113	+6**
ft./century	−0.71	−0.49	−0.67	−0.33	−0.37	+0.02**

*Data in ft./century from Clark and Persoage (1970, Table 1) and from Coordinating Committee on Great Lakes Basic Hydraulic and Hydrologic Data (1977).

**Positive value indicates Cleveland is rising relative to Port Colborne; the standard error for 1977 value is ± 9 mm.

Nature and Interpretation of the Deformation

The first mapping of warped lake planes was undertaken by DeGeer (1892), using the methods of Gilbert (1890) to draw lines of equal deformation, called "isobases". The use of the term "hinge line" for the "zero isobase" and delineation of the warped zone from that of "horizontality" is credited to J.W. Goldthwait (1908). These concepts of Goldthwait need careful re-evaluation; however, they have been applied almost universally up to the present to describe glacioisostatic deformation in the Great Lakes area. The paragraphs below summarize the results of this application in the Erie basin.

The first "hingeline" to be recognized in the Great Lakes may have been that of the Lake Whittlesey strand in Ohio, which Leverett (1902, p. 755) placed at Ashtabula (Figs. 1 and 6). The Maumee "zero isobase" was also identified here by Leverett and Taylor (1915, p. 337), because the northward rise of its shoreline, initiated south of Cleveland, was sustained only northward from Ashtabula. In Michigan, the Lake Whittlesey, Lake Maumee, and Lake Arkona beaches were all observed to rise northward from within an area located about 8 km north of Birmingham (Fig. 1).

The "hingeline" of the Lake Warren (Forest) and Lake Wayne strands, and of Lakes Grassmere and Lundy (Elkton), were recognized (Leverett and Taylor, 1915, Plate XX, text p. 396, Fig. 15) in the Lake Huron basin about 20 km and 117 km respectively north of the Whittlesey "hingeline". However, respective positions of these hingelines cannot be projected across the Lake Erie parallel to the other isobases without falling well within the tilted zone (Hough, 1958; Schooler, 1974; Totten, 1982, 1985). Totten (1982, 1985) has determined a significantly different set of assumed hinge positions for these Erie basin Great Lakes that occur along the lake plain between Cleveland and the Ohio/Pennsylvania state line area. The hinge point positions are compatible with Totten's concept that in the Great Lakes succession, lower beaches are successively younger.

Careful replotting of Lake Whittlesey strand elevation points measured by Leverett and Taylor (1915), as well as more recent workers (Barnett, 1979), yields a direction of maximum differential uplift of 027° (Fig. 6). This figure is compatible with most earlier studies (Calkin, 1970). The reconstruction incorporates the Ubly outlet as 244 m (800 ft.) and suggests that post-Whittlesey uplift, relative to altitudes

in the "zone of horizontality", has been 52 m (172 ft.) at Buffalo. Similarly, relative uplift since the Lowest Lake Warren time has been about 43 m (140 ft.) at Buffalo (Calkin, 1970). Maximum total rebound for Lowest Warren relative to the "zone of horizontality" has been 66 m (217 ft.) where the strand occurs at its most northern point, 13 km north of Batavia, New York (Fairchild, 1916).

Present Deformation

The degree to which glacioisostatic deformation or warping of any origin continues to affect Lake Erie has been studied by many workers (see MacLean, 1961, 1963; Clark and Persoage, 1970). Although the Lake Nipissing "zero isobase" of Leverett and Taylor (1915) could be projected into the Erie basin south of Buffalo, Taylor (Leverett and Taylor, 1915, p. 467) noted that "it seems almost certain... the isobases bend gradually to the east in southwestern Ontario so as to leave the outlet of Lake Erie at or south of the hinge line." Taylor (1928) later changed his mind on this matter; however, Hough (1958), provided support for this 1915 conclusion.

A number of workers have presented estimates of crustal movement for each of the Great Lakes. For the most part, they used the general methods of Gilbert (1898) and compared pairs of water level gauge readings for the summer months. Their results (Clark and Persoage, 1970; Coordinating Committee... 1977) suggest that differential vertical movement is going on throughout the Great Lakes region. Isobases of apparent zero "uplift" cross the southern part of Lake Michigan and through the NE − SW axis of Lake Erie. The uplift measured for Cleveland, Ohio, relative to Port Colborne, Ontario (Fig. 1; 24 km west of Buffalo), is given in Table I.

MacLean (1961, 1963) noted that such apparent rates of crustal movement in the Erie basin may be explained as due to net summer wind set-up; however, this type of interpretation probably applied to "short term (a few years) fluctuation" and the position of the leveling gauges may have an even greater effect than atmospheric factors (Coordinating Committee..., 1977, p. 8). The 1977 study (Table I) showed that all relative rates of deformation for the Erie basin are less than 64 mm per century and are compatible with the conclusions of Clark and Persoage (1970, p. 632) drawn from earlier surveys. These conclusions were that "crustal movement rates for Lake Erie suggest minimal, if any relative movement between the inlet and the outlet of the lake and consequently little effect on its mean lake level with time." The data did show, however, that there was increasing upward tilt from southeast to northwest. In marked contrast to the other Great Lakes basins, present relative uplift of Lake Erie is very small and shows contour trends which do not correspond with those of the probable glacioisostatic uplift shown by the warped strands (Fig. 6).

Alternative Models of Post-Glacial Deleveling and Warped Shore Features

The concept of the "hingeline" or "zero isobase" that separates an area of relative stability or even near-horizontality on the south from one of isostatically uplifted shore features on the north is inconsistent with measurements that suggest that continuous vertical movements are still occurring over the whole Great Lakes (Larsen, 1985b). That an area of no deformation or true horizontality could be expected in the glacioisostatically-affected Great Lakes area has been considered unlikely for some time based on theoretical grounds (MacLean, 1961; McGinnis, 1968; Walcott, 1972; Clark *et al.*, 1978). Some examples of alternative working concepts or models of isostatic reponse that may be considered for application in the Lake Erie basin, are outlined below.

McGinnis (1968), in consideration of evidence for a "forebulge" of glacial deflection, contoured data of Moore (1948) to suggest a zone of current subsidence that closely followed the southern margins of the Great Lakes. In addition, McGinnis (1968, p. 772) indicated that glacial crustal warping would parallel the lobate ice margins so that the "area of horizontality" may be that "where ice fronts were parallel to shore features, and the horizontal attitude of beaches indicates a region of uniform movement."

Numerical calculations developed by Clark (Clark *et al.*, 1984, 1985) that predict the amount of vertical movement of an earth model for any glacial history support the subsidence in the southern Great Lakes considered by McGinnis; they also match the trends of recent lake-level gauge readings. The area of subsidence predicted by Clark *et al.* (1985) is separated from that of isostatic uplift to the north by an isobase of "zero" deformation; this has slowly migrated northward since deglaciation. Their studies in the Lake Michigan basin predict that some older strands cross below younger ones southward from the mapped "hingelines" there.

Larsen (1985a, 1985b), in an attempt to correlate discontinuous, raised strand terraces in the Lake Michigan and Lake Huron basins, derived a new relative lake level model. This is based on the apparent similarity of recent vertical movements in the Great Lakes and the exponential decay of the rate of uplift following deglaciation that is observed in the area of Arctic ice masses.

The importance of these or other preliminary models of glacioisostatic reponse, to the evolution of the Great Lakes of the Erie basin, needs to be tested. Many existing correlations of shore features considered in this summary may merit careful re-evaluation in the context of the new concepts.

Particularly good candidates for a second evaluation are correlations of discontinuously-exposed strands (e.g., for Lakes Arkona, Grassmere, Lundy) made by long-distance projection of isobases as straight lines or from assumed lines of maximum tilt. Future workers may also want to avoid the assumption of areas of stability or even of continuous "uplift" in a zone of ice marginal fluctuations.

SOME CONCLUSIONS AND POINTS OF CONTROVERSY

1) Lake Maumee is represented by three strand levels and two or three different outlets. Much work, both recent and old, suggests that the classic sequence of Highest-Lowest-Middle must be complemented by a succeeding, "reoccupied" Lowest Maumee phase, or replaced by a descending sequence of Highest-Middle-Lowest phases.

2) There appears to be good stratigraphic evidence in the Lake Huron basin and on the west margin of the Lake Erie basin that Lake Arkona occurred prior to the higher, Lake Whittlesey phase. However, Arkona beaches are difficult to define or trace through most of the Erie basin and sedimentologic evidence for submergence by Whittlesey waters is rare or not definitive.

3) Support continues to be assembled for a pre-Whittlesey low water (Ypsilanti) interval between 14 000 and 13 000 B.P.

4) Lake Whittlesey strands are the best developed of any in the basin; however, some of the topography associated with this lake phase, as well as others, may be a product of earlier events.

5) Lake Warren had two or possibly three phases that drained westward, but evidence, mainly in southeastern Michigan, suggests that Lowest Warren was preceded by the low, Lake Wayne phase. Drainage of Lake Wayne, as well as drawdown from the succeeding Lowest Warren and subsequent drainage of proglacial lake waters from the Erie basin, was probably to the east and may be explained by ice marginal fluctuations east of Buffalo, New York.

6) Evidence for control of Lakes Grassmere, Lundy, or the hypothetical Erie arm of an Early Lake Algonquin, by proglacial lake levels in the Michigan basin is contradictory.

7) The name "Dana" for a post-Lundy proglacial lake in the Erie basin is no longer appropriate.

8) Present relative uplift between the inlet and the outlet of Lake Erie is minimal; the direction of maximum tilt is substantially different from that of the apparent postglacial tilting suggested by correlations of the Late Wisconsin beaches. Models of lake history should be tested with correlations of strand features that take into account the continuous deformation of the Erie basin and of the elastic response of the crust.

ACKNOWLEDGEMENTS

We are very grateful to Jane Forsyth, David Fullerton, and Ernest Muller for many discussions over the years and for their constructive criticism of this and assorted earlier manuscripts relative to the Great Lakes of the Erie basin. However, they are in no way responsible for any inadequacies nor should they be held to any interpretations herein.

REFERENCES

American Falls International Board, 1974, Preservation and Enhancement of the American Falls at Niagara: Final Report to the International Joint Commission, Appendix D-Hydraulics, 41 p.

Barnett, P.J., 1978, Quaternary Geology of the Simcoe Area, Southern Ontario: Ontario Division of Mines Geoscience Report 162, 74 p.

————, 1979, Glacial Lake Whittlesey: The Probable Ice Frontal Position in the Eastern End of the Erie Basin: Canadian Journal of Earth Sciences, v. 16, p. 568-574.

————, 1982, Quaternary Geology of the Tillsonburg Area, Southern Ontario: Ontario Geological Survey Report 220, 87 p.

————, 1985, Glacial Retreat and Lake Levels, North Central Lake Erie Basin, Ontario: in Karrow, P.F., and Calkin, P.E., eds., Quaternary Evolution of the Great Lakes: Geological Association of Canada Special Paper 30.

Bleuer, N.K., and Moore, M.C., 1972, Glacial Stratigraphy of the Fort Wayne Area and the Draining of Glacial Lake Maumee: Proceedings of the Indiana Academy of Science, 1971, v. 81, p. 195-209.

Brennan, W.J., Hamilton, M.J., Kilbury, R.K., Reeves, R.L., and Covert, L.J., 1984, Late Quaternary Secular Variation of Geomagnetic Declination in Western New York: Earth and Planetary Science Letters, v. 70, p. 363-372.

Bretz, J.H., 1951, Causes of the Glacial Lake Stages in Saginaw Basin, Michigan: Journal of Geology, v. 59, p. 244-258.

————, 1959, The Double Calumet Stage of Lake Chicago: Journal of Geology, v. 67, p. 675-684.

————, 1964, Correlation of Glacial Lake Stages in the Huron-Erie and Michigan Basins: Journal of Geology, v. 72, p. 618-627.

Burgis, W.A., and Eschman, D.F., 1980, The Imlay Channel and Glacial Lake Maumee: Geological Society of America Abstracts with Programs, v. 12, no. 5, p. 221.

Calkin, P.E., 1970, Strand Lines and Chronology of the Great Lakes in Northwestern New York: Ohio Journal of Science, v. 70, p. 78-96.

————, 1982, Glacial Geology of the Erie Lowland and Adjoining Alleghany Plateau, Western New York: in Buehler, E.J., and Calkin, P.E., eds., Field Trips Guidebook: New York State Geological Association, 54th Annual Meeting, Amherst, New York, p. 121-148.

Calkin, P.E., and Brett, C.E., 1978, Ancestral Niagara River Drainage: Stratigraphic and Paleontologic Setting: Geological Society of America Bulletin, v. 89, p. 1140-1154.

Calkin, P.E., and McAndrews, J.H., 1980, Geology and Paleontology of Two Late Wisconsin Sites in Western New York State: Geological Society of America Bulletin, Part 1, v. 91, p. 295-306.

Calkin, P.E., and Wilkinson, T.A., 1982, Glacial and Engineering Geology Aspects of the Niagara Falls and Gorge: in Buehler, E.J., and Calkin, P.E., eds., Field Trips Guidebook: New York State Geological Association, 54th Annual Meeting, Amherst, New York, p. 247-283.

Carter, C.H., 1977, Sediment Load Measurements Along the United States Shore of Lake Erie: Ohio Geological Survey Report of Investigations, no. 10, 24 p.

Chapman, L.J., and Putnam, D.F., 1966, The Physiography of Southern Ontario: Toronto, Ontario, University of Toronto Press, 386 p.

Clark, J.A., Farrell, W.E., and Peltier, W.R., 1978, Global Changes in Postglacial Sea Level: A Numerical Calculation: Quaternary Research, v. 9, p. 265-287.

Clark, J.A., Pranger, H.S., Primus, J.A., and Walsh, J.K., 1984, Holocene Sea Level and Proglacial Lake Indicators of Vertical Crustal Movement: American Geophysical Union, Chapman Conference on Vertical Crustal Motion, Measurement and Modeling, October 22-26, 1984, Harpers Ferry, West Virginia, Program with Abstracts.

Clark, James A., Walsh, Jeffrey K., Primus, John A., Pranger, Harold S.,1985, A Model of Proglacial Lake Strandline Delevelling During the Past 18000 years: Stratigraphic Implications: Geological Society of America Abstracts with Programs, v. 17, no. 5, p. 283.

Clark, R.H., and Persoage, N.P., 1970, Some Implications of Crustal Movement for Engineering Planning: Canadian Journal of Earth Sciences, v. 7, p. 628-633.

Coakley, J.P., and Lewis, C.F.M., 1985, Postglacial Lake Levels in the Erie Basin: in Karrow, P.F., and Calkin, P.E., eds., Quaternary Evolution of the Great Lakes: Geological Association of Canada Special Paper 30.

Cooper, A.J., 1979, Quaternary Geology of the Grand Bend-Parkhill Area, Southern Ontario: Ontario Geological Survey Report 188, 70 p.

Coordinating Committee on Great Lakes Basic Hydraulic and Hydrologic Data, 1977, Apparent Vertical Movement Over the Great Lakes: Chicago, Detroit District, Corps of Engineers, 71 p.

Cowan, W.R., Sharpe, D.R., Feenstra, B.H., and Gwyn, Q.H.J., 1978, Glacial Geology of the Toronto-Owen Sound Area: in Currie, A.L. and Mackasey, W.O., eds., Toronto '78 Field Trips Guidebook for a Joint Meeting of the Geological Society of America, Geological Association of Canada, and Mineralogical Association of Canada, p. 1-16.

DeGeer, G.J., 1892, On Pleistocene Changes in Level in Eastern North America: Boston Society of Natural History Proceedings, v. 25, p. 454-477.

Dewey, Chester, 1818, Appendix: in Configuration of the Country Lying South of Lake Erie: in Mitchell, S.L., Observations on the Geology of North America; Illustrated by the Description of Various Organic Remains Found in that Part of the World: in Cuvier, Georges, Essay on the Theory of the Earth: New York, p. 417-419.

Dorr, J.A., Jr., and Eschman, D.F., 1970, Geology of Michigan: Ann Arbor, Michigan, University of Michigan Press, 476 p.

Dreimanis, Aleksis, 1963, Pleistocene Geology of the London-St. Thomas and Port Stanley Areas: Ontario Department of Mines Progress Report 1963-2, p. 33-34.

————, 1964, Lake Warren and the Two Creeks Interval: Journal of Geology, v. 72, p. 247-250.

————, 1966, Lake Arkona-Whittlesey and Post-Warren Radiocarbon Dates from ''Ridgetown Island'' in Southwestern Ontario: Ohio Journal of Science, v. 66, p. 582-586.

————, 1969, Late-Pleistocene Lakes in the Ontario and Erie Basins: Proceedings 12th Conference on Great Lakes Research, International Association for Great Lakes Research, p. 170-180.

Dreimanis, Aleksis, and Goldthwait, R.P., 1973, Wisconsin Glaciation in the Huron, Erie, and Ontario Lobes: in Black, R.F., Goldthwait, R.P., and Willman, H.B., eds., The Wisconsinan Stage: Geological Society of America Memoir 136, p. 71-106.

Dreimanis, Aleksis, and Karrow, P.F., 1972, Glacial History of the Great Lakes-St. Lawrence Region, the Classification of the Wisconsin(an) Stage, and Its Correlatives: 24th International Geological Congress, Montreal, Quaternary Geology, Section 12, p.5-15.

Dryer, C.R., 1888, Geology of Allen County, Indiana: Geological Survey of Indiana, 16th Annual Report, p. 107-126.

Eschman, D.F., and Farrand, W.R., 1970, Glacial History of the Glacial Grand Valley: in Guidebook for Field Trips: East Lansing, Michigan, Michigan Basin Geological Society, p. 131-157.

Eschman, D.F., and Karrow, P.F., 1985, Huron Basin Glacial Lakes: A Review: in Karrow, P.F., and Calkin, P.E., eds., Quaternary Evolution of the Great Lakes: Geological Association of Canada Special Paper 30.

Evenson, E.B., 1973, Late Pleistocene Shorelines and Stratigraphic Relations in the Michigan Basin: Geological Society of America Bulletin, v. 84, p. 2281-2298.

Evenson, E.B., and Dreimanis, Aleksis, 1976, Late Glacial (14 000-10 000 years B.P.) history of the Great Lakes Region and Possible Correlation: in Easterbrook, D.J. and Sibrava, Vladimir, eds., Quaternary Glaciations in the Northern Hemisphere, Project 73-1-24, Report no. 3 on the Session in Bellingham, Washington, USA, September, 1975; IUGS-UNESCO International Geological Correlation Program, p. 217-239.

Fairchild, H.L., 1897, Lake Warren Shorelines in Western New York and the Geneva Beach: Geological Society of America Bulletin, v. 8, p. 269-286.

_____, 1899, Glacial Waters in the Finger Lakes Region of New York: Geological Society of America Bulletin, v. 10, p. 27-68.

_____, 1907, Glacial Waters in the Erie Basin: New York State Museum Bulletin 106, 86 p.

_____, 1909, Glacial Waters in Central New York: New York State Museum Bulletin 127, 66 p.

_____, 1916, Pleistocene Uplift of New York and Adjacent Territory: Geological Society of America Bulletin, v. 27, p. 235-262.

_____, 1932, Closing Stages of New York Glacial History: Geological Society of America Bulletin, v. 43, p. 603-626.

Farrand, W.R., and Eschman, D.F., 1974, Glaciation of the Southern Peninsula of Michigan — A Review: Michigan Acadamician, v. 7, p. 31-56.

Farrand, W.R., Zahner, Robert, and Benninghoff, W.S., 1969, Cary-Port Huron Interstade — Evidence from a Buried Bryophyte Bed, Cheboygan County, Michigan: Geological Society of America Special Paper 123, p. 249-262.

Feenstra, B.H., 1974, Quaternary Geology of the Dunnville Area, Southern Ontario: Ontario Division of Mines Preliminary Map P. 981. Scale 1:50 000.

_____, 1981, Quaternary Geology and Industrial Minerals of the Niagara-Welland Area, Southern Ontario: Ontario Geological Survey Open File Report 5361, 260 p.

Fitzgerald, W.D., and Hradsky, M., 1980, Quaternary Geology of the Wallaceburg-St. Clair Flats Area, Lambton and Kent Counties, Southern Ontario: Ontario Geological Survey Preliminary Map P. 2368. Scale 1:50 000.

Flint, J.J., and Lalcoma, J.L., in press, Buried Ancestral Drainage Between Lakes Erie and Ontario: Geological Society of America Bulletin.

Forsyth, J.L., 1959, The Beach Ridges of Northern Ohio: Ohio Geological Survey Information Circular 25, 10 p.

_____, 1973, Late-Glacial and Postglacial History of Western Lake Erie: Compass, v. 51, p. 16-26.

Fullerton, D.S., 1980, Preliminary Correlation of Post-Erie Interstadial Events (16 000-10 000 Radiocarbon Years Before Present), Central and Eastern Great Lakes Region, and Hudson, Champlain, and St. Lawrence Lowlands, United States and Canada: United States Geological Survey Professional Paper 1089, 52 p.

Geier, R.J., and Calkin, P.E., 1983, Stratigraphy and Bluff Recession Along the Lake Erie Coast, New York: Albany, New York Sea Grant Institute, 58 p.

Gilbert, G.K., 1871, Surface Geology of the Maumee Valley: American Journal of Science, 3rd Series, v. 1, p. 339-345.

_____, 1890, Lake Bonneville: United States Geological Survey Monograph 1, 438 p.

_____, 1898, Recent Earth Movements in the Great Lakes Region: United States Geological Survey 18th Annual Report, Part 2-H, p. 595-648.

Goldthwait, J.W., 1908, A Reconstruction of Water Planes of the Extinct Glacial Lakes in the Lake Michigan Basin: Journal of Geology, v. 16, p. 459-476.

Goldthwait, R.P., 1958, Wisconsin-age Forests in Western Ohio, Part 1-Age and Glacial Events: Ohio Journal of Science, v. 58, p. 209-219.

Hall, James, 1842, Niagara Falls, Their Physical Changes and the Geology and Topography of the Surrounding Country: Boston Journal of Natural History, v. 4, p. 206-234.

Hansel, A.K., Mickelson, D.M., Schneider, A.F., and Larsen, C.E., 1985, Late Wisconsinan and Holocene History of the Lake Michigan Basin: in Karrow, P.F., and Calkin, P.E., eds., Quaternary Evolution of the Great Lakes: Geological Association of Canada Special Paper 30.

Hough, J.L., 1958, Geology of the Great Lakes: Urbana, Illinois, University of Illinois Press, 313 p.

_____, 1963, The Prehistoric Great Lakes of North America: American Scientist, v. 51, p. 84-109.

_____, 1966, Correlation of Glacial Lake Stages in the Huron-Erie Basins: Journal of Geology, v. 74, p. 62-77.

Hubbard, Bela, 1840, Report on Lenawee, Hillsdale, Branch, St. Joseph, Cass, Berrian, Washtenaw, Oakland, and Livingston Counties, with Notes on the Lake Ridges and Great Lakes: Michigan State Geological Survey Annual Report 3, p. 77-111.

International Joint Commission, 1953, Preservation and Enhancement of Niagara Falls: Washington, D.C., 354 p.

Karrow, P.F., 1963, Pleistocene Geology of the Hamilton-Galt Area: Ontario Department of Mines Geology Report 16, 68 p.

_____, 1973, Bedrock Topography in Southwestern Ontario: A Progress Report: Geological Association of Canada, Proceedings, v. 25, p. 67-77.

Karrow, P.F., Clark, J.R., and Terasmae, Jaan, 1961, The Age of Lake Iroquois and Lake Ontario: Journal of Geology, v. 69, p. 659-667.

Kindle, E.M., and Taylor, F.B., 1913, Description of the Niagara Quadrangle: United States Geological Survey Geological Atlas, Folio 190, 26 p.

Kunkle, G.R., 1963, Lake Ypsilanti: A Probable Late Pleistocene Low-Lake Stage in the Erie Basin: Journal of Geology, v. 71, p. 72-75.

Lane, A.C., 1900, Geological Report on Huron County: Michigan Geological Survey, v. 7, Part 2, 324 p.

Larsen, Curtis E., 1985a, Glacio-Isostasy — An Alternative to the Hinge-Line Models in the Southern Lake Michigan Basin: Geological Society of America, Abstracts with Programs, v. 17, no. 5, p. 298.

_____, 1985b, Lake Level, Uplift, and Outlet Incision, the Nipissing and Algoma Great Lakes: in Karrow, P.F., and Calkin, P.E., eds., Quaternary Evolution of the Great Lakes: Geological Association of Canada Special Paper 30.

Leverett, Frank, 1895, On the Correlation of New York Moraines with Raised Beaches of Lake Erie: American Journal of Science, v. 50, p. 1-20.

_____, 1902, Glacial Formations and Drainage Features of the Erie and Ohio Basins: United States Geological Survey Monograph 41, 802 p.

_____, 1931, Quaternary System: in Cushing, H.P., Leverett, F., and Van Horn, F.R., Geology and Mineral Resources of the Cleveland District, Ohio: United States Geological Survey Bulletin 818, p. 57-81.

_____, 1939, Correlations of Beaches with Moraines in the Huron and Erie Basins: American Journal of Science, v. 237, p. 456-475.

Leverett, Frank, and Taylor, F.B., 1915, The Pleistocene of Indiana and Michigan and the History of the Great Lakes: United States Geological Survey Monograph 53, 529 p.

Lewis, C.F.M., 1969, Late Quaternary History of Lake Levels in the Huron and Erie Basins: Proceedings 12th Conference on Great Lakes Research: International Association for Great Lakes Research p. 250-270.

Lewis, C.F.M., Anderson, T.W., and Bertie, A.A., 1966, Geological and Palynological Studies of Early Lake Erie Deposits: Proceedings 9th Conference on Great Lakes Research, University of Michigan Great Lakes Research Division Publication 15, p. 176-191.

Lyell, Charles, 1842, A Memoir on the Recession of the Falls of Niagara: Geological Society of London Proceedings, v. 3, p. 595-602.

MacLachlan, D.C., 1939, Warren Shoreline in Ontario and in the Thumb of Michigan and its Deformation: Ph.D. Thesis, Ann Arbor, Michigan, University of Michigan, 89 p.

MacLean, W.F., 1961, Postglacial Uplift in the Great Lakes Region: Ann Arbor, Michigan, University of Michigan, Great Lakes Research Division Special Report No. 14, 234 p.

_____, 1963, Modern Pseudo-Upwarping Around Lake Erie: Proceedings 6th Conference on Great Lakes Research, International Association for Great Lakes Research, p. 158-168.

McGinnis, Lyle D., 1968, Glacial Crustal Bending: Geological Society of America Bulletin, v. 79, p. 769-776.

Mickelson, D.M., Clayton, Lee, Fullerton, D.S., and Borns, H.W., Jr., 1983, The Late Wisconsin Glacial Record of the Laurentide Ice Sheet in the United States: in Porter, S.C., ed., Late Quaternary Environments of the United States, Volume 1, The Late Pleistocene: Minneapolis, Minnesota, University of Minnesota Press, p. 3-37.

Moore, Sherman, 1948, Crustal Movement in the Great Lakes Area: Geological Society of America Bulletin, v. 59, p. 697-710.

Muller, E.H., 1965, Quaternary Geology of New York: in Wright, H.E., Jr., and Frey, D.G., eds., The Quaternary of the United States: Princeton, New Jersey, Princeton University Press, p. 99-112.

_____, 1977a, Late Glacial and Early Post-Glacial Environments in Western New York: Annals of the New York Academy of Sciences, v. 288, p. 223-233.

_____, 1977b, Quaternary Geology of New York, Niagara Sheet: New York State Geological Survey Map and Chart Series No. 28, Scale 1:250 000.

Muller, E.H., and Prest, V.K., 1985, Glacial Lakes in the Ontario Basin: in Karrow, P.F., and Calkin, P.E., eds., Quaternary Evolution of the Great Lakes: Geological Association of Canada Special Paper 30.

Muller, E.H., Young, R.A., Rhodes, D.D., Willette, Paul, Wilson, M.P., and Fakundiny, R.H., 1981, Surficial Geology of the Genesee Valley: New York State Geological Survey Open File Report No. 2102.056, 174 p.

Prest, V.K., 1970, Quaternary Geology of Canada: in Geology and Economic Minerals of Canada: Geological Survey of Canada, Economic Geology Report 1, 5th ed., p. 675-764.

Russell, I.C., and Leverett, Frank, 1908, Description of the Ann Arbor Quadrangle: United States Geological Survey Geological Atlas, Folio 155, 15 p.

Schooler, E.E., 1974, Pleistocene Beach Ridges of Northwestern Pennsylvania: Pennsylvania Geological Survey, General Geology Report 64, 38 p.

Sly, P.G., and Lewis, C.F.M., 1972, The Great Lakes of Canada – Quaternary Geology and Limnology: Guidebook for Field Excursion A 43, 24th International Geological Congress, Montreal, 92 p.

Spencer, J.W., 1888, The St. Lawrence Basin and the Great Lakes: Science, v. 12, p. 99-100.

_____, 1891, High-level Shores in the Region of the Great Lakes and Their Deformation: American Journal of Science, 3rd Series, v. 41, p. 201-211.

_____, 1894a, Deformation of the Lundy Beach and Birth of Lake Erie: American Journal of Science, 3rd Series, v. 147, p. 207-212.

_____, 1894b, The Duration of Niagara Falls: American Journal of Science, 3rd Series, v. 48, p. 455-472.

Taylor, F.B., 1897, Correlation of Erie-Huron Beaches with Outlets and Moraines in Southwestern Michigan: Geological Society of America Bulletin, v. 8, p. 31-58.

_____, 1905, Relation of Lake Whittlesey to the Arkona Beaches: Michigan Academy of Science, 7th Annual Report, p. 29-36.

_____, 1928, The Status of Lake Erie in Present and Recent Land-Tilting: Michigan Academy of Science Papers, v. 10, p. 251-260.

_____, 1939, Correlations of the Port Huron Morainic System of Michigan in Ontario and Western New York: American Journal of Science, v. 237, p. 375-388.

Totten, S.M., 1982, Pleistocene Beaches and Strandlines Bordering Lake Erie: in White, G.M., Glacial Geology of Northeastern Ohio: Ohio Geological Survey Bulletin 68, p. 52-60.

_____, 1985, Chronology and Nature of the Pleistocene Beaches and Wave-Cut Cliffs and Terraces, Northeastern Ohio: in Karrow, P.F., and Calkin, P.E., eds., Quaternary Evolution of the Great Lakes: Geological Association of Canada Special Paper 30.

Vagners, U.J., 1972, Quaternary Geology of the Windsor-Essex Area [Western Part], Southern Ontario: Ontario Department of Mines, Preliminary Map P.749. Scale 1:50 000.

Walcott, R.I., 1972, Late Quaternary Vertical Movements in Eastern North America: Quantitative Evidence of Glacio-Isostatic Rebound: Reviews of Geophysics and Space Physics, v. 10, p. 849-884.

Wall, R.E., 1968, A Sub-Bottom Reflection Survey in the Central Basin of Lake Erie: Geological Society of America Bulletin, v. 79, p. 91-106.

Wayne, W.J., and Zumberge, J.H., 1965, Pleistocene Geology of Indiana and Michigan: in Wright, H.E., Jr., and Frey, D.G., eds., The Quaternary of the United States: Princeton, New Jersey, Princeton University Press, p. 63-84.

White, G.W., 1982, Glacial Geology of Northeastern Ohio: Ohio Geological Survey Bulletin 68, 75 p.

Whittlesey, Charles, 1838, Report on the Geology and Topography of a Portion of Ohio: Ohio Geological Survey Annual Report 2, p. 41-71.

_____, 1850, On the Natural Terraces and Ridges of the Country Bordering Lake Erie: American Journal of Science, 2nd Series, v. 10, p. 31-39.

Williams, S.J., and Meisburger, E.P., 1982, Geological Character and Mineral Resources of South Central Lake Erie: United States Army Corps of Engineers, Coastal Engineering Research Center, Miscellaneous Report 82-9, 62 p.

Winchell, N.H., 1872, The Surface Geology of Northwestern Ohio: Proceedings of the American Association for the Advancement of Science, v. 21, p. 152-186.

Quaternary Evolution of the Great Lakes,
edited by P.F. Karrow and P.E. Calkin,
Geological Association of Canada Special Paper 30, 1985

CHRONOLOGY AND NATURE OF THE PLEISTOCENE BEACHES AND WAVE-CUT CLIFFS AND TERRACES, NORTHEASTERN OHIO

Stanley M. Totten
Department of Geology, Hanover College, Hanover, Indiana 47243

ABSTRACT

Two prominent sets of Wisconsinan strandlines occur along the south shore of Lake Erie. The older set, probably dating from the Plum Point (Farmdalian) Interstadial (about 35 000 − 23 000 B.P.) when lake levels were mostly higher than present, consists of wave-cut cliffs and terraces developed primarily in till. These strandlines were developed at elevations of 241, 236, 230, 218, 201, and 186 m. The younger set of strandlines consists of 20 beach ridges, which represent stages of lakes Maumee, Whittlesey, Arkona, and others which formed on the terraces following retreat of the ice sheet that deposited the Ashtabula Till. These ridges were deposited by the action of longshore currents and waves on deltaic river sediment at elevations between 238 and 186.5 m during a gradual lowering of lake level from about 14 500 to 12 700 B.P. The distribution of sediment in the ridges and on the interridge flats indicates the beach ridges probably formed in a regular sequence according to topographic position − the lower the ridge elevation, the younger the age of the beach. The traditional view that certain Maumee, Arkona, and Wayne ridges were drowned and washed over by higher lake levels is not supported by sedimentologic and geomorphic evidence from northeastern Ohio.

RÉSUMÉ

Deux séries importantes de rivages wisconsiniens s'observent le long de la côte sud du lac Érié. La série la plus ancienne, datant probablement de l'interstade Plum Point (± 35 000 − 23 000 B.P.) a été formée lorsque les niveaux lacustres ont atteint des altitudes plus élevées qu'actuellement. Cette série consiste en falaises et plate-formes littorales d'abrasion construites principalement dans du till d'âge altonien (début du Wisconsin) et recouvertes d'une mince couche d'alluvions d'âge woodfordien (fin du Wisconsin). Ces formes littorales ont été peu affectées par l'avancée glaciaire subséquente et le ruissellement.

La seconde série de rivages consiste en 20 levées de plage représentant les niveaux des lacs Maumee, Whittlesey, Arkona et autres. Ces lacs se sont formés sur les terrasses à la suite du retrait de la glace ayant déposé le till d'Ashtabula. Les levées de plage ont été déposées par l'action des vagues et des courants de dérive littorale sur les sédiments deltaïques situés entre 238 et 186.5 m. Cette déposition s'est effectuée lors d'une baisse graduelle du niveau lacustre entre 14 500 et 12 700 ans B.P. Le long de la côte sud du lac Érié, la série la plus complète et les plages les mieux développées se rencontrent au nord-est de l'état d'Ohio. Là, les rivières drainant l'escarpement et les versants raides des moraines ont procuré aux lacs une grande quantité de sédiments.

La répartition des sédiments sur les crêtes de plage et entre les crêtes indique que les plages se sont formées de façon ordonnée en accord avec leur position topographique: les plages les plus basses en altitude étant les plus récentes.

Dans le nord-est de l'Ohio, aucune preuve géomorphologique et sédimentologique ne soutient l'opinion traditionnelle selon laquelle certaines plages des lacs Maumee, Arkona et Wayne auraient été inondées et délavées par des niveaux lacustres supérieurs.

La courbe des datations au carbone − 14 suggère que la baisse du plan d'eau s'est faite de façon graduelle à un taux relativement constant entre 14 500 et 12 900 B.P. Durant cette période le lac se drainait vers l'ouest et d'importantes levées de plage étaient construites. Entre 12 900 et 12 660 B.P. le niveau du lac a baissé rapidement suite à l'ouverture de nouveaux exutoires vers l'est de l'état de New York (ceux des rivières Mohawk et Niagara). La courbe des plans d'eau déduite des datations au carbone − 14 permet d'extrapoler l'âge des plages non-datées. En ce qui a trait à la durée de chaque épisode lacustre on trouve alors une bonne correspondance entre les données fournies par les courbes des plans d'eau et celles basées sur le volume de sédiments.

INTRODUCTION

A strip of land 3 to 19 km wide bordering Lake Erie in northeastern Ohio was greatly affected by wave action, longshore currents, and wind when lake levels in the Erie Basin were considerably higher than the present 174-m surface elevation of Lake Erie. During each of the interglacial and interstadial (warm) periods, when ice retreated north of Ohio, lakes existed as they had in the time since the last ice left. In the early stages of each series of lakes, water was enclosed between higher land elevations to the south and the thick ice sheet to the north. At lower levels the water occupied only the Erie Basin itself, just as does present Lake Erie.

For the most part, in the earlier episodes prior to the last ice advance, the major activity was wave erosion forming cliffs and terraces as the modern lake is now doing. At the various lake levels following the retreat of the last (Woodfordian) glaciers from Ohio, the major activity was the deposition of beach and dune ridges, rather than cliff and terrace cutting.

The strandlines are represented on Figure 1 by a few of the most prominent beach ridges. The less prominent ridges and the cliffs, which closely parallel the beach ridges, are not shown on Figure 1 but are shown on maps in the more detailed reports of the following counties: Ashtabula (White and Totten, 1979), Lake (White, 1980), Cuyahoga (John Ford, unpublished manuscript, 1978), and Lorain (Stanley Totten, unpublished manuscript, 1978).

PREVIOUS STUDIES

One of the earliest investigations of the geology of northeastern Ohio was made by Colonel Charles Whittlesey (1848, 1850, 1867) who described a series of terraces and ridges that occurred along the south shore of Lake Erie at an altitude of 21 to 62 m above the present lake level. He included (1848) a cross-section sketch of the lacustrine deposits in the Cleveland area that were especially prone to slumping. Whittlesey (1850) concluded that the terraces represented ''ancient beaches'' of the lake, and that the ridges were ''submarine deposits'' of the lake.

Gilbert (1871, 1873) mapped the beach ridges of extreme northwestern Ohio, and he believed the ridges represented strandlines formed when Lake Erie stood at higher levels. As explained by Leverett (1892, p. 284), Gilbert ''discovered that several of the raised beaches of Lake Erie do not completely encircle that body of water but terminate in a successive series from higher to lower in passing eastward from northern Ohio to southwestern New York... . In explanation of the termination of these beaches, Mr. Gilbert has entertained the theory that they represent successive positions of the ice-front in its northeastward retreat across the Lake Erie Basin, but has held that the complete verification of this theory depends upon the occurrence of moraines which are demonstrable correlatives of the beaches. Such moraines have now been discovered and traced into connection with the eastern ends of the three beaches which terminate in Ohio.'' Leverett (1902) included a comprehensive report on the beach ridges in his monograph on the Erie Lobe, and later he collaborated with Taylor (Leverett and Taylor, 1915) to propose a chronology of lake stages. Hough (1958) followed the descriptions and interpretations of Leverett and Taylor (1915) in his discussion of Lake Erie history with only slight modification.

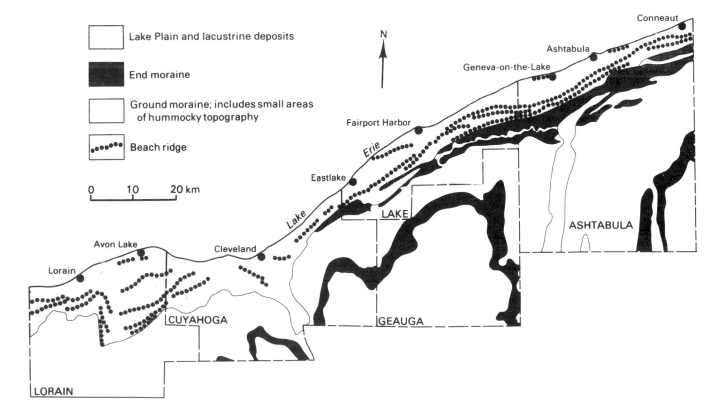

Figure 1. Map of northeastern Ohio showing physiography and location of beach ridges.

Shortly after the Leverett study, Carney (1910, 1911, 1916) remapped the beach ridges in northeastern Ohio, and he demonstrated the multiple nature of several ridges. More recently, Calkin (1970) in New York and Schooler (1974) in Pennsylvania have studied the strandlines northeast of Ohio. Other papers regarding the ancient strandlines in northeastern Ohio such as those by Forsyth (1959) and by Goldthwait *et al.* (1965) are useful summaries of previously published papers. This study finds little or no support for many of the "yo-yo" fluctuations of water level found in these early classic studies.

CLIFFS AND TERRACES CUT INTO BEDROCK

The bedrock surface buried beneath till and the surficial strandlines was reconstructed from well records for Ashtabula County (White and Totten, 1979). Profiles of the bedrock surface show a series of steps (Fig. 2) which are believed to represent wave-cut cliffs and terraces cut at strandline elevations of 225, 210, 193, and 168 m. These strandlines are developed in shale and are not controlled by any known bedrock units. Farther west in Lorain County, outliers of Berea Sandstone display nearly vertical cliffs and broad terraces partly buried beneath till (Totten, unpublished Lorain County manuscript). These partly buried cliffs and terraces in Lorain County and the completely buried

cliffs and terraces in Ashtabula County probably represent pre-Wisconsinan erosion by an early predecessor of Lake Erie. The occurrence of thin Keefus Till (early Wisconsinan ?) overlying the bedrock terraces in northwestern Ashtabula County and northeastern Lake County suggests the lake around which these strandlines formed dates at least as far back as the Sangamonian Stage.

CLIFFS AND TERRACES CUT INTO TILL

The wave-cut cliffs and terraces cut into till are the most prominent strandline features that occur at the surface along the narrow belt of Lake Plain (Fig. 1) south of Lake Erie. Whittlesey (1850) and Leverett (1902, 1931) recognized the cliffs and terraces as wave-cut features separate from and predating the beach ridges. Neither geologist developed this idea to any extent, and more recent studies (Carney, 1910, 1911, 1916; Schooler, 1974) make little or no distiction between cliff and terrace cutting and beach-ridge formation. Phillips (1977) demonstrated for Lake Superior that the cliffs and terraces predate the beach deposits there, just as in the case for Lake Erie.

The terraces, which are underlain by till, slope gently toward the lake, and the different terrace levels are separated by steep slopes or cliffs. The line of intersection of the two slopes (the shoreline angle), as seen in profile (Figs. 2, 3 and

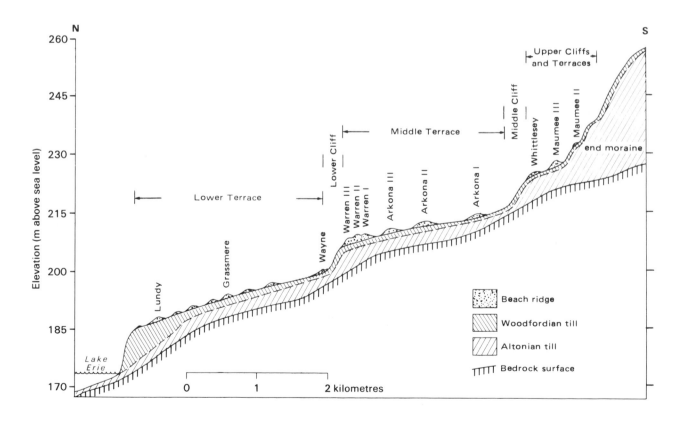

Figure 2. Composite cross-section of strandlines south of Lake Erie in Lake and Ashtabula Counties. Three features are evident: 1) cliffs and terraces cut into bedrock; 2) cliffs and terraces cut into Altonian till and later mantled with Woodfordian till; and 3) beach ridges on terraces. Vertical exaggeration X 55

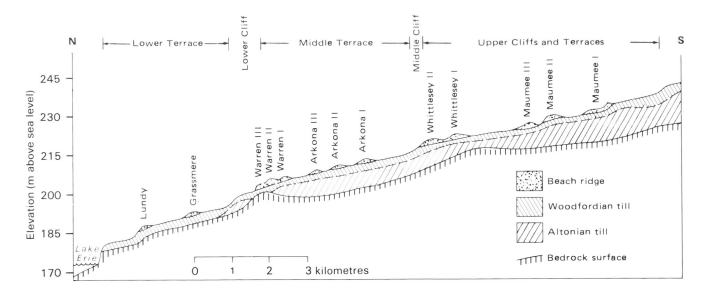

Figure 3. Composite cross-section of strandlines south of Lake Erie in Lorain and western Cuyahoga Counties. Three features are evident: 1) cliffs and terraces cut into bedrock; 2) cliffs and terraces cut into Altonian till and later mantled with Woodfordian till; and 3) beach ridges on terraces. Vertical exaggeration X 65

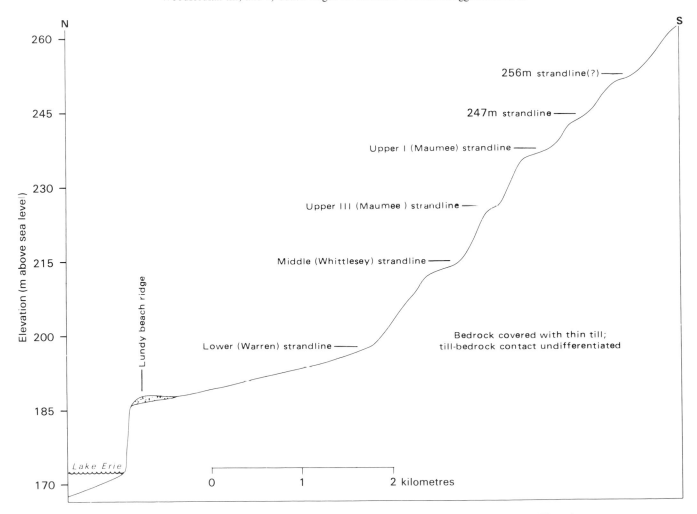

Figure 4. Composite profile of strandlines south of Lake Erie in eastern Cuyahoga County showing cliffs and terraces cut mainly in bedrock. Note absence of beach ridges with the exception of Lundy. Vertical exaggeration X 55

4) represents the strandline for that particular wave-cutting episode. The cliffs and terraces are cut into Titusville-Millbrook Till (White, 1982) of Altonian (early and/or middle Wisconsinan) age, and have been covered with a thin veneer of till of Woodfordian (late Wisconsinan) age, so that the actual lake levels responsible for the strandlines were 1.5 to 3 m lower than indicated by surface elevations. The terraces apparently were eroded or modified very little by the subsequent Woodfordian ice advance, and little postglacial dissection of the terrace surfaces by running water has occurred.

Three prominent wave-cut cliffs (or sets of cliffs) and terraces occur south of Lake Erie, and on each terrace are two to six beach ridges. The most prominent beach ridges recognized south of the lake, from highest to lowest, are designated in this paper as Maumee I, II, III, Whittlesey, Arkona I, II, III, Warren I, II, III, Grassmere, and Lundy. This designation differs slightly from that of Forsyth (1959) and of Fullerton (1980). The wave-cut strandlines do not occur at exactly the same elevations as the beach ridges. However, the Maumee, Whittlesey, and Warren beach ridges occur at the top of prominent cliffs; consequently the cliff and overlying ridge share a common frontal slope and hitherto have been considered a single feature. The cliff and terrace features have long been identified with the associated beaches. However, these erosional forms are earlier than the beaches which are in front or upon them. In this paper, therefore, the cliffs and terraces are given separate designa-tions of Upper, Middle, and Lower, with the former names of Maumee, Whittlesey, and Warren in parentheses.

The present cliff of Lake Erie and its bench form a model for the much earlier features. If the Lake Erie water level fell, the present cliff, which would soon assume a stable slope, and the bench, now under water, would form an almost exact analogue of the higher cliffs and terraces.

Upper (Maumee) Cliffs and Terraces

Three distinct levels of cliff-terrace development referred to as Upper (Maumee) Stage I, II, III are traceable across northeastern Ohio at elevations of 241, 236, and 230 m respectively (Fig. 5). In Lorain County and western Cuyahoga County, west of Cleveland, where the topographic relief is low, the Upper terraces are well developed and the cliffs generally are low and indistinct. The highest level, Upper I, is represented by a terrace between the Maumee I beach ridge and the 241-m elevation (Fig. 3). No distinct cliff is present above the 241-m elevation, only a steeper slope. The middle of the three levels, Upper II, is not a prominent feature and the cliff is masked by a Maumee beach ridge. The lowest level, Upper III, at an elevation of 230 m, is represented by a well-developed cliff and terrace. The cliff, 3 to 4.5 m high, forms the steep frontal (northern) slope of Butternut Ridge. A thin covering of Maumee beach sand is spread over the cliff. The terrace associated with this cliff attains a maximum width of about 4.5 km and is poorly

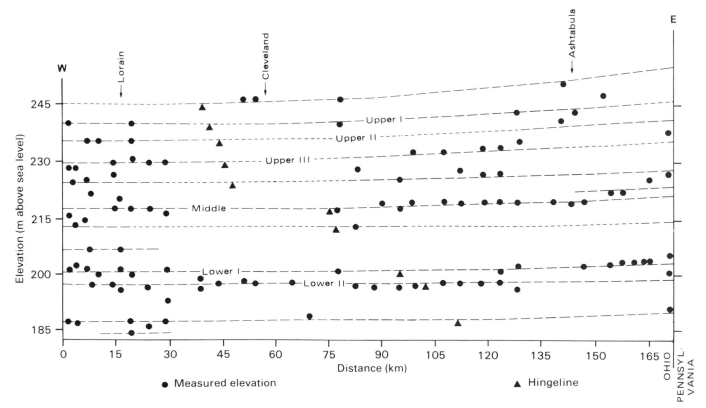

Figure 5. Elevations of intersections of cliffs and terraces in northeastern Ohio. Long-dashed lines represent good correlations, short-dashed lines are projections over greater distances where data are lacking. Distances shown were measured along the Middle Cliff.

drained except for the Maumee III and Whittlesey beach ridges developed on it.

In eastern Cuyahoga County, the Euclid Moraine and the Escarpment have combined to produce elevations exceeding 244 m within 3 km of Lake Erie, and the strandline appears as a cliff or series of cliffs up to 49 m high, broken in places by narrow terraces. Above the Upper strandlines, an additional strandline occurs at an elevation of 247 m and extends eastward into Lake County. The 247-m strandline may represent a smaller localized lake episode or it may correlate with a high terrace at an elevation of 262 m near Erie, Pennsylvania. In a few places in eastern Cuyahoga County yet another terrace-like feature of undetermined significance is present at an elevation of about 256 m (Fig. 4).

In Lake and Ashtabula Counties (Fig. 2) the Upper strandlines generally are notches cut into the steep proximal (northern) slopes of the Ashtabula, Painesville, and Euclid Moraines. The terraces tend to be very narrow and commonly are absent. The major topographic expression is a cliff that may reach a height of 18 to 24 m, especially where the Upper and the Middle Cliffs are combined. The Upper III Terrace attains a maximum width of about 600 m in western Ashtabula and eastern Lake Counties, and is overlain by the Maumee III beach ridge and by the Whittlesey beach-dune ridge. Similarly, the Upper II Terrace widens to 300 m and is overlain by the Maumee II beach ridge. The Upper I strandline cannot be traced farther east than the western part of Ashtabula County and the Upper II strandline can be traced a little farther east to Kingsville in the same county. Ashtabula County may represent the eastern margin of Upper I and II lakes when terracing occurred. The Upper III strandline is the highest and earliest that can be traced eastward into Pennsylvania.

The Upper strandline elevations rise northeastward due to glacio-isostatic rebound (Fig. 5). The hingeline marking the beginning of rise for the Upper strandlines is located in western Cuyahoga County between Cleveland and Lorain. The amount of tilting increases northeastward, being greatest in Ashtabula County, where the Upper I strandline attains an elevation of 247 m.

Middle (Whittlesey) Cliff and Terrace

The Middle (Whittlesey) strandline consists of a prominent cliff and terrace that formed during a major stillstand of lake level at an elevation of 218 m. The Middle Cliff is the single most imposing strandline feature in Lake and Ashtabula Counties. Generally the cliff rises 6 to 9 m above the terrace, but in places where it has cut into end moraines, the height may reach 15 m or more. Between the Middle Cliff and the Lake Erie shoreline, all traces of the Ashtabula, Painesville, and Euclid Moraines have been removed by wave erosion.

From Conneaut Creek in Ashtabula County, Ohio, to the Pennsylvania state line, a distance of 10 km, the Middle and Upper Cliffs are joined against the steep northern slope of the Ashtabula Moraine to form a steep cliff that towers 15 m or more above Under Ridge Road at its base (Fig. 2). The combined cliffs are 15 to 24 m high against the northern slope of the Painesville Moraine in Lake County. The Middle Cliff maintains its prominence westward across Cuyahoga

County, but is reduced in height to about 9 m, and to 3 m in Lorain County. The base of the Middle Cliff rises northeastward from an elevation of 218 m in eastern Cuyahoga County to an elevation of 221 m at the Ohio-Pennsylvania state line as a result of glacio-isostatic uplift.

The Middle Terrace north of its cliff ranges in width from nearly 0 in eastern Cuyahoga County to 3.5 km in Ashtabula County and 7.2 km in eastern Lorain County. The broad gentle terrace slope provided optimum conditions for beach-ridge formation during a later episode, and several beach ridges – Arkona I, II, and III and Warren I, II, and III – occur on its surface.

Lower (Warren) Cliffs and Terraces

The Lower (Warren) strandline consists of two closely related sets of cliffs and terraces north of the Warren beach ridges. The Lower I cliff, with a base elevation of 201 m, forms the moderately steep northward-facing slope of North Ridge. The cliff or slope is only 3 to 6 m high in Ashtabula and Lorain counties, but is 9 to 14 m high across much of Cuyahoga and Lake Counties. A second cliff, Lower II, has a base elevation of 198 m and occurs a very short distance north of Lower I. The Lower II Cliff, which is about 3 m high, commonly is joined with the Lower I Cliff to from a more or less continuous feature. The Lower strandlines gradually rise about 3 m in elevation due to glacio-isostatic rebound as they are traced eastward to the Ohio-Pennsylvania state line (Fig. 5).

The Lower Terrace north of its cliff ranges in width from 0.5 km in Cleveland to a maximum of 6 km in Lorain and Ashtabula Counties. At its widest part, the slope of the terrace is about 2 m/km, and the low gradient combined with the low permeability of the subsoil has produced swampy conditions in many places. Several low sandy segments of beach ridges, including the more continuous Grassmere and Lundy ridges, occur on the Lower Terrace.

Cliffs and Terraces Below the Lower (Warren) Terrace

The Lower (Warren) Terrace is the lowest erosional level that is clearly evident at the surface in northeastern Ohio, but sketchy evidence exists for still lower erosion surfaces. A cliff about 1.5 m high and with a base elevation of 187.5 m occurs in Lorain County (Stanley Totten, unpublished manuscript, 1978) near the modern Lake Erie shoreline, and a low terrace with an elevation of about 186 m in Ashtabula County has been described by White and Totten (1979). In addition, a thick wedge-shaped mass of Ashtabula Till of Woodfordian age has been plastered against the face of one or more cliffs at low elevations near the present Lake Erie shoreline in Ashtabula County, burying the cliffs in the process. Other cliffs and terraces at lower elevations may have been destroyed by modern lake erosion of lake bluffs during the past few hundred to few thousand years.

Dating of Cliffs and Terraces

The cliffs and terraces were eroded by wave action during an ice-free interval in northeastern Ohio when water levels were higher than the present. The cliffs and terraces are younger than the Ashtabula, Painesville, and Euclid Moraines as evidenced by the truncation of moraines at the Middle (Whittlesey) Cliff and complete removal of the moraines from the Lake Plain in northeastern Ohio. The moraines are composed primarily of Titusville Till of Altonian (early and/or middle Wisconsinan) age (White and Totten, 1979; White, 1982).

The thickness of Hiram Till of Woodfordian age in Lorain County (Stanley Totten, unpublished manuscript, 1978) is similar on the lake plain and on the till plain to the south, demonstrating that extensive wave action did not occur after the last glaciation. The valleys of many northward flowing streams tributary to Lake Erie contain very wide cut-terraces that correlate with elevations of wave cut strandlines. Terraces of several of these valleys are mantled by till of Woodfordian age in the same fashion as the wave-cut features.

The wave-cut terraces have a collective width of about 8 km in northeastern Ohio, which is an indication of the minimum amount of cliff retreat required to form the terraces. Based on the erosion rate of about 0.7 m/yr for the modern Lake Erie cliff in northeastern Ohio (Carter, 1976), the wave-cut terraces would require more than 10 000 years to form. Even allowing for greater erosion rates when the lake was higher and more extensive, the cliffs and terraces represent several thousand years of wave erosion. Postglacial lake levels fell to below present day levels in about 1800 years (14 500 to 12 700 B.P.) much too short a period for extensive wave erosion. Thus the cliffs and terraces most likely formed after the disappearance of ice that deposited the Titusville-Millbrook Till more than 35 000 (?) years ago and prior to the advance of the earliest Woodfordian glacier which deposited the Kent-Navarre Till about 23 000 years ago. This ice-free period is known as the Farmdalian Substage in the north-central United States and as the Plum Point Interstadial in the northeastern Great Lakes region.

All of the wave-cut strandlines in northeastern Ohio exhibit about the same amount of glacio-isostatic rebound (Fig. 5). This similarity in tilting indicates that a substantial, relatively stable ice mass remained in the northeastern Erie Basin during the period of shoreline erosion.

BEACH RIDGES

The sand and gravel ridges on the terraces previously described are conspicuous features on the otherwise flat Lake Plain. These ridges record shorelines of a series of late-glacial and postglacial lakes which stood at higher levels than present Lake Erie.

Following the retreat of Late Woodfordian ice from northern Ohio between 14 000 and 15 000 years ago, a series of high lake levels originated that were direct ancestors of present Lake Erie. These lakes were considerably more extensive than present Lake Erie and existed in the depression between the northward-sloping surface of northern Ohio and the final wasting ice masses in the Erie Basin, which blocked drainage northward and eastward. These late-glacial lakes, each lasting from about 50 to 300 or more years, left their record on the Ohio landscape mainly in the form of beach and sand-dune ridges.

These beach-dune ridges figured prominently in the settlement of northeastern Ohio because the sandy, slightly elevated ground provided well-drained, nearly level transportation routes and homesites. Somewhat later, the beach ridges gained importance as a source of sand and gravel aggregate for the construction industry.

The beach ridges interrupt the low but continuous northward slope of the terraces, thereby ponding the natural northward drainage. Swamps, many now artificially drained, are common along the southern margin of the ridges, and the smaller drainage lines tend to parallel the beach ridges. The beach ridges, like the cliffs and terraces, rise in elevation northeastward owing to glacio-isostatic uplift (Figs. 6 and 7).

Maumee Beach Ridge

The last of the continental ice sheets to advance as far south as Ohio advanced into the northeastern part of Ohio about 15 000 years ago and deposited the Ashtabula Till which occurs in eastern Cuyahoga, northern Lake, and northern Ashtabula Counties. Northern Ohio, west of Cleveland, was not covered by the Ashtabula ice advance (White, 1982). Ashtabula ice blocked northward and eastward drainage in the Erie Basin north of Ohio, and a large lake known as Lake Maumee gradually formed between the ice and higher land to the south of the present shoreline of Lake Erie. The highest lake-level elevation recorded by a beach ridge, nearly 238 m, was reached about 14 500 years ago, probably during the retreat phase of the ice which deposited the Ashtabula Till.

The three major Maumee beach ridges are termed, from earliest to latest, I, II, III. In Lorain County the Maumee I ridge has a crest elevation of 238 m, with a secondary crest in places at an elevation of 236 m (the crest elevation is 1.5 to 3 m higher than the actual lake level when the ridge formed). Maumee II has a crest elevation of 233 m and Maumee III has a crest elevation of 229.5 m (Fig. 6).

The Maumee beach ridges typically are no more than 1.5 to 3 m high and 150 to 450 m wide. The Maumee I ridge, known as Butternut Ridge in eastern Lorain and western Cuyohoga Counties, can be traced as far east as Lake County, where Lake Maumee presumably terminated against the retreating ice sheet. The Maumee II ridge is poorly developed because the 233-m crest elevation is near the top of the Upper III (Maumee) Cliff, a poor place for beach development. The Maumee II ridge can be traced eastward nearly to the Ohio Pennsylvania state line which approximates the eastern boundary of Lake Maumee II. The Maumee III ridge is nearly continuous in eastern Lorain and western Cuyahoga Counties, where it is known as Chestnut Ridge. Farther east in Lake and Ashtabula Counties, the ridge is discontinuous and has been extensively dissected by streams flowing northward down the proximal slope of the Ashtabula and Painesville Moraines. At Kingsville, Ashtabula County, sediments discharged into the lake by Conneaut Creek were incorporated to form ridges 4.5 m or more high. An excavation cut into one broad ridge segment at the south edge of Kingsville, exposed 2 m of coarse sand and fine gravel consisting of flat siltstones and rounded crystalline cobbles arranged as beach shingle.

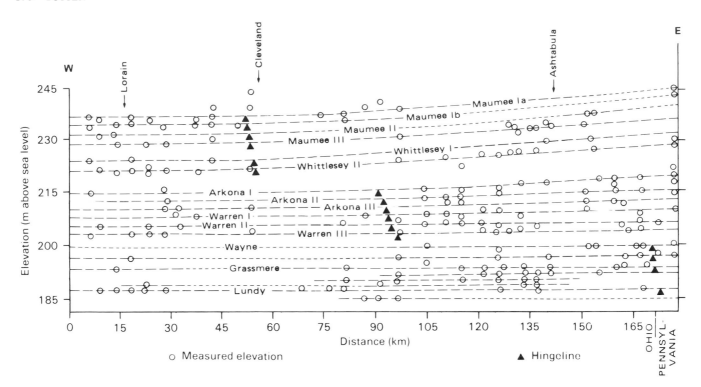

Figure 6. Elevations of beach-ridge crests in northeastern Ohio. Long-dashed lines represent good correlations, short-dashed lines are projections over greater distances where data are lacking. Distances shown were measured along the Whittlesey beach ridge.

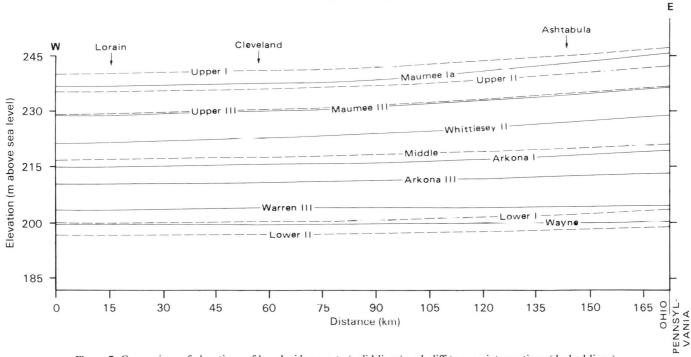

Figure 7. Comparison of elevations of beach-ridge crests (solid lines) and cliff-terrace intersections (dashed lines). Distances shown were measured along the Whittlesey beach ridge.

Beach ridge sediment volume was computed for each 2-km ridge segment utilizing closely spaced profiles and well logs to determine sediment thickness (Fig. 8). The Maumee beach ridges comprise 29.4% of the beach-ridge sediment in northeastern Ohio (Table I; Fig. 8), the largest volume of any ridge complex. The major bulk of the beach sediment was contributed by West Branch and East Branch of Black River in Lorain County, and Cowles Creek and Conneaut

TABLE 1

SEDIMENT VOLUME OF BEACH RIDGES AND
DURATION OF BEACH STAGES IN
NORTHEASTERN OHIO

Beach Stage	Sediment Volume m³ × 10⁶	Percent of Total Sediment Volume	Duration in Years (Based on Sediment Volume)	Duration in Years (from Fig. 9)
Post-Warren	16.3	6.9	125	130
Warren	64.0	27.1	487	320
Arkona	56.3	23.9	430	460
Whittlesey	30.0	12.7	229	380
Maumee	69.3	29.4	520	510

TABLE II

BEACH RIDGES OF NORTHEASTERN OHIO.
ELEVATIONS ARE OF RIDGE CRESTS, AND AGES
WERE DETERMINED FROM FIGURE 9

Beach Ridge	Elevation (Metres)	Age (Yrs. B.P.)	Outlet
Maumee Ia	238	14,500	Wabash River, Indiana
Maumee Ib	236	14,450	Wabash River, Indiana
Maumee II	233	14,250	Wabash River, Indiana
Maumee III	229.5	14,100	Wabash River, Indiana
Whittlesey I	225.5	13,950	Grand River, Michigan
Whittlesey II	223	13,850	Grand River, Michigan
Arkona I	217	13,500	Grand River, Michigan
Arkona II	213	13,350	Grand River, Michigan
Arkona III	212	13,300	Grand River, Michigan
Warren I	209	13,050	Grand River, Michigan
Warren II	207	13,000	Grand River, Michigan
Warren III	204	12,900	Grand River, Michigan
Wayne	201	12,850	Mohawk River, New York
Grassmere	195	12,800	Mohawk River, New York
Lundy	189	12,750	Mohawk River, New York

Creek in Ashtabula County. Longshore currents apparently did not spread the sediment far from where it entered Lake Maumee as evidenced by the sharp histogram peaks (Fig. 8) corresponding with the river mouths. The valleys of the two largest rivers that flow into Lake Erie, the Cuyahoga and Grand Rivers, were the sites of extensive glacial lakes and lacustrine deposition during the ice advance which immediately preceded the Maumee lake stages. Thus their resulting low gradients and clayey sediments were not conducive to providing sand and gravel for beach sediment. The major reason that the Maumee beach complex contains the greatest amount of sediment most likely is a function of time. The Maumee beach ridges may represent about 500 years of beach formation, nearly 30% of the available time for beach sedimentation in northeastern Ohio (Fig. 9; Table II).

Leverett (1902) has reported an earlier, higher Maumee beach ridge in northwestern Ohio at an elevation of 244 m, which Forsyth (1959) identified as Maumee I. This earlier beach, which occurs only in northwestern Ohio, was associated with a relatively small proglacial lake probably dammed by Hiram ice. This early beach clearly predates the Ashtabula ice advance and cannot be related to the succession of beaches that began with Maumee I at an elevation of 238 m about 14 500 years ago. During the short interval covering the retreat of Hiram ice and the advance of Ashtabula ice, lake level dropped from 244 m to 238 m or lower. It is possible that considerable lake sediment, including the Oak Openings sand, an extensive glaciofluvial deltaic deposit in northwestern Ohio (Anderhalt et al., 1984), accumulated during this interval. Likewise, beach gravel that occurs beneath till in northern Ohio, such as the gravel reported by Echelbarger (1978), is pre-Lake Maumee, pre-Hiram Till, and may predate the Woodfordian ice advance. Buried beach gravels related to pre-Woodfordian cliff-and-terrace erosional stages previously described may be expected in embayments west of the study area where the terraces are very wide and the cliffs are low or absent.

The Maumee strandlines rise in elevation about 9 m from Cleveland eastward to Ashtabula County owing to isostatic uplift following ice retreat. Uplift was occurring while the ridges were forming (and as the glacier was retreating) as evidenced by greater tilt of the higher elevation ridges as compared with those of lower elevations (Fig. 6).

Whittlesey Beach Ridges

The Whittlesey II beach ridge has a crest elevation of 223 m and generally has been regarded as the most prominent beach in northern Ohio (Forsyth, 1959, p. 6). Much of its prominence actually is due to its position at the brow of the prominent Middle (Whittlesey) Cliff. The Whittlesey beach, known as Center Ridge in eastern Lorain and western Cuyahoga Counties, where it is followed by U.S. Route 20, is a ridge 1.5 to 3 m high and 90 to 244 m wide. In Lake and Ashtabula Counties, the Whittlesey beach is known as South Ridge and is traversed by Ohio Route 84; it can be traced as a continuous ridge, 150 to 300 m wide and about 3 m high, for 40 km from Painesville northeastward to Ashtabula. The ridge is covered by dunes in many places, and the continuity of the ridge is broken by small streams that head in the moraines south of the ridge. Near Ashtabula, Whittlesey gravel bars connect several "islands" of the Ashtabula Moraine which had been isolated from the main morainic ridge by wave erosion at an earlier time. Commercial quantities of sand and gravel have been obtained from these beach deposits in Ashtabula.

A second Whittlesey beach ridge, with a crest elevation of 225.5 m, occurs a short distance south of the main ridge in widely scattered areas in northeastern Ohio. This poorly developed Whittlesey ridge is most continuous across Mentor and Painesville Townships in Lake County (White, 1980).

The Whittlesey beach ridges constitute 12.7% of the beach ridge sediment in northeastern Ohio (Table I), a relatively small amount considering the Whittlesey beach is a prominent feature in many places, and that it may represent approximately 380 years, or about 21% of the available time for beach building. Whittlesey beach sediment is relatively well-distributed and no single river basin appears to have been a dominant sediment producer. Evidently longshore currents effectively redistributed the sediment deposited at the river mouths both to the northeast and the southwest in nearly equal amounts (Fig. 8). The small amount of

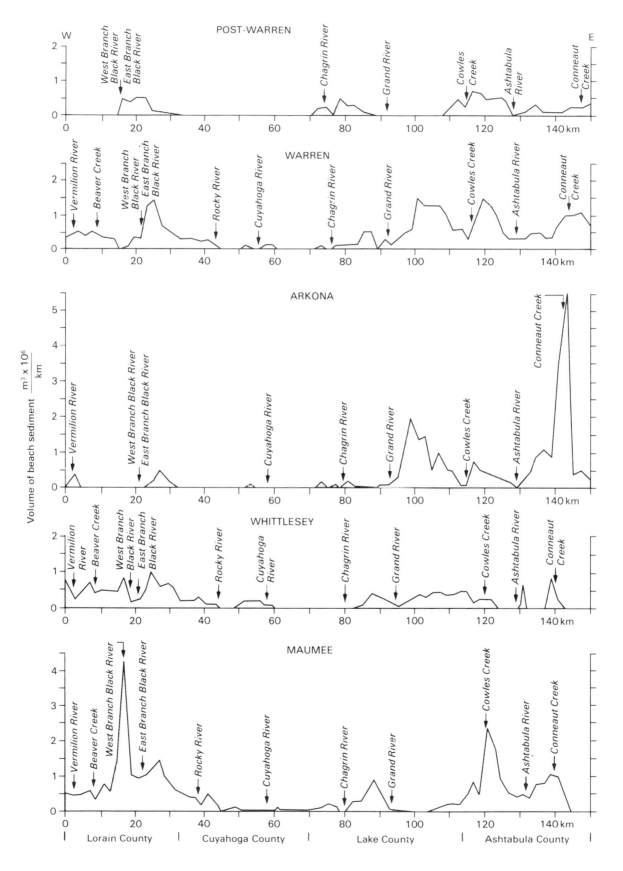

Figure 8. Histograms showing volume and distribution of beach ridge sediment in northeastern Ohio.

Whittlesey beach sediment in Ashtabula County is likely to be a result of nondeposition on the steep Middle Cliff, which occurs at the Whittlesey beach elevation. No doubt much of the sediment which entered the lake during the Whittlesey beach stage was swept down the steep cliff into deeper water, to be incorporated later in the large Arkona beach ridges in Ashtabula County.

Whittlesey beach-ridge crests rise gradually in elevation about 6 m owing to glacio-isostatic uplift, as they are traced northeastward from Cuyahoga County to the Ohio-Pennsylvania state line (Fig. 6).

Arkona Beach Ridges

Lake Arkona was initiated when ice of the Huron-Erie lobe retreated northward and opened a drainage route through the Grand River (of Michigan) channel (Hough, 1958). The Grand River channel was eroded during Arkona time, lowering the lake level. Three separate ridges, designated Arkona I, II, and III, were developed with crest elevations of 217, 213, and 212 m respectively. Arkona ridges typically show poor development in northern Ohio and they were not recognized by Carney (1910, 1911, 1916) during early mapping of the ridges.

The Arkona beach ridges comprise 23.9% of the beach-ridge sediment in northeastern Ohio (Table I). Nearly all of the Arkona beach-ridge sediment is concentrated in eastern Lake County and in Ashtabula County, where the major sediment contributors were the Grand River (of Ohio), Cowles Creek, the Ashtabula River, and Conneaut Creek.

Longshore currents distributed the sediment primarily to the northeast of the river mouths (Fig. 8).

In many places extensive sheets of sand rather than distinct ridges are common midway on the broad, gently sloping Middle (Whittlesey) Terrace surface separating the Lower (Warren) and Middle (Whittlesey) Cliffs. Consequently, the Arkona ridges, where developed, are not associated with any cliffs, a fact which contributed to the late recognition of the Arkona strandlines.

In Lorain County, Arkona beaches tend to be discontinuous ridge segments, each 2 km or less in length and 150 to 300 m wide. They are composed of sand about 1.5 m thick. In Lake and Ashtabula Counties, the Arkona ridges are broad discontinuous subtle rises, which show distinctly on cross sections (Fig. 2) as broad mounds that contain relatively large quantities of sand and gravel. It is not possible to follow a single ridge any great distance, and the ridges have a tendency to merge and then diverge again, adding to the difficulty of tracing strandlines.

The Arkona I ridge is 3 to 4.5 m high and 460 m wide in eastern Ashtabula County, where it blocked an earlier outlet of Conneaut Creek. Conneaut Creek was diverted 4.5 km eastward to a low place in the Arkona I ridge. Four gravel pits are located in this segment of the Arkona I ridge.

The Arkona II ridge in eastern Ashtabula County is about 1 km wide and 4.5 to 6 m high. At least seven gravel pits are located in this ridge between Amboy and Kingsville, giving the Arkona II ridge the distinction of producing the best quality and largest quantity of gravel of any beach ridge in all

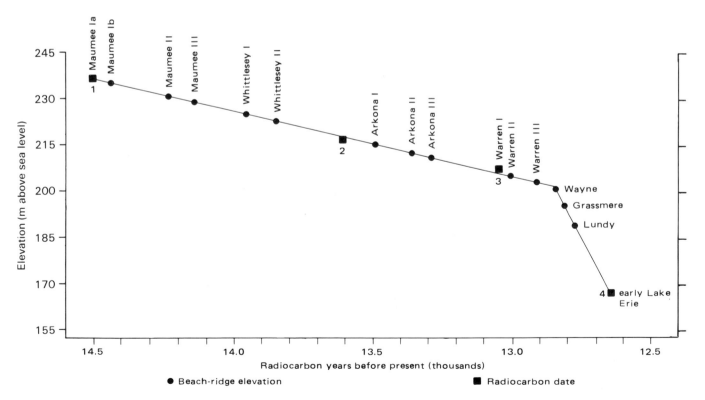

Figure 9. Relationship between the elevations of beach ridges and their ages. The break in slope represents the change from the Grand River, Michigan, outlet to the Mohawk River, New York, outlet. Sources of radiocarbon dates: 1, ISGS-402; 2, W-33; 3, ISGS-437; 4, W-861.

of northeastern Ohio. In the largest pits, sand and gravel as much as 6 m thick are exposed. A section through the centre of the broad ridge showed 2.5 to 4 m of gravel at the surface overlying sand 2.5 m thick that rested on till. The gravel on the north slope of the ridge is much coarser and consists of pebbles and cobbles as large as 8 cm in diameter. Dune sand overlies the beach deposits in places, particularly in western Ashtabula County between Saybrook and Geneva. The Arkona ridges rise slightly toward the northeast in Ashtabula County, with Arkona I rising more than II, and II rising more than III.

Warren Beach Ridges

A series of three ridges, designated Warren I, II, and III, with crest elevations of 209, 207, and 204 m respectively, were created as the level of Lake Warren fell in response to lowering of the Grand River (of Michigan) channel (Hough, 1958). The three ridges are grouped as a single complex ridge in some places; in a few places, particularly on broad flats, the three ridges are separate and well defined. The Warren ridge complex is located on the gently sloping Middle (Whittlesey) Terrace at the brow of the Lower (Warren) Cliff and in places Warren beach deposits partially obscure the cliff. The composite Lower Cliff and Warren beach, known as North Ridge, is the prominent ridge closest to Lake Erie and is followed by major highways, most notably U.S. Route 20 between Cleveland and the Ohio-Pennsylvania state line.

The Warren beach ridges constitute 27.1% of the beach ridge sediment of northeastern Ohio (Table I). This sediment was evenly distributed across Lorain, Lake, and Ashtabula Counties by longshore currents which transported sediment in a northeastward direction from the river mouths (Fig. 8).

The Warren I beach in Lorain and western Cuyahoga Counties consists of a broad sheet of sand in places heaped into a broad ridge 1.5 to 3 m high and 150 to 300 m wide. The Warren II ridge, of similar proportions, occurs in proximity to Warren III, and it is not always possible to distinguish them as separate ridges. The combined ridges near Avon, Lorain County, contain one of the largest surface deposits of gravel in that county. West Branch and East Branch of Black River contributed the greatest amount of sediment for Warren beach building in Lorain County; Beaver Creek and the Vermilion River contributed lesser amounts. Wood collected from the base of Warren I beach sand between Avon and Sheffield has a date of 13,050 ± 100 B.P. (ISGS-437). The Warren III ridge is not well developed in Lorain and Cuyahoga Counties because its crest elevation of 204 m occurs near the brow of the prominent Lower (Warren) Cliff.

In Lake and Ashtabula Counties, the Warren beach ridge complex is 1.5 to 4.5 m high, up to 600 m wide, and is mantled in many places by irregular patches and ridges of dune sand, which increase the ridge height by 3 to 4.5 m. The Warren beach sediment is predominantly sand as evidenced in many small borrow pits opened in the ridge complex. Most of the Warren beach sediment in these two counties was supplied by the Grand River, Cowles Creek, and Conneaut Creek (Fig. 8). The Warren beach-ridge complex rises less than 3 m toward the northeast owing to glacio-isostatic rebound. Beach ridges in Ohio with elevations lower than the

Warren complex show no effects of glacio-isostatic rebound (Fig. 6).

Other Beach Ridges

Between the Lower (Warren) Cliff and the Lake Erie bluff is a wide, gently sloping, poorly drained terrace on which are situated numerous low sandy mounds which have been variously interpreted as beach ridges, offshore bars, and dunes. These low mounds or ridges, each about 1.5 m high or less, occur between the elevations of 201 and 186.5 m at 1.5- to 3-m intervals (Figs. 2 and 6). These ridges are composed of sand, have a linear distribution parallel to the more prominent beach ridges, and probably represent a succession of short-lived strandlines formed as the lake level gradually lowered. Three of these ridges, Wayne at 201 m, Grassmere at 195 m, and Lundy at 189 m have regional significance according to earlier reports; the others may not be traceable beyond northeastern Ohio.

The post-Warren beach ridges constitute only 6.9% of the beach ridge sediment in northeastern Ohio (Table I). This sediment was contributed primarily by 5 rivers, West Branch and East Branch Black River in Lorain County, Chagrin River in Lake County, and Cowles Creek and Conneaut Creek in Ashtabula County. These sediments were swept a short distance northeastward from the river mouths by longshore currents (Fig. 8).

The Wayne beach is indistinct in most places in northeastern Ohio, primarily because its crest (201 m) coincides with the Lower (Warren) Cliff. The only place the Wayne beach ridge is recognized with certainty is in eastern Ashtabula County, where a few low ridge segments with crests reaching an elevation of 201 m occur a short distance north of the Lower (Warren) Cliff. The separation between cliff and beach ridge near the Ohio-Pennsylvania state line is due to the greater amount of glacio-isostatic uplift of the Lower Cliff and Terrace as compared to the beach ridge (Fig. 7).

The Grassmere beach ridge, about 150 m wide and 1.5 m high, occurs close to the brow of the Lake Erie bluffs in eastern Ashtabula County, where it is traversed by Lake Road. The beach can be traced as a discontinuous ridge southwestward from Ashtabula into Lake County, where the beach becomes indistinct.

The Lundy beach ridge is characterized by very discontinuous elongate sandy mounds 1.5 m high or less. The mounds are primarily east of major streams and rivers.

Chronology of Beach Ridges

The chronology of the beach ridges, including both the order and dates of formation, has been the subject of disagreement for some time. Leverett (1892), following a suggestion from Gilbert, correlated the beach ridges of Ohio with end moraines. Leverett (1902) assumed the chronological order of the beach ridges was the same as the topographical order, i.e., that the ridges formed in simple sequence from highest to lowest as lake levels dropped due to the erosion of outlets and the opening of new, lower outlets. Taylor (1905; in Leverett and Taylor, 1915), from a study of moraines in Michigan, devised a sequence that required rapid fluctuation of lake levels during which the lowest Maumee, Arkona I, II, III, and Wayne beach ridges were submerged beneath rising waters that built ridges at higher elevations.

Taylor (1897, 1905) concluded that each moraine in Ohio and Michigan required a readvance of 50 km or more of an active ice sheet, and he believed that each moraine represented a duration of 5000 to 10 000 years. He soon realized that such large oscillations of the ice sheet would alternately uncover and block outlets of the lake, causing lake levels to fluctuate. This complex sequence, although later adopted by Hough (1958), is not supported by the evidence from northeastern Ohio.

Evidence accumulated over the past 20 years indicates that the end moraines in northeastern Ohio have cores of Titusville (early and/or middle Wisconsinan) Till (Totten, 1969; White and Totten, 1979; White, 1982). These moraines predate the Woodfordian ice advance and they do not correlate with lake stages or beach ridges. Also, it is generally agreed that moraine formation does not require ice readvance and the time framework for beach ridge formation is only a fraction of that envisioned by Taylor (1897). Thus Taylor's sequence of lake level fluctuation is open to question.

Evidence presented by Taylor (1905) for the "washed over" appearance of beach ridges included low relief of the ridges, particularly far from protected bays, and clay matrix in some beach gravels which he believed was introduced when the beach ridge was submerged. Taylor's (1905) arguments are not supported by geomorphic and sedimentologic evidence from northeastern Ohio. The rise in lake levels probably would have been sufficiently slow to allow wave action to destroy or greatly alter drowned ridges. If a submerged beach survived wave erosion, sediment entering the lake from the river mouths should have been trapped behind the submerged ridge, partially burying the ridge. The terrace surfaces between beach ridges commonly contain only a thin veneer of lacustrine sediment. Much of the sediment previously regarded as lacustrine clay actually is clayey Hiram Till.

The occurrence of coarse beach gravel overlying sand in the Arkona ridges is indicative of normal regression of lake level. If the beaches had been "washed over", silty deposits characteristic of deeper water should overlie the sand and gravel. The typical fine grained sediment found on the ridges is sand of probable eolian origin. The clay matrix referred to by Taylor (1905) probably was not introduced during submergence, but most likely is indigenous to the beach sediment. Arkona beaches typically are finer grained and more poorly sorted than Whittlesey beaches. Weathering of the shale fragments in the gravel is the most likely source of the clay coatings on beach pebbles and granules.

The low relief of the Arkona ridges mentioned by Taylor (1905) may be explained by the process of beach ridge formation on a broad, very gently sloping terrace in response to gradual lowering of lake level due to erosion of the lake outlet. The excellent development of Arkona ridges near river mouths is not a result of protection from wave action in sheltered bays during submergence as believed by Taylor

(1905) but is most likely a direct result of closeness to river mouths that supplied abundant sediment for the beach ridges. Leverett and Taylor's (1915) argument that the coarse material from the Arkona beach was torn up by wave action in water 6 to 12 m deep, and then moved shoreward a distance measured in kilometres to the top to the Middle Cliff to form the Whittlesey beach is not substantiated by modern sedimentologic theory.

Somewhat later, Leverett (1931) offered new evidence to substantiate the submergence of beach ridges. He suggested that the ridges occurring on the terraces represent a series of offshore bars that formed concurrently with cliff-terrace cutting. Thus ridges at higher elevations would be younger than ridges at the lower elevations. According to Leverett (1931), an episode of wave erosion was followed by a significant rise in lake level and subsequently a beach ridge would be formed on the next higher terrace above the cliff. One major conclusion of the Leverett hypothesis is that all of the strandline features – ridges, cliffs, and terraces could be formed during one episode of mainly rising lake levels. This hypothesis of Leverett's also is not substantiated by modern sedimentologic theory or by the geologic evidence.

Determining the sequence of beach ridge formation on the basis of radiocarbon dates is confusing and risky, due to the short time intervals involved, to generally poor stratigraphic control, and to possible contamination of the materials being dated. For example, Fullerton (1980) shows a range of dates of 11 080 to 15 172 B.P. for Lake Grassmere, 10 890 to 14 400 B.P. for Lake Wayne, and 11 950 to 12 900 B.P. for Lake Whittlesey.

A few radiocarbon dates from northeastern Ohio offer some evidence of the chronological age of the beach ridges. Maumee beach-ridge formation was contemporaneous with the retreat of the ice sheet that deposited the Ashtabula Till and the earliest post-ice dates in northern Ohio are about 14 500 B.P. (Stanley Totten, unpublished manuscript, 1979). The lake level dropped below the present Lake Erie level of 174 m by 12 660 B.P. (W-861, Lewis, 1969), the earliest date for Early Lake Erie, and the lake level remained below 170 m until recent time. A plot of the pertinent radiocarbon dates (Fig. 9) suggests the decline of lake level was gradual and relatively constant from 14 500 B.P. to about 12 900 B.P. when the lake outlet was toward the west and while the prominent beach ridges were forming. From about 12 900 to 12 660 B.P., the lake level dropped rapidly as a result of the opening of the Mohawk and Niagara outlets to the east in New York. The lake-level curve constructed from the radiocarbon dates (Fig. 9) permits age assignment of the remaining ridges (Table II). The duration in years determined for each beach stage based on lake levels (Fig. 9) compares favorably with the duration based on sediment volume (Table I).

The geologic evidence cited in this paper does not preclude the possibility of fluctuating lake levels during ice retreat from the Erie Basin. Frequent fluctuations of 1 or 2 m similar to modern fluctuations probably were common. Larger fluctuations could have occurred, and it is possible that one or more beaches such as the Arkona ridges may have had a complex history. The evidence from northeastern

Ohio suggests that the beach ridges preserved in Ohio south of Lake Erie most likely originated in a sequence according to their geographic and topographic position—the ridges are progressively younger toward the north, and the lower the elevation, the younger the ridge.

ACKNOWLEDGEMENTS

Field work for this project was sponsored by the Ohio Department of Natural Resources, Division of Geological Survey as a part of the Ohio county mapping project. Much of the field work in Ashtabula and Lake Counties was done with George W. White, who has offered invaluable advice and encouragement. Horace R. Collins, State Geologist of Ohio, kindly consented to the publication of this paper, parts of which have been published previously by the Ohio Geological Survey (White and Totten, 1979; Totten, 1982). Figures were drafted by James Brown and technical assistance was offered by Merrianne Hackathorn, both of the Ohio Geological Survey.

REFERENCES

Anderhalt, R., Kahle, C.F., and Sturgis, D., 1984, Field Guidebook to the Glaciolacustrine Deltaic Deposits in the Oak Openings Sand of Northwestern Ohio: Fourteenth Annual Field Conference of the Great Lakes Section, Society of Economic Paleontologists and Mineralogists, Part 2, p. 59-90.

Calkin, Parker E., 1970, Strandlines and Chronology of the Glacial Great Lakes in Northwestern New York: Ohio Journal of Science, v. 70, p. 78-96.

Carney, Frank, 1910, The Abandoned Shore Lines of the Oberlin Quadrangle, Ohio: Denison University Scientific Laboratories Bulletin, v. 16, p. 101-117; Abstract, Science, n.s., v. 32, p. 187.

_____, 1911, The Abandoned Shore Lines of the Vermilion Quadrangle, Ohio: Denison University Scientific Laboratories Bulletin, v. 16, p. 233-244.

_____, 1916, The Abandoned Shore Lines of the Ashtabula Quadrangle, Ohio: Denison University Scientific Laboratories Bulletin, v. 18, p. 362-369.

Carter, C.H., 1976, Lake Erie Shore Erosion, Lake County, Ohio: Setting, Processes, and Recession Rates from 1876 to 1973: Ohio Geological Survey Report of Investigations 99, 105 p.

Echelbarger, M.J., 1978, Glacial Geology of Seneca County, Ohio: Master's Thesis, Bowling Green, Ohio, Bowling Green State University, 76 p.

Forsyth, J.L., 1959, The Beach Ridges of Northern Ohio: Ohio Geological Survey Information Circular 25, 10 p.

Fullerton, D.S., 1980, Preliminary Correlation of Post-Erie Interstadial Events (16 000-10 000 Radiocarbon Years Before Present), Central and Eastern Great Lakes Region, and Hudson, Champlain, and St. Lawrence Lowlands, United States and Canada: United States Geological Survey Professional Paper 1089, 52 p.

Gilbert, G.K., 1871, Report on the Geology of Williams, Fulton, and Lucas Counties: Ohio Geological Survey, Report of Progress, 1870, pt. 7, p. 485-499.

_____, 1873, Geology of Williams County: Ohio Geological Survey, v. 1, pt. 1, p. 557-566.

Goldthwait, R.P., Dreimanis, Aleksis, Forsyth, J.L., Karrow, P.F., and White, G.W., 1965, Pleistocene Deposits of the Erie Lobe: in Wright, H.E., Jr., and Frey, D.G., eds., The Quaternary of the United States: Princeton University Press, p. 85-97.

Hough, J.L., 1958, Geology of the Great Lakes: University of Illinois Press, 313 p.

Leverett, Frank, 1892, On the Correlation of Moraines with Raised Beaches of Lake Erie: American Journal of Science, v. 43, p. 281-301.

_____, 1902, Glacial Formations and Drainage Features of the Erie and Ohio Basins: United States Geological Survey Monograph 41, 802 p.

_____, 1931, Quaternary System, in Cushing, H.P., Leverett, Frank, and Van Horn, F.R., Geology and Mineral Resources of the Cleveland District, Ohio: United States Geological Survey Bulletin 818, p. 57-81.

Leverett, Frank, and Taylor, F.B., 1915, The Pleistocene of Indiana and Michigan and the History of the Great Lakes: United States Geological Survey Monograph 53, 529 p.

Lewis, C.F.M., 1969, Late Quaternary History of Lake Levels in the Huron and Erie Basins: International Association for Great Lakes Research: Proceedings 12th Conference on Great Lakes Research, International Association for Great Lakes Research, p. 250-270.

Phillips, B.A.M., 1977, Shoreline Inheritance in Coastal Histories: Science, v. 195, p. 11-16.

Schooler, E.E., 1974, Pleistocene Beach Ridges of Northwestern Pennsylvania: Pennsylvania Geological Survey General Geology Report 64, 38 p.

Taylor, F.B., 1897, Moraines of Recession and Their Significance in Glacial Theory: Journal of Geology, v. 5, p. 421-466.

_____, 1905, Relation of Lake Whittlesey to the Arkona Beaches: 7th Annual Report, Michigan Academy of Science, p. 29-36.

Totten, S.M., 1969, Overridden Recessional Moraines in North-Central Ohio: Geological Society of America Bulletin, v. 80, p. 1931-1946.

_____, 1982, Pleistocene Beaches and Strandlines Bordering Lake Erie: in White, George, W., Glacial Geology of Northeastern Ohio: Ohio Geological Survey Bulletin 68, p. 52-60.

White, G.W., 1980, Glacial Geology of Lake County, Ohio: Ohio Geological Survey Report of Investigations 117, 20 p.

_____, 1982, Glacial Geology of Northeastern Ohio: Ohio Geological Survey Bulletin 68, 75 p.

White, G.W., and Totten, S.M., 1979, Glacial Geology of Ashtabula County, Ohio: Ohio Geological Survey Report of Investigations 112, 52 p.

Whittlesey, Charles, 1848, Notes Upon the Drift and Alluvium of Ohio and the West: American Journal of Science, v. 5, p. 205-217.

_____, 1850, On the Natural Terraces and Ridges of the Country Bordering Lake Erie: American Journal of Science, 2nd series, v. 10, p. 31-39.

_____, 1867, On the Fresh-Water Glacial Drift of the Northwestern States: Smithsonian Contributions to Knowledge, v. 15, 38 p.

Quaternary Evolution of the Great Lakes,
edited by P.F. Karrow and P.E. Calkin,
Geological Association of Canada Special Paper 30, 1985

GLACIAL RETREAT AND LAKE LEVELS,
NORTH CENTRAL LAKE ERIE BASIN, ONTARIO

Peter J. Barnett

Ontario Geological Survey, 77 Grenville Street, Toronto, Ontario M5S 1B3

ABSTRACT

The patterns of ice margin retreat and their relationship to water level in the Lake Erie basin were determined from Quaternary geological mapping along the north central shore of Lake Erie. Ice marginal positions are marked by moraines, of which 10 are present in the study area. Ancestral lake levels are recorded by shoreline features such as bluffs, deltas, beach bars, and spits, as well as by their sediments.

Two sequences of deglacial lakes are recorded in the study area: 1) an early sequence during the Port Bruce (Cary) Stadial and Mackinaw Interstadial and 2) a younger sequence during and following the Port Huron Stadial ice advance. The early sequence begins during ice-marginal retreat from the Port Bruce Stadial maximum at the Ingersoll Moraine. Lakes Maumee I and II are believed to have existed in the western end of the Erie basin during the early stages of this retreat. The waters of Lake Maumee III were the first to inundate the study area. This lake was followed by a series of lower lake levels, including Lake Arkona, which are marked or inferred by buried features and/or sediments. This sequence of deglacial lakes ends with the deepening of Lake Erie basin waters to form glacial Lake Whittlesey during the Port Huron Stadial maximum.

The younger sequence begins with Lake Whittlesey and includes Lakes Warren, Wayne, Grassmere and Lundy as well as nonglacial Early Lake Erie. A series of deltas about 5 m above present day Lake Erie records a high water level in the Erie basin that existed approximately 2000 years ago.

RÉSUMÉ

La configuration de la marge glaciaire lors de son retrait et ses rapports avec les niveaux d'eau dans le bassin du lac Érié a été reconstituée à partir de la cartographie géologique quaternaire le long de la rive nord du lac Érié. La forme et l'orientation du bassin du lac Érié représentent un élément des plus importants puisqu'ils ont contrôlé la direction du retrait glaciaire, la forme de la marge glaciaire, les environnements de déposition, ainsi que la nature, les propriétés et la distribution des sédiments retrouvés dans le bassin.

L'exutoire naturel du lac Érié est situé à son extrémité nord-est, par conséquent un barrage glaciaire à cet endroit entraînera une augmentation du niveau d'eau. Plusieurs autres exutoires ont été empruntés au cours du dernier épisode glaciaire.

Au cours du Wisconsinien récent, la région a été marquée par trois avancées glaciaires ou stades et deux périodes de récession générale ou interstades. Le maximum d'extension glaciaire du lobe Érié lors du stade de Port Bruce se situe à la moraine d'Ingersoll. En tout dix moraines ont été retracées dans cette région: huit se composent du till de Port Stanley et deux plus récentes, les moraines de Paris et de Galt, du till de fond de Wentworth.

Deux séquences de lacs proglaciaires ont été identifiées. La première séquence appartient au stade de Port Bruce et à l'interstade Mackinaw et débute avec le lac glaciaire Maumee dont on a retrouvé les traces de Maumee III et Maumee IV. Vient ensuite le lac Arkona formé lorsque le glacier de "Port Stanley" se retirait vers l'est.

Au cours de la formation des moraines de Paris et de Galt (moraine de fond de Wentworth) le niveau d'eau était bas dans le bassin du lac Érié comme le montrent les deltas enfouis à Jacksonburg et à Simcoe. À la suite de ces niveaux, le lac Ypsilanti exista dans le bassin du lac Érié juste après que la marge glaciaire se soit retirée dans le bassin du lac Ontario ouvrant ainsi de nouveaux exutoires à l'est.

La seconde séquence débute avec la formation du lac Whittlesey. Ce lac aurait été formé lorsque l'avancée glaciaire de Port Huron jusqu'à la limite du till d'Halton fit monter le niveau d'eau dans le bassin du lac Érié. Les différents niveaux de plage dans la région permettent de retracer, après le lac Whittlesey, la succession suivante: lacs Warren, Wayne (entre les niveaux de Warren), Grassmere et Lundy. On a également retrouvé des évidences d'un haut niveau lacustre (5 m au-dessus du niveau actuel du lac Érié) qui aurait existé il y a environ 2000 ans.

INTRODUCTION

This paper presents evidence of ancestral lakes in the Lake Erie basin north of the central sub-basin of Lake Erie (Fig. 1). In this area, the pattern of deglaciation and its relationships to water levels in the Erie basin are well recorded by a series of morainic ridges, abandoned shoreline features and sediments exposed at the surface, and in excellent river and lake bluff exposures. Information on these features was collected during Quaternary geology field mapping programs of the Ontario Geological Survey (Barnett, 1978, 1982, 1983; Barnett and Zilans, 1983). A summary of the ancestral lakes in the Erie basin has been presented by Calkin and Feenstra (1985) and only concepts essential to an understanding of this paper will be presented here.

GENERAL BACKGROUND

Lake Erie Basin

The shape and orientation of the Lake Erie basin played an important role in determining the direction of ice movement, the shape of the ice margin, the environments of deposition, and hence the distribution, type, and characteristics of the sediments that were deposited within the basin. The northeast-southwest orientation of the basin and the barrier of the Appalachian Plateau to the south, deflected the flow of the continental glacier westward along the trend of the basin (Chamberlain, 1883, 1888; Carman, 1946). Initially, the continental glacier entered the northeastern end of the Lake Erie basin and spread southwestward along the basin (Erie Lobe) until it coalesced with a lobe of ice flowing southward in the Lake Huron basin (Leverett, 1902; Leverett and Taylor, 1915). During deglaciation, the reverse occurred and the northeastern end of the Lake Erie basin was the last part to be deglaciated.

The present day, natural outlet of Lake Erie is the Niagara River located at the northeastern end of the lake. As the continental glacier entered the Erie basin, this outlet became ice-covered, causing the water in the basin to rise. In general, the farther the glacier extended into the basin, the higher the lake level became. However, because several of these high level lakes occupied portions of both the Lake Huron and the Lake Erie basins, the water level also depended on the position of the ice margin in the Lake Huron basin (Huron Lobe). Major outlets controlling ancestral lake levels in the Erie basin include (Fig. 1): 1) the Wabash River, Indiana 2) the Imlay Channel, Michigan, 3) the Ubly Channel, Michigan, 4) the Grand River, Michigan, 5a) the Indian River Lowlands, Michigan, and/or 5b) the Straits of Mackinac, 6) the Syracuse Channels, New York, 7) the Mohawk River Valley, New York, and 8) the Niagara River.

Because of the above factors there are 3 main variables in reconstructing ancestral lakes in the Erie basin: the position of the Huron Lobe margin or grounding line, the position of the Erie Lobe margin or grounding line, and the location of the lowest uncovered outlet. This assumes that the topography of the basin and the position of the outlets remained relatively constant during deglaciation. However, several other factors, including isostatic tilting, the deepening of certain outlets by erosion, and the covering and possible filling of outlets as a result of glacial readvance (especially the Port Huron readvance), must be considered.

For most of the ancestral lakes in the Erie basin, the position of the Huron Lobe margin and the outlet for the lake are

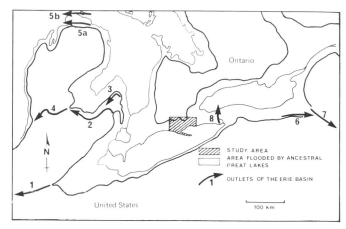

Figure 1. Location of study area and ancestral outlets of the Lake Erie basin. Explanation of numbers: 1) Wabash River, Indiana; 2) Imlay Channel, Michigan; 3) Ubly Channel, Michigan; 4) Grand River, Michigan; 5a) Indian River Lowlands, Michigan; 5b) Straits of Mackinac, Michigan; 6) Syracuse Channels, New York; 7) Mohawk River Valley, New York; 8) Niagara River.

intimately associated. The position of the Erie Lobe margin is more difficult to locate.

Stratigraphy and Nomenclature

The stratigraphic framework and the nomenclature of Quaternary sediments pertaining to the study area have been summarized by Dreimanis and Karrow (1972), Karrow (1974), Cowan et al. (1975, 1978) and Barnett (1978, 1982, 1984). During the Late Wisconsinan three major periods of ice advance or stadials, termed the Nissouri, Port Bruce, and Port Huron, directly affected the Erie basin (Dreimanis and Karrow, 1972) (Fig. 2). These stadials were separated by two periods of general ice recession called the Erie and Mackinaw Interstadials.

In Ontario, the Nissouri Stadial is represented by the Catfish Creek Drift (Catfish Creek Till). The Kent and Lavery Tills in Ohio are thought to have been deposited during this stadial (Goldthwait et al., 1965; White, 1982). The Port Stanley Drift (Port Stanley Till) represents the Port Bruce Stadial in Ontario and is, in part, probably the correlative of the Hiram Till. The Ashtabula Till is probably correlative with the Port Stanley Till, however, its youngest member, related to the Girard Moraine, may correlate with the Wentworth Till in Ontario (Leverett, 1902; Mickelson et al., 1983).

The writer believes that the Wentworth Till represents a period of readjustment of the Erie and Ontario ice lobes during the early part of the Mackinaw Interstadial. Several small oscillations of the ice margin probably were involved (Barnett, 1984). The Port Huron advance of the Erie Lobe is represented by the Halton Till in Ontario (Barnett, 1979). This advance reached only as far as the eastern end of the Erie basin and did not reach the present study area (Feenstra, 1974; Barnett, 1979).

Proglacial lakes existed in the Lake Erie basin dating from the time the continental glacier first shrank back from the southern divides allowing water to accumulate between the divides and the glacial front (Fenneman, 1938; Hough, 1958). The proglacial lakes that existed in the Lake Erie basin during ice recession in the later part of the Nissouri Stadial and the Erie Interstadial have been described by Dreimanis (1969) and Mörner and Dreimanis (1973). During the subsequent Port Bruce Stadial readvancing ice occupied most of the Erie basin and overrode much of the evidence for these lakes. No shoreline features of these earlier proglacial lakes were recognized in the study area. However, two younger sequences of deglacial lakes are recorded: 1) an early sequence during the Port Bruce (Cary) Stadial and Mackinaw Interstadial, and 2) a later sequence during and following the Port Huron Stadial ice advance.

ICE MARGINAL POSITION

Ten end moraines mark positions of ice margin stillstand or readvance in the study area (Fig. 3). The Ingersoll, Westminster, St. Thomas, Norwich, Tillsonburg, Courtland, Mabee and Lakeview Moraines are composed, at least in part, of Port Stanley Drift. The Lakeview Moraine, as defined here, marks the termination of a small readvance. It lacks surface expression, however, it can be traced in the subsurface from the Lake Erie shore near Lakeview, inland to Vienna (Fig. 3). All of these moraines are oriented roughly parallel or slightly oblique to the present Lake Erie shoreline.

The Paris and Galt Moraines are composed primarily of Wentworth Till. These two moraines are oriented north-northeast to south-southwest or nearly perpendicular to the local trend of the present Lake Erie shoreline west of Long Point.

The Ingersoll Moraine marks the northwestern extent of the Port Stanley Till in the study area. The remaining moraines record an oscillating recession of the margin of the Erie Lobe following the Port Bruce maximum. Several of these document minor readvance, such as the St. Thomas, Tillsonburg, Courtland, Mabee, and Lakeview Moraines.

The Ingersoll, Westminster, St. Thomas, and Norwich Moraines were deposited in a terrestrial environment. During their deposition meltwater from the receding ice margin flowed northward to the Thames River and then southwestward to the Komoka Delta at London. However, as the ice margin receded from the Norwich Moraine, waters of a large proglacial lake flooded the ground between the ice margin and that moraine. The younger moraines, the Tillsonburg, Courtland, Mabee, and Lakeview, located south of the Norwich Moraines, also formed in proglacial lakes in the study area. The relationships of interfingering glaciolacustrine and glacial sediments provide information on the relationships of water levels in the Erie basin and ice-marginal positions.

During the formation of the Paris and Galt Moraines, the margin of the glacier continued to support proglacial lakes in the Erie basin.

EVIDENCE OF ANCESTRAL LAKES

Ancestral lakes in the study area are recorded directly by

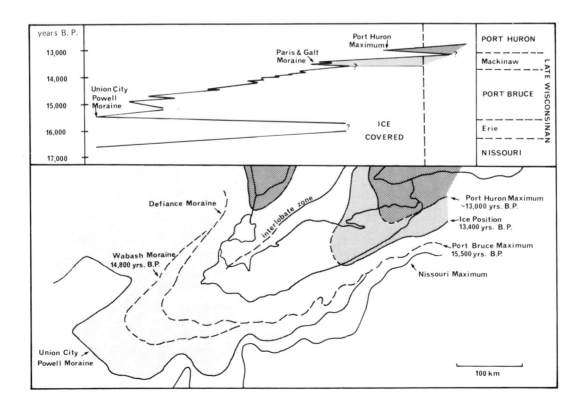

Figure 2. Time-space diagram of the Erie Lobe. Modified after Dreimanis and Karrow (1972), Dreimanis (1977), and Mickelson *et al.* (1983).

shoreline features, such as bluffs, deltas, beach bars, and spits, and indirectly by their sediments, sediment relationships, and by river terraces. Shoreline features range in elevation from 271 m (890 ft.) to below present Lake Erie level (173 m, 570 ft.). They are generally fragmented. Most of the shoreline features discussed here have been described previously in individual areal geology reports and preliminary maps (Barnett, 1978, 1979, 1982, 1983; Barnett and Zilans, 1983, and references therein), but have not been previously discussed as entities in the present form.

Lake Whittlesey created the most distinct and continuous shoreline features in the study area. The Whittlesey shoreline (Barnett, 1979) was used as the "local datum" in this study for the identification and correlation of shoreline features and deposits of the other ancestral lakes in the Lake Erie basin. The locations of Lake Whittlesey shoreline features are presented in Figure 4, along with the other shoreline features discussed below. Lake Whittlesey shoreline features rise from 241 m to 256 m (790 to 840 ft.) across the study area. The maximum direction of tilting of the waterplane was in the direction of 027°N azimuth (Barnett, 1979).

In general, shorelines of lakes older than Lake Whittlesey are tilted more than the Lake Whittlesey shoreline; younger lakes, less. In order to compare the shoreline data, elevations from the study area of the shoreline features will be given along with the corresponding elevation of the shoreline in the essentially untilted portion of the uplift curve, the "area of horizontality". The evidence of ancestral lake levels in the study area will be discussed from oldest to youngest.

Glacial Lake Maumee

At least three phases of Lake Maumee and sometimes four have been recognized (Fullerton, 1980). These include Lake Maumee I (244 m, 800 ft.) and Maumee III (239 m, 780 ft.), and Maumee II and Maumee IV (232 m, 760 ft.). Drainage is considered to have been via one or a combination of the Wabash River, the Imlay Channel, and a buried valley north of Imlay.

Only two shoreline features in the study area are present above those of Lake Whittlesey. An abandoned shorebluff located 3.5 km. north of Bookton (Fig. 4) occurs along the

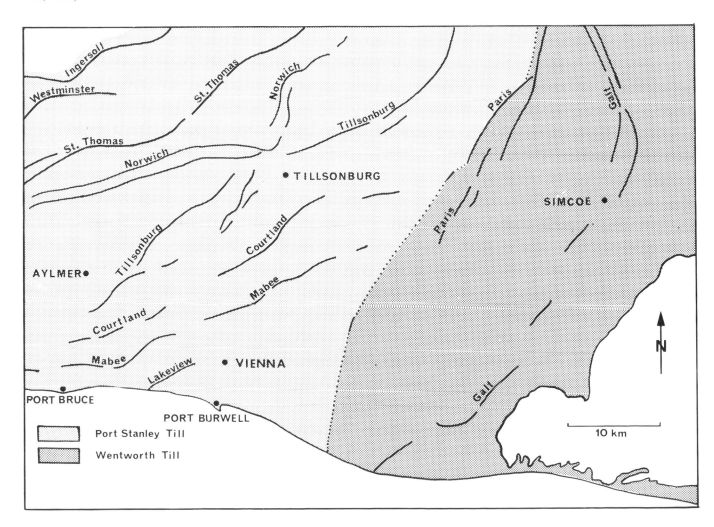

Figure 3. Moraines of the study area. Modified after Barnett (1978, 1982, 1984) and Chapman and Putnam (1984).

proximal side of the Tillsonburg Moraine between 271 and 274 m (890 and 900 ft.). A small beach bar (262 m, 860 ft.) is found on the proximal flank of the Norwich Moraine 1.5 km northwest of Delmer (about 262 m, 860 ft.). These two shoreline features were previously assigned to Maumee III (Barnett, 1982); however, they now appear to be the products of the glacial Lake Maumee IV of Fullerton (1980). They are too low for Maumee III, when compared to the Maumee III features identified by Dreimanis (1964, 1970) in the London area. The lake in which these shoreline features were deposited appears to have had an outlet similar in elevation to that of Maumee II, but at a later time, since the uplift of these features is less than Maumee II features from adjoining areas.

Several areas of glaciolacustrine silts and clays occur above these shoreline features assigned to Maumee IV. Some were deposited in local pondings between the ice margin and higher land; however, others can only be explained by the incursion of a large proglacial lake in the Erie basin, probably glacial LLLake Maumee III.

Glacial Lake Arkona

At least three levels of Lake Arkona (216, 213, 210 m; 710, 700, 690 ft.) have been recognized in the Lake Erie basin, all of which drained via the Grand River into the Lake Michigan Basin (Hough 1958). Several shoreline features in the study area have been assigned to glacial Lake Arkona. These features have been modified by glacial Lake Whittlesey and are buried below its sediments. Evidence for more than one level is lacking. The shoreline features occur approximately 11 m below Lake Whittlesey features and rise towards the northeast from 230 m (755 ft.) up to 235 m (770 ft.) (Fig. 4). These features occur on the proximal sides of the Courtland and Mabee Moraines and can be traced up to the Paris Moraine. However, the relationship of these features to the Paris Moraine is difficult to determine because the deposits of both the Lake Arkona shoreline and the moraine are buried beneath Lake Whittlesey sediments in the critical area.

Jacksonburg Delta Level

A sequence of buried deltaic and near shore sediments is exposed along the Lake Erie shorebluffs east of Port Burwell (Fig. 4). The uppermost unit of this sequence, containing low

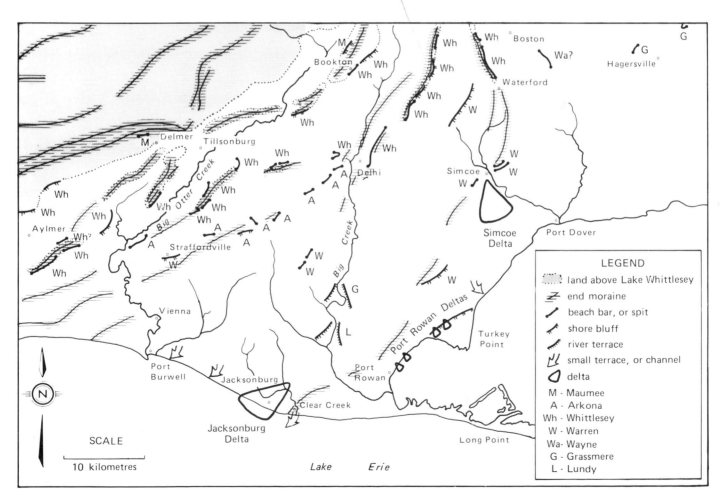

Figure 4. Evidence of ancestral lakes in study area.

angle cross-beds, plane beds, and minor trough cross-beds, defines a lake level between 190 and 198 m (625 and 650 ft.). Assuming a level of tilt similar to the Lake Whittlesey shoreline, this would correspond to a level somewhere between 175 and 183 m (573 and 598 ft.) in the "area of horizontality".

The upper part of this deltaic and nearshore sediment sequence contains glacially derived debris flows (flow tills) of Wentworth Till which are intimately associated with the formation of the Paris and Galt Moraines. Detrital organic matter was also recovered from these sand units. Wood fragments from this deposit displaying a high degree of rounding were dated at 25 800 ± 600 B.P. (BGS-884). They possibly were eroded from older deposits and subsequently redeposited. However, very delicate and well preserved leaves of *Dryas* and *Salix*, which would probably not have survived erosion and redeposition, were dated at 13 360 ± 440 B.P. (BGS-929). This date more closely reflects the age of these sediments and the formation of the Paris and Galt Moraines. Glacial ice in the Lake Huron basin must have uncovered the Indian River Lowlands at this time.

Simcoe Delta Level

The buried Simcoe delta (Fig. 4) was first recognized by Taylor (1913, p. 71). Located immediately south of Simcoe, this delta is covered by up to 8 m of fine-textured glaciolacustrine sediments. The top of the buried deltaic sediments occurs at approximately 213 m (700 ft.). Assuming that uplift has been similar to that of the Lake Whittlesey strands, this would correspond to a lake at about 186 m (610 ft.) in the "area of horizontality".

This delta is located on the proximal side (southeast) of the Galt Moraine. The river which fed this delta flowed southward in front of this moraine, then breached it at Simcoe and entered a proglacial lake present in the Erie basin. The elevation of the shoreline of this lake projected south in the "area of horizontality" is estimated to be 186 m (610 ft.). It existed in the Erie basin as the ice margin was receeding from the Galt Moraine and may have drained via the Indian River Lowlands or the Straits of Mackinac (Fig. 1).

Lake Ypsilanti

No features in the study area could be directly related to Lake Ypsilanti. However, a channel was identified that cut deeply into the Simcoe delta bottomset sediments east of Turkey Point. This channel is filled with trough cross-bedded sands and covered by silts and clays of Lake Whittlesey. The base of the channel occurs approximately 5 m above present Lake Erie or about 180 m (590 ft.). It was graded to a lake level that must have been lower than the base of the channel and would correspond to a water level of less than 161 m (528 ft.) in the "area of horizontality". This level falls within the range of elevations of Lake Ypsilanti suggested by Kunkle (1963). Drainage may have been eastward during Lake Ypsilanti and along the Erie-Ontario glacial lobe margin north of the Niagara Escarpment (Kunkle, 1963).

Glacial Lake Whittlesey

The Lake Whittlesey shoreline as mentioned previously rises from 241 to 256 m (790 to 840 ft.) across the study area. Its features, water plane, and paleogeographic distribution have been summarized previously (Barnett, 1979).

Lake Whittlesey formed during the Port Huron advance approximately 13 000 B.P. This advance is marked by the Port Huron and Wyoming Moraines in the Lake Huron basin and by the maximum extent of the Halton Till in the Erie basin (Barnett, 1978, 1979). The advancing glacier covered several of the lower outlets, raising the water-levels in the Erie basin to Lake Whittlesey level which was controlled by the Ubly Channel outlet (Fig. 1). Lake Whittlesey begins the second sequence of deglacial lakes recorded in the study area.

Glacial Lake Warren

The Lake Warren shoreline is well defined at Straffordville (Fig. 4) where a high shorebluff marks the water level at about 228 m (750 ft.). At Simcoe, a pair of beach ridges which occur at 238 m (780 ft.) and 235 m (770 ft.) have been assigned to Lake Warren.

A beach or offshore bar partially covered by sand at an elevation of approximately 228 m (750 ft.) is located 3 km southeast of Boston (Fig. 4). This feature may be an offshore bar of Lake Warren or, possibly, a partially buried Lake Wayne shoreline feature.

Lakes Grassmere and Lundy

Lake Grassmere is recorded by several small beach bars and a spit in the northeast corner of the study area at an elevation of 220 m (710 ft.). A fanning out of river terraces along Big Creek at approximately 206 m (675 ft.) may also mark the shoreline of Lake Grassmere. A similar fanning out of river terraces along Big Creek at approximately 198 m (650 ft.) may mark the shoreline of Lake Lundy in the study area. Lake Grassmere occurs at an elevation of 195 m (640 ft.) and Lake Lundy at 189 m (620 ft.) in the "area of horizontality" (Hough, 1958). Burgis (1977) suggested that Grassmere drained eastward (Syracuse Channels) and Lundy westward via the Indian River Lowlands.

Early Lake Erie

Two hanging fluvial terraces are exposed in the Lake Erie shorebluffs between Port Burwell and Jacksonburg (Fig. 4). At the first locality, 3 km east of Port Burwell, the base of the older alluvium occurs at approximately 19 m (62 ft.) above the present level of Lake Erie. Preliminary pollen analysis of the older alluvium indicated deposition prior to the spruce-pine transition (approximately 10 500 B.P. in this part of Ontario). Spruce pollen (*picea*) make up over 80% of the tree pollen, and non-tree pollen, ranges from 8 to 21% of all pollen (C.E. Winn, pers. commun., 1984). A radiocarbon age obtained on wood from within the alluvial sediments was 11 070 ± 140 B.P. (BGS-882) and appears reasonable in relationship to the pollen spectra.

At the second locality, 8 km southeast of Port Burwell, the

base of the older alluvium occurs about 15 m (49 ft.) above the present level of Lake Erie. Here, preliminary pollen analysis indicates deposition of the alluvium during the spruce-pine transition. A large log taken from near the base of the alluvium was dated at 9750 ± 150 B.P. (BGS-883) and is not unreasonable for this site.

Neither of these terraces can be related directly to the water level that existed in the Lake Erie basin during their formation. However, the levels in the Lake Erie basin were probably lower than 189 m (620 ft.) and the shoreline must have been located farther out in the Lake Erie basin than at present.

At Clear Creek, an abandoned channel of Clear Creek is cut 5 m (16 ft.) below the present level of Lake Erie. Sedimentological and palynological studies of this site suggest that this abandoned channel began infilling approximately 9500 to 9000 years ago based on the pollen record (Barnett *et al.*, in press). Infilling was completed sometime after 3900 ± 100 (BGS-898) based on a radiocarbon date on wood from near the top of the channel fill (Barnett *et al.*, 1985). The sediment and pollen records at this site suggest that the water level in the Lake Erie basin was lower than the present level during this time interval.

Port Rowan Deltas Level

Several delta-like features, occurring approximately 5 m (18 ft.) above the present Lake Erie level, were identified at the base of a stretch of Lake Erie shorebluff protected by Long Point (Fig. 4). It is difficult to confirm whether these are deltas or alluvial fans due to the lack of exposure of internal characteristics. However, the coincidence of the elevations to which these features are built, combined with older alluvial terraces graded to them, strongly suggests that they are deltas.

These deltas are relatively young features which indicate that the water level in the Erie basin rose above the present level of Lake Erie well after Early Lake Erie existed in the Lake Erie basin and before the present level was obtained. Radiocarbon dating on organic detritus and on wood from older alluvium graded to two of these deltas yielded dates of 960 ± 80 B.P. (BGS-980) and 1900 ± 80 B.P. (BGS-928).

The outlet sill for this lake was probably the Fort Erie Moraine at Fort Erie. There, a river terrace cut into the moraine occurs at 180 m (590 ft.). A younger terrace is present at 174 m (570 ft.). Shoreline features recognized by Feenstra (1981) occurring at Shisler Point (181 m, 595 ft.) and at Erie Beach, south of Fort Erie (180 m, 590 ft.) may also mark the shoreline of this post-Early Lake Erie lake.

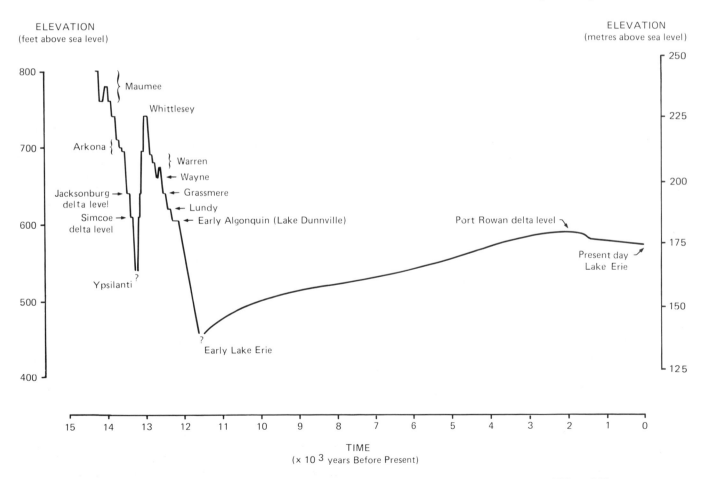

Figure 5. Sequence of ancestral lakes in the Lake Erie basin. Modified after Lewis (1969), Fullerton (1980), and Chapman and Putnam (1984).

However, Feenstra (1981) related these features to falling levels in the Erie basin and the beginning of Early Lake Erie.

The presence of these relatively young delta features suggests that the controlling sill along the Niagara River up until this stage was the 180-m (590-ft.) level terraces across the Fort Erie Moraine. Downcutting of this sill to the present sill on bedrock probably occurred as a result of the return of upper Great Lakes drainage via Port Huron into the Lake Erie basin.

GLACIAL HISTORY

A general account of Late Wisconsinan ice movements and associated till deposits was presented previously (General Background). The account of the glacial history presented here will concentrate on the history of the Erie Lobe commencing at the Port Bruce Stadial maximum. In the study area this maximum is associated with the Ingersoll Moraine. It will attempt to trace the steps of this recession in relationship to ancestral lake levels in the Erie basin as indicated by the deposits and features preserved in the study area. The general sequence of ancestral lake levels in the Erie basin is summarized in Figure 5.

During the Port Bruce Stadial, the Erie Lobe eventually coalesced with the Huron Lobe and advanced to the Union City-Powell Moraine in the United States (Mickelson et al., 1983). The northern extent of the Erie Lobe in the study area is marked by the Port Stanley Till and the Ingersoll Moraine. Recession and oscillations probably occurred at the western extremity of the Erie Lobe prior to the actual formation of the Ingersoll Moraine. The entire study area was probably still ice covered during the Glacial Lake Maumee I phase in the western end of the Erie basin.

During ice marginal recession in the study area, the ice margin paused or readvanced slightly to form part of the Westminster Moraine, the St. Thomas Moraine, and the Norwich Moraine (Fig. 3). Meltwater flowed freely from these ice margins northward to the Thames River, then southwestward along the Ingersoll Moraine to the Komoka Delta at London. This, in turn, was being built into Lake Maumee I and Lake Maumee II. Dreimanis (1970) suggested that the Glacial Lake Maumee II phase occurred in the Erie and Huron basins during ice marginal fluctuations along the St. Thomas Moraine. Maumee II waters probably did not enter the study area at this time.

As the glacier retreated from the Norwich Moraine, a high-level glacial lake (Lake Maumee II or III) flooded the ground between this moraine and the ice front. At this time, rivers draining the ice margin carried sediment into the lake. Deltaic sands were deposited along the ice front and silts and clays farther out in the basin. The ice front receded to a position south of the Tillsonburg Moraine, then readvanced, over-riding the glaciolacustrine sediments to form the "northern limb" of the Tillsonburg Moraine. The "middle" and "southern" limbs of this moraine were formed in a similar manner (Barnett, 1982).

The ice front then receded to a position south of the Courtland Moraine. Deltaic sediments continued to be deposited along the ice margin. Glacial Lake Maumee III existed in the Erie basin by this time, flooding the land be-

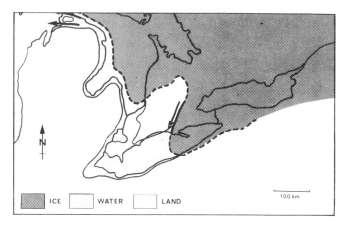

Figure 6. Paleogeographic map of the Erie basin, 13 400 years ago (Jacksonburg delta level).

tween the St. Thomas Moraine and the ice margin. A minor readvance of the ice margin formed the Courtland Moraine. The Mabee and Lakeview Moraines formed in a similar fashion, probably during glacial Lake Maumee IV. Subsequently, the margin of the glacier continued its retreat farther eastward into the Lake Erie basin.

In the Lake Erie shorebluff, a coarsening upward sequence of glaciolacustrine sediments indicates that a regional shallowing of water levels occurred following the Port Bruce Stadial. Lake Arkona features are well developed on Port Bruce Stadial sediments such as those forming the Mabee Moraine, and probably were formed during the initial stages of ice retreat near the beginning of the Mackinaw Interstadial. The Paris and Galt Moraines, formed of Wentworth Till, represent a readjustment of the Erie Lobe during the Mackinaw Interstadial. The relationship of the Paris Moraine to Lake Arkona is not clear.

During the formation of the Galt Moraine, however, the water level in the Lake Erie basin is recorded by the Jacksonburg delta 175 m to 183 m, (575 to 600 ft.). Because the Erie Lobe blocked eastward drainage, the Michigan and Huron Lobes must have receded northward far enough to uncover the Indian River Lowlands or the Straits of Mackinac in order to form a lake at this level (Fig. 6). Deglaciation of most of Michigan must have occurred at the time of the formation of the Jacksonburg delta, about 13 400 B.P. This may be supported by dates on the Cheyboygan Bryophyte Bed (Miller and Benninghoff, 1969). However, dates of the Cheyboygan site range from 13 300 ± 400 B.P. to as young as 9960 ± 350 B.P. and their interpretation is not without controversy (see Fullerton, 1980).

The Simcoe delta records water level in the Erie basin following the formation of the Galt Moraine. Again, westward drainage, possibly along the Indian River Lowlands or Straits of Mackinac, must have occurred. However, with recession of the Erie Lobe margin toward the Lake Ontario basin during the latter part of the Mackinaw Interstadial, eastward outlets opened and Lake Ypsilanti formed.

During the Port Huron advance and deposition of the Halton Till, ice entered the eastern end of the Erie basin and raised the water level in the basin to that of Lake Whittlesey (Barnett, 1979). The recession of the ice margin from this maximum gave rise to the remaining sequence of glacial lakes in the Erie basin. Lake Whittlesey, two Lake Warrens, possible Lake Wayne, Lake Grassmere, and Lake Lundy features have been identified.

Early Lake Erie, or at least lakes with shorelines south of the present day Lake Erie shoreline, may be represented by the hanging terraces in the shorebluffs east of Port Burwell or the abandoned channel cut and fill at Clear Creek (Fig. 4). The Port Rowan deltas record a water level about 5 m above the present Lake Erie level which occurred about 2000 years ago.

SUMMARY

This paper has presented the record of ancestral lakes in the Erie basin from an area north of Lake Erie. The Erie glacial lobe was active in this area during the existence of these lakes. Ice-marginal positions have been suggested for several of the lake levels and several new levels were proposed.

The Jacksonburg delta provides evidence that the Paris and Galt Moraines were formed in shallow water (Fig. 5). This occurred before the Port Huron readvance raised the water level in the Erie basin to the Lake Whittlesey level (Barnett, 1979).

ACKNOWLEDGEMENTS

This paper is published with the permission of the Director, Ontario Geological Survey. I am grateful for discussions with B.H. Feenstra, P.F. Karrow, and D.E. Lawson, and for critical review of the manuscript by W.R. Cowan, Aleksis Dreimanis, P.F. Karrow, P.E. Calkin, and M.J. Ford. The assistance of A.F. Bajc and B.F. Carswell in the preparation of the diagrams and Jennifer John in the typing of the manuscript is gratefully acknowledged.

REFERENCES

Barnett, P.J., 1978, Quaternary Geology of the Simcoe Area, Southern Ontario: Ontario Division of Mines, Geoscience Report 162, 74 p.

———, 1979, Glacial Lake Whittlesey: The Probable Ice Frontal Position in the Eastern End of the Erie Basin: Canadian Journal of Earth Sciences, v. 16, p. 568-574.

———, 1982, Quaternary Geology of the Tillsonburg Area, Southern Ontario: Ontario Geological Survey Report 220, 87 p.

———, 1983, Quaternary Geology of the Port Burwell Area, Southern Ontario: Ontario Geological Survey, Preliminary Map P.2624, Geological Series, Scale 1:50 000.

———, 1984, Glacial Stratigraphy and Sedimentology Central North Shore Area, Lake Erie, Ontario: Geological Association of Canada-Mineralogical Association of Canada, Joint Annual Meeting, Field Trip Guidebook 12, 42 p.

Barnett, P.J. and Zilans, A., 1983, Quaternary Geology of the Long Point Area, Southern Ontario: Ontario Geological Survey Preliminary Map P.2616, Geological Series, Scale 1:50 000.

Barnett, P.J., Coakley, J.P., Terasmae, J. and Winn, C.E., 1985, Chronology and Significance of a Holocene Sedimentary Profile from Clear Creek, Lake Erie Shoreline, Ontario: Canadian Journal of Earth Sciences, v. 22, p. 1133-1138.

Burgis, W.A. 1977, Late-Wisconsinan History of Northeastern Lower Michigan: Ph.D. Thesis, Ann Arbor, University of Michigan, 396 p.

Calkin, P.E., and Feenstra, B.H., 1985, Evolution of the Erie-Basin Great Lakes: in Karrow, P.F., and Calkin, P.E., Quaternary Evolution of the Great Lakes: Geological Association of Canada Special Paper 30.

Carman, J.E., 1946, The Geological Interpretation of Scenic Features in Ohio: Ohio Journal of Science, v. 46, p. 241-283.

Chamberlain, T.C., 1883, Preliminary Paper of the Terminal Moraine of the Second Glacial Epoch: United States Geological Survey, Third Annual Report, 1881-82, p. 291-402.

———, 1888, Rock-Scorings of the Great Ice Invasion: United States Geological Survey, 7th Annual Report, 1885-86, p. 155-248.

Chapman, L.J. and Putnam, D.F., 1984. The Physiography of Southern Ontario: Ontario Geological Survey Special Volume 2, 270 p.

Cowan, W.R., Karrow, P.F., Cooper, A.J. and Morgan, A.V., 1975, Late Quaternary Stratigraphy of the Waterloo-Lake Huron Area, Southwestern Ontario, Field Trip 7: in Telford, P.G., ed., Waterloo '75, Field Trips Guide Book: Geological Association of Canada, p. 180-222.

Cowan, W.R., Sharpe, D.R., Feenstra, B.H., and Gwyn, Q.H.J., 1978, Glacial Geology of the Toronto-Owen Sound Area: in Currie, A.L. and Mackasey, W.O., eds., Field Trips Guidebook: Geological Society of America and Geological Association of Canada, p. 1-6.

Dreimanis, A., 1964, Pleistocene Geology of the St. Thomas Area (West Half), Southern Ontario: Ontario Department of Mines Preliminary Geological Map P.238, Scale 1:50 000.

———, 1969, Late-Pleistocene Lakes in the Ontario and Erie Basins: Proceedings 12th Conference on Great Lakes Research, International Association for Great Lakes Research, p. 170-180.

———, 1970, Pleistocene Geology of the St. Thomas Area (East Half), Southern Ontario: Ontario Department of Mines, Preliminary Geological Map P.606, Scale 1:50 000.

———, 1977, Late Wisconsin glacial retreat in the Great Lakes region, North America: in Newman, W.S., and Salwen, Bert, eds., Amerinds and Their Paleo-Environments in Northeastern North America, Annals of the New York Academy of Sciences, v. 288, p. 70-89.

Dreimanis, A., and Karrow, P.F., 1972, Glacial History of the Great Lakes-St. Lawrence Region, the Classification of the Wisconsin(an) Stage, and its Correlatives: 24th International Geological Congress, Montreal, Quaternary Geology, Section 12, p. 5-15.

Feenstra, B.H., 1974, Quaternary Geology of the Dunnville Area, Southern Ontario: Ontario Division of Mines Preliminary Map P.981, Geological Series, Scale 1:50 000.

———, 1981, Quaternary Geology and Industrial Minerals of the Niagara-Welland Area, Southern Ontario; Ontario Geological Survey, Open File Report 5361, 260 p.

Fenneman, N.M., 1938, Physiography of Eastern United States: New York, McGraw-Hill, 714 p.

Fullerton, D.S., 1980, Preliminary Correlation of Post-Erie Interstadial Events (16 000-10 000 Radiocarbon Years Before Present), Central and Eastern Great Lakes Region, and Hudson, Champlain, and St. Lawrence Lowlands, United States and Canada: United States Geological Survey Professional Paper 1098, 52 p.

Goldthwait, R.P., Dreimanis, A., Forsyth, J.L., Karrow, P.F., and White, G.W., 1965, Pleistocene deposits of the Erie lobe: in Wright, H.E., Jr., and Frey, D.G., eds., The Quaternary of the United States, Princeton, N.J., Princeton University Press, p. 85-97.

Hough, J.L. 1958, Geology of the Great Lakes: Urbana, Illinois, University of Illinois Press, 313 p.

Karrow, P.F., 1974, Till Stratigraphy in Parts of Southwestern Ontario: Geological Society of America Bulletin, v. 85, p. 761-768.

Kunkle, G.R., 1963, Lake Ypsilanti: A Probable Late Pleistocene Low-Lake Stage in the Erie Basin: Journal of Geology, v. 71, p. 72-75.

Leverett, F., 1902, Glacial Formations and Drainage Features of the Erie and Ohio Basins: United States Geological Survey Monograph 41, 802 p.

Leverett, F. and Taylor, F.B., 1915, The Pleistocene of Indiana and Michigan and the History of the Great Lakes: United States Geological Survey Monograph 53, 529 p.

Lewis, C.F.M., 1969, Late Quaternary History of Lake Levels in the Huron and Erie Basins: Proceedings 12th Conference on Great Lakes Research, International Association for Great Lakes Research, p. 250-270.

Mickelson, D.M. Clayton, L., Fullerton, D.S., and Borns, H.W., Jr., 1983, The Late Wisconsin Glacial Record of the Laurentide Ice Sheet in the United States: in Wright, H.E., Jr., ed., Late-Quaternary Environments of the United States, v. 1: The Late Pleistocene, Porter, S.C., ed., Minneapolis, Minnesota, University of Minnesota Press, p. 3-37.

Miller, N.G., and Benninghoff, W.S., 1969, Plant Fossils from a Cary-Port Huron Interstade Deposit and their Paleoecological Interpretation: Geological Society of America Special Paper 123, p. 225-248.

Mörner, N.A. and Dreimanis, A., 1973, The Erie Interstadial: in Black, R.F., Goldthwait, R.P., and Willman H.B., eds., The Wisconsin Stage: Geological Society of America Memoir 136, p. 107-134.

Taylor, F.B., 1913, The Moraine Systems of Southwestern Ontario: Royal Canadian Institute Transactions, v. 10, p. 57-79.

White, G.W., 1982, Glacial Geology of Northeastern Ohio: Ohio Geological Survey Bulletin 68, 75 p.

Quaternary Evolution of the Great Lakes,
edited by P.F. Karrow and P.E. Calkin,
Geological Association of Canada Special Paper 30, 1985

POSTGLACIAL LAKE LEVELS IN THE ERIE BASIN

J.P. Coakley

Hydraulics Division, National Water Research Institute, Canada Centre for Inland Waters, Burlington, Ontario L7R 4A6

C.F.M. Lewis

Geological Survey of Canada, Atlantic Geoscience Centre, Bedford Institute of Oceanography, Dartmouth, Nova Scotia B2Y 4A2

ABSTRACT

New data have led to the revision of the empirical curve of postglacial levels in the Erie Basin originally proposed by Lewis in 1969. The new data were compiled from a variety of sources, both published and unpublished, and comprise a total of 50 radiocarbon dates, geomorphological and fluvial indicators, and detailed profiles of postglacial sediments below the present lake. The resulting revised curve differs significantly from the earlier version. A major difference is the higher placement of the lake level trend between 10 000 and 3000 B.P. Another significant change is in the interpretation of lake levels up to 5 m above the present datum during the period 5000 to shortly after 4000 B.P. This interval is coincident with the initiation of full Nipissing drainage into the Erie basin. Between 3000 B.P. and the present, both curves are virtually identical, showing a slow rising trend to present levels. Causal factors in the above lake level trends are still not well understood. Important processes in this regard could be the changing pattern of inflows from the upper Great Lakes, the nature and postglacial tectonics of the lake outlet, and paleoclimatic influences.

RÉSUMÉ

Le lac Érié, le plus vieux des Grands Lacs laurentiens, a été libéré de l'action directe des glaciers il y a environ 12 000 ans lorsque le retrait de la glace de Port Huron a dégagé l'exutoire de Niagara. L'ouverture de cet exutoire a pratiquement entraîné la vidange complète du lac glaciaire. Ce lac, de la phase initiale du lac Érié, comprenait un certain nombre de petits sousbassins presqu'entièrement séparés. L'analyse de nouvelles données se rapportant aux événements postglaciaires survenus dans le bassin du lac Érié nous a incités à réviser la courbe empirique des divers niveaux lacustres du bassin du lac Érié telle que proposé par Lewis en 1969. Ces données incluent 50 datations au radiocarbone, des indicateurs géomorphologiques et fluviatiles de même que des analyses détaillées des sé-quences sédimentaires postglaciaires. La courbe revisée des niveaux lacustres diffère de la courbe de Lewis: d'une part, la nouvelle courbe indique un niveau d'eau beaucoup plus élevé pour la période de 10 000 à 3000 B.P.; d'autre part, pour la période entre 5000 et 4000 B.P., la courbe revisée montre un niveau à 5 m au-dessus du niveau actuel. A partir de 3000 B.P., les deux courbes ont une allure semblable. Elles indiquent une lente remontée du niveau lacustre vers les niveaux actuels.

Les causes des variations du niveau lacustre sont encore mal comprises. Cependant, il semble que la première montée du niveau lacustre entre 12 000 et 10 000 B.P. soit liée aux apports d'eau importants provenant du lac glaciaire Algonquin et au soulèvement rapide de l'exutoire. Après cette période jusqu'à environ 5000 B.P. la pente de la courbe des niveaux d'eau a tendance à devenir de plus en plus horizontale. Cela s'expliquerait par une réduction des apports d'eau provenant de la partie supérieure des Grands Lacs, au reflux dans la partie occidentale du lac Érié ou à une amélioration climatique. La montée rapide du niveau d'eau entre 4000 et 5000 B.P. est liée à la reprise du drainage de la partie supérieure des Grands Lacs lors de la phase finale du lac Nipissing. Le renversement ultérieur, c'est-à-dire la baisse du niveau d'eau, est attribué à l'élargissement du chenal de la rivière Niagara. Depuis cette période jusqu'à aujourd'hui, la lente remontée du niveau d'eau semble être principalement le résultat de soulèvements non-glaciaires de la croute dans le bassin du lac Érié.

INTRODUCTION

Lake Erie is the southernmost of the Laurentian Great Lakes, and thus was the first to be uncovered by the retreat of the continental glaciers of the Late Wisconsinan stage. The subsequent high-level proglacial lake stages, Maumee (elevation 244 m a.s.l.) to Dana (158 m a.s.l.), ended when the glacier retreated into the Ontario basin, opening up the lake outlet at Niagara (Fig. 1). Rapid drainage through this glacio-isostatically depressed outlet brought the level in

Lake Erie to its most recent minimum, tens of metres below its present elevation. This was the stage referred to by Hough (1966) as Early Lake Erie, and later interpreted by Lewis (1969) to have occurred around 12 500 B.P. The age was based on the oldest radiocarbon date for marsh-related plant debris collected in lake-bottom cores from the western sub-basin of the lake. Lewis (1969) placed the initial elevation of Early Lake Erie at about 48 m below present level.

Lewis (1969) and Sly and Lewis (1972) concluded that from about 12 500 B.P. to the present, Lake Erie levels have followed a fairly uniform upward trend, responding primarily to the crustal rebound of the outlet. The first curve of postglacial lake levels, published by Lewis (1969), and reproduced here as Figure 2, was based primarily on 17 radiocarbon ages (Fig. 1, Table I). Almost all these ages were on samples obtained in the shallow western sub-basin of the lake (Fig. 3). The placement of the initial lake elevation was based on estimates of uplift inferred from the tilted and uplifted shorelines of the Whittlesey and Warren proglacial lake stages.

More recent investigations into lake sediment history, especially in the sparsely reported eastern and central areas of the lake, by the authors and others (Williams and Meisburger, 1982; Guy, 1983; Ontario Hydro, 1981; Barnett and Zilans, 1983; and Barnett et al. 1985) have contributed much additional data. These are mostly in the form of radiocarbon-dated or palynologically controlled sediment profiles and geophysical surveys of lake sediment stratigraphy and relict geomorphological features, all related to past lake levels. However, these data and the inferences they permit are sometimes in conflict with the earlier work. The nature of the contradictionu suggests that the evolution from the initial lows to present-day levels might have been much more complex than that implied by Lewis (1969).

The prime objective of this paper is to re-examine the postglacial evolution of Lake Erie levels in the light of the expanded data base. After a critical review of the new and previous data, we derive an updated model of lake level history for the period following the regression of the Late Wisconsinan glacial lake phases.

BASIS FOR LAKE LEVEL INTERPRETATION

Radiocarbon Dates and Elevations

A total of 50 postglacial radiocarbon dates (obtained by the authors or others) that relate to Lake Erie history, are presented in Table I. A brief description of the material dated and its sediment matrix, as presented in the source reports, is also included. Dates no. 1 to 17 were the ones used by Lewis (1969). Note that a minor error in these data (e.g., typographical error in the age of No. 10) has been corrected. Note also that all elevations have been referred to International Great Lakes Datum for Lake Erie (173.3 m a.s.l.).

Estimates of the contemporary lake level associated with the samples were deduced primarily from the texture of the sediment matrix. For instance, for open lake samples, a sand

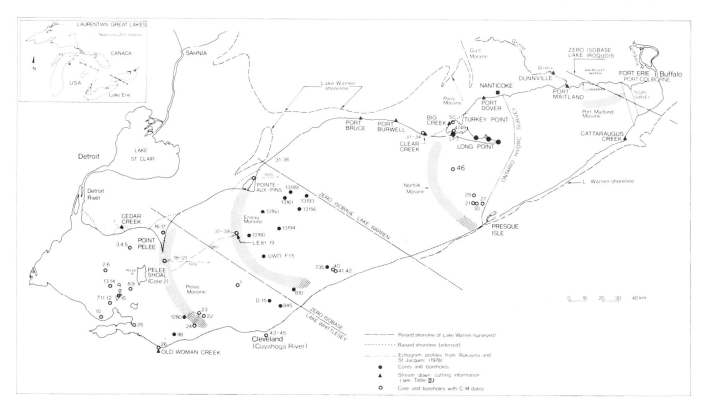

Figure 1. Map of Lake Erie, showing place names and physiographic features referred to in the text. Also shown are the locations of boreholes and sites (numbered 1 to 50) where radiocarbon-dated samples were collected (Table I). The shaded area along the south side of the lake marks the area surveyed and cored by the U.S. Army Corps of Engineers and the Ohio Division of Geological Survey.

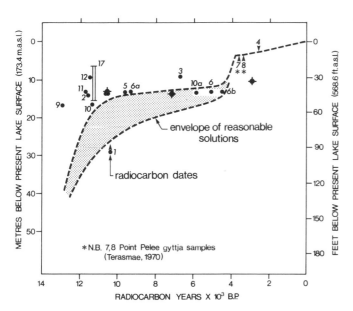

Figure 2. Postglacial history of Lake Erie levels as interpreted by Lewis (1969). Numbers refer to Lewis' original list of radiocarbon dates, which are included in Table I.

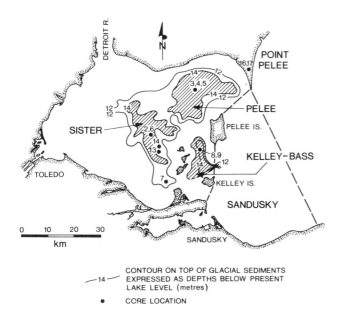

Figure 3. Minor sub-basins in western Lake Erie, interpreted from glacial sediment and bedrock surface topography (modified after Lewis, 1969). Shaded areas show location of organic deposits which were cored and dated (sites numerically keyed to radiocarbon dates in Table I). Dashed lines indicate major sub-basin sills.

matrix was related to water depths of up to 5 m, silty sand, 5 to 10 m, and mud, 10 m or more. In sheltered areas, these depths were reduced somewhat. Prior to this step, however, an attempt was made to assess the reliability of the radiocarbon dates as objectively as possible. The more important factors in this assessment are discussed below.

Sampling Errors. Virtually all the dates were obtained on plant material (wood, gyttja, peat) collected using a variety of coring techniques. Some of these techniques can lead to sample disturbance and contamination by organics from above the sampled horizon. For this reason, dates no. 10 to 14, which were collected using a technique of water-jetting to remove the overlying sediments, followed by coring of the target layer, must be treated with caution until confirmed by other data. Sampling contamination might explain why dates no. 11 and 14, although stratigraphically equivalent to dates no. 12 and 13, yielded considerably younger radiocarbon ages. Dates where sampling errors might be significant are designated (S) in the "Comments" column of Table I.

Allochthonous or Transported Organic Material. Pleistocene glacial sediments, exposed along much of the shoreline of the Erie basin, have long been subjected to erosion and redeposition elsewhere in the basin. Organic matter incorporated in these older deposits has also been reworked, and may occur as detrital organic matter included within relatively younger deposits. Clues to such older detrital organics are usually provided by the character of the organic matter (disseminated organics, or broken and eroded fragments), or by the nature of the sediment/organic matter association. For instance, wood fragments or terrestrial plant detritus in a lacustrine mud matrix often suggest transport and redeposition downslope from an original subaerial position. Stratigraphic inferences based on such materials are thus subject to some inaccuracy, insofar as the age of the matrix deposits are concerned, unless supported by other means (e.g., pollen dating).

Wood in sand deposits, however, is expected to date these deposits and their corresponding lake level fairly accurately, because older wood, introduced to the nearshore zone, is more likely to be recycled to the offshore basin or destroyed in the high-energy environments characterized by sand deposition. Furthermore, the deposition of the wood as driftwood close to its terrestrial source area on or near the waterline (shoreface sand deposit or river bar) is a more natural and likely scenario.

In general, dates obtained from wood samples that are apparently in growth position are the most reliable of all. Date no. 27, on wood fragments in firm, glacial clay was believed by the collector (S.J. Williams, pers. commun., 1982) to be on in situ root material. This date is seen as being reasonably reliable, although the relationship of the "roots" to the ambient lake level cannot be verified, other than the requirement that the living tree had to be located above lake level. However, its location and preservation suggest to us that it was buried in situ below the lake level soon after death. Dates on wood in peaty sequences also are generally reliable, as allochthonous wood inputs or local transport of the wood after death is judged to be minimal in such environments. Dates on material probably transported to the sampling site are labelled (T) in the Comments column in Table I.

In situ Contamination and Isotopic Fractionation. The anomalously old ages commonly obtained on fresh-water mollusc shells and humified plant detritus have been discussed by a number of workers (Mott, 1975; Karrow and

TABLE I

COMPREHENSIVE LISTING OF RADIOCARBON DATES FROM THE ERIE BASIN NEAR OR BELOW THE LAKE. DESCRIPTION OF ORGANIC MATERIALS USED, SOURCES, AND A SUBJECTIVE APPRAISAL OF THE RELIABILITY OF THE DATE ARE ALSO GIVEN. DATE NUMBERS ARE KEYED TO SIMILAR NUMBERS IN THE LOCATION MAP (FIG. 1)

No.	Location	Metres below datum		C-14 age		Comments	Source
		Sample	Est. lake level	(yrs. B.P.)	Lab. No.		
1	*Central sub-basin (Core 2226)	28.5	above 18	10,200 ± 180	GSC-330	DRIFTWOOD at base of offshore muds (T)	Lewis et al. (1966), Lewis (1969)
2	*Sister sub-basin (Core 1240)	14.0	below 13	11,300 ± 160	GSC-382	BASAL PLANT DETRITUS in local ponding (C,P)	Lewis et al. (1966), Lewis (1969)
3	*Pelee sub-basin (Core 68-6)	16.7	below 12	12,650 ± 170	I-4040	BASAL PLANT DETRITUS in local ponding (C,O,P) Note: Pollen stratigraphy suggests age of around 12,000 years B.P. for this level.	Lewis (1969), T.W. Anderson (pers. commun. 1983)
4	*Pelee sub-basin (Core 68-6)	16.3	below 12	11,140 ± 160	I-4041	TOP OF PLANT DETRITUS in local ponding (C,O,P) Note: Pollen strat. suggests 10,600 B.P.	Lewis (1969), T.W. Anderson (pers. commun. 1983)
5	*Pelee sub-basin (Core 68-6)	13.4	3 to 11	5,750 ± 180	GSC-1165	DISSEM. ORGANIC MATTER at upward transition from clay to clayey silt (T,O,C,P) Note: Pollen age – 4000 to 5000B.P.	Lewis (1969), T.W. Anderson (pers. commun. 1983)
6	*Sister sub-basin (Core 68-16)	13.6	below 13	11,430 ± 150	I-4035	BASAL PLANT DETRITUS in local ponding (repl. of (2)) (C,P)	Lewis (1969)
7	*Sister sub-basin (Core 68-20)	9.1	below 13	11,200 ± 180	GSC-1136	BASAL PLANT DETRITUS in fringing marsh of local pond (C)	Lewis (1969)
8	*Kelley-Bass sub-basin (Core 67-10)	14.0	below 10	10,370 ± 150	I-4034	BASAL PLANT DETRITUS in local pond open to Sandusky sub-basic (C)	Lewis (1969)
9	*Kelley-Bass sub-basin (Core 67-10)	13.8	below 10	10,340 ± 150	I-4033	TOP OF PLANT DETRITUS in local pond open to Sandusky s.b. (C)	Lewis (1969)
10	?Portage River mouth (Core 1-57)	9.2	?	6,550 ± 134	OWU-110	WOOD (oak) at base of plant detritus layer (T,S)	Ogden and Hay (1965), Herdendorf and Braidech (1972), Lewis (1969)
11	?Sister sub-basin (Core WR-31)	12.5	?	4,335 ± 135	OWU-318	FRAGMENTED PLANT DETRITUS (T,C,S)	Ogden and Hay (1969), Herdendorf and Braidech (1972), Lewis (1969)
12	?Sister sub-basin (Core WR-32)	12.5	?	9,115 ± 210	OWU-319	FRAGMENTED PLANT DETRITUS (T,S)	Ogden and Hay (1969), Herdendorf and Braidech (1972), Lewis (1969)
13	?Sister sub-basin (Core WR-33)	12.6	?	9,440 ± 315	OWU-350	FRAGMENTED PLANT DETRITUS (T,S)	Herdendorf and Braidech (1972), Lewis (1969)
14	?Sister sub-basin (Core WR-34)	12.5	?	5,097 ± 175	OWU-351	FRAGMENTED PLANT DETRITUS (T,S)	Herdendorf and Braidech (1972), Lewis (1969)
15	*Terwilliger's Pond Bass Island	3.0	close to 3	2,500 ± 270	OWU-275	WOOD in subaerial swampy soil overlain by marsh deposits (P)	Ogden and Hay (1969) Lewis (1969), Stevenson and Benninghoff (1969)
16	*Redhead Pond Point Pelee	3.5	above 3	3,520 ± 100	I-3992	BASAL GYTTJA (C,O)	Terasmae (1970), Lewis (1969)
17	*Big Pond Point Pelee	3.5	above 3	3,310 ± 100	I-3993	BASAL GYTTJA (C,O)	Terasmae (1970), Lewis (1969)
18	*Point Pelee Shoal (Core 6)	10.5	above 2	3,600 ± 140	BGS-256	WOOD FRAGMENTS near base of transgressive sequence (T)	Coakley et al (1977)
19	*Point Pelee Shoal (Core 5)	12.3	above 2	6,600 ± 180	BGS-252	WOOD FRAGMENTS near base of transgressive sequence (T)	Coakley et al (1977)
20	?Point Pelee Shoal (Core 5)	16.0	?	8,100 ± 300	BGS-255	SHELLS in lag gravel layer over silt at base of transgressive sequence (O,X)	Coakley et al (1977)

TABLE I (CONTINUED)

No.	Location	Metres below datum		C-14 age		Comments	Source
		Sample	Est. lake level	(yrs. B.P.)	Lab. No.		
21	? Point Pelee Shoal (Core 2)	12.6	?	10,260 ± 325	BGS-254	PLANT DETRITUS in fine sand/silt sequence (T,X) Note: pollen strat. suggests age of less than 7000 yrs.	Coakley *et al* (1977)
22	? Sandusky sub-basin (Core 85)	18.6	above 18	12,180 ± 400	BGS-608	PLANT DETRITUS within sandy silt 3 m below lake bed (T,X)	Guy (1983), C.H. Carter (pers. commun. 1983), J.A. Fuller (pers. commun. 1983)
23	? Sandusky sub-basin (Core 86)	17.4	?	10,330 ± 560	BGS-610	WOOD in surficial sandy silt 1.5 m below lake bed (T,X)	C.H. Carter (pers. commun. 1983), J.A. Fuller (pers. commun. 1983)
24	? Sandusky sub-basin (Core 91)	15.9	?	6,490 ± 140	BGS-612	SHELL LAYER in sandy silt (C,O,T,X)	Guy (1983), C.H. Carter (pers. commun. 1983), J.A. Fuller (pers. commun. 1983)
25	? Sandusky sub-basin (Core 101)	7.4	?	7,730 ± 400	BGS-609	WOOD in surficial sand (T,X)	Guy (1983), C.H. Carter (pers. commun. 1983), J.A. Fuller (pers. commun. 1983)
26	* Old Woman Creek Estuary, Ohio	5.2	below 5	7,690 ± 210	DIC-1134	WOOD in coarse sand/ silt alluvial complex (T)	D. Buchanan (pers. commun. 1981)
27	* Norfolk Moraine (Core 28)	22	close to 22	10,800 ± 190	UM-1706	WOOD in firm silty clay over till. Believed to be *in situ* root fragments	Williams and Meisburger (1982) Williams *et al* (1980)
28	* Norfolk Moraine (Core 23)	21	11-16	8,545 ± 150	UM-1705	WOOD at base of clean medium sand with clay layers (T)	Williams and Meisburger (1982) Williams *et al* (1980)
29	* Norolk Moraine (Core 4)	21	11-16	8,240 ± 210	UM-1703	WOOD in interbedded sand/ clay unit (T)	Williams and Meisburger (1982) Williams *et al* (1980)
30	* Norolk Moraine (Core 18)	22	above 17	6,870 ± 150	UM-1704	WOOD at the base of massive fine – medium sand (T)	Williams and Meisburger (1982) Williams *et al* (1980)
31	* Clear Creek, Ontario	−1.8	above 2	3,900 ± 100	BGS-898	LARGE WOOD FRAGMENT, *in situ* in well preserved forest bed.	Coakley, this study Barnett *et al.* (1985)
32	* Clear Creek, Ontario	−0.5	below 0	5,975 ± 150	BGS-899	PEAT layers in silt	Coakley, this study Barnctt *et al* (1985)
33	* Clear Creek, Ontario	−0.3	below 0	6,460 ± 125	BGS-900	PEAT layers in silt	Coakley, this study Barnett *et al* (1985)
34	* Clear Creek, Ontario	0.7	below 1	6,980 ± 120	BGS-901	PEAT layers in silt	Coakley, this study Barnett *et al.* (1985)
35	* Rondeau Prov. Park, Pointe-	6.3	0-5	5,330 ± 250	WAT-378	PEAT with shells and silt above silty clay layer	A.J. Cooper, Ontario Geological Survey (1982,
36	* aux-Pins			5,180 ± 370	WAT-379	(C,O)	pers. commun.)
37	? S. of Pointe-aux Pins (Core LE8119)	23.2	?	5,420 ± 150	WAT-1081	Whole silty clay sample (O,X)	Coakley, this study
38	* S. of Pointe-aux Pins (Core LE81-19)	23.5	above 13	3,140 ± 110	WAT-946	WOOD FRAGMENT in shelly, gravelly layer with silt and clay (T)	Coakley, this study
39	? S. of Pointe-aux Pins (Core LE81-19)	23.5	?	7,000 ± 370	WAT-970	SHELLS picked from the above layer (T,O)	Coakley, this study
40	* Central sub-basin (Core 62)	20.8	above 15	8,250 ± 145	DIC-1329	WOOD FRAGMENTS in muddy sand (T)	Carter (1984)
41	? Central sub-basin (Core 62)	18.9	above 14	4,020 ± 190	DIC-1328	WOOD FRAGMENTS in sandy silt 2 m below lake bed (T)	Carter (1984)
42	? Central sub-basin (Core 61)	17.4	above 12	3,360 ± 160	BGS-611	WOOD AND ORGANICS in surficial sandy silt (T)	Carter (1984)
43	* Lower Cuyahoga River, Ohio	−4.7	below −4.7	8,540 ± 70	DIC-1137	WOOD from vegetation-rich layers in top section of cross-bedded alluvial sand	Miller (1983)
44	* Lower Cuyahoga River	−1.7	below −1.7	8,760 ± 90	DIC-1136	(Same as above)	Miller (1983)
45	* Lower Cuyahoga River	−0.7	below −0.7	8,780 ± 80	DIC-1135	(Same as above)	Miller (1983)
46	? Eastern sub-basin south of Long Point	18.5	?	4,100 ± 100	BGS-363	WOOD at base of silty clay/ fine sand surficial deposit (T)	Rukavina (1981)
47	? Long Point (Borehole 3)	6.0	?	7,420 ± 280	WAT-1079	WHOLE ORGANIC SILT sample (O,X) Note: Pollen strat. suggests an age of less than 5000 B.P.	Coakley, this study

TABLE I (CONTINUED)

No.	Location	Metres below datum		C-14 age		Comments	Source
		Sample	Est. lake level	(yrs. B.P.)	Lab. No.		
48	?Long Point (Borehole 3)	6.4	?	11,280 ± 380	WAT-1080	WHOLE ORGANIC SILT sample, same as above (O,X)	Coakley, this study
49	?Long Point (Borehole 3)	19.5	?	8,490 ± 330	WAT-1083	WHOLE SILTY CLAY sample (O,P)	Coakley, this study
50	?Small unnamed stream flowing into Long Point Bay	−4	?	960 ± 80	BGS-908	ORGANIC MATTER in silt and sand alluvium (T,O)	P.J. Barnett, Ontario Geol. Survey (pers. commun., 1983)

LEGEND: T − Probably transported
         O − Possibly contaminated by "old" carbon
         C − Probably underwent some compaction
         S − Possibly contaminated during sampling
         P − Pollen stratigraphy exists as a check on date
         X − Date judged unreasonable, rejected
         ? − Age or elevation cannot be assessed with confidence
         * − Age/elevation are definitive, or can be deduced with confidence

Anderson, 1975; Keith and Anderson, 1963; and Rubin and Taylor, 1963). Silt-sized detritus from inorganic carbonate terrains such as the Lake Erie watershed could introduce significant inaccuracy to shell dates as it is virtually impossible to remove these isotopically-depleted particles completely from the shell samples before dating. This could account for the anomalously older shell date (date no. 39), compared with the stratigraphically equivalent wood sample (date no. 38). Also, date no. 50, on shallow alluvial materials, could be either too old (humified modern organics), or too young (older organics contaminated by modern roots). Dates where such errors are likely are labelled (O) in Table I.

Post-depositional Compaction. This refers to the time-dependent process whereby columns of cohesive sediments with initially high water contents are compressed due to the gradual escape of porewaters. The release of the excess pore pressures is caused by the increasing weight of the overlying sediments. Depending on the texture and original water content of the sediments, their rate of sedimentation, and the time following deposition, such reductions could exceed 50%. Similar compaction effects are also common in peat deposits. The main effect of this process would be the overestimation of the dated sample's depth below datum, particularly for those samples overlying substantial thicknesses of compressible (or compressed) sediments. Thus, the estimated lake-level ranges stated in Table I for peat samples and those from organic matter in cohesive materials such as silty clays have been broadened to reflect this possibility. Samples probably affected to an undetermined degree by this process are labelled (C) in Table I.

Other Factors. In reviewing the reliability of the radiocarbon dates, other indicative factors were considered where relevant. One crude indicator of reasonable dates is the existence of a proper younging-upward relationship in cases where a vertical sequence of dates was involved (dates no. 3 to 5, 31 to 34, 43 to 45). Another is the existence of confirmatory pollen data from the sampled borehole (dates no. 31 to 34). Such pollen examination resulted in the revisions to dates no. 1 to 7 noted in Table I. Consideration was given,

when using dates and elevations from streams now located close to the lake shoreline, to the fact that the elevations refer to the river channel level, and not to the base or lake level at the time. Because neither the distance from the lake nor the stream gradient at the time is precisely known, lake levels inferred from such data must be regarded as maximum values only.

Summary. Taking all these factors into account, the perceived reliability of the dates and elevations presented in Table I was subjectively appraised. This appraisal is included in the table in the form of estimated lake-level ranges, as well as notations regarding possible sources of error. The lake level referred to in the table is that of the central sub-basin. Levels in the small, isolated pondings, which presumably occupied the western sub-basin, were apparently controlled at higher elevations for much of their early history by the elevations of the sills separating them (Fig. 3).

The lake level estimate for samples suspected of being transported is placed above a minimum value, or questioned (?) if uncertain. Some dates are clearly spurious, for instance, those on whole sediment samples such as dates no. 47 to 49, and date no. 21 on disseminated plant detritus. In both cases, pollen profiles suggest very different ages. Such dates are indicated by an (X) in the "Comments" column of Table I. Those dates whose elevations could not be estimated with confidence, or which were deemed highly questionable are indicated by a (?) next to the date number. Dates designated by either an (X) or a (?) were disregarded in subsequent analyses. Definitive dates and elevations, i.e., those with higher perceived reliability, are indicated with an asterisk in Table I. Of the original 50 dates, only 30 were eventually used.

Relict Geomorphological Features

Relict features indicative of previous lake levels, both below and above the present lake datum (173.3 m a.s.l.) were interpreted from subsurface records and topographic maps. In view of the general scarcity of absolute dates for these features, their relative ages can only be inferred. In the

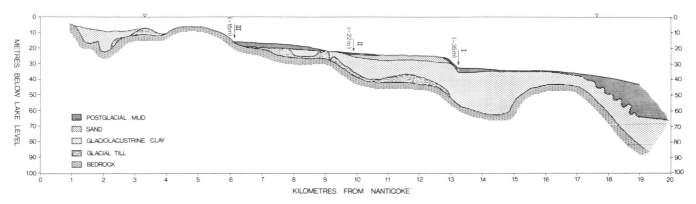

Figure 4. Interpreted geological section through Quaternary deposits along a seismic reflection survey line near Nanticoke, Ontario (Fig. 1). Slope-breaks and sand-veneered offshore terraces were used to define previous shoreline positions I, II, and III. Seismic survey data provided courtesy of Ontario Hydro.

discussion below, they will be grouped as follows: 1) sub-surface lake level indicators (from acoustical profiling and borehole data); and 2) lake level indicators provided by shoreline topographical features and depths of tributary stream erosion.

Subsurface Lake-Level Indicators. The most definitive indicators consist of wave-eroded terraces or platforms cut into the pre-Lake Erie glacial sediments, and sharply defined slope breaks offshore beneath modern sediments. The latter may be suggestive of an earlier shore-bluff or shoreface profile. Most of these features were identified in the more sheltered eastern sub-basin of the lake. This was partly because of bias in the location of acoustical profiles, and partly due to better preservation prospects. In addition, one co-author (Lewis) had already made surveys in the area and seismic profiles were made available to us by private firms (Ontario Hydro and Transcontinental Gas Pipe Line, Inc.; see Fig. 1). A sub-bottom seismic and borehole survey of the Norfolk Moraine ridge south of Long Point (Williams and Meis-

burger, 1982; and hatched in Fig. 1) suggests two distinct episodes of east-west channelling into glacial materials, now infilled with more recent sediment. The base of the lower channel is more than 45 m below datum (b.d.), and that of the upper (more recent) channel occurs at around 30 m b.d. One borehole on Long Point (BH3; Coakley, 1984) and others in the central sub-basin near Pointe-aux-Pins (Lewis *et al.*, 1973) also recorded diagnostic erosional features. These features comprised signs of a prior history of erosion, e.g., truncation of sediment layers, overconsolidation, desiccation of the glacial sediment surfaces, and the presence of a lag sediment cover.

A total of 26 measurements of the depth to the lowest eroded glacial sediment surface was provided by echograms from the eastern sub-basin. The elevation of such erosion limits rose in an eastward direction from around 39 m b.d. in the west (Long Point Bay), to 25 m b.d. in the east (off Port Colborne). This figure contrasts with a present nearshore erosion limit of less than 10 m in Long Point Bay (St.

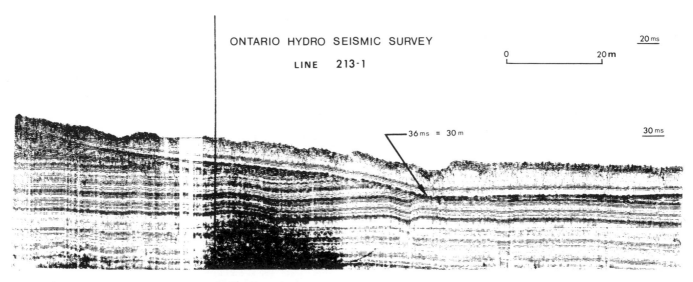

Figure 5. Example of a seismogram from the Ontario Hydro survey, showing the feature interpreted in Figure 4 as relict shoreline I, at approximately 30 m b.d., cut into laminated glaciolacustrine deposits. The vertical black line is a distance fix marker. Reproduced with permission of Ontario Hydro (J. Godawa, pers. commun., 1984).

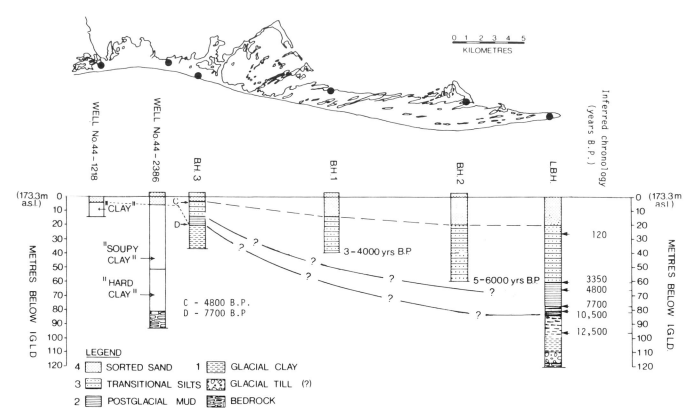

Figure 6. Longitudinal section through boreholes drilled on Long Point, including interpreted lithology and pollen-based chronology. Note the sharp slope break inferred from borehole logs occurring west of BH3, interpreted as a possible relict shoreline. Boreholes west of BH3 were for water supply purposes andnonly drillers' sediment descriptions were available.

Jacques and Rukavina, 1973), and is strong evidence of a much lower lake phase. In addition, abrupt slope breaks were noted in the Ontario Hydro seismic profiles off Nanticoke (Shoreline I, Fig. 4) at between 30 and 35 m b.d. A representative seismic record for this feature is shown in Figure 5. Less defined shoreline indications were noted at 20 to 22 and 10 to 15 m b.d. in the same area. Comparable features were noted also along the TCGPL seismic profile between Port Colborne and Sturgeon Point, N.Y., at depths of 25 to 30 m b.d. Other such features were resolved from the echograms in the Long Point Bay area at depths of 28 to 32 m b.d. In the cross-section through the Long Point boreholes (Fig. 6), a scarp-like feature was inferred in the eroded glacial sediment surface at around 20 m b.d. The erosion limit in the Pointe-aux-Pins boreholes and echograms was recorded at around 30 m b.d.

Figure 7 shows the elevations of these subsurface features, and the estimated lake level to which they refer, plotted against distance from an arbitrary point west of the presumed zero isobase for the most recent glacial lakes. Elevations were projected to the line of maximum tilt, N 24° E, according to Leverett and Taylor (1915) and Calkin (1970). When compared to similar plots of corresponding raised and tilted shorelines in the eastern part of the basin, it is clear that the above features lie considerably below the westward projection of the raised features that Feenstra (1981) linked to Early Lake Erie. Furthermore, no reasonable line fitted to all or combinations of these features, and parallel to the water-planes above them, could intersect or pass above the

present bedrock sill across the Niagara River at Buffalo. This sill and the yet higher crests of the Fort Erie Moraine (180 m) and Niagara Falls Moraine (183 m) were potential outlet controls for Early Lake Erie (Fig. 7). Moreover, no correlation of these features could be made either with Feenstra's Early Lake Erie stage or with Calkin and Brett's Lake Tonawanda stage shown in Figure 7 (Feenstra, 1981; Kindle and Taylor, 1913; Calkin and Brett, 1978).

This lack of correlation suggests that the geomorphologic features noted could not be related to the initial low-level stage of Early Lake Erie except under an unusual combination of circumstances (see Discussion and Summary). Based on the relatively high slope of the line joining maximum erosion depths at Long Point Bay and Port Colborne (dotted line, Fig. 7), we suggest that the sub-bottom features described above could predate Early Lake Erie. They may have either been preserved near the surface since then, or were uncovered intact by recent bottom erosion. Clearly, more information is needed before the significance of these features can be assessed further.

Shoreline Topography and Stream-downcutting Indicators. Raised shorelines below the Lake Warren level were identified mainly in the eastern portion of the basin (Feenstra, 1981; Leverett and Taylor, 1915) (Figs. 1 and 7). Feenstra (1981) attributed three slightly raised shoreline features (between 177 and 180 m) in the Niagara River area to Early Lake Erie. Kindle and Taylor (1913) and Calkin (1970) identified low, raised shorelines in the Niagara Falls

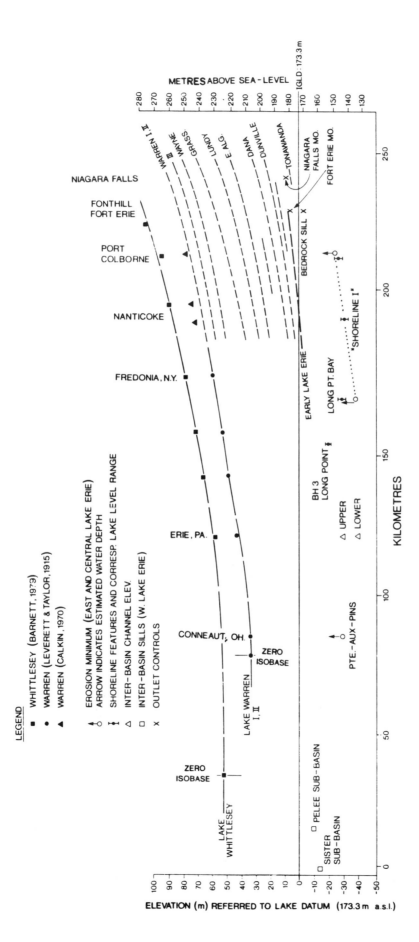

Figure 7. Plot of elevation versus distance of raised and uptilted shorelines of the Whittlesey and subsequent lake phases (modified after Feenstra, 1981; Leverett and Taylor, 1915; Calkin, 1970; Barnett, 1979). Profile is oriented N 24° E, the direction of maximum tilting. Also plotted are submerged geomorphological features noted on or below the lake bottom, and their relationship to possible outlet controls at the Niagara River (Fig. 10).

area as vestiges of Lake Tonawanda.

In the Long Point area, a slightly raised bluff shoreline, now separated from the lake, extends from the western end of Long Point to its truncation by the modern shoreline east of Turkey Point. The base elevation of the bluff is estimated from topographic maps at between 175 and 185 m a.s.l. Lobate features, suggestive of small deltas extending from stream valleys cut into this bluff, were identified in the area west of Turkey Point (Barnett and Zilans, 1983). The flattened surface of one of these features was determined to be about 6 m above datum (P.J. Barnett, pers. commun., 1983). If this feature is comparable to a Gilbert-type delta, then the above elevation is a reasonable estimate of the level of the lake into which the stream once flowed, i.e., 5 to 10 m above datum. Alluvial organic matter from a terrace associated with one of these features yielded a radiocarbon age of 960±180 B.P. (BGS-908, date no. 50, Table I), but for reasons outlined earlier, this date needs further confirmation before it can be accepted as a reliable age for these deltoid features.

Suggestions of an abandoned shoreline at the same height above datum occur landward of the Point Pelee and Pointe-aux-Pins (Erieau) forelands, and along the north shoreline of the western sub-basin. The apparent lack of tilting suggests that this shoreline trace is more recent than Early Lake Erie, although no other dates are presently available.

The vertical channel geometry and sedimentation patterns of streams entering the lake can also provide useful information regarding stream base-level changes, and thus indirectly, the contemporaneous lake level. A total of 10 measurements and descriptions of sediment sequences were taken from borehole records associated with bridge construction over major streams flowing into Lake Erie (Table II). These data were provided by the Ontario Ministry of Transportation and Communication, the U.S. Army Corps of Engineers, and the Ohio Department of Natural Resources. Stream locations are shown in Figure 1.

The lowest down-cutting (>11 m b.d.) of entering streams is recorded in the eastern sub-basin at the mouths of the Grand River and Big Creek (Fig. 1), neither of these channels was controlled by bedrock. At Big Creek, the original alluvial deposits are apparently being re-channelled again, indicating a more recent change to lower base levels.

The only stream whose sedimentation sequence was accurately dated was Clear Creek (Fig. 1). Pollen profiles, controlled by 4 radiocarbon dates (no. 31 to 34), were obtained here (Barnett et al., 1985). The stream channel was cut to a depth of 5 m b.d., and basal sediments were determined to have an age around 9500 B.P. on the basis of pollen. Pollen-dating was supported in part by the identification of diagnostic events in the pollen record for this area (Ogden, 1967; Davis, 1981; Mott and Farley-Gill, 1978; Terasmae, 1981). Where necessary, approximate ages were also obtained by comparison of pollen profiles with radiocarbon-dated profiles in the area (Winn, 1977).

Because the distance to the lake and the stream gradient at the time of this Clear Creek sedimentation are unknown, the channel elevation figure cited above represents a maximum for lake levels. The sedimentary sequence shows a steady fining-upward trend from a fluvial environment to marsh

conditions which were established by around 7000 B.P. (date no. 34). Arboreal vegetation was apparently drowned by high water levels at around 4000 B.P. This is based on date no. 31 obtained on a 50-cm-thick layer composed almost entirely of logs and peat. The sequence strongly suggests the existence of lake levels 2 m or more above present datum. Assuming base level changes in the lake as the underlying cause for this sequence, the pattern indicates a rising trend from at least around 9500 B.P. Lake levels apparently reached their present elevation around 4000 to 5000 B.P. and continued rising for an interval on the order of a few hundred years.

Using extensive borehole data from the lower Cuyahoga River valley (approximately 5 km from the present lakeshore near Cleveland; Fig. 1), Miller (1983) defined an episode of channel aggradation to a base level higher than that at present. Radiocarbon dates on wood from these channel sands indicated that this event occurred around 8500 B.P. (dates no. 43 to 47). The minimum elevation of previous channels at the site was 165 m a.s.l. (8 m b.d.). At present, the river channel at the site is at 174 m a.s.l. (about 1 m above lake datum). Therefore, if uniform stream gradients are assumed, the sequence might be interpreted to support a rising trend in lake levels from around 8 m b.d. to a level above that at present beginning prior to 9000 B.P. Sometime afterward, lake level then fell to its present elevation, or alternatively, the stream gradient was increased due to shore erosion, as is indicated by the re-entrenchment of the river to 174 m a.s.l. In general the trend here is in good agreement with that indicated by the Clear Creek profile, although the event is dated earlier at the Cuyahoga River site.

Borehole Sediments

Postglacial sediments sampled in boreholes below Long Point and Point Pelee (Fig. 8) have been dated using pollen profiles and, in a few cases, radiocarbon dating (dates no. 18 to 21). Further details regarding sediment analyses and lithology are presented in Coakley (1984). Of particular relevance here are estimates of original deposit thickness, and thus minimum lake levels, based on consolidation tests carried out at selected horizons in the cores.

The sediment data indicate that at the site of BH3 on Long Point, sediment accumulation began around 8000 B.P. on an over-consolidated glaciolacustrine clay surface at 20 m b.d. (Fig. 6). Consolidation tests and shear strength profiles indicate that prior to this time the surface underwent considerable erosion, and might even have been subjected to subaerial exposure and desiccation some time after deposition. Pollen assemblages at the base of the initial postglacial sediments indicate a closed boreal or mixed hardwood forest environment and suggest a minimum age of between 7500 and 9000 B.P. for this horizon (Winn, 1977).

Six metres of uniform, quiet-water sediments (silty clays) were deposited at the site up to around 7000 B.P. (Unit 2, Fig. 8). If allowance is made for post-depositional compaction (discussed above), the thickness of the original sediment column may be conservatively estimated at 10 to 15 m. Furthermore, if a water depth of at least 10 m is assumed reasonable for such fine sediments, the lake level around 7000 B.P. would have been between 20 and 25 m above the

TABLE II

VERTICAL SEDIMENTARY RELATIONSHIPS AND CHANNEL GEOMETRY OF STREAM MOUTHS ALONG THE SHORE OF LAKE ERIE. LOCATION OF SITES IS GIVEN IN FIGURE 1

Stream	Distance from mouth (km)	Water elev. (m)	Water depth /Bott. elev. IGLD	Sed. materials below channel (glac./postgl. contact)	Contact elevation	Bedrock elevation	Comments
Grand River:							
Port Maitland	0	173	7.6 m/166.4	Alluvial sand over lacustrine clay (glacial)	162.4	160.8	Stream apparently cut into glaciolacustrine clay deposit. Change of stream regime apparent in upward transition from loose, fine to coarse sand with shells, to soft silty clay with organic matter. Stream *not* bedrock-controlled.
	0 - 0.5 (offsh.)	173	7.9/166.4	Loose sand and gravel over clay	161.5	154	
Dunnville	6.0 (upstream)	176	2/173.7	"Marly" loose sand over reddish gray clay (glac.). Broad (500 m) valley cut in clay.	161.5	152	
Lynn River:							
Port Dover	0.8 (upstream)	174	3.3/170.7	Thin layer of loose to compact alluvial sand over firm (glac.?) clay.	170	170	Stream has apparently cut down into soft surficial silty clay and then into loose sand and glac. clay. Stream not bedrock-controlled.
Big Creek:							
(vic. Port Rowan)	2.0 (upstream)	175	1/173	Alluvial sand, gray silty and organic, over reddish gray stiff clay.	unknown; below 165	not observed	Channel originally cut into glac. clay to around 160m or less. Sands originally laid down now being channeled again.
Cattaraugus Creek:							
New York	0.2 (offsh.)	174	2.5/171.5	Sand and gravel over glacial till and glac. clay.	167.3	—	Channel cut through glaciolacustrine clay down to till.
Clear Creek:							
	at shoreline	174.5	175.6	Glacial till	168.9	—	Narrow channel silted up and abandoned. Sediments grade down from a 1 m thick surface layer of logs and peat, through coarsening-downward series of silt, sand, and gravel to pinkish till.
Otter Creek:							
Port Burwell	0.5 (upstream)	173.8	—	Loose to compact gray silty fine sand with wood over stiff clay (till?)	168.5	—	Port entrance dredged often so relationships might be disturbed.
	"	"	6.3/167.5	(same as above)	165.7	—	Stream probably cut in till to 165.7 m. Top loose organic sediment represents modern deposits while loose sands repr. aggradation phase as lake rose.
Catfish Creek:							
Port Bruce	0.5 (upstream)	174	1.2/172.8	Fine to coarse sand with fine gravel and organic matter over very stiff, truncated silty clay surface (till?)	169.5 to 170	—	Stream cut into sand layer of alluvial or nearshore origin

TABLE I (CONTINUED)

Cedar Creek:	4.8 (upstream)	173.9	Borehole on land	Peat over compact to very dense silty fine to coarse sand. Glacial sed. base not encountered.	lower than 168.5	—	Borehole stopped in sand at 168.5. Sand probably laid down at a high lake stage.
Old Woman Creek:							
Ohio	0.3 (upstream)	—	174	Silty clay layers with organic matter over undetermined substrate. Coarse pebbly layer at base probably alluvial.	lower than 167.8	—	Contact could be lower than that noted, as bore hole did not reach glacial substrate.

glacial sediment surface, i.e., within 5 m of the present datum.

At Point Pelee (Fig. 8) the situation is strikingly similar, except that the base of the silty clay unit was not reached. Therefore no accurate figure for the total sediment thickness was possible. However, the unit is more than 6 m thick, so a compaction history comparable to that at Long Point is likely. In other words, the unit surface, pollen-dated at around 7000 B.P. and at an elevation of 13 m b.d., could also have been originally at least 5 m higher, providing further support for the idea of lake levels at the time being close to the present datum. The bottom of Core 2, 18 m b.d. in silty clay, was dated at around 10 000 B.P. on the basis of pollen, indicating that lake levels were somewhere above that elevation; possibly they were as high as 10 m b.d. at that time. Unlike the stream data described above, the elevations of sediment horizons provide only a minimum estimate of lake levels.

DISCUSSION

The inferences resulting from the above data sources were synthesized to create the revised postglacial history of lake levels in the Erie basin shown in Figure 9. No attempt was made to have the curve pass through all data points. Rather, we attempted to fit as smooth a curve as possible to the points used, with more weight given to dates judged to be definitive (dates no. 15 and 27, in particular). Sharp changes in trend were avoided as much as possible.

Early Lake Erie

As a result of pollen analysis on Core 68-6 (T.W. Anderson, pers. commun., 1984), the age of the basal plant detritus in western Lake Erie (dates no. 3 and 4), may be younger than previously thought (Lewis, 1969). Sediments enclosing the uppermost plant detritus zone, which has a radiocarbon age of 11 140 BP (date no. 4), were found to occur at the boundary between spruce-dominated and pine-dominated pollen assemblages. This transition has been well-documented elsewhere in the Great Lakes (Ogden, 1967; Karrow *et al.*, 1975; Terasmae, 1981), and was dated at around 10 600 BP. Thus, the uppermost plant detritus appears to be 500 years older than its pollen-defined age of deposition.

The age of deposition of the lower plant detritus in Core 68-6 may also be younger than its radiocarbon assay age (12 650 BP, date no. 3). The dated level bears a maximum concentration of spruce pollen (T.W. Anderson, pers. commun., 1984), a characteristic of pollen profiles in southern Ontario dating about 12 000 BP (Terasmae, 1981).

The foregoing adjustments imply that low lake levels and early postglacial marsh deposition existed in western Lake Erie from about 12 000 BP to after 11 100 BP, but prior to 10 600 BP. This period correlates with the low-water phase of glacial Lake Algonquin in the Huron basin while it drained into the Ontario basin through the Kirkfield outlet (Karrow *et al.*, 1975). The resulting diversion of glacial meltwater around the Erie basin would reduce circulation as well as water levels, and may account for the marsh development in restricted parts of western Lake Erie. The termination of marsh deposition thus correlates with the inception of main Lake Algonquin. It also presumably reflects the passage of Algonquin discharge (possibly augmented by Moorhead phase discharge from glacial Lake Agassiz into the western Superior basin (Teller, 1985)) through the Erie basin when the closing of the Kirkfield outlet diverted drainage southward.

The overall distribution of lake levels in the various subbasins corresponding to Early Lake Erie appears to have been rather complex. In general, waters in western Lake Erie appear to have been controlled at levels above 10 m b.d. by local sills between the sub-basins (Fig. 3). In central Lake Erie, no radiocarbon dates of comparable age were available, so the original lake elevation must be inferred, with special reference to the depth of the buried channel through the Norfolk Moraine, and the lower limit of the wave-eroded glacial sediment surface. These indicate a level of approximately 30 m or more below present datum (Lewis, 1969).

Undated indications of a low-level stage in eastern Lake Erie at around 30 to 36 m b.d., interpreted from geomorphological features in the sub-bottom, however, do not appear to be related to Early Lake Erie raised shoreline traces and outlet controls mapped onshore (Feenstra, 1981). Furthermore, their geometric relationship with erosion limits in central Lake Erie does not accommodate the necessary differential tilting expected for Early Lake Erie shorelines. Such discrepancies could possibly be explained by nonconfluence between these sub-basins, especially if lake levels were temporarily free of outlet controls in the initial stages. The possibility of a period of minimal outflow from Lake Erie, caused by rapid uplift of the outlet sill, is discussed later. However, for now, the discussion will assume that lake waters of central and eastern sub-basins were more-or-less confluent at around 30 m b.d. or lower, while initial levels in the western sub-basins were at the elevation of the relevant sills (i.e., 10 to 15 m b.d.).

Lake Level History

From the above minimum at around 12 000 to 10 000 B.P.,

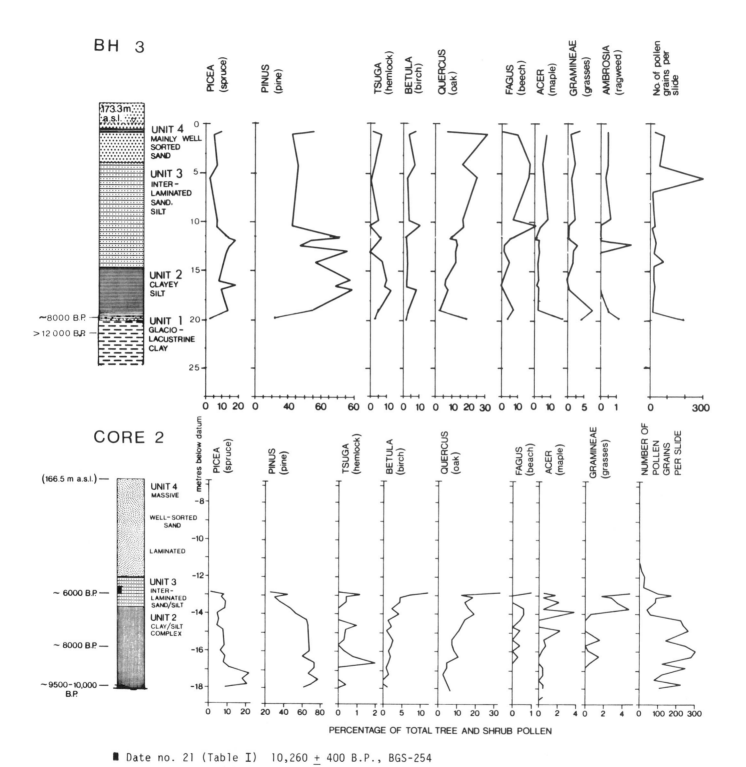

Figure 8. Representative sedimentary sequence and pollen profiles from below Long Point (BH3) and Point Pelee (Core 2). Relative dating based on pollen species trends and one radiocarbon date are also shown. Note discrepancy between pollen and radiocarbon dates in Core 2.

the lake level apparently rose rapidly from elevations of at least 30 m below datum, to around 15 m b.d. This trend is in agreement with the erosion limits for glacial sediments occurring on the periphery of the central sub-basin and below Long Point. The curve was deliberately drawn to pass close to date no. 27, judged to be a definitive date.

From around 10 000 to 7000 B.P., the trend slope declines noticeably to accommodate minima imposed by the postglacial sediment columns below Long Point and Point Pelee (pollen-dated), and maxima imposed by channel elevations of major inflowing streams. Four factors might have contributed to this slope change.

1) Back-flooding of the topographically-higher western Lake Erie, and the resulting increased surface area and storage volume would result in a slower rise in levels for unchanged inflow and outflow volumes.

2) The opening of northern outlets for glacial Lake Algonquin at around 10 500 B.P. (Karrow *et al.*, 1975) would greatly reduce inflows into Lake Erie.

3) Down-cutting of the lake outlet through the Fort Erie Moraine to bedrock would result in increased outflows.

4) The gradual onset of a period of climatic improvement (warmer, drier), as suggested by the contemporaneous vegetational change in the basin (pine-dominated closed boreal to mixed hardwood forests), could increase evaporation losses.

From around 7000 to 5000 B.P., the interpreted trend in lake level is almost flat at around 5 m b.d. This is to accommodate maximum values provided by the Clear Creek dated sequence (dates no. 31 to 34), minima imposed by the marsh peat at Pointe-aux-Pins (dates no. 35 and 36), and deep-water sediments dated on the basis of pollen (date no. 5). The stability of levels during this interval agrees well with the earlier curve (Lewis, 1969), except that the lake level is placed some 10 m higher in this interpretation as a result of our critical evaluation of previous radiocarbon dates. Such a stable interval could be linked to a climatic optimum, perhaps the mid-Holocene Hypsithermal interval, and is consistent with the fact that trees grew to maturity on marsh sediments at Clear Creek at that time.

From around 5000 to 3900 B.P., the curve shows an abrupt rise to levels as high as 5 m above datum. The most direct evidence for this is date no. 31 on the "drowned forest" bed at Clear Creek, described above. Topographic contours and deltoid features along the north shore of the lake also suggest a relatively recent shoreline position consistent with such a level. Although the surficial alluvium in the deltoid features contains organic matter dated at 960 BP (date no. 50), the features themselves possibly correlate with the above-mentioned lake rise, given the potential for contamination by younger organics discussed earlier. The time interval of this rise coincides with the onset of the single-outlet Nipissing II phase in the Upper Great Lakes (Lewis, 1969), when full drainage, via the St. Clair River, returned to the Erie basin.

From 3900 B.P. to present, the lake level trend is not fully resolved, and the curve can be interpreted in two distinct ways. If the deltoid features are assumed to be around 1000 years old, then the curve must pass through them, and a gradually lowering trend is suggested from 3900 B.P. to the present. If date no. 50 is discounted and the deltas linked

chronologically with the Nipissing event, then the lake level trend must undergo a sharp drop in order to have it conform with dates no. 15, 16, and 17, all of which are judged to be reliable. For this reason, this latter opinion is favoured.

The sharp drop can best be explained by the widening of the Niagara outlet to carry higher post-Nipissing outflow volumes. Because it is bedrock-bound, sufficient deepening of the outlet is inconceivable in such a short time. The possibility that other outlet pathways could have been temporarily activated, such as the Lowbanks site suggested by B.H. Feenstra (pers. commun., 1981), cannot be ruled out. This site, located some 50 km to the west of the Niagara River outlet (Fig. 1), corresponds with low points both in the northeast Lake Erie shoreline, as well as the Onondaga escarpment. Moreover, its location is just south of the Welland (Wainfleet) Bog. If this explanation is indeed valid, then it would explain the presence of the Wainfleet Bog linked to an earlier lake stage by Feenstra, and the persistence of Lake Tonawanda features to the present (Calkin and Brett, 1978).

The slow rise in levels (approximately 10 cm/century) from around 3000 B.P. to the present is difficult to explain in terms of hydrological changes. With the outlets in apparent equilibrium with even maximum outflows, levels should be stable over the long term. However, comparable vertical differential movements over historical time have been reported based on water-level comparisons between Lake Erie long-term gauges (Kite, 1972; Co-ordinating Committee on Great Lakes Basic Hydraulic and Hydrological Data, 1977), and on regional geodetic re-levelling (Hands, 1977). Rates of differential movement obtained range from 6 cm/century (gauge comparison; Buffalo rising with respect to Cleveland) to 30 cm/century (geodetic re-levelling; north shore rising with respect to the south). These results are in agreement with the trend in Figure 9, and suggest that differential crustal movements are continuing long after postglacial isostatic adjustments have ended. Such movements, though still not fully explained, might be likely causes for the level rise inferred over the past 3000 years. Small-scale fluctuations in lake level due to climatically-induced changes in water supply, as interpreted for Lake Michigan by Larsen (1985), may have been superimposed on the long-term rising trend.

Outlet Control of Lake Erie Levels

Earlier publications on Lake Erie levels consistently assumed that the elevation of the rebounding outlet was the only controlling factor at all times, and that inflows were always sufficient to fill the lake to this level. Figure 10 shows the outlet on a bedrock sill that is presently only 5 m or so below lake datum. End moraine ridges that trend across the outlet channel may have initially added several metres to the outlet elevation.

Conservative exponential models of the postglacial rebound of the outlet, illustrated in Figure 11, and proposed by Andrews (1970) and Washburn and Stuiver (1962), were superimposed onto the empirical lake-level curve (Fig. 9). The model shown in Figure 11 as a thin solid line was based on a half-response time (time for the uplift remaining to be reduced to half of its initial value on unloading) of 700 years, as was used by Washburn and Stuiver (1962). This value was chosen to accommodate the fact that, based on the rate of

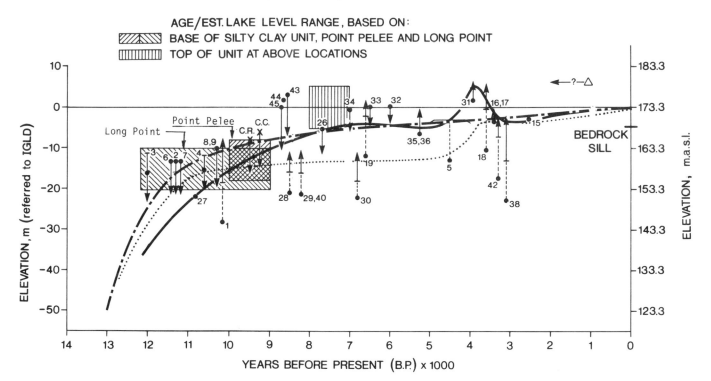

Figure 9. Revised interpretation of lake level history in Lake Erie (central sub-basin), indicated by the solid line. The dotted line shows the position of the earlier lake level interpretation by Lewis (1969), i.e., the top of the envelope of reasonable solutions in Figure 2. The dashed line represents the theoretical lake level at the outlet sill (assuming an overlying depth of water similar to that at present) based on a composite model of sill rebound. Arrows indicate the direction and estimated distance to the contemporary lake level (the base of the solid portion of the arrow represents estimated minimum water depth over the organic sample). The small triangle (upper right) indicates the position of date no. 50, and the arrow shows its possible link with the peak at around 4000 B.P.

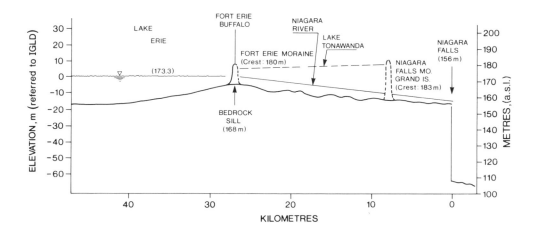

Figure 10. Cross-section through the Lake Erie outlet at the Niagara River, showing the relationship between the bedrock sill and the two major transverse moraines at the outlet.

migration of zero isobases of the post-Port Huron lakes (Fig. 1), postglacial isostatic adjustment in the Erie basin was complete by around 8000 B.P. On the other hand, the half-response time of 1800 years suggested by Andrews (1970) (thin dashed line in Fig. 11) would have extended isostatic rebound up to the present, contradicting the evidence of the zero isobases.

In any event, neither of the exponential rebound models was entirely compatible with the lake level curve. In both, the sill rebound curve persisted several metres above the lake level up until around 7000 BP, thus implying no outflow over this 5000 year period. Such a long discontinuity in outflow is in conflict with Niagara River chronology (Calkin and Brett, 1978). A much better fit to the empirical lake-level curve was obtained by using a composite model of sill uplift (bold line in Fig. 11), in which a concurrent linear uplift component was added to the above exponential component. Similar models for postglacial uplift were proposed for Fennoscandia by Mörner (1980), and for New Quebec by Hillaire-Marcel (1980). The equation for the linear component was obtained by fitting a straight line through the origin and through dates 15, 16, and 17 in Figure 9. The bold dashed line in Figure 11 shows theoretical sill elevation changes with time according to the composite model.

Even using this unusual concept of outlet rebound, it appears that the sill lay above the empirical lake-level curve for considerable periods of time prior to around 8500 B.P. Two possible explanations for this are considered here. The first is that neither the exponential nor the composite model provide anything but a crude approximation of the actual uplift process. Such a view is supported by Walcott (1970), who predicted oscillatory uplift processes following glacial unloading. This view is attractive in that it explains why the raised shorelines of the most recent glacial lakes are still apparently horizontal west of their respective zero isobases, despite the measured modern uplift. This test might not be conclusive, however, if the uplift hypothesized is restricted to the vicinity of the outlet, where raised shorelines are sparse and discontinuous. The second possible explanation is that lower outlets might have existed to the west of the Niagara outlet, which even during the initial period of rapid uplift could have maintained lake outflow. As mentioned earlier, B.H. Feenstra (pers. commun., 1981) speculated on such outlets in the Lowbanks area. This idea was prompted by topographic considerations alone, and no confirmation in the field has been reported to date.

If either of the above uplift models for the present outlet is accepted, then the conclusion follows that a period of minimal outflows via the Niagara River occurred until around 8500 B.P. The notion of variable outflow volumes through the Niagara outlet during postglacial time was previously advanced by Kindle and Taylor (1913). Such periods of minimal outflow would have been further enhanced by the loss of upper Great Lakes (Lake Algonquin) drainage to Lake Erie around 10 500 B.P. (Karrow *et al.*, 1975) due to the opening of northern outlets. In any event, this question of the underlying causes of lake level trends, and the possible association with the neotectonics of the lake outlet after glacial unloading, are areas where further research is needed.

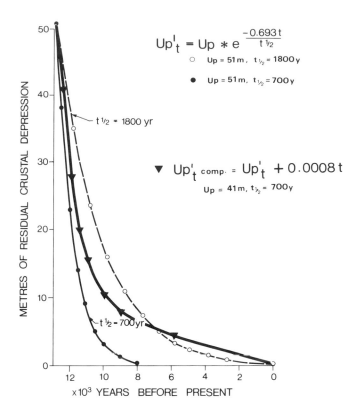

Figure 11. Residual crustal depression (or uplift remaining) at the Lake Erie outlet at Niagara versus time before present. Plots are based on three separate theoretical models for postglacial crustal rebound, two of which are exponential (with different half-response times) and one is a composite of exponential and linear components.

CONCLUDING REMARKS

Radiocarbon-dated sediments related to previous water levels are still the prime data sources for investigations into lake level history, although a variety of processes are apparently active in reducing the reliability of the ages obtained. Examples of these processes are detrital transport, hardwater and inorganic carbon contamination, postdepositional compaction, and sampling procedures. Supplementary data from postglacial stream channeling and depositional history, relict geomorphological shore features below the present lake level, and from muddy offshore sediment sequences beneath progradational beach (spit) sediments were all valuable in our reinterpretation of postglacial lake level trends.

The postglacial history of lake levels in the Erie basin is clearly more complex than is indicated by previous models (Lewis, 1969). A number of factors, hydrologic, physiographic, and tectonic, were apparently important. The curve presented in this paper best fits the data presently available. However, for more accurate resolution of postglacial lake levels in the Erie Basin, further work should be focused on the critical periods, 12 800 to 12 000 B.P. and 6000 B.P. to the present. In the case of the latter period, such work should include a better definition of the role of Holocene glacio-isostatic crustal warping and climate-related hydrological fluctuations on postglacial levels in Lake Erie.

ACKNOWLEDGEMENTS

The authors acknowledge the assistance of S.J. Williams, (United States Geological Survey), P.J. Barnett and A. Cooper (Ontario Geological Survey), N.A. Rukavina (National Water Research Institute), D. Guy, D. Buchanan, J.A. Fuller and C.H. Carter (Ohio Department of of Natural Resources), the staff of Ontario Hydro, Transcontinental Gas Pipe Line, Inc., and the U.S. Army Corps of Engineers for making unpublished dates and material available to us. Pollen analysis was carried out by C.E. Winn (Barnett-Winn Palynological Consultants). Discussions with P.F. Karrow, T.W. Anderson, P.J. Barnett, and B.H. Feenstra were most helpful.

REFERENCES

Andrews, J.T., 1970, Present and Postglacial Rates of Uplift for Glaciated Northern and Eastern North America derived from Postglacial Uplift Curves: Canadian Journal of Earth Sciences, v. 7, p. 703-727.

Barnett, P.J., 1978, Quaternary Geology of the Simcoe Area, Southern Ontario: Ontario Division of Mines Geoscience Report 162, 74 p.

———, 1979, Glacial Lake Whittlesey: the Probable Ice-frontal Position in the Eastern End of the Erie Basin: Canadian Journal of Earth Sciences, v. 16, p. 568-574.

Barnett, P.J., and Zilans, A., 1983, Quaternary Geology of the Long Point Area, Southern Ontario: Ontario Geological Survey Preliminary Map P. 2616, Geological Series. Scale 1:50 000.

Barnett, P.J., Coakley, J.P., Terasmae, J., and Winn, C.E., 1985, Chronology and Significance of a Holocene Sedimentary Profile from Clear Creek, Lake Erie Shoreline, Ontario: Canadian Journal of Earth Sciences, v. 22, p. 1133-1138.

Calkin, P.E., 1970, Strand Lines and Chronology of the Glacial Great Lakes in Northwestern New York: Ohio Journal of Science, v. 70, p. 78-96.

Calkin, P.E. and Brett, C.E., 1978, Ancestral Niagara River Drainage: Stratigraphic and Paleontologic Setting: Geological Society of America Bulletin, v. 89, p. 1140-1154.

Carter, C.H., 1984, An Early Lake Erie Delta: the Fairport Harbor, Ohio, Sand Deposit: Abstracts 27th Conference on Great Lakes Research, International Association for Great Lakes Research, p. 32.

Clark, R.H., and Persoage, N.P., 1970. Some Implications of Crustal Movement in Engineering Planning: Canadian Journal of Earth Sciences, v. 7, p. 628-633.

Coakley, J.P., 1984, Subsurface Sediments and Late Quaternary History of Long Point, Lake Erie: Unpublished Report, Hydraulics Division, National Water Research Institute, Burlington, Ontario, 50 p.

Coakley, J.P., Zeman, A.J., and Kalas, L.L., 1977, Lithology and Geotechnical Properties as Indicators of the Depositional History of Late Quaternary Sediments from the Pelee Shoal, Western Lake Erie: Unpublished Report, Hydraulics Research Division, National Water Research Institute, Burlington, Ontario, 47 p.

Coordinating Committee on Great Lakes Basic Hydraulic and Hydrological Data, 1977, Apparent Vertical Movement Over the Great Lakes: Detroit District, United States Army Corps of Engineers, 70 p.

Davis, M.B., 1981, Outbreaks of Forest Pathogens in Quaternary History: Proceedings 4th International Palynological Conference, Lucknow, India (1976-77), p. 216-227.

Feenstra, B.H., 1981, Quaternary Geology and Industrial Minerals of the Niagara-Welland Area, Southern Ontario: Ontario Geological Survey, Open File Report 5361, 260 p.

Guy, D.E., Jr., 1983, Origin and Evolution of Bay Point Sand Spit, Lake Erie, Ohio: Master's Thesis, Bowling Green, Ohio, Bowling Green State University, 205 p.

Hands, E.B., 1977, Implications of Submergence for Coastal Engineers: Proceedings Coastal Sediments '77, Charleston, South Carolina: American Society of Civil Engineers, p. 149-166.

Herdendorf, C.E., and Braidech, L.L., 1972, Physical Characteristics of the Reef Area of Western Lake Erie: Ohio Division of Geological Survey Report of Investigations 82, 90 p.

Hillaire-Marcel, Claude, 1980, Multiple Component Postglacial Emergence, Eastern Hudson Bay, Canada: in Mörner, Nils-Axel, Earth Rheology, Isostasy and Eustasy: International Union of Geological Sciences Geodynamics Project, Report no. 49, p. 215-230.

Hough, J.L., 1966, Correlation of Glacial Lake Stages in the Huron-Erie and Michigan Basins: Journal of Geology, v. 74, p. 62-67.

Karrow, P.F., and Anderson, T.W., 1975, Palynological Study of Lake Sediment Profiles from Southwestern New Brunswick: Discussion: Canadian Journal of Earth Sciences, v. 12, p. 1808-1812.

Karrow, P.F., Anderson, T.W., Clarke, A.H., Delorme, L.D., and Sreenivasa, M.R., 1975, Stratigraphy, Paleontology, and Age of Lake Algonquin Sediments in Southwestern Ontario, Canada: Quaternary Research, v. 5, p. 49-87.

Keith, M.L., and Anderson, G.M., 1963, Radiocarbon Dating: Fictitious Results from Mollusk Shells: Science, v. 141, p. 634-636.

Kindle, E.M. and Taylor, F.B., 1913, Description of the Niagara Quadrangle: United States Geological Survey Geological Atlas, Folio 190, 26 p.

Kite, G.W., 1972, An Engineering Study of Crustal Movements Around the Great Lakes: Environment Canada, Inland Waters Branch, Technical Bulletin 63, p. 57.

Larsen, C.E., 1985, Lake Level, Uplift, and Outlet Incision, the Nipissing and Algoma Great Lakes: in Karrow, P.F., and Calkin, P.E., eds., Quaternary Evolution of the Great Lakes: Geological Association of Canada Special Paper 30.

Leverett, F., and Taylor, F.B., 1915, The Pleistocene of Indiana and Michigan and the History of the Great Lakes: United States Geological Survey Monograph 53, 529 p.

Lewis, C.F.M., 1969, Late Quaternary History of Lake Levels in the Huron and Erie Basins: Proceedings 12th Conference on Great Lakes Research, International Association for Gerat Lakes Research, p. 250-270.

Lewis, C.F.M., Anderson, T.W., and Berti, A.A., 1966, Geological and Palynological Studies of Early Lake Erie Deposits: Proceedings 9th Conference on Great Lakes Research, Ann Arbor, Great Lakes Research Division Publication 15, p. 176-191.

Lewis, C.F.M., Wooton, A.E., and Davis, J.B., 1973, Stratigraphic and Engineering Studies of Unconsolidated Sediments in Central Lake Erie Near Erieau, Ontario: Geological Survey of Canada Report of Activities Part A: April to October 1972, Geological Survey of Canada Paper 73-1, p. 205-209.

Miller, B.B., 1983, Late Quaternary Fluvial History of the Lower Cuyahoga River in Northeastern Ohio: Journal of Great Lakes Research, v. 9, p. 97-105.

Mörner, Nils-Axel, 1980, The Fennoscandian Uplift: Geological Data and their Geodynamic Implications: in Mörner, Nils-Axel, ed., Earth Rheology, Isostasy and Eustasy: International Union of Geological Sciences Geodynamics Project, Report no. 49, p. 251-284.

Mott, R.J., 1975, Palynological Studies of Lake Sediment Profiles from Southwestern New Brunswick: Canadian Journal of Earth Sciences, v. 12, p. 273-288.

Mott, R.J., and Farley-Gill, L.D., 1978. A Late Quaternary Pollen Profile from Woodstock, Ontario: Canadian Journal of Earth Sciences, v. 15, p. 1101-1111.

Ogden, J.G., 1967, Radiocarbon and Pollen Evidence for a Sudden Change in Climate in the Great Lakes Region Approximately 10,000 Years Ago: in Cushing, E.J., and Wright, H.E., Jr., eds. Quaternary Paleoecology, New Haven, Connecticut, Yale University Press, p. 117-127.

Ogden, J.G., III, and Hay, R.J., 1965, Ohio Weslyan University Natural Radiocarbon Measurements, II: Radiocarbon, v. 7, p. 166-173.

————, 1969, Ohio Weslyan University Natural Radiocarbon Measurements, IV: Radiocarbon v. 11, p. 137-149.

Ontario Hydro, 1981, Lake Erie Marine Cable Crossing, Geotechnical Investigation – 1980 Program: Unpublished Report 81169, 8 p.

Rubin, M, and Taylor, D.W., 1963, Radiocarbon Activity of Shells from Living Clams and Snails: Science, v. 141, p. 637.

Rukavina, N.A., 1981, Lake Erie Nearshore Sediment and Acoustic Data, Long Point Area: Hydraulics Division, National Water Research Institute, Burlington, Ontario, Technical Note 81-92, 4 p.

Rukavina, N.A. and St. Jacques, D.A., 1978, Lake Erie Nearshore Sediments, Point Pelee to Port Burwell, Ontario: Environment Canada, Inland Waters Directorate Scientific Series No. 99, 44 p.

St. Jacques, D.A., and Rukavina, N.A., 1973, Lake Erie Nearshore Sediments, Mohawk Point to Port Burwell, Ontario: Proceedings 16th Conference on Great Lakes Research, International Association for Great Lakes Research, p. 454-467.

Sly, P.G., and Lewis, C.F.M., 1972, The Great Lakes of Canada – Quaternary Geology and Limnology: in 24th International Geological Congress, Montreal, Guidebook for Field Excursion A 43, 92 p.

Stevenson, A.L., and Benninghoff, W.S., 1969, Late Post-Glacial Rise of Lake Erie and Changes in Vegetation of the Maumee Lake Plain: Proceedings 12th Conference on Great Lakes Research, International Association for Great Lakes Research, p. 347-350.

Teller, J.T., 1985, Lake Agassiz and its Possible Influence on the Other Great Lakes: in Karrow, P.F., and Calkin, P.E., eds., Quaternary Evolution of the Great Lakes: Geological Association of Canada Special Paper 30.

Terasmae, J., 1970, Report on Stratigraphic Drilling in Point Pelee National Park, Ontario: Contract Report 68-200, National and Historic Parks Branch, Department of Indian and Northern Affairs, 6 p.

————, 1981, Late-Wisconsin Deglaciation and Migration of Spruce into Southern Ontario, Canada: in Roman, R.C., ed., Geobotany II: New York, Plenum Press, p. 75-90.

Walcott, R.I., 1970, Isostatic Response to Loading of the Crust in Canada: Canadian Journal of Earth Sciences, v. 7, p. 716-727.

Washburn, A.L., and Stuiver, M., 1962, Radio-Carbon-Dated Postglacial Delevelling in Northeast Greenland and its Implications: Arctic, v. 15, p. 66-73.

Williams, S.J., and Meisburger, E.P., 1982, Geological Character and Mineral Resources of South Central Lake Erie: U.S. Army Corps of Engineers Coastal Engineering Research Center, Miscellaneous Report 82-9, 62 p.

Williams, S.J., Carter, C.H., Meisburger, E.P., and Fuller, J.A., 1980, Sand Resources of Southern Lake Erie, Conneaut to Toledo, Ohio – A Seismic Reflection and Vibracore Study: U.S. Army Corps of Engineers, Coastal Engineering Research Center, Miscellaneous Report 80-10, 883 p.

Winn, C.E., 1977, Vegetational History and Geochronology of Several Sites in South Southwestern Ontario With Discussion on Mastodon Extinction in Southern Ontario: M.Sc. Thesis, St. Catharines, Ontario, Brock University, 374 p.

Quaternary Evolution of the Great Lakes,
edited by P.F. Karrow and P.E. Calkin,
Geological Association of Canada Special Paper 30, 1985

GLACIAL LAKES IN THE ONTARIO BASIN

E.H. Muller
204 Heroy Geology Laboratory, Syracuse University, Syracuse, New York 13210

V.K. Prest
Veekay Consultants Limited, 1465-#405 Baseline Road, Ottawa, Ontario K2C 3L9

ABSTRACT

Following ice sheet withdrawal from the Valley Heads Moraine, primitive lakes impounded in troughs of the New York plateau first drained south, but later coalesced, draining either east or west as lower outlets opened along the north edge of the plateau. These lakes were correlatives of glacial Lakes Maumee through Lundy in the Erie Basin. Prominent meltwater channels were cut during eastward drainage and lowering of glacial Lake Warren and younger local glacial Lakes Avon and Dawson in the Genesee Valley.

Glacial Lake Iroquois, with outlet near Rome and initially limited to the Oneida Basin, expanded westward about 12 500 B.P. as ice receded from the Lockport Escarpment in western New York. Northward diverging strands record isostatic adjustment as the lake, still draining past Rome, flooded the Trent embayment and north to Lake Mazinaw.

Retreating eastward north of the Adirondacks, the ice uncovered a lower col and glacial Lake Iroquois gave way to glacial Lake Frontenac draining eastward through Covey Hill gap to the Champlain Trough.

Following abandonment of Covey Hill gap, the lakes in the Ontario/St. Lawrence Valley merged with the Fort Ann phase of Lake Vermont in the Champlain Trough; this lake phase is represented by the Belleville strand in the Trent embayment. The somewhat lower Trenton strand, rather than relating to the Champlain Sea, probably corresponds to a post-Fort Ann low phase in the Champlain Basin. About 12 000 B.P., ice retreat near Quebec permitted the glacial lake to drain and the Champlain Sea to invade the St. Lawrence Valley as far as the Thousand Islands.

RÉSUMÉ

Suite au retrait de la calotte glaciaire à partir de la moraine des Valley Heads, des lacs glaciaires, retenus dans des auges du plateau de New York, se sont drainés d'abord vers le sud, puis plus tard en se joignant les uns aux autres, vers l'est ou l'ouest à mesure que des exutoires plus bas

étaient déglacés. Ces lacs peuvent être mis en corrélation avec la séquence de lacs glaciaires dans le bassin du lac Érié (partant du lac Maumee jusqu'au lac Lundy). Des chenaux ont été entaillés lors de l'abaissement vers l'est du lac glaciaire Warren et des lacs locaux, Avon et Dawson, ont existé dans la vallée de la rivière Genesee.

Le lac glaciaire Iroquois, dont l'exutoire était situé près de Rome, a d'abord été restreint au bassin du lac Oneida. Dès 12 500 B.P., à mesure que le glacier se retirait du bassin du lac Ontario, le lac Iroquois s'est étendu d'abord vers l'ouest, puis vers le bassin de Trent et vers le nord jusqu'au lac Mazinaw alors que l'exutoire de Rome fonctionnait toujours. Avec le retrait du lobe ontarien, le lac Iroquois a continué à s'étendre vers l'est, entre le front glaciaire et les Adirondacks, jusqu'à ce qu'il cède la place au lac glaciaire Frontenac qui se drainait vers la dépression du lac Champlain par le col de Covey Hill.

Lorsque l'exutoire du col de Covey Hill fut abandonné, le lac du bassin du lac Ontario et de la vallée du Saint-Laurent s'est fusionné avec les eaux de la phase Fort Ann du lac Vermont dans le bassin du lac Champlain. Cette phase lacustre est représentée par la phase Belleville dans le bassin de Trent. La ligne de rivage plus basse rencontrée à Trenton correspond peut-être à une phase ultérieure à la phase Fort Ann plutôt qu'à un plan d'eau relié à la mer de Champlain. Vers 12 000 B.P., avec le retrait du culot de glace près de Québec, le lac glaciaire s'est vidangé et la mer de Champlain a envahi la vallée du Saint-Laurent jusqu'aux Mille Îles.

INTRODUCTION

This review of the proglacial lake history of the Ontario Basin incorporates the results of recent research, both published and unpublished. It differs from previous summaries primarily in its perspective on the transitional lake phases that followed glacial Lake Warren, and on the expansion of Lake Iroquois through the basin. This study is otherwise in general accord with classic and accepted interpretations

(Leverett, 1902; Leverett and Taylor, 1915; Hough, 1958; Calkin, 1970; Prest, 1970). For additional details the interested reader is referred to these works, and particularly to Fullerton's (1980) monograph which provides the most current and comprehensive documentation of regional correlations and radiocarbon chronology for the Ontario Basin, as well as for the Great Lakes as a whole.

Glacial lake histories have been interpreted on the basis of: a) their stratigraphic record, b) their geomorphic expression in littoral and strandline features, and c) their former outlet controls. Lake sediments in drill core or bluff exposure clearly define the stratigraphic relationships, but the identification of a specific group of beds with a particular outlet or strandline is usually ambiguous. Similarly, difficulty often arises in determining the relationships of discontinuous, tilted and diverging shorelines to shifting, ephemeral, and ill-defined outlets. In blending three different kinds of chronology – based respectively on intrepretation of stratigraphy, of strandlines, and of outlet history – unwarranted assumptions have been too often concealed.

Within the Ontario Basin, past usage has been inconsistent. Some authorities identify the proglacial lake in the Ontario Basin, represented by lacustrine sediments as well as by multiple and diverging strandlines, as Lake Iroquois throughout a complex history of shifting outlets. Glacial Lake Warren, on the other hand, is recognized as having existed only while the outlet control was westward directly into the Grand River, Michigan.

For clarity and consistency, we adopt the following usages: A lake is defined by its outlet. Drainage of the Ontario Basin by the Rome outlet to the Mohawk River is considered to define a single lake, that is, glacial Lake Iroquois, in spite of changing extent and complexity of strandlines. Glacial Lake Iroquois ceased to exist, however, when outflow from the Ontario Basin shifted north of the Adirondack Mountains.

A lake level is named for its strand. Multiple strands, due to incision of the outlet or strands that diverge due to regional upwarping, relate to the same lake phase as long as the outlet location remains unchanged. Lakes which existed in

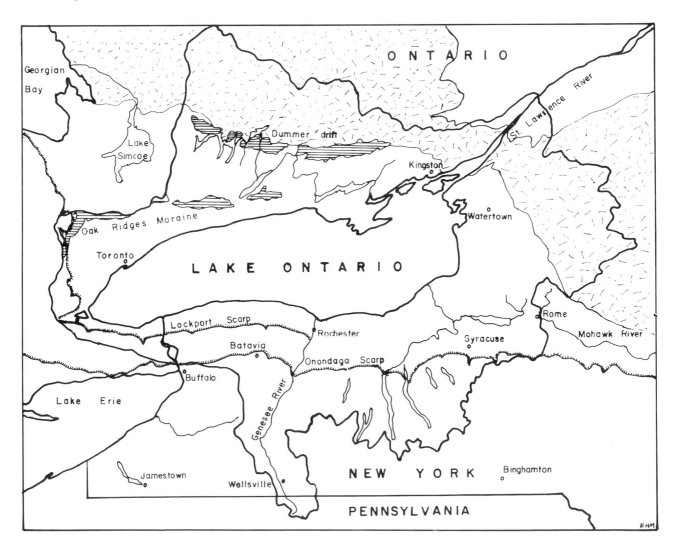

Figure 1. Location map showing outlines of the Lake Ontario drainage basin and northern margins of Lockport Dolomite and Onondaga Limestone outcrop belts.

contact with the ice sheet are identified as glacial lakes, e.g., glacial Lake Iroquois.

PHYSIOGRAPHIC SETTING

The Ontario Basin occupies the eastern end of the Central Lowland where it lies between the Canadian Shield on the north and the Allegheny Plateau on the south (Fig. 1). A southward extension of Precambrian rocks links the Adirondacks to the rest of the Shield, closing off the eastern end of the basin. South of the lake, the lowlands rise in cuestaform fashion over the Lockport and Onondaga limestone outcrop belts to the glacially dissected southern New York upland. Two minor salients of the Onondaga bench in New York – north of Batavia and west of Syracuse – play key roles in the history of ancestral lakes in the Ontario Basin.

Among rivers in western New York, only the Genesee rises at the Wisconsinan terminal moraine in Pennsylvania and flows north across New York. Because the Genesee Valley contained ponded meltwater from the onset of Late Wisconsinan ice recession, it is there that the history of proglacial lakes in the Ontario Basin must begin. Initial outflow south into the basin of the Susquehanna River gave way early to westward drainage (glacial Lake Wellsville) (Table I) across the Stone Dam col via Honeoye Creek to the Allegheny River (Outlet 2, Fig. 2).

In the westernmost part of the Ontario Basin, the proglacial lake history began as that in the Erie Basin was ending. Glacial Lake Arkona (Calkin and Feenstra, 1985) may be presumed to have extended into western New York.

PORT BRUCE STADIAL

Across most of New York, the Valley Heads Moraine, here taken as marking the extent of ice late in the Port Bruce Stadial, is also the southern border of the Ontario drainage basin. Its massive valley-blocking deposits comprise the watershed in all major basins west of Utica, except that of

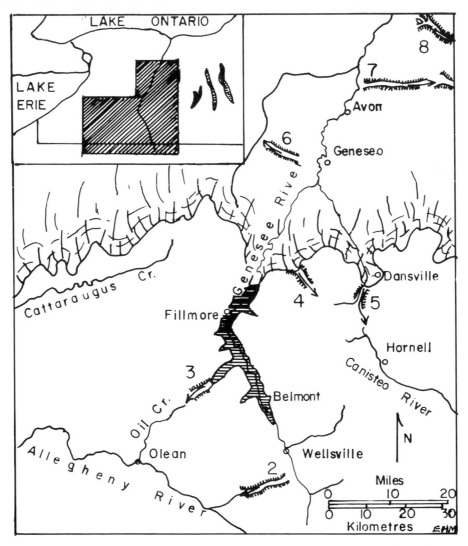

Figure 2. Central New York showing the Valley Heads Moraine impounding glacial Lake Belmont-Fillmore. Numbered outlets of Genesee Valley glacial lakes are 2) Stone Dam Col, outlet of Lake Wellsville; 3) Black Creek outlet of Lake Belmont-Fillmore; 4) and 5) outlets via Canisteo River to the Susquehanna; 6) Pearl Creek outlet of Lake Hall; 7) Rush-Victor channels of Lake Avon; 8) Fairport channels of Lake Dawson.

TABLE I

LAKE STAGES IN THE ONTARIO BASIN

Showing approximate temporal and spatial relationships of lake stages

Erie Basin	Genesee Valley	Eastern Ontario Basin
	PENNSYLVANIA LAKES, S to Susquehanna and Allegheny Rivers	
	WELLSVILLE, W by Honeoye Cr. to Allegheny River	
Maumee	BELMONT-FILLMORE, W by Oil Cr. to Allegheny R.	
Arkona	NUNDA, SE via Canisteo to Susquehanna River	PRIMITIVE LAKES, S across Valley Heads Moraine
	DANSVILLE, SE via Cohocton to Susquehanna R.	ITHACA and WATKINS merge as
Whittlesey		NEWBERRY, S past Horseheads to Susquehanna R.
	HALL, W via Pearl Cr. outlet; ended by spread	
Warren	of WARREN into Genesee V.	
		VANUXEM, transitory falling and rising lake phases due
	Transitory lowering due	to opening and closure of
Wayne	to opening of eastward	channels along plateau edge
	drainage to Mohawk River	draining east to Mohawk R.
Warren		
Grassmere	AVON, E via Rush-Victor	
and Lundy	Channels	Inception of IROQUOIS in Oneida Basin, E past Rome
	DAWSON, E via Fairport	the Mohawk River
	Channels	
		IROQUOIS expanding west to
Early Erie	IROQUOIS, E past Rome	Hamilton, then N in Trent
	to Mohawk River	Basin, NE down St. Lawrence
	Lowering stages not	Outlets north of Adirondacks lower lake through
	delineated	FRONTENAC, SYDNEY, BELLE-VILLE, TRENTON phases to
	EARLY (LOW) ONTARIO with	EARLY (LOW) ONTARIO with
	depressed threshold	depressed threshold.
	Gradual rebound raises	Gradual rebound raises
	lake to level of present	lake to level of present
Erie	ONTARIO	ONTARIO

the Genesee River (Fig. 2) (Muller *et al.*, 1981). At the Valley Heads maximum, synchronous with glacial Lake Maumee in the Erie Basin, glacial Lake Belmont-Fillmore in the Genesee Valley had its outflow southwest past Cuba and Olean to the Allegheny River (Outlet 3, Fig. 2).

Recession from the massive, divide-forming moraines of the Valley Heads complex initiated glaciomarginal ponding in most troughs across New York State. These "primitive lakes" drained south across end moraines either to the Susquehanna or Allegheny river systems. Many were short-lived, however, as the receding ice margin uncovered lower outlets that permitted them to coalesce with or drain into lakes in neighboring troughs.

In this manner, the Erie Basin lakes extended their influ-

ence eastward. An impoundment in the Cattaraugus Creek Valley (Fig. 2), coexistent with glacial Lake Maumee III, drained south to the Allegheny River. Glacial Lakes Arkona and Whittlesey received inflow from as far east as East Aurora (Fig. 3). Only southwest of Hamburg and the Hamburg Moraine could the strandline of glacial Lake Arkona have escaped subsequent glacial erosion or burial. Although no shore features in New York have been conclusively ascribed to glacial Lake Arkona, the Whittlesey strand is prominently developed.

GLACIAL LAKE WHITTLESEY

In recognition of early pioneering work by Charles Whittlesey (1850), F.B. Taylor (1897) proposed the name

Lake Whittlesey for the proglacial lake which had formed the Belmore Beach in Michigan. As early as 1848, Whittlesey had recognized strand features of ancestral lakes in the Erie Basin, and by 1850 had traced them eastward into New York, though without any clear concept of their relationship to the continental ice sheet.

Glacial Lake Whittlesey (Fig. 4-1) was initiated by the advance of the ice margin to the Port Huron Moraine, and use of the Ubly Channel across "The Thumb" of eastern Michigan to glacial Lake Saginaw (Leverett and Taylor, 1915, p. 377). In western New York, glacial Lake Whittlesey is represented by a generally well developed and nearly continuously traceable strand that rises northeastward from 241 m a.s.l. at the Pennsylvania State Line to 276 m near Marilla (Fig. 3), a distance of 130 km (Leverett, 1902; Muller, 1963; Calkin 1970).

The relationship of moraines to the Whittlesey shoreline (Fig. 3), therefore, holds the key to correlation with the Port Huron Stadial of Michigan. Diversion of Buffalo Creek westward along the ice margin at the Hamburg Moraine built gravel plains graded to the Whittlesey level at East Aurora

and Orchard Park (Symecko, 1967). An exposure near Cayuga Creek, 5 km east-northeast of Marilla, shows a bouldery lag at the contact between till and overlying sand in a manner suggestive of a transgressive strandline. Existence of the Whittlesey strand in the lee of the Marilla Moraine (Fig. 3) is further evidence of minor ice readvance, for shelter afforded by an ice cliff would otherwise have prevented effective wave erosion. The Whittlesey strand transects the Hamburg, but not the Marilla Moraine, indicating that lowering from the Whittlesey to the Warren level took place before significant retreat by the ice margin from the Marilla Moraine. The Hamburg and Marilla Moraines are considered, therefore, to be of Port Huron age.

In the Genesee Valley, retreat from the Valley Heads Moraine opened outlets lower than the Black Creek Valley (Outlet 3, Fig. 2) initiating drainage southeast via the Cantisteo River (Outlet 4) and subsequent inception of Lake Dansville (Outlet 5) (Fairchild, 1896, 1928; Chadwick and Dunbar, 1924).

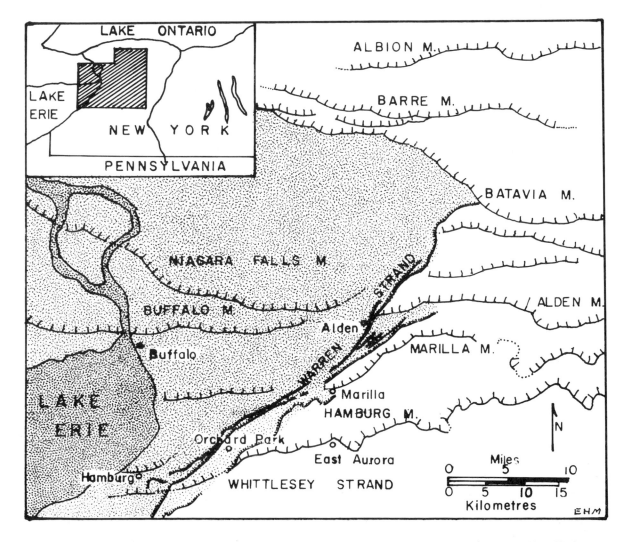

Figure 3. Relationships of moraines to shorelines of glacial Lakes Whittlesey and Warren in western New York.

GLACIAL LAKE WARREN

The name Lake Warren, in honor of G.K. Warren, "the father of lacustrine geology in North America", was first applied by J.W.W. Spencer (1888) to a body of water that built high level beaches throughout the Great Lakes basins. F.B. Taylor (1897) proposed a more restricted usage, applying the name Lake Warren to the proglacial lake that drained directly into the Grand River across Michigan and shaped strand features correlative with the Forest Beach in Michigan and Ontario. In New York, Fairchild (1897) traced the Warren strand into the Genesee Valley, whereas Leverett (1902) mapped it only as far northeast as Indian Falls, 50 km east of Buffalo.

Glacial Lake Whittlesey gave way to glacial Lake Warren with the opening of direct outflow to the Grand River across Michigan (Fig. 4-2). This occurred while the ice margin stood at the Marilla Moraine in western New York (Fig. 3), as indicated by a gravel surface just west of Marilla that is graded to the strand of Warren I at 259 m (Blackmon, 1956). The magnificent set of barrier bars rises to 264 m near Alden, where it truncates the Marilla Moraine. Curving eastward

sub-parallel to the Alden Moraine, it has a strength of development that would not have been possible if the glacier had not withdrawn, exposing the shore to effective wave action before readvance to the Alden Moraine. These bars relate to the highest stand of glacial Lake Warren (Calkin, 1970).

The strongly developed strand and compound spit north of Alden (Fig. 3), representing the lower level of glacial Lake Warren, cuts across the Alden, Buffalo (East Pembroke Kames), and Niagara Falls Moraines, which therefore mark recessional positions of the ice margin after the Port Huron maximum.

In the Genesee Valley, withdrawal of the ice margin from the Marilla Moraine (Muller, 1977b) uncovered the Pearl Creek Channel (Outlet 6, Fig. 2) westward to Oatka Trough. Under control by this new outlet, drainage to the Susquehanna ceased and glacial Lake Dansville gave way to glacial Lake Hall. The discharge from Lake Hall incised a 30 m channel and built a sizeable fan into Oatka Trough. Escaping by a plexus of shifting channels along the disintegrating ice border, the discharge continued west to To-

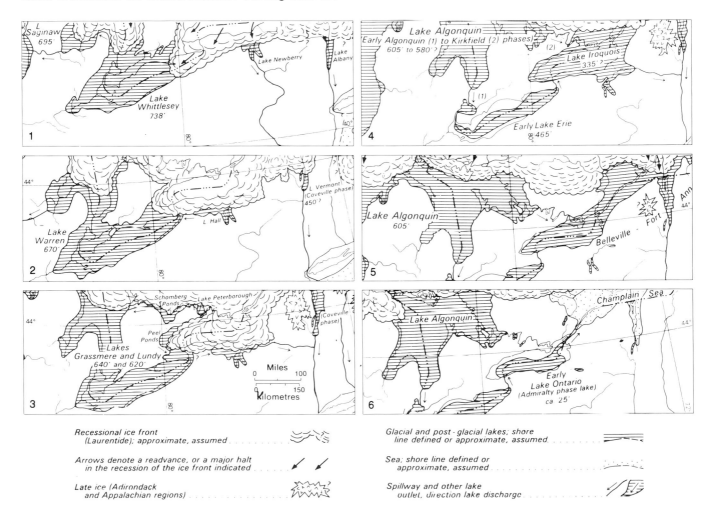

Figure 4. Lake phases in the Lake Ontario basin. 1) Whittlesey, 2) Warren, 3) Grassmere-Lundy, 4) Iroquois, 5) Belleville, 6) Early Lake Ontario. Adapted from Prest (1970).

nawanda Trough, south of Batavia, and thence to glacial Lake Warren.

NORTH MARGIN OF THE ALLEGHENY PLATEAU

In the Finger Lake area, glacial Lakes Ithaca in Cayuga Trough and Watkins in Seneca Trough had merged to form glacial Lake Newberry (Fairchild, 1899, 1934a, 1934b) with its outflow south across the Valley Heads Moraine, past Horseheads to the Susquehanna River (Fig. 4-1). At maximum extent, Lake Newberry received drainage from most of the glacial troughs along the north margin of the Allegheny Plateau between the Genesee River and Syracuse.

The events by which this southward drainage shifted to eastward escape of the ponded water toward the Mohawk Valley (Fig. 4-3) are complex and incompletely understood. Fairchild (1909) recognized that meltwater channels along the north margin of the Allegheny Plateau in central New York record at least two episodes of eastward drainage discharge from the Great Lakes. The channels between Rush and Syracuse were initiated during the earlier episode of glacial recession from the plateau. Fairchild inferred that during the second episode of glacial recession, the ice dam held against the Onondaga scarp west of Syracuse long enough to permit expansion of glacial Lake Warren eastward into the Genesee Valley. Each recession from the Onondaga bench west of Syracuse induced a transitory sequence of lake levels which Fairchild named glacial Lake Vanuxem. Although Fairchild ascribed primary control to the Syracuse channels (Fairchild, 1909; Muller, 1964; Hand and Muller, 1972), a controlling threshold was 20 km to the west at the head of the Gulf Channel (Fairchild, 1909; "Guppy Gulf" of Blagbrough, 1951); the Syracuse Channels controlled only the levels of local ponding in Onondaga Trough immediately south of Syracuse.

This episode of eastward meltwater drainage is correlated with glacial Lake Wayne, a low stage in the western Great Lakes (Leverett and Taylor, 1915; Hough, 1958; Fullerton, 1980). Hough (1963), however, expressed reservation about the proposed eastward outflow which he had earlier accepted.

The Batavia Moraine cuts obliquely across the trend of earlier moraines in western New York (Fig. 3) in a manner that suggests either a significant readjustment of glacier flow lines or, perhaps, a change in ice surface gradient of the kind associated with glacier surging. In either case, the Batavia Moraine restored Lake Warren to its final stand before it was lowered to the glacial Grassmere and Lundy Lake levels.

GLACIAL LAKES GRASSMERE AND LUNDY

Strand features below the Warren level in Monroe (Lane, 1900) and Huron (Scherzer, 1900) Counties in eastern Michigan were named the Grassmere Beach. Subsequently, closely related features 6 m below the Grassmere level that had been mapped as the Elkton Beach (Lane, 1900), were correlated with beach deposits described by Spencer (1894) at Lundy(s) Lane, west of Niagara Falls (Leverett and Taylor, 1915; Calkin and Feenstra, 1985). Leverett and Taylor assigned both the Grassmere and Elkton (Lundy) Beaches to Lake Lundy (Lake Elkton), loosely equating

them as well to Lake Dana of Fairchild (1909), a usage that is justified only if they shared a common outlet.

Uncertainty persists relative to the outlet controls that briefly stabilized impoundment at the Grassmere and Elkton levels. Because Leverett and Taylor (1915) ruled out drainage westward across Michigan, they were receptive to Fairchild's (1909) suggestion that outflow was eastward, controlled by a threshold in the Syracuse area (Fig. 4-3). Hough (1963) adopted an alternative view, inferring a corridor north of the Lower Peninsula of Michigan to account for the coincidence of levels of Grassmere and Elkton with phases of Lake Chicago. A further possibility has not been ruled out – the Grassmere Beach may have marked the end of westward drainage and the weaker Elkton Beach, the beginning of eastward escape across New York to the Mohawk River.

The relationship of the Grassmere and Elkton Beaches in Michigan to the ice border in New York has never been clearly established. Leverett (1902, p. 773) acknowledged the weakness of correlation and "lack of harmony" in fragmentary beaches that he assigned to Fairchild's (1899) Lake Dana. Although both Grassmere and Lundy lake stages must have extended into the Ontario Basin, their shore features are weakly developed in New York. Correlation of their scattered remnants (Leverett, 1902; Kindle and Taylor, 1913; Leverett and Taylor 1915; Blackmon, 1956; Symecko, 1967) remain weakly supported and Leverett (1939) doubted the validity of previously accepted correlations.

The problem has not been simplified by the practice of equating glacial Lakes Lundy, Elkton, and Dana as though they shared a common outlet. Whereas the outlets of Grassmere and Lundy have been conjectural, Dana was defined by Fairchild (1899) on the assumed correlation of the "Geneva Beach" to the Cedarvale Outlet at Marcellus. This limestone threshold seems, by reason of location, to be a very unlikely control for major impoundment to the west. Withdrawal of the ice margin that might have allowed ponded water in western New York to reach this threshold, would first have exposed either the Gulf Channel (Guppy Gulf) north of Skaneateles (20 km west of Syracuse), or a drainage–way below the Onondaga bench past the north end of Ninemile Trough.

Aside from the improbability that the threshold at Marcellus could have exerted other than local control on lake level, recent studies in the Genesee Basin (Muller, 1977b; Muller et al., 1981; Wilson, 1980) indicate that Lake Dana, if it ever existed, probably played no part in the history of recession. Rather, it seems now that the controls on changing levels in the western Ontario Basin following the lowering of glacial Lake Warren are to be sought in the plexus of channels east of Batavia, the LeRoy Channels (Fairchild, 1909), which in turn built their deltas into lakes in the Genesee Valley.

The relationship of strands in the Erie and Huron Basins to outlets in central New York must continue to be conjectural. The presumed eastward drainage of Lake Lundy may have been responsible for, and controlled by, incision of Taylor Channel south of LeRoy, building a cobble gravel delta on the edge of the Genesee Valley at 220 m. During the operation of Taylor Channel, the lake level control in the Genesee Valley was lowered, causing dissection of the delta and aggradation of an ice-marginal gravel surface at 207 m. Ice recession from the Onondaga Scarp at LeRoy induced meltwater floods (*jokulhlaups*) which cut the anastamotic Dugan and White Creek Channel complex. Deltas were built at 183 m where these streams flowed into glacial Lake Avon controlled by the Rush-Victor Channels (Fairchild, 1909) that drained east to glacial Lake Iroquois (Outlet 7, Fig. 2).

INCEPTION OF GLACIAL LAKE IROQUOIS

Raised beach ridges recognized in pioneer days (Clinton, 1825; Bigsby, 1829; Roy, 1837) were investigated by Spencer (1888, 1890, 1894) as evidence of an ancestral lake in the Ontario Basin. This body of water, with outflow east to the Mohawk River across the col at Rome, New York, was named Lake Iroquois by Spencer after the Indians whose trails followed its strand.

Free drainage east past Rome may have developed during the Erie Interstadial (Mörner and Dreimanis, 1973) and again, at least briefly, immediately prior to the Stanwix readvance (Fullerton, 1971; Wright, 1972). It has continued without interruption since recession from the Stanwix Moraine. Based on tentative correlation of the Stanwix Moraine with the Batavia-Waterloo-Auburn Moraine, this early phase of Lake Iroquois, limited initially to the east end of the Ontario Basin, may have been contemporaneous with glacial Lake Lundy in the Erie and Huron Basins (Fig. 4-3). The early uncovering of the east end of the Ontario Basin may well be reflected in differential postglacial rebound. Whereas isobases for most of the basin are internally consistent, the outlet at Rome is low relative to the remainder of the basin, suggesting that partial recovery had taken place before development of the main Iroquois strand. The isobase pattern of Kirkland and Coates (1977) schematically shows isobases deflected around the Adirondacks, but does not conform well to Iroquois strand data.

Drainage toward the Mohawk from the western part of the Ontario Basin was controlled by thresholds west of the Genesee Valley. These streams built deltas into glacial Lake Avon in the Genesee Valley with outflow by way of the Rush-Victor Channels (Outlet 7, Fig. 2) and glacial Lake Dawson south of the Albion (Pinnacle Hills) Moraine controlled by the Fairport Channels (Outlet 8, Fig. 2) (Fairchild, 1909). Fairchild referred to these early eastward-draining lake phases as "Hyper-Iroquois" because "they had the same ultimate escape as the Iroquois waters and were tending to the Iroquois level" (Fairchild, 1909, p. 53). In this sense "Hyper-Iroquois" includes glacial Lakes Grassmere, Avon, and Dawson. As understanding of the lake succession is refined the term "Hyper-Iroquois" becomes decreasingly useful.

The inception of lake phases in the Ontario Basin distinct from those of the Erie Basin relates to emergence of the Niagara Escarpment. Estimated ages for inception of ponding below the Escarpment are listed below. 1) Fossil wood collected behind the Iroquois bar at Lewiston yielded radiocarbon ages of 12 660 ± 400 B.P. and 12 080 ± 300 B.P. (Muller, 1965). 2) Lewis (1969) listed 12 650 B.P. as the end of the Erie proglacial lake sequence. 3) Prest (1970) showed Lake Iroquois at maximum development at 12 500 to 12 400

B.P. 4) Calkin (1982) suggested that "Early Lake Iroquois formed earlier than 12 200 B.P." 5) Clark and Karrow (1984) and Karrow (1981) took 12 100 B.P., the average of wood dates, as chronologic control for Lake Iroquois.

These data indicate that the western end of the Ontario Basin was deglaciated by about 12 500 B.P. This, however, did not immediately lower impoundment, for remnants of the Ontario Lobe still projected onshore in central New York obstructing meltwater escape from the western to the eastern end of the basin where early glacial Lake Iroquois was draining across the Rome outlet.

The Barre Moraine (Fig. 3) was built in glacial Lake Lundy which is considered here to have had its outflow eastward into glacial Lake Avon in the Genesee Valley and thence east to the Mohawk Valley. The ice sheet at the Albion Moraine (Fig. 3) continued to obstruct eastward outflow from the western part of the Ontario Basin. This drainage passed into glacial Lake Dawson in the Genesee Valley, controlled by the Fairport Channels southeast of Rochester, at an elevation of 145 m or about 12 m above the main Iroquois beach. Only after the ice withdrew from the Carlton (Oswego?) Moraine (Muller, 1977a, 1977b) did early glacial Lake Iroquois of the eastern end of the Ontario Basin extend into the western end as well. Chute (1979) has recently detailed the distribution of Lake Iroquois features in central New York.

NORTHWARD EXPANSION OF LAKE IROQUOIS INTO ONTARIO

The Schomberg Pondings (glacial Lake Schomberg) (Chapman and Putnam, 1951, 1966) were formed as the northern or Algonquin highland ice receded from the Oak Ridges Interlobate Moraine (Fig. 4-3) ponding the water between the ice and the moraine. Its discharge was southward into the Peel pondings (glacial Lake Peel) between ice of the Ontario lobe and the Niagara Escarpment. Lake Peel drained into ponded waters in the west end of the Ontario Basin.

Chapman and Putnam (1951, 1966) did not extend the Schomberg pondings eastward to the Peterborough basin although Deane (1950) had done so. Gravenor (1957) used the name Schomberg pondings in his discussion of the Peterborough lowland, but he could find no connection between glacial Lakes Peterborough (Coleman, 1904) and Schomberg as Deane had implied, nor could he find evidence for southward drainage across a low col in the Oak Ridges Moraine into Lake Iroquois. Thus Gravenor considered that Lake Peterborough discharged eastward through the Rice Lake basin into glacial Lake Iroquois somewhat farther east. Johnston (1916) had concluded that Iroquois penetrated into the Rice Lake Basin to the mouth of Indian River where a delta was constructed below the level of the present lake.

Coleman (1937) conceived of glacial Lake Peterborough as a bay of Lake Iroquois, and it is so indicated by Chapman and Putnam. Mirynech (1962) mapped the Trent Basin in detail and showed that glacial Lake Iroquois did indeed penetrate into the Rice Lake Basin (Fig. 5) but he did not pursue the problem with regard to Lake Peterborough which was outside his map area. Prest (this report), using all available data on Iroquois shorelines and a somewhat different isobase trend from that of Mirynech, considers, as did Coleman, that an arm of Lake Iroquois occupied the Rice Lake and Peterborough lowlands. The large delta at Peterborough was built by the Algonquin River which, for a time, drained glacial lake Algonquin into Lake Iroquois (Fig. 4-4) (Coleman, 1937, p. 25).

The controversy as to the Iroquois shorelines in the northern part of the Trent Valley stems in large part from the weak development of the strandlines due to divergence of the beaches caused by rapid isostatic rebound during high level phases of Iroquois. This phenomenon, recognized by Spencer (1888, 1890), has been confirmed by all subsequent workers. One cannot assume with any degree of confidence that limited strandline data points on former islands in the eastern and generally lower side of the Trent Basin match with a particular shoreline farther west; thus there is leeway

in plotting the trend of the isobases in this region. This is in marked contrast with the main Iroquois terrace and/or bluff near the Lake Ontario shore westward from Trenton. Also, it is evident that Lake Iroquois was in contact with the northern ice when the ice front was along the Dummer Moraine. Rapid uplift may have lowered the lake level by several metres before ice receded from this position and the lake flooded the low areas north of the moraine (Fig. 5).

In a careful survey from Oshawa, Ontario to Rochester, New York, Wilkinson (1959) found the trend of isobases veering eastward from N 111° E to N 108° E. The work of Mirynech (1962) is vital in regard to the Iroquois strandlines and provides many additional data points. Although he accepted the commonly reported isobase trend of N 110° E, he shows the trends shifting toward the north and east, and also changing during the time of falling water levels.

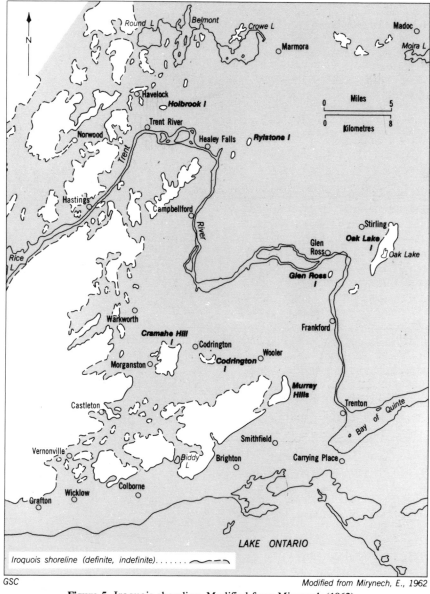

Figure 5. Iroquois shoreline. Modified from Mirynech (1962).

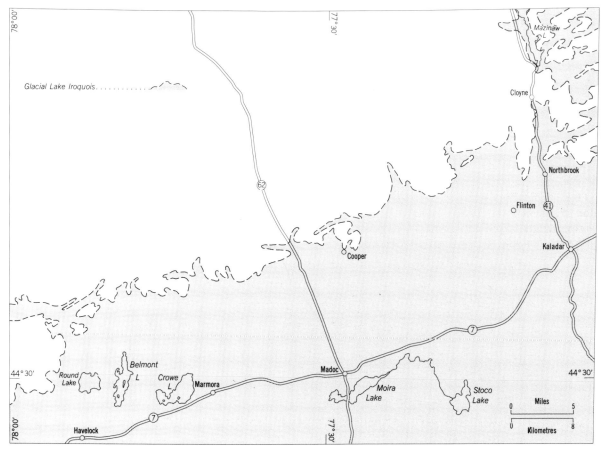

Figure 6. North shore of glacial Lake Iroquois.

In attempting a regional synthesis of all available data, Prest (this report) finds the isobase trend during the Belleville phase to be mainly close to N 100° E. Projection of this trend across the northeastern end of Lake Ontario, yields fairly good agreement with available Iroquois shoreline determinations in the Pulaski-Watertown area of New York. The isobase may indeed be swinging closer to N 100° E near Watertown. In the Malone area of New York, Clark (1980) inferred a nearly east-west trend.

North of the Trenton-Belleville area of Ontario, Prest notes an isobase trend of only N 100° E; he uses this trend and an uplift rate of 1.6 m/km in plotting the northern limit of Lake Iroquois (Fig. 6). On this basis he projects the maximum shoreline as being north of Cloyne. Near Round Lake, this projection is thus somewhat different from that of Mirynech (Fig. 5).

Accounting for the presence of *Mysis relicta,* a freshwater shrimp, in Mazinaw Lake north of Cloyne has been a problem. This tiny shrimp has been recognized as being a pioneer species that occurs in glacial lakes along a retreating ice border. It is sensitive to light, settling into deeper water at break of day, and is unable to migrate upstream (Dadswell, 1974). Thus it is restricted to present-day lakes and ponds that lie within the limit of former glacial lakes such as Iroquois. Henderson (1973) showed that outwash on high ground between Cloyne and the Mazinaw Basin argued against Iroquois having followed the ice front northward into the Mazinaw Basin. Retreat of the ice sheet, however, exposed lower ground east of Cloyne enabling Iroquois water

to enter Mazinaw basin from the southeast after the ice had withdrawn.

The level of Iroquois in the supposedly unwarped area southwest of the Ontario Basin has been taken as 102 m. Below the Niagara escarpment between Hamilton and Niagara Falls the Iroquois strand is at about 105 m. As determined by Coleman (1937) and confirmed by Mirynech (1962) and Leyland (1984), it rises to a maximum of 222.5 m on Pancake Hill, 24 km north of Belleville in an area of bifurcating strandlines. Current investigations by Prest find evidence of an Iroquois level at 232 m near Round Lake; 238 m near Madoc; 259 m near Cooper; 274 m near Northbrook and higher than 285 m at Cloyne.

In many places west of Trenton on the Ontario shore and west of Rochester in New York, lake sands are observed behind and above the main Iroquois bar. The origins of these scattered deposits have not been established. They may relate to initial flooding as the eastward retreating Ontario ice lobe withdrew from the basin border; or they may relate to a pre-Iroquois level, prior to early downcutting at the Rome outlet that controlled glacial Lake Iroquois.

LAKE IROQUOIS IN THE ST. LAWRENCE VALLEY

Ice recession from the northeastern end of the Ontario Basin was not without interruption. Mapping by Leyland (1982) in the Trenton area indicates that the limit of a westward readvance of the Ontario ice lobe abutted against the eastern end of the Dummer drift, extended southwestward through Trenton and across the present Ontario shoreline south of Brighton. Where it abuts the broad belt of Dummer drift, the Ontario Lobe formed a discrete end moraine. Elsewhere this readvance is marked by distinct west-northwesterly trending striations and drumlinoid forms in the Belleville-Trenton area (Leyland, 1982, 1984). This trend is in marked contrast with the south-southwesterly trend of the drumlins and striae to the west, northwest, and north which indicates flow direction during withdrawal of the main northern ice toward the Algonquin uplands. The western and southern limits of this Ontario lobe advance are not known; nor has its relationship been determined to moraines mapped by Taylor (1924), Stewart (1958), and Muller and Miller (1980a, 1980b) who record interrupted and oscillatory retreat in northern New York.

MacClintock and Stewart (1965) reviewed the history of strandline investigations in the St. Lawrence Lowlands. Nonetheless, numerous questions remain unsettled regarding the manner in which glacial Lake Iroquois expanded northeast against the retreating ice margin along the north flank of the Adirondacks.

South of Massena (Fig. 1), ice-marginal meltwater channels descend no lower than the Iroquois strand. In general, the channels debouched into lakes that were ponded against the margin of the Ontario Lobe above the level of Lake Iroquois. As far east as Churubusco, 70 km east of Massena, the pattern of glaciomarginal meltwater channels consistently reflects the levels of lakes dammed by a westward declining ice margin. The ridge that extends south from Covey Hill, for instance, is crossed by small but distinct westward-drained, abandoned channels with thresholds ranging from 398 to 407 m above sea level.

Prest (1970), Denny (1974), and Clark (1980) inferred an eastward extension of glacial Lake Iroquois across the ridge south of Covey Hill as high as 380 m (Prest) or 330 m (Denny). In the escape of these waters they find explanation for the thinness of drift on the east flank of the ridge and for the bare rock area called the Altona Flatrocks. This area, devoid of drift and lacking in erratics, is, at least in part, too high to have been washed clean by subsequent flood discharge through the Covey Hill gap as has heretofore been claimed (Woodworth, 1905). Partly to account for these relationships, Denny (1974) postulated the Chateaugay Episode that involved uncovering of the ridge south of Covey Hill nearly to the International Boundary, followed by readvance to a position 3 miles south of Churubusco (ice border 6 on Plate 1 of Denny, 1974).

COVEY HILL GULF PHASE

Woodworth (1905) and Fairchild (1912) described the Covey Hill gap, but Leverett and Taylor (1915) first recognized its crucial role in the history of the Great Lakes. They considered that a transitory lake phase must have been controlled by the bare rock threshold above The Gulf southwest of Covey Hill. Because the ice barrier, which supported the lake in the St. Lawrence Valley, rested on the Frontenac axis of Precambrian rocks, they named this body of water glacial Lake Frontenac.

In the Trenton embayment, beaches 16 to 32 m below Iroquois level (129 to 167 m above the marine limit) have

been ascribed to glacial Lake Frontenac by Mirynech (1962) and others, implying that they were controlled by the 310 m rock threshold above The Gulf. Clark (1980) and Clark and Karrow (1984) identified geomorphic evidence of five tilted water planes that washed the southeastern slope of the St. Lawrence Valley west of Covey Hill. The two highest, Levels I and II, diverge northeastward in a manner that suggests uplift during the interval they represent. The limited data suggest correlation of Level I with glacial Lake Iroquois and Level II with glacial Lake Fronteanc.

Denny (1974) suggested that deglaciation of the north flank of the Adirondacks took place between 12 700 and 12 000 B.P. Prest (1970) proposed 12 200 B.P. as an approximate age for temporary stabilization recorded by the Frontenac strand.

SYDNEY, BELLEVILLE, AND TRENTON STRANDS

In general terms, just as the Frontenac and Iroquois strands are commonly considered together, so also the lower beaches can be given parallel treatment. All three were identified in the Trent Valley embayment and named by Mirynech (1962).

Mirynech described the Sydney beach as being best developed near Stirling off the east end of the Oak Ridges interlobate Moraine (Fig. 7). Leyland (1982) considers these materials to be outwash and the prominent development of this surface to be largely a consequence of the ready availability of sand due to reworking of a portion of the Collinton Esker, rather than being indicative of prolonged stabilization of lake level. Clark (1980) and Clark and Karrow (1984) indicate that the Sydney strand is represented on the north slope of the Adirondack uplands by beaches some 80 m below Level II.

Mirynech inferred that waters of glacial Lake Algonquin in the Huron Basin, draining across the threshold at Fenelon Falls and through the Trent Valley system, debouched into Ontario basin lakes as they lowered from Frontenac to Sydney levels. Below the Sydney level, Mirynech recognized only evidence of diminished discharge that shaped the lower Trent Valley. Leyland (1984), on the other hand, discounts the significance of the Sydney level and finds no evidence that the "Algonquin River" ceased to flow until after waters in the Ontario Basin had dropped below present lake level.

Clark (1980) recognized on air photos more than 30 apparent strandlines that wrap around the north flank of Covey Hill and range in altitude from 268 down to 207 m. Chapman (1937, 1942) considered these features to be single-walled meltwater channels even though they conform closely to contour lines instead of the gradient of the assumed ice margin. Clark acknowledged a disparity between lake levels as represented by these apparent strands and by deltas of major streams down to the lowest level. The lowest of the apparent strands, however, corresponds to his level IV as distinguished on the basis of elevations of hanging deltas built into the ponded waters of the St. Lawrence Valley by north-flowing rivers that drained from the Adirondacks. Clark further calls attention to the contrast in degree of dissection of higher deltas as compared to those of level IV. He ascribes the deeper and more confined dissection of level IV deltas to a drop in base level more rapid than the gradual lowering which had preceded it. Clark and Karrow (1984) correlate the deltas of level IV with Mirynech's Belleville strandline.

The strongest of the strandlines below the Iroquois beach was first recognized by Bigsby (1829), and later by Spencer (1883) and Coleman (1901). Mirynech (1962, 1967) named it the Belleville Beach for its prominent development west of Belleville along Route 401, north of the Bay of Quinte (Fig. 8). Clark (1980) and Clark and Karrow (1984) correlate 13 hanging deltas and a beach remnant 23 meters below Level III on the south slope of the St. Lawrence Lowlands with the Belleville Beach. South of the St. Lawrence the Belleville Beach may be represented by the Sandy Creek strand mapped by Sutton *et al.* (1972) east of Lake Ontario. Like Prest (1970), Clark and Karrow consider that the

Belleville Beach represents stabilization of level correlative with the Fort Ann phase of Lake Vermont (Chapman, 1937). The Fort Ann phase involved merger of impounded waters in the Champlain trough with those of the St. Lawrence Lowlands (Fig. 4-5). It had its outlet south across a metamorphic rock sill near Fort Ann at the south end of the Champlain trough. Prest (1970) suggested 12 000 B.P. as the approximate age of the Belleville shoreline.

The Belleville lake phase ended when a lower outlet opened eastward to the Chaudière Valley and thence around an ice lobe into the sea near Quebec. The Trenton shoreline, lying close along and 9 to 12 m above the north shore of Lake Ontario in the Trenton-Belleville area (Mirynech, 1962), has been interpreted as marking a brief stabilization of lake level before invasion of the upper St. Lawrence Valley by the

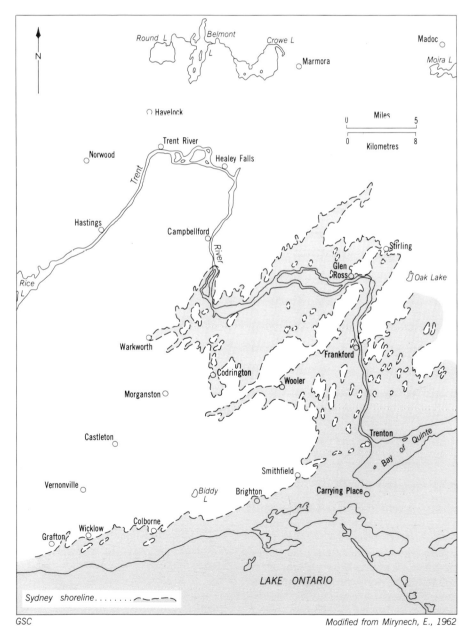

Figure 7. Sydney shoreline. Modified from Mirynech (1962).

Champlain Sea. On the north slop of the Adirondack Uplands, Clark and Karrow (1984) identify the Level V water plane represented by beaches 26 m below the Belleville phase. Westward projection of this water plane suggests correlation with Mirynech's Trenton shoreline. Clark and Karrow consider that Level V strand features were probably formed early in the history of the Champlain Sea. A viable alternative, however, suggests correlation to the lowermost Fort Ann phase lake in the Champlain Valley, named glacial Lake New York (Wagner, 1967)

MARINE PHASE

J.W. Goldthwait (Gadd, 1971) identified the marine limit on Covey Hill as marked by a strand at 160 m above present sea level and about 84 m below the lowest lake strand on Covey Hill.

Gilbert traced what he considered to be the marine limit from Covey Hill south to Oswego (Leverett and Taylor, 1915). Coleman (1901) likewise traced a strand from the westernmost occurrence of marine fossils then known, near Prescott, into the Ontario Basin. Fairchild (1907) assigned the name Gilbert Gulf to the early post-glacial, sea level waterway which, on the basis of these prior studies, he believed to have linked the Hudson Estuary with the St. Lawrence Valley and the Ontario Basin. Leverett and Taylor (1915) appear to have accepted the existence of a sea level stage in the Ontario Basin.

Fairchild's Gilbert Gulf in the Champlain-Hudson trough is no longer accepted, however, and reason exists to question whether the strands traced into the lake basin by Gilbert

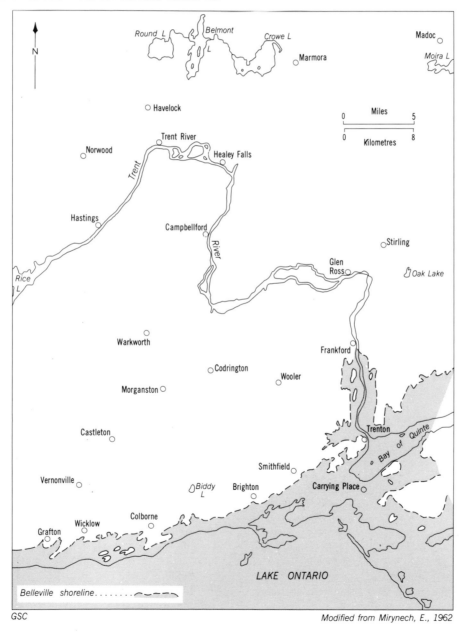

Figure 8. Belleville shoreline. Modified from Mirynech (1962).

and Coleman do, indeed, represent the marine limit. Goldthwait (Gadd, 1971), Karrow *et al.* (1961), and Henderson (1973) projected the marine limit as passing below the Ontario threshold, some 30 km west of Brockville, Ontario. If this were so, the Ontario Basin never contained an extension of the Champlain Sea, but always existed as a freshwater lake, an interpretation accepted by Prest (1970).

Henderson (1973) and Sharpe (1979) reported marine fossils in the Merrickville area, Ontario, and Clark (1980) discovered a new site southwest of Ogdensburg. In contrast to Henderson, both Sharpe and Clark project the marine limit into the Ontario Basin. Sharpe suggested that marine invertebrates may have failed to reach the proposed sealevel lake in the Ontario Basin because the overriding freshwater lens extended to the depth of the Ontario threshold across the Frontenac arch.

Investigations of Ontario lake-bottom sediments have so far yielded very inconclusive evidence of possible marine incursion into the Ontario Basin. Schroeder and Bada (1978) report a high concentration of acidic amino acids in the lower part of the glaciolacustrine clay of a core from the Rochester (easternmost) subbasin of Lake Ontario. On the basis of the prevailing view that Ontario began as a freshwater lake, they consider it unlikely that the acidic amino acid concentration indicates a local marine influence. Clark and Karrow (1984) accept the amino acid data as supporting their correlation of marine strandlines in the St. Lawrence Valley with the Trenton-phase strand of Mirynech.

Marine invertebrates of the Champlain Sea afford the best basis for dating deposits in the lowlands. In the Maitland area, Sharpe (1979) reported shells found at 137 m above present sea level which were dated at 11 600 B.P. Marine shells collected from a gravel pit on the Salmon River, 12 km northwest of Malone, New York, (and hence southeast of Maitland) at 76 m above sea level, were dated at 10 630 ± 249 B.P. (Clark, 1980).

SUBSEQUENT DEVELOPMENTS

Fairchild (1907) and Coleman (1922) hypothesized the existence of a low-water phase below present Ontario lake level. As evidence of this lake stage, which he named the Admiralty Lake, Coleman (1922) cited the entrenchment of the Trent Valley beyond the present shoreline. Subsequent investigators, including Karrow *et al.* (1961), Mirynech (1962), Sutton *et al.* (1972), and Young (1983) supplied confirming evidence of this low-level stage which is more commonly called Early Lake Ontario (Fig. 4-6). Additional documentation is becoming available through studies of lake-bottom sedimentation and profiling, such as those of Sly and Prior (1984) and Anderson and Lewis (1985).

Because isostatic recovery has been greatest at the northeastern end of the basin, postglacial rebound has raised the level of the St. Lawrence outlet, tilting and submerging older strandline features and flooding the mouths of valleys in the southern and western part of the basin. Sly and Prior (1984) show that the slope of the lowest water plane closely parallels that of the Belleville isobases. This is in accord with radiocarbon data indicating that the low-water stage was initiated by 11 500 B.P.

During subsequent rebound and rise toward present lake level, temporary stabilization was apparently achieved at an intermediate level, the Dunes stage of Sutton *et al.* (1972). The slope of the Dunes stage water plane closely approaches the horizontal, departing from present Ontario level enough to accord with observation that rebound continues at rates measurable in fractions of a metre per century in all but the southwestern part of the Ontario Basin (Kite, 1972).

CONCLUSIONS

1. The Late-Wisconsinan history of proglacial lake impoundment in the Ontario Basin probably began with eastward expansion of glacial Lake Arkona although no remnants of the Arkona strand are definitively identified in the basin.
2. Glacial readvance raised lake level to the glacial Lake Whittlesey strand which is well defined southwest of Hamburg and traceable to the Marilla Moraine. The Hamburg and Marilla Moraines, therefore, are considered to be Port Huron correlatives. Glacial Lakes Newberry in the Finger Lake Region and Danville in the Genesee Valley were partially contemporary.
3. Well-developed strand features that transect the Marilla Moraine, but not the younger Alden Moraine, represent glacial Lake Warren I, which initially received outflow from Lake Hall in the Genesee Valley, but later itself expanded into the Genesee Valley before lowering by eastward drainage to the Mohawk Valley.
4. Strand features of glacial Lake Warren III, 6 m below the earlier Warren beach, mark impoundment by glacial readvance to the Batavia Moraine.
5. Glacial Lake Iroquois, controlled by drainage across the Rome Outlet to the Mohawk Valley, initially occupied only the eastern end of the Ontario Basin. The glacier barrier receding from the north margin of the plateau impounded Lake Lundy in the Erie Basin, as well as Lake Avon and subsequently Lake Dawson in the Genesee Valley.
6. Glacial Lake Iroquois spread rapidly to the western end of the Ontario Basin by about 12 500 B.P. As the lake expanded northward in the Trent Valley, isostatic rebound produced northward diverging strandlines. At maximum extent the lake extended north into the Mazinaw lake basin.
7. With exposure of the gap at Covey Hill, glacial Lake Iroquois gave way to short-lived glacial Lake Frontenac which drained into the Fort Ann phase of Glacial Lake Vermont in the Champlain Trough.
8. The level of proglacial ponding north of the Adirondacks lowered rapidly through the Sydney phase to stabilize at the level of the Fort Ann phase of Glacial Lake Vermont and produce the Belleville strand.
9. As the ice sheet receded completely from the St. Lawrence Valley, early Lake Ontario was diminished to a fraction of its present volume at an elevation 5 to 8 m a.s.l.
10. Postglacial rebound at rates exceeding the eustatic rise of sea level raised the St. Lawrence threshold, further tilted strandlines and flooded southshore rivermouths. Measurable rebound continues today (Kite, 1972).

ACKNOWLEDGEMENTS

The authors acknowledge with appreciation their indebtedness to J.G. Leyland and P.E. Calkin for suggestions received during the course of this investigation and to J.S. Vincent for translating our abstract into French. We have benefited from suggestions by P.F. Karrow, J. Terasmae, and R.A. Young who read an early draft of the manuscript. V.K. Prest gratefully acknowledges the support of the Geological Survey of Canada.

REFERENCES

Anderson, T.W., and Lewis, C.F.M., 1985, Postglacial Water-level History of the Lake Ontario Basin: *in* Karrow, P.F., and Calkin, P.E., eds., Quaternary Evolution of the Great Lakes: Geological Association of Canada Special Paper 30.

Bigsby, J.J., 1829, A Sketch of the Topography and Geology of Lake Ontario: Philosophical Magazine, series 2, v. 5, p. 1-15.

Blackmon, Paul, 1956, Glacial Geology of the East Aurora, New York Quadrangle: M.S. Thesis, Buffalo, New York, University of Buffalo, 100 p.

Blagbrough, J.W., 1951, The Red Clay Deposits of Otisco Valley: M.S. Thesis, Syracuse, New York, Syracuse University, 97 p.

Calkin, P.E., 1970, Strandlines and Chronology of the Glacial Great Lakes in Northwestern New York: Ohio Journal of Science, v. 70, p. 78-96.

————, 1982, Glacial Geology of the Erie Lowland and Adjoining Allegheny Plateau, Western New York: New York State Geological Association Guidebook, 54th Annual Meeting, Buffalo, p. 121-139.

Calkin, P.E., and Feenstra, B.H., 1985, Evolution of the Erie-basin Great Lakes: *in* Karrow, P.F., and Calkin, P.E., eds., Quaternary Evolution of the Great Lakes: Geological Association of Canada Special Paper 30.

Chadwick, G.H. and Dunbar, E.V., 1924, Genesee Glacial Lakes: Geological Society of America Bulletin, v. 35, p. 669-676.

Chapman, D.H., 1937, Late-glacial and Postglacial History of the Champlain Valley: American Journal of Science, 5th series, v. 34, p. 85-124.

————, 1942, Late-glacial and Postglacial History of the Champlain Valley: Report to the State Geologist on the Mineral Industries and Geology of Vermont, 1941-1942: Vermont Geological Survey, 23rd Report, p. 48-83.

Chapman, L.J. and Putnam, D.F., 1951, The Physiography of Southern Ontario: Toronto, Ontario, University of Toronto Press, 284 p.; Second Edition, 1966, 386 p.

Chute, N.E., 1979, Glacial Lake Iroquois in Central New York: Northeastern Geology, v. 1, p. 69-105.

Clark, P.U., 1980, Late Quaternary History of the Malone area, New York: M.Sc. Thesis, Waterloo, Ontario, University of Waterloo, 188 p.

Clark, P.U. and Karrow, P.F., 1984, Late Pleistocene Water Bodies in the St. Lawrence Lowland, New York, and Regional Correlations: Geological Society of America Bulletin, v. 95, 805-813.

Clinton, De Witt, 1825, On Certain Phenomena of the Great Lakes of North America: Literary and Philosophical Society of New York Transactions, v. 2, p. 1-33.

Coleman, A.P., 1901, Marine and Fresh-water Beaches of Ontario: Geological Society of America Bulletin, v. 12, p. 129-146.

————, 1904, Iroquois Beach in Ontario: Geological Society of America Bulletin, v. 15, p. 347-368.

————, 1922, Glacial and Post-glacial Lakes in Ontario: University of Toronto Studies, Biological Series, No. 21.

————, 1937, Lake Iroquois: Ontario Department of Mines, 45th Annual Report, v. 2, pt. 7, p. 1-36.

Dadswell, Michael, 1974, Distribution, Ecology and Postglacial Dispersal of Certain Crustaceans and Fishes in Eastern North America: Ottawa, Ontario, National Museums of Canada, Publications in Zoology, No. 11, 110 p.

Deane, R.E., 1950, Pleistocene Geology of the Lake Simcoe District, Ontario: Geological Survey of Canada Memoir 256, 108 p.

Denny, C.S., 1974, Pleistocene Geology of the Northeast Adirondack Region, New York: United States Geological Survey Professional Paper 786, 50 p.

Fairchild, H.L., 1896, Glacial Genesee Lakes: Geological Society of America Bulletin, v. 7, p. 423-452.

————, 1897, Lake Warren Shorelines in Western New York and the Geneva Beach: Geological Society of America Bulletin, v. 8, p. 269-284.

————, 1899, Glacial Lakes Newberry, Warren, and Dana in Central New York: American Journal of Science, v. 7, p. 249-263.

————, 1907, Gilbert Gulf (Marine Waters in Ontario Basin): Geological Society of America Bulletin, v. 17, p. 712-718.

————, 1909, Glacial Waters in Central New York: New York State Museum Bulletin 127, 66 p.

————, 1912, The Closing Phase of Glaciation in New York: New York State Museum Bulletin 158, p. 32-35.

————, 1928, Geologic Story of the Genesee Valley: Rochester, New York, Published by the author, 193 p.

————, 1934a, Cayuga Valley Lake History: Geological Society of America Bulletin, v. 45, p. 233-280.

————, 1934b, Seneca Valley Physiographic and Glacial History: Geological Society of America Bulletin, v. 45, p. 1073-1110.

Fullerton, D.S., 1971, The Indian Castle Glacial Readvance in the Mohawk Lowland, New York and its Regional Implications: Ph.D. Dissertation, Princeton, New Jersey, Princeton University, 270 p.

————, 1980, Preliminary Correlation of Post-Erie Interstadial Events (16 000-10 000 Radiocarbon years Before Present) Central and Eastern Great Lakes Region, and Hudson, Champlain, and St. Lawrence Lowlands, United States and Canada: United States Geological Survey Professional Paper 1089, 52 p.

Gadd, N.R., 1971, Pleistocene Geology of the Central St. Lawrence Lowland: Geological Survey of Canada Memoir 359, 153 p.

Gravenor, C.P., 1957, Surficial Geology of the Lindsay-Peterborough Area, Ontario: Geological Survey of Canada Memoir 288, 68 p.

Hand, B.M. and Muller, E.H., 1972, Syracuse Channels: Evidence of a Catastrophic Flood: p. I-1 to I-12 *in* McLelland, J., ed., New York State Geological Association Guidebook, 44th Annual Meeting, Hamilton, New York.

Henderson, E.P., 1973, Surficial Geology of Kingston (North Half) Map-Area, Ontario: Geological Survey of Canada Paper 72-48, 6 p.

Hough, J.L., 1958, Geology of the Great Lakes: Urbana, Illinois, University of Illinois Press, 313 p.

————, 1963, Prehistoric Great Lakes of North America: American Scientist, v. 51, p. 84-109.

Johnston, W.A., 1916, The Trent Valley Outlet of Lake Algonquin and the Deformation of the Algonquin Water-plane in the Lake Simcoe District, Ontario: Geological Survey of Canada Museum Bulletin 23, 27 p.

Karrow, P.F., 1981, Late-glacial Regional Ice-flow Patterns in Eastern Ontario: Discussion: Canadian Journal of Earth Sciences, v. 18, p. 1386-1390.

Karrow, P.F., Clark, J.R. and Terasmae, J., 1961, The Age of Lake Iroquois and Lake Ontario: Journal of Geology, v. 69, p. 659-667.

Kindle, E.M. and Taylor, F.B., 1913, Description of the Niagara Quadrangle: United States Geological Survey Geological Atlas, Folio 190, 26 p.

Kirkland, J.T. and Coates, D.R., 1977, The Champlain Sea and Quaternary Deposits in the St. Lawrence Lowland, New York: in Newman, W.S., and Salwen, Bert, eds., Amerinds and their Paleoenvironments in Northeastern North America: New York Academy of Science Annals, v. 288, p. 498-507.

Kite, G.W., 1972, An Engineering Study of Crustal Movement Around the Great Lakes: Inland Waters Branch Technical Bulletin No. 23, 57 p.

Lane, A.C., 1900, Geological Report on Huron County: Ann Arbor, Michigan, Geological Survey of Michigan, v. VII, Part 2, 379 p.

Leverett, Frank, 1902, Glacial Formations and Drainage Features of the Erie and Ohio Basins: United States Geological Survey Monograph 41, 802 p.

————, 1939, Correlations of Beaches with Moraines in the Huron and Erie Basins: American Journal of Science, v. 237, p. 456-475.

Leverett, Frank, and Taylor, F.B., 1915, The Pleistocene of Indiana and Michigan and the History of the Great Lakes: United States Geological Survey Monograph 53, 529 p.

Leyland, J.G., 1982, Quaternary geology of the Tweed Area, Southern Ontario: Ontario Geological Survey Map P-2615, Geological Series-Preliminary Map, Scale 1:50 000.

————, 1984, Quaternary geology of the Northeastern Lake Ontario Basin: M.S. Thesis, St. Catharines, Ontario, Brock University, 68 p.

Lewis, C.F.M., 1969, Late Quaternary History of Lake Levels in the Huron and Erie Basins: Proceedings 12th Conference on Great Lakes Research, International Association for Great Lakes Research, p. 250-270.

MacClintock, Paul, and Stewart, D.P., 1965, Pleistocene Geology of the St. Lawrence Lowland: New York State Museum Bulletin 394, 152 p.

Mirynech, Edward, 1962, Pleistocene Geology of the Trenton-Campbellford Map Area, Ontario: Ph.D. Dissertation, Toronto, Ontario, University of Toronto, 176 p.

————, 1967, Pleistocene and Surficial Geology of the Kingston-Cobourg-Tweed Area, Ontario: in Jenness, S.E., ed., Geology of Parts of Eastern Ontario and Southeastern Quebec: Geological Association of Canada Guidebook, p. 183-198.

Mörner, Nils-Axel and Dreimanis, Aleksis, 1973, The Erie Interstade: in Black, R.F., Goldthwait, R.P., and Willman, H.B., eds., The Wisconsinan Stage: Geological Society of America Memoir 136, p. 107-134.

Muller, E.H., 1963, Geology of Chautauqua County, New York, Part II, Pleistocene Geology: New York State Museum and Science Service Bulletin 392, 60 p.

————, 1964, Surficial Geology of the Syracuse Field Area: New York State Geological Association Guidebook, 36th Annual Meeting, p. 25-35.

————, 1965, Quaternary Geology of New York: in Wright, H.E. and Frey, D.G., eds., The Quaternary of the United States: Princeton, New Jersey, Princeton University Press, p. 99-112.

————, 1977a, Late Glacial and Early Postglacial Environments in Western New York: in Newman, W.S. and Salwen, Bert, eds., Amerinds and their Paleoenvironments in Northeastern North America: New York Academy of Science Annals, v. 228, p. 223-233.

————, 1977b, Quaternary Geology of New York, Niagara Sheet: New York State Geological Survey Map and Chart Series No. 28, Scale 1:250 000.

Muller, E.H. and Miller, T.S., 1980a, Surficial Geology of New Haven Quadrangle, Oswego County, New York: United States Geological Survey Water Resources Investigations, Open File Report 80-1208.

Muller, E.H. and Miller, T.S., 1980b, Surficial Geology of Oswego East Quadrangle, Oswego County, New York: United States Geological Survey Water Resources Investigations, Open File Report 80-1209.

Muller, E.H., Young, R.A., Rhodes, D.D., Willette, P.W., Wilson, M.D., and Fakundiny, R.H., 1981, Surficial Geology of the Genesee Valley: New York State Geological Survey Open File Report 2102.056, 174 p.

Prest, V.K., 1970, Quaternary Geology of Canada: Chapter XII in Douglas, R.J.W., ed., Geology and Economic Minerals of Canada: Geological Survey of Canada Economic Geology Report No. 1, Fifth Edition, p. 676-764.

Roy, Thomas, 1837, On the Ancient State of the North American Continent: Geological Society of London Proceedings v. 2, p. 537-538.

Scherzer, W.C., 1900, Geological Report on Monroe County: Michigan Geological Survey, v. VII, Part 1, 240 p.

Schroeder, R.A. and Bada, J.L., 1978, Aspartic Acid Racemization in Late Wisconsin Lake Ontario Sediments: Quaternary Research, v. 9, p. 193-204.

Sharpe, D.R., 1979, Quaternary Geology of the Merrickville Area, Southern Ontario: Ontario Geological Survey Report 180, 54 p.

Sly, P.G. and Prior, J.W., 1984, Late glacial and Postglacial geology in the Lake Ontario Basin: Canadian Journal of Earth Sciences, v. 21, p. 802-821.

Spencer, J.W.W., 1883, Terraces and Beaches about Lake Ontario: American Journal of Science, series 3, v. 24, p. 409-416.

————, 1888, Notes on the Origin and History of the Great Lakes of North America: Proceedings of the American Association for the Advancement of Science, v. 37, p. 197-199.

————, 1890, The Deformation of Iroquois Beach and Birth of Lake Ontario: American Journal of Science, v. 40, p. 433-451.

————, 1894, Deformation of the Lundy Beach and Birth of Lake Erie: American Journal of Science, series 3, v. 147, p. 207-212.

Stewart, D.P., 1958, The Pleistocene geology of the Watertown and Sackets Harbor Quadrangles: New York State Museum Bulletin 369, 79 p.

Sutton, R.G., Lewis, T.L. and Woodrow, D.L., 1972, Post-Iroquois Lake Stages and Shoreline Sedimentation in Eastern Ontario Basin: Journal of Geology, v. 80, p. 340-356.

Symecko, R.E., 1967, Glacial Geology of the Orchard Park, New York, Quadrangle: M.S. Thesis, Buffalo, New York, State University of New York at Buffalo, 64 p.

Taylor, F.B., 1897, Correlation of Erie-Huron Beaches with Outlets and Moraines in Southeastern Michigan: Geological Society of America Bulletin, v. 8, p. 31-58.

_____, 1924, Moraines of the St. Lawrence Valley: Journal of Geology, v. 32, p. 641-667.

Wagner, W.P., 1969, The late Pleistocene of the Champlain Valley, Vermont: *in* Barnett, S.G., ed., Guidebook: 41st Annual Meeting, New York State Geological Association, Plattsburg, New York, p. 65-80.

Whittlesey, Charles, 1848, Notes upon the Drift and Alluvium of Ohio and the West: American Journal of Science, Series 2, v. 5, p. 205-217.

_____, 1850, On the Natural Terraces and Ridges of the Country Bordering Lake Erie: American Journal of Science Series 2, v. 10, p. 31-39.

Wilkinson, R.S., 1959, Differential Uplift of the Iroquois Shoreline: B.Sc. Thesis, Toronto, Ontario, Department of Geology, University of Toronto, 20 p.

Wilson, M.P., 1980, Catastrophic Discharge of Lake Warren in the Batavia-Genesee Region: Ph.D. Dissertation, Syracuse, New York, Syracuse University, 99 p.

Woodworth, J.B., 1905, Pleistocene Geology of the Mooers Quadrangle, New York: New York State Museum Bulletin 83, 60 p.

Wright, F.M., III, 1972, The Pleistocene and Recent Geology of the Oneida-Rome District, N.Y.: Ph.D. Dissertation, Syracuse, New York, Syracuse University, 181 p.

Young, R.A., 1983, The Geologic Evolution of the Genesee Valley Region and early Lake Ontario: Rochester Academy of Science Proceedings, v. 15, p. 85-98.

Quaternary Evolution of the Great Lakes,
edited by P.F. Karrow and P.E. Calkin,
Geological Association of Canada Special Paper 30, 1985

POSTGLACIAL WATER-LEVEL HISTORY OF THE LAKE ONTARIO BASIN

T.W. Anderson
Geological Survey of Canada, 601 Booth Street, Ottawa, Ontario K1A 0E8

C.F.M. Lewis
Geological Survey of Canada, Bedford Institute of Oceanography, Dartmouth, Nova Scotia B2Y 4A2

ABSTRACT

Piston coring in Lake Ontario has revealed sand and gravel, fossiliferous stratified sand and silt, marl, and peat below silty clay at depths ranging from about 102 m to 13 m below present lake level. Plant and insect remains, molluscs, and ostracodes contained in stratified sand and silt overlying laminated clay provide evidence of extremely low lake levels in Lake Ontario following the draining of glacial Lake Iroquois and the expansion of post-Iroquois glacial lakes into the Ottawa and upper St. Lawrence valleys. Pollen records spanning the shallow-water deposits at lowest elevation in western Lake Ontario indicate that the low-level stage was reached at 11 400 B.P. About this time, water levels were confluent with the Champlain Sea (Gilbert Gulf phase) though marine fossils were not observed in Ontario basin cores. Presumably the freshwater supply and outflow were sufficiently strong to prevent incursion of saline waters into the Lake Ontario basin. Once lake levels separated from the Champlain Sea, Early Lake Ontario water levels rose rapidly with steadily diminishing rates as the outlet area rebounded isostatically.

The drainage history of the Ontario basin, shown in a set of maps of former shoreline positions at 12 000 B.P. (Lake Iroquois), 11 400, 10 000, 8000, 6000, and 4000 B.P., is reconstructed from paleowater-planes defined in a shoreline displacement diagram, from shallow-water sediment occurrences, profiles of interpreted relative lake-level change, and predicted outlet-uplift histories.

Following diversion of Upper Great Lakes drainage to the Ottawa River at 10 500 B.P., the Lake Ontario basin experienced a long period of reduced water supply in which lake levels closely followed rising eastern outlets. Water levels in the Kingston basin and North Channel were controlled separately until they became confluent with Early Lake Ontario about 9000 B.P. With the return of Upper Lakes drainage, the increased outflow of Lake Ontario overtaxed the capacity of outlet channels causing water levels to rise significantly. The ensuing Nipissing Flood phase, peaking about 4000 B.P., surpassed present levels in eastern Lake Ontario. Levels subsided within 1000 years as outlet channels ad-

justed to increased outflow and subsequently rose slowly again under the influence of uplifting outlet channels.

RÉSUMÉ

Des carottages effectués dans le lac Ontario ont révélé du sable et du gravier, du sable et des limons stratifiés fossilifères, de la marne et de la tourbe sous de l'argile silteuse à des profondeurs variant d'un peu plus de 100 mètres à 13 mètres sous le niveau actuel du lac. Les débris de plantes et d'animaux, les mollusques et les ostracodes trouvés dans le sable et les limons stratifiés recouvrant de l'argile laminée révèlent que le lac Ontario a atteint de très bas niveaux à la suite de la vidange du lac glaciaire Iroquois et de l'extension des lacs post-Iroquois dans les vallées de l'Outaouais et du cours supérieur du Saint-Laurent. L'analyse du pollen contenu dans des dépôts d'eau peu profonde (dépôts présents à une plus grande profondeur dans la partie ouest du lac) suggère que le lac Ontario a atteint un niveau extrêmement bas vers 11 400 B.P. A ce moment, le plan d'eau du lac était au même niveau que celui de la mer de Champlain (phase du golfe de Gilbert). La présence de fossiles marins n'a pas été observée dans les carottes provenant du bassin du lac Ontario; on pense que le courant d'eau douce était suffisamment fort pour empêcher l'infiltration de l'eau de mer. Lorsque les exutoires de la partie est du bassin du lac Ontario atteignirent le niveau de la mer, le lac s'isola de la mer de Champlain. Par la suite, les niveaux d'eau de la phase initiale du lac Ontario s'élevèrent rapidement, à un taux décroissant, suivant le relèvement de l'exutoire. La courbe générale du relèvement, d'après une analyse de l'inclinaison des plans d'eau antérieurs, est exponentielle pour un facteur temps d'environ 2500 à 3000 ans.

L'accumulation massive de sable et de gravier, enfouie sous de la vase et traversant la partie ouest du lac Ontario entre Grimsby et Oakville, pourrait appartenir à un ancien cordon littoral. Celui-ci se serait formé, d'abord par l'accumulation de sédiments transportés par les courants durant l'épisode de transition entre la phase du golfe de Gilbert et la phase initiale du lac Ontario, ensuite par l'accumulation de détritus provenant de la gorge Saint-David et entraînés le long de la rivière Niagara il y a environ 10 000 B.P.

L'évolution du bassin du lac Ontario, résumée par une série de figures montrant les positions de rivages vers 12 000 (lac Iroquois), 11 400, 10 000, 8000, 6000 et 4000 B.P., est reconstituée à partir des plans d'eau des paléolacs. Ces plans d'eau sont déduits d'un diagramme montrant la déformation des rivages reconstitués à partir des dépôts d'eau peu profonde, des profils des variations des niveaux du lac ainsi que de l'histoire proposée du relèvement des exutoires.

A la suite du déversement des eaux de la partie supérieure des Grands Lacs vers la rivière Outaouais il y a 10 500 B.P., le bassin du lac Ontario connut une période d'apport réduit en eau. Durant cette période, les niveaux d'eau du lac suivirent d'assez près le relèvement du déversoir à l'est du lac. Le déversement des eaux vers l'est était contrôlé par des seuils: un entre les Îles Main Duck et Galloo; un autre près du cap Vincent, dans l'état de New York; et un autre dans la région des Mille Îles, dans la partie supérieure du fleuve Saint-Laurent. Les niveaux d'eau dans le bassin de Kingston et dans la région de North Channel furent contrôlés séparément jusqu'au moment où ils devinrent confluents avec les eaux de la phase initiale du lac Ontario, vers 9000 B.P. Lorsque le drainage de la partie supérieure des Grands Lacs fut rétabli, l'écoulement accru vers le lac Ontario dépassa la capacité de drainage des chenaux, entraînant ainsi une hausse marquée des niveaux d'eau. La phase à crues du lac Nipissing qui en résulta et qui se situe vers 4000 B.P. entraîna des niveaux d'eau plus élevés que les niveaux actuels dans la partie est du lac Ontario. Les niveuax d'eau baissèrent pendant environ 1000 ans alors que les chenaux s'ajustaient au débit accru. Par la suite, ils s'élevèrent encore lentement à cause du relèvement des exutoires.

INTRODUCTION

The late Wisconsinan history of the Lake Ontario basin, as currently understood, has Port Huron ice retreating from the Ontario basin followed by the formation of glacial Lake Iroquois by about 12 400 B.P. (Muller, 1977) and prior to about 12 200 B.P. (Fullerton, 1980). Lake Iroquois drained to the southeast via the Mohawk Valley, New York; subsequently a series of lower lake phases (Ellenburg, Frontenac, Sydney, Belleville, Sandy Creek, Trenton, Skinner Creek) came into existence when ice recession in the upper St. Lawrence Valley uncovered lower outlets to the northeast (Prest, 1970; Clark and Karrow, 1984). Extremely low levels were established in the Ontario basin because of glacio-isostatic depression of the upper St. Lawrence outlet area (Prest, 1970). Coleman (1922) called the low-level lake, the Admiralty Phase, based on what he thought to be the controlling sill in the Admiralty Islands area, upper St. Lawrence River. The classic view of postglacial history shows Lake Ontario water levels rising as the outlet area to the northeast rebounded isostatically.

The surficial sediments and depositional features of Lake Ontario are described in Lewis and McNeely (1967) and Thomas et al. (1972). Recently, Sly and Prior (1984) discussed the stratigraphy and lake history near the Niagara

River and Kingston areas as derived from acoustic data in conjunction with sediment sampling.

Evidence for lower water levels in the Lake Ontario basin was confirmed from borings into buried shallow-water deposits in the Burlington bar in western Lake Ontario (Karrow et al., 1961), and by the recovery of gyttja, peat and wood at depths below present lake level in eastern Lake Ontario (Lewis and McNeely, 1967; Sutton et al., 1972). Other sedimentary sequences or sub-bottom features suggestive of lower water levels include buried, organic bay deposits and a drowned beach near Braddock Heights, New York (Sutton et al., 1965a, 1965b; Woodrow et al., 1967), a mud-buried, sand and gravel barrier beach between Grimsby and Oakville, Ontario (Lewis, 1969; Lewis and Sly, 1971), buried peat-over-sand sequences in borings obtained from Irondequoit Bay, near Rochester, New York (Young, 1983), well-sorted, fine- and medium-grained sand concentrates overlying glaciolacustrine clay in cores collected from Lake Ontario (Lewis and McNeely, 1967), and erosional features at the base of the Toronto Scarp (Lewis and Sly, 1971).

In the present study, piston cores ranging from a few metres to as much as 18 m in length have been obtained from the bottom sediments of Lake Ontario in an effort to understand the late Quaternary history of the Lake Ontario basin. Several of these piston cores contain shallow-water deposits consisting of shell-bearing, stratified sand and silt, gravel, peat, wood, and marl at depths well below the present lake level (Fig. 1 and Table I). This study attempts to document the postglacial changes in lake level inferred from evidence in these cores and explains the relative lake-level history in terms of a five-factor model based on glacial lake drainage, differential crustal uplift, sea-level incursion, outlet adjustments, and upstream drainage diversions. A possible origin of the massive, buried, offshore Grimsby-Oakville bar is correlated with this history.

FIELD AND LABORATORY PROCEDURES

The bottom sediments of Lake Ontario were sampled between 1966 and 1974 by means of piston and gravity coring during several echo-sounding surveys from research vessels. The full shipboard procedures are detailed in Thomas et al. (1972). The piston cores were recovered with a 450-kg, Alpine piston corer fitted with a 12.2 m core barrel and 5.7 cm I.D. plastic liner. The cores were logged and described in the laboratory using Munsell soil colour charts. Samples were removed from selected cores to undertake various sedimentological analyses, studies of plant and animal fossils, and radiocarbon dating.

Samples for pollen analysis were treated with HF and KOH followed by acetolysis. The sand and silt fractions were decanted prior to acid treatment and samples having low pollen concentrations were sieved through a 10 μ m mesh to concentrate the pollen. Counts of at least 200 tree and shrub pollen provide the basic pollen sum.

Plant and animal macrofossils, i.e., seeds, fruits, leaves, needles, insects, molluscs, and ostracodes, were extracted from the more fossiliferous layers. The core increments were first scraped to remove surface contamination after which the sediment was soaked in water and washed through a

TABLE I

SEDIMENTS RELATED TO PREVIOUS WATER LEVELS IN LAKE ONTARIO BASIN

SITE NO.	LOCATION	LATITUDE	LONGITUDE	SEDIMENT	METRES BELOW DATUM SAMPLE	ESTIMATED LAKE LEVEL (MAIN BASIN)	[14]C DATE (YR BP) AND LAB. NO. (AGE OF POLLEN HORIZON, YR BP)	REFERENCE (S)
1a	Cootes Paradise (Hamilton, Ontario)	43°17.3'	79°53.8'	wood	18.6	above 18.6	4400 ± 50 (WAT-343)	Berry and Drimmie (1982)
1b	Cootes Paradise (Dundas, Ontario)	43°16.2'	79°55.5'	organic silt	9.6	above 9.6	3690 ± 50 (GSC-2706)	This study
2	Core 68-0-17-4 (Hamilton, Harbour)	43°16.8'	79°52.2'	Plant detritus below silty clay	17.3	close to 17.3	5140 ± 200 (GSC-2164)	This study
3	Core 68-0-18-38 (Hamilton, Harbour)	43°17.0'	79°48.6'	woody gyttja over sand	17.3	close to 17.3	5260 ± 90 (GSC-2147)	This study
4	Core 75-00-006-42 (Hamilton, Harbour)	43°18.0'	79°49.9'	peat over sand	21.8	close to 21.8		This study
5a	Burlington Bar	43°18.0'	79°48.0'	wood in silt and sand	15.2	above 15.2	2820 ± 160 (Y-613A)	Karrow et al. (1961)
5b	Burlington Bar	43°18.0'	79°48.0'	wood in silt and sand	24.4	above 24.4	5240 ± 140 (Y-614A)	Karrow et al. (1961)
5c	Burlington Bar	43°18.0'	79°48.0'	wood in silt and sand	62.2	below 62.2	10,150 ± 450 (I-GSC-11)	Walton et al. (1961) Karrow et al. (1961)
6	Core 69-0-13-3 (Western Lake Ontario)	43°18.5'	79°43.1'	clay	38.9	above 38.9	(5000 - 7000)	This study
7	Core 69-0-13-1 (Western Lake Ontario)	43°18.5'	79°41.0'	clay	54.9	above 54.9	(7690)	This study
8	Core 69-0-13-13 (Western Lake Ontario)	43°16.2'	79°21.0'	clay over till	72.0	above 72.0	(9000)	This study
9	Core 69-0-13-7 (Western Lake Ontario)	43°22.0'	79°35.4'	clay over sand	75.6	above 75.6		This study
10	Core 69-0-13-14 (Western Lake Ontario)	43°22.5'	79°34.2'	stratified sand and silt under silty clay	84.8	above 84.8	(10,000)	This study
11a	Core 69-0-16-1 (Western Lake Ontario)	43°26.0'	79°30.7'	stratified sand and silt under silty clay	102.6	above 102.6	(11,400)	This study
11b	Core 69-0-16-1 (Western Lake Ontario)	43°26.0'	79°30.7'	clay over stratified sand and silt	102.5	above 102.5	(9000)	This study
12	Fifteen-Sixteen Mi. Creeks, (St. Catherines, Ontario)	43°11.0'	79°20.0'	gyttja	1.6 - 5.8	above 1.6	400 ± 100 to 3225 ± 100	Otto and Dalrymple (1983)
13a	Irondequoit Bay (Rochester, New York)	43°13.0'	77°32.0'	peat over sand	12.2	close to 12.2		Young (1983)
13b	Irondequoit Bay (Rochester, New York)	43°13.0'	77°32.0'	peat over sand	42.7	close to 42.7		Young (1983)
13c	Irondequoit Bay (Rochester, New York)	43°13.0'	77°32.0'	sand and gravel	60.9	close to 60.9		Young (1983)
14a	Core 68-0-18-33 (Sodus Bay, New York)	43°15.0'	76°57.4'	peat over sand	16.2	close to 16.2	5200 ± 300 (GSC-2017)	This study
14b	Core 68-0-18-33 (Sodus Bay, New York)	43°15.0'	76°57.4'	peat below silty clay	15.5	close to 15.5	4950 ± 260 (GSC-2012)	This study
15	Mexico Bay (Eastern Lake Ontario)	43°36.0'	76°14.0'	wood in peat	12.2	close to 12.2	4810 ± 180 (GX-1627)	Sutton et al. (1972)
16	North Pond (Eastern Lake Ontario)	43°40.0'	76°11.0'	peat above present lake level	-0.6	at -0.6		Sutton et al. (1972)
17	Core 68-0-18-25 (Eastern Lake Ontario)	43°35.9'	76°24.6'	clay over stratified sand and silt	96.7	above 96.7	(9000)	This study
18	Core 68-0-13/14-3 (Eastern Lake Ontario)	43°49.0'	76°47.2'	clay over sand	52.9	above 52.9		This study
19a	Core 67-0-18-28 (Eastern Lake Ontario)	43°53.6'	76°32.6'	stratified sand and silt under clayey silt	57.8	at 57.8		This study
19b	Core 67-0-18-28 (Eastern Lake Ontario)	43°53.6'	76°32.6'	stratified sand and silt under clayey silt	57.0	above 57.0	(10,400)	This study
19c	Core 67-0-18-28 (Eastern Lake Ontario)	43°53.6'	76°32.6'	stratified sand and silt under clayey silt	56.8	above 56.8	(10,000)	This study
20	Core 67-0-18-27 (Eastern Lake Ontario)	43°58.9'	76°29.7'	clay	60.4	above 60.4	(9000)	This study
21	Core 69-0-16-3 (Eastern Lake Ontario)	43°59.7'	76°51.0'	plant detritus under silty clay	34.9	close to 34.9		This study
22	Core 67-0-18-24 (Eastern Lake Ontario)	43°51.6'	76°20.7'	plant detritus under sand	34.0	close to 34.0		This study
23	Core 67-0-18-23 (Eastern Lake Ontario)	43°53.0'	76°24.9'	plant detritus under silty clay	30.5	close to 30.5		This study

TABLE I (CONTINUED)

SITE NO.	LOCATION	LATITUDE	LONGITUDE	SEDIMENT	METRES BELOW DATUM SAMPLE	ESTIMATED LAKE LEVEL (MAIN BASIN)	^{14}C DATE (YR BP) AND LAB. NO. (AGE OF POLLEN HORIZON, YR BP)	REFERENCE (S)
24	Core 67-0-18-25 (Eastern Lake Ontario)	43°53.3'	76°28.0'	plant detritus	28.7	close to 28.7		This study
25	Core 66-0-15-79 (Eastern Lake Ontario)	43°53.1'	76°24.8'	gyttja under clay	18.0	below 18.0	8790 ± 170 (GSC-742)	Lewis and McNeely (1967)
26a	Core 69-0-16-2 (Bay of Quinte)	44°02.1'	77°05.0'	peat over sandy clay	15.75	below 15.75	7920 ± 120 (GSC-3441)	This study
26b	Core 69-0-16-2 (Bay of Quinte)	44°02.1'	77°05.0'	gyttja over marl	15.7	above 15.7	6080 ± 100 (GSC-3300)	This study
26c	Core 69-0-16-2 (Bay of Quinte)	44°02.1'	77°05.0'	gyttja	15.1	above 15.1	4790 ± 80 (GSC-3460)	This study
26d	Core 69-0-16-2 (Bay of Quinte)	44°02.1'	77°05.0'	gyttja	14.0	above 14.0	3550 ± 80 (GSC-3464)	This study
27	Rossmore Bog (Bay of Quinte)	44°07.0'	77°23.0'	gyttja over marl	3.2	below 3.2	9480 ± 70 (GSC-157)	Terasmae and Mirynech (1964)
28	Core 68-0-18-22 (Henderson Harbour)	43°53.7'	76°11.1'	marl under silty gyttja	13.6	close to 13.6	(5000 - 6000)	This study
29	Core 70-0-34-Long Point (Eastern Lake Ontario)	44°06.3'	76°31.8'	fossiliferous sand under sandy clay	19.6	close to 19.6		This study
30	Core 74-00-102-20 (Eastern Lake Ontario)	44°09.3'	76°39.1'	plant detritus	21.7	at 21.7	8160 ± 120 (GSC-2115)	This study
31	St. Lawrence River	44°14.7'	76°15.5'	plant detritus over sand	16.6	below 16.6	8560 ± 200 (GSC-2252)	Johnston (1978)
32a	Cataraqui River (Kingston, Ontario)	44°15.2'	76°28.8'	wood below peat	2.5	at 2.5	3610 ± 60 (GSC-2499)	Lowdon et al. (1977)
32b	Cataraqui River (Kingston, Ontario)	44°12.0'	76°30.0'	wood below peat	2.5	at 2.5	4840 ± 360 (WAT-300)	Berry and Drimmie (1982)
33	Cataraqui River (Kingston, Ontario)	44°17.0'	76°27.0'	gyttja	2.0	below 2.0	10,200 ± 500 (GSC-I-1223)	Terasmae (1980)

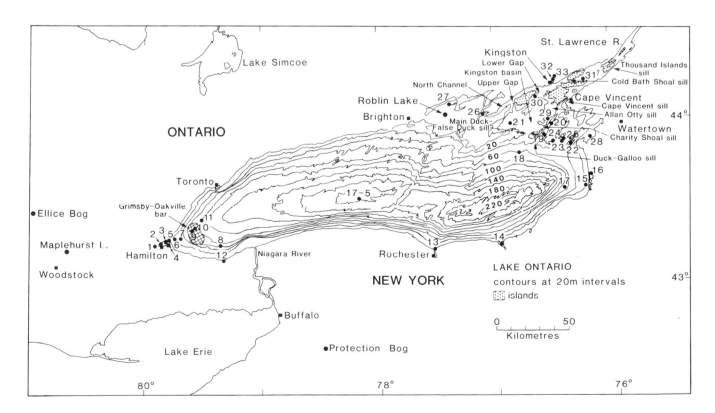

Figure 1. Bathymetry of Lake Ontario and locations of sites and features discussed in text. The Lake Ontario basin sites are described in Table I.

149-μ m sieve. The concentrate was examined under a dissecting microscope and all identifiable specimens were picked out and stored in a mixture of alcohol and glycerin, or stored dry for later examination. The plant macrofossils were identified with the aid of a reference collection of modern fruits and leaves which is housed at the Geological Survey of Canada; all other fossils were forwarded to specialists for identification.

STRATIGRAPHY, CHRONOLOGY AND PALEOENVIRONMENTAL DATA

Nearshore and Embayment Sites

The stratigraphy of several cores from sites in the nearshore zone and bays of present-day Lake Ontario are shown in Figure 2. These and additional nearshore and embayment sites are described in Table I.

Sites 2, 3, and 4 are from Hamilton Harbour where peat admixed with marl is underlain by coarse beach sand and overlain by silty clay with streaks of iron sulphide (FeS) scattered throughout. Dates on plant detritus at the top and bottom of the organic interval are 5140 ± 200 B.P. (GSC-2163) and 5260 ± 90 B.P. (GSC-2147) from separate cores.

Site 14 is in Sodus Bay, where peat is underlain immediately by medium- to coarse-grained sand, and deeper by laminated silty clay, and overlain by massive silty clay. Dates at the base and top of the peat are 5200 ± 300 B.P. (GSC-2017) and 4950 ± 260 B.P. (GSC-2012), respectively.

Site 26 is in Bay of Quinte, where basal peat overlies sandy clay which in turn overlies laminated silty clay; the peat grades upward into marl which is overlain by gyttja to the surface. The peat produced a date of 7920 ± 120 B.P. (GSC-3441); dates on the gyttja range upward in age from 6000 to 3500 B.P. (Table I).

The stratigraphic sequence in Henderson Harbour (site 28) is basal till, overlain by laminated silty clay, which is overlain by massive silty clay. Marl unconformably overlies the silty clay. The marl changes upward into a thin layer of silty gyttja which is overlain by massive silty clay to the top of the core.

Sites 30 and 31, in the Kingston area, show peat over sandy clay over laminated silty clay and peat over medium- to coarse-grained sand, respectively; marl overlies peat at both sites. Dates on the respective peat beds are 8160 ± 120 B.P. (GSC-2115) and 8560 ± 200 B.P. (GSC-2252).

Pertinent radiocarbon dates on other sites in the eastern end of Lake Ontario include 9480 ±70 B.P. (GSC-157) and 10 200 ± 500 B.P. (GSC-I-1223) on gyttja at sites 27 and 33, respectively, 4810 ± 180 B.P. (GX-1627) on buried wood at site 15 and two dates of 4840 ± 350 B.P. (WAT-360) and 3610 ± 60 B.P. (GSC-2499) on drowned tree stumps (sites 32a, 32b). Dates from other embayment sites in western Lake Ontario include 4400 ± 50 B.P. (WAT-343) on wood and 3690 ± 50 B.P. (GSC-2706) on organic silt (sites 1a, 1b) and eleven dates ranging between 400 B.P. and 3200 B.P. on gyttja at site 12.

Pollen and plant macrofossils extracted from the Sodus Bay core (site 14) are shown in Figure 3. Pollen of *Cephalanthus occidentalis, Ilex*, grasses, sedges, and of the waterlilies, *Nuphar* and *Nymphaea*, and seeds of *Carex*,

Scirpus validus, Eleocharis palustris, Typha, Sagittaria latifolia, Zannichellia palustris, Decodon verticillatus, Rorippa islandica, Utricularia, Ceratophyllum demersum, Potamogeton, and *Najas* are dominant throughout the peat interval. These plant taxa are typical representatives of shallow-water, lagoonal and marsh-like habitats. Their presence in the peat suggests that wetland conditions existed in Sodus Bay from 5200 B.P. to about 5000 B.P.

Similar marsh and lagoonal environments are inferred from buried peat or marl sediments in Hamilton Harbour, Bay of Quinte, Henderson Harbour, and at other buried peat sites in the Kingston basin. Corresponding dates on wood from the Burlington bar (site 5b) and on basal peat in Hamilton Harbour (sites 2 and 3) show the close association that existed between barrier beach formation and lagoonal development in Hamilton Harbour. Lagoonal conditions continued to the present in Hamilton Harbour because the upward growth of Burlington bar provided continued barrier protection between the lagoon and the isostatically rising main lake.

Offshore Sites

Sediment logs for several offshore core sites are shown in Figure 4. The cores bottomed either in till-like stony sandy clay, sand and gravel, laminated silty clay, or stratified sand and silt. The stratigraphic sequence at the base of most cores is laminated silty clay over stony, sandy clay or gravel. At sites 8 and 11, stony sandy clay is immediately overlain by massive sandy clay and massive silty clay with clay blebs, respectively. The buried Grimsby-Oakville bar is well marked on seismic reflection profiles (Lewis, 1969) and is shown to be composed of stratified sand and gravel in cores from sites 9 and 10. The surface of this buried sand and gravel deposit, a presumed ancient barrier beach, lies between 74 and 84 m below present level of Lake Ontario. Several of the cores contain shell-bearing, stratified sand and silt overlying laminated silty clay and underlying massive silty clay. The deepest fossiliferous beds occur at sites 11, 17 and 19, respectively at 102.5 m, 96.7 m, and 56.7 m below the present level of Lake Ontario.

Macrofossil Analyses

The more fossiliferous sand and silt beds were analyzed for molluscs, ostracodes, plant macrofossils, and insect remains (Table II). The molluscs are dominated by the two sphaeriids, *Pisidium lilljeborgi* and *P. conventus* with lesser numbers of *P. casertanum* and *Sphaerium nitidum*, and by the gastropod *Valvata sincera*. Both *Pisidium* species are typical inhabitants of freshwater oligotrophic lakes in central and northern Canada (Clarke, 1973). *Pisidium conventus* can be found in large numbers in the profundal zone of deep lakes or in shallow, cold lakes throughout the Northwest Territories; *P. lilljeborgi* and *Sphaerium nitidum* are also characteristic of oligotrophic lakes but they are not found in as deep water as *P. conventus* (G. Mackie, pers. commun., 1981). *P. casertanum*, on the other hand, is one of, or perhaps the most tolerant of eutrophic conditions (G. Mackie, pers. commun., 1981). *Valvata sincera* prefers a substrate of mud, with or without coarser sediments, and pres-

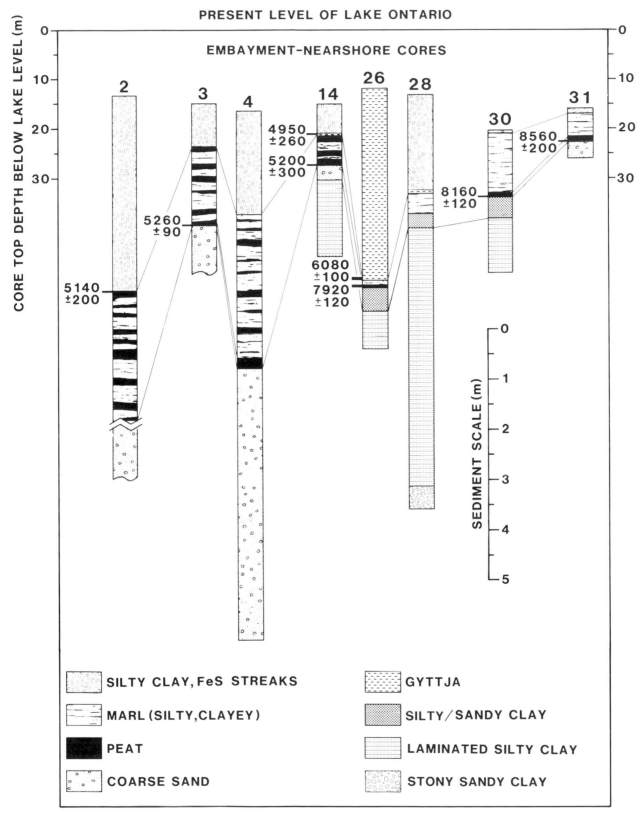

Figure 2. Stratigraphy and radiocarbon dates (years B.P.) obtained from several nearshore and embayment cores, Lake Ontario. Inset scale refers to core lengths (sediment depths). Sites are located in Figure 1 and are described in Table I.

Note that lake transgression, signified by the onset of organic sedimentation, occurred earliest at the eastern end of the lake (sites 26 to 31).

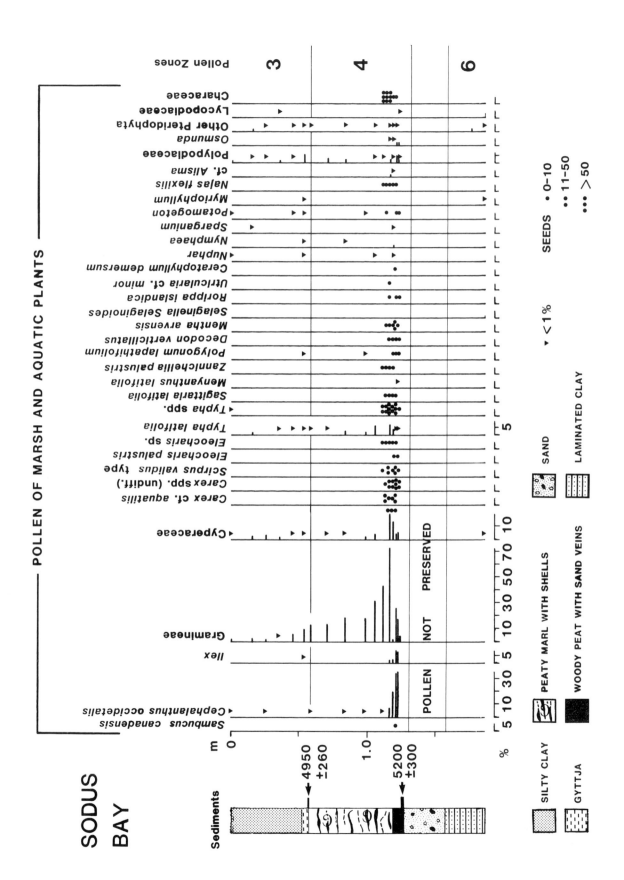

Figure 3. Pollen and macrofossils of aquatic and marsh plants in a core from Sodus Bay, New York (site 14).

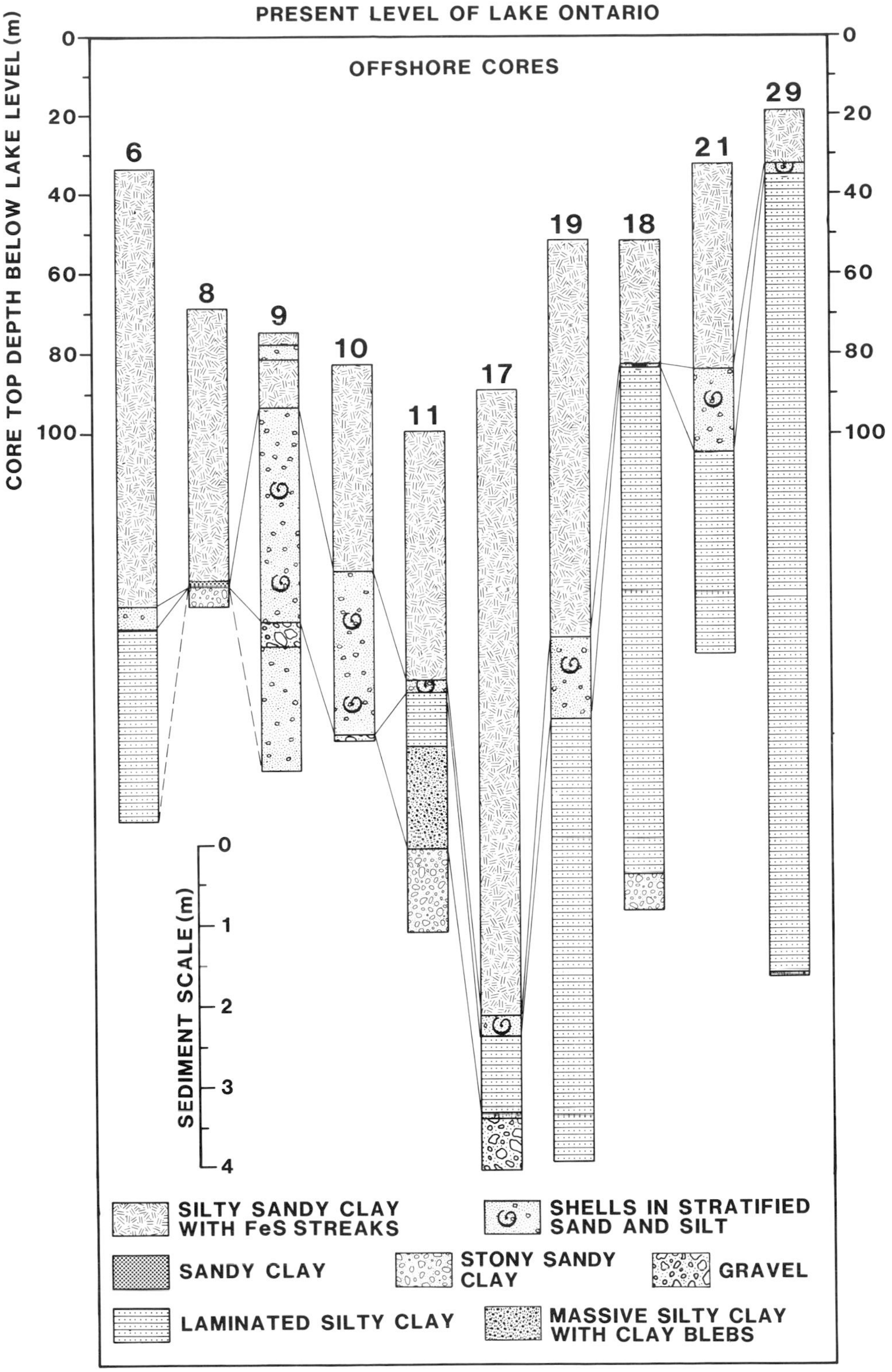

Figure 4. Stratigraphy of several offshore cores, Lake Ontario. Inset scale refers to core lengths (sediment depths). Sites are located in Figure 1 and are described in Table I.

TABLE II

FOSSIL OCCURRENCES IN SHALLOW-WATER SEDIMENTS, OFFSHORE LAKE ONTARIO

SITE 11 (310-320 cm)

PLANT MACROFOSSILS
- *Larix laricina* (needles)
- *Picea mariana* (needles)
- *Picea sp.* (seed cases)
- *Selaginella selaginoides* (macrospores)
- *Eleocharis palustris* (fruits)
- *Najas flexilis* (fruits)
- *Typha sp.* (fruits)
- *Juncus* sp. (fruits)
- Characeae (oogonia)
- Moss fragments

FOSSIL INSECTS
- Carabidae (Ground Beetles)
  - *Agonum (Europhilous)* sp.
- Hydraenidae (Ephemeral Pond Beetles)
- Staphylinidae (Rove Beetles)
  - *Quedius sp.*
  - Omaline types
- Leiodidae (Burying Beetles)
- Helodidae (Swamp Beetles)
  - *Cyphon sp.*
- Phalacridae (Shining Flower Beetles)
- Lathridiidae (Minute Scavenger Beetles)
- Scolytidae (Bark Beetles)
- Diptera (Flies)
- Hymenoptera (Wasps and Bees)

SITES 8, 10, 17

MOLLUSCS	%
Pisidium conventus	100

SITE 18 (154-156 cm)

MOLLUSCS	%
Pisidium conventus	99
P. nitidum f. contortum	3 valves

OSTRACODES	
Candona spp.	13 valves

MOLLUSCS	approx. %
Pelecypods	
Pisidium lilljeborgi	50
P. conventus	45
P. casertanum	5
Sphaerium nitidum	1 valve
Gastropods	
Gyraulus sp.	1
Valvata sincera	7

OSTRACODES	%
Candona candida	0.5
C. caudata	11
C. ohioensis	0.5
C. rawsoni	2.7
C. rectangulata	1
C. subtriangulata	38
Cytherissa lacustris	30
Ilyocypris bradyi	1
I. gibba	3.4
Limnocythere friabilis	6
Limnocythere sp.	5.5

SITE 19

MOLLUSCS (495-500cm)	%
Pisidium conventus	90
P. lilljeborgi	5
P. casertanum	5

OSTRACODES (495-500 cm)	%
Candona subtriangulata	60
C. rawsoni	40

OSTRACODES (513-516cm)	
Candona subtriangulata	50
C. rawsoni	38
Cytherissa lacustris	12

OSTRACODES (532-537cm)	
Candona subtriangulata	43
Cytherissa lacustris	7
Limnocythere friabilis	50

ence of submersed vegetation (Clarke, 1973).

The ostracodes at site 11 are dominated mainly by *Candona subtriangulata* and *Cytherissa lacustris* and to a lesser extent by *Candona caudata*, *C. rawsoni*, *Limnocythere friabilis*, and *Ilyocypris gibba*. The overall ostracode assemblage is indicative of an oligotrophic lake having few dissolved solids (less than 100 mg/l); water depth may have been as shallow as 8 m at the site (L.D. Delorme, pers. commun., 1981). The ostracodes *Candona subtriangulata* and *C. rawsoni* dominate in the upper part of the sand-silt unit at site 19, but *Limnocythere friabilis* and lesser amounts of *Cytherissa lacustris* replace *Candona rawsoni* with increase in depth. An oligotrophic lake is also implied at site 19 but the fewer number of shells of *Pisidium lilljeborgi* at this site indicates that the lake may have been relatively deeper than at site 11.

Plant macrofossils and insect fragments also occur in the sand-silt unit at site 11. The plant macrofossils are represented by needles of *Picea mariana* and *Larix laricina* and

fruits of aquatic and marsh plants such as *Eleocharis palustris*, *Juncus*, *Typha*, *Chara*, and *Selaginella selaginoides*. The fossil beetles include the Hydraenidae, which inhabit ephemeral ponds, species within the genus *Cyphon*, which are commonly found in swamps, and members of the Scolytidae, the bark beetles.

Pollen Analysis

Pollen studies were carried out on the fossiliferous sand and silt beds and overlying and underlying sediments at sites 11, 17, and 19 (Fig. 5). The abbreviated pollen diagram for site 11 shows two major pollen boundaries, an *Artemisia-Picea* boundary within the massive clay unit below laminated clay and a *Picea-Pinus* boundary near the top of the sand-silt unit. The lower pollen boundary is characterized by a decline in *Artemisia* from 12% to less than 5%. The high *Picea*, *Pinus*, and *Quercus* values of the *Artemisia* zone are attributed to long-distance dispersal over a tundra landscape at this early stage. *Artemisia* remains low (5% or less) but *Picea* increases upward to peak percentages (30% and more) in the *Picea* zone throughout the laminated clay. *Picea* remains high into the overlying stratified sand and silt unit and is replaced near the top of this unit by sharp increases in *Pinus*.

Pollen analyses at site 19 (Fig. 5) extend only into the upper part of the laminated clay. As at site 11, *Picea* reaches a maximum 30% and *Artemisia* 5% and less in the laminated clay and overlying sand-silt sequence. *Picea* gives way to maximum values in *Pinus* in the overlying silty clay. The *Picea-Pinus* transition takes place within the upper part of

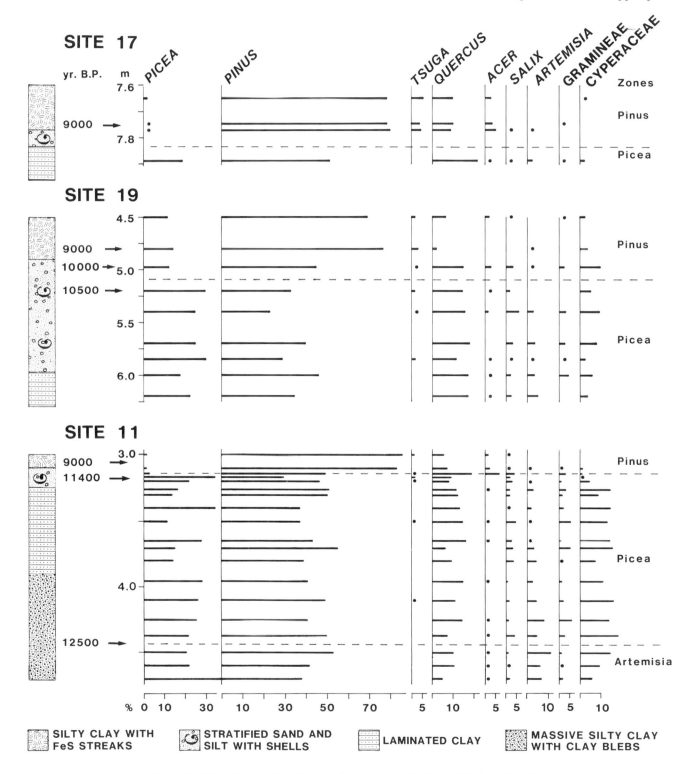

Figure 5. Abbreviated pollen diagrams for core sites 11, 17, and 19, Lake Ontario.

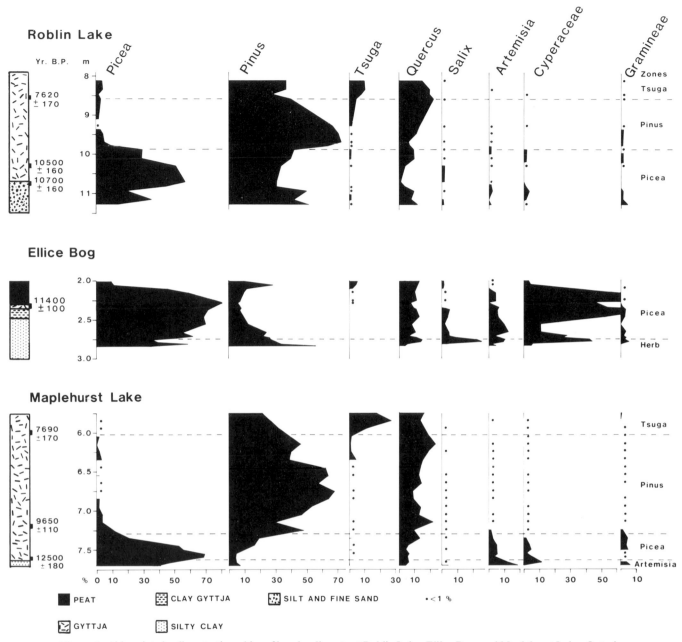

Figure 6. Abbreviated pollen stratigraphies of basal sediments at Roblin Lake, Ellice Bog, and Maplehurst Lake, Ontario. The Roblin Lake and Maplehurst Lake diagrams are redrawn from Terasmae (1980) and Mott and Farley-Gill (1978), respectively. The Ellice Bog diagram is an expanded version of that in Anderson (1971).

the sand-silt unit. Only a few analyses were carried out on core sites 17 and 18 as the sediments were moderately to highly oxidized. The much-abbreviated pollen diagram at site 17 (Fig. 5) shows a sharp pollen change from relatively high *Picea* percentages in the laminated clay to high *Pinus* percentages in the silty clay that overlies the sand and silt layer. The *Picea-Pinus* transition also takes place across a similar shelly sand layer at site 18.

The pollen segments show similar trends to those of the basal pollen record from the conformable sediments at site 17-5 in central Lake Ontario (McAndrews, 1971; 1973). As at sites 11 and 19, *Picea* and Cyperaceae dominate in the laminated silty clay and give way to a *Pinus*-dominated zone

in the overlying massive clay. Unlike core site 11, the central-basin core does not extend into the *Artemisia*-dominant zone at the base.

Comparison with the radiocarbon-dated pollen record at Maplehurst Lake (Mott and Farley-Gill, 1978) places the *Artemisia-Picea* pollen boundary at site 11 at approximately 12 500 B.P. (Fig. 6). In like manner, the stratified sand and silt sequence at site 11 was deposited by about 11 400 B.P. based on pollen correlation with corresponding high *Picea* percentages dating 11 400 ± 100 B.P. (GSC-3730) at Ellice Bog (Fig. 6). Stratified sand and silt were still being deposited until the time of the *Picea-Pinus* transition (about 10 500 B.P.) after which silty clay deposition took place.

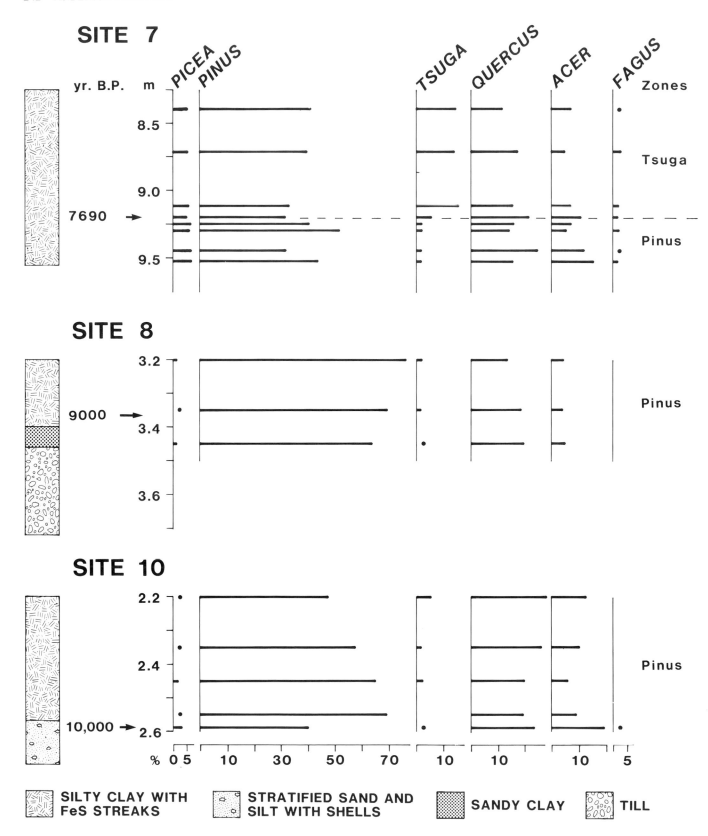

Figure 7. Abbreviated pollen diagrams for core sites 7, 8, and 10, Lake Ontario.

The pollen record for the fossiliferous sand-silt sequence at site 19 in easternmost Lake Ontario corresponds with similar percentages in the *Picea* profile dated 10 500 ± 160 B.P. (GSC-925) at Roblin Lake (Terasmae, 1980). Stratified sand and silt were deposited at this site until at least 10 000 B.P. followed by silty clay deposition.

Inferred ages from pollen correlation are also placed on core sites 7, 8, and 10 located above site 11 in the western end of Lake Ontario (Fig. 7). Sand was still being deposited at site 10 until 10 000 B.P. based on correlation with the composite pollen diagram in Terasmae (1981). Silty clay deposition was dated at 9000 and 7700 B.P. at sites 8 and 7 by correlating the *Pinus* maximum and rise in *Tsuga* with corresponding horizons in Protection Bog, New York (Miller, 1973) and Maplehurst Lake, Ontario (Mott and Farley-Gill, 1978), respectively.

POSTGLACIAL LAKE-LEVEL HISTORY

Paleowater-Planes

Table I lists all known buried organic, shallow-water, and inorganic sequences which are indicative of lake-level change in the Lake Ontario basin. Many of these sediments have been radiocarbon-dated or dated by pollen correlation with similar radiocarbon-dated pollen records from land.

The dated intervals were plotted relative to the present level of Lake Ontario and projected onto a curved line of section oriented N 10° E to N 20° E through the Sodus Bay area and Kingston (Fig. 8). The line of section represents the direction of maximum uplift drawn perpendicular to isobases on the Iroquois and post-Iroquois beaches in eastern Lake Ontario region (Coleman, 1937; Muller and Prest, 1985). The dashed liens on the section of Figure 8 are the present positions of paleowater-planes which join sites of similar age in

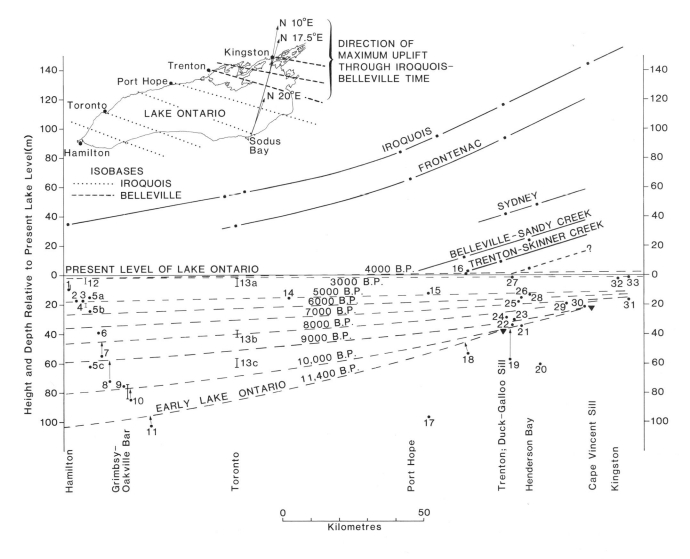

Figure 8. Paleowater-planes of the Lake Ontario basin relative to present lake level and plotted in section normal to isobases of glacial Lakes Iroquois and Belleville. Arrow lengths denote estimated water depths at sites at various times. Shoreline positions of Lake Iroquois and post-Iroquois lake phases are from Coleman (1937), Mirynech (1962), Sutton *et al.* (1972), and Muller and Prest (1985).

TABLE III

EXPONENTIAL COEFFICIENT FOR DIFFERENTIAL UPLIFT OF ONTARIO BASIN

| Water-plane age t B.P. | Water-plane height/depth | | Elevation difference $\triangle E$ m | Relative coefficient $k = \dfrac{1}{t_1 - t_2} \log_e \left(\dfrac{\triangle E_{t_2}}{\triangle E_{t_1}} \right)$ |
	Kingston m	Hamilton m		
12000	153	35	118	
8000	−20	−44	24	> −0.398 ka^{-1}
5000	−11	−18	7	> −0.411
12000	153	35	118	> −0.404
				$k = -0.404$
				± 0.006

the eastern and western extremities of Lake Ontario.

Laminated silty clay at or near the base of the cores is interpreted to be glaciolacustrine in origin and is attributed to glacial Lake Iroquois and the post-Iroquois glacial lakes. Stratified sand and silt and the contained fossil remains overlying the laminated silty clay deep in the basin form a record of an extremely low-water stage. Hence water levels fell about 140 m from high-level Lake Iroquois through a series of intermediate stages (Frontenac to Trenton-Skinner Creek) to low-level Early Lake Ontario (Fig. 8).

The Skinner Creek level was named from an exposure of beach sands (elevation: 77.7 m) located along Skinner Creek in the North Pond area, eastern Lake Ontario (Sutton et al., 1972). The beach sands correspond to the Trenton water plane, suggesting that the Trenton and Skinner Creek levels are equivalent (Sly and Prior, 1984). The benches formed by the Skinner Creek phase in the Henderson Bay area (Sutton et al., 1972) may not be correlative with the shoreline deposits of the Skinner Creek type locality, but possibly represent a lower (yet unnamed) lake phase.

The best dated of the lowest water-planes is that at 11 400 B.P., when lake levels were as low as 90 to 100 m below present level in western Lake Ontario (site 11). Inferred shallow-water and marsh-like habitats at site 11 undoubtedly were part of a lagoonal deposit in a nearshore zone of the low-level lake. The 11 400 B.P. water-plane is projected to site 18 in eastern Lake Ontario and over site 19 in the St. Lawrence trough (Sly and Prior, 1984). The sand-silt interval at site 19 is related to the silty-sandy horizon under postglacial mud on seismic surface II of Sly and Prior (1984). This surface extends to about 37 m and slopes southwest like the inferred 11 400 B.P. water-plane. The curvature of the 11 400 B.P. water-plane closely parallels that of Lake Iroquois suggesting that perhaps only a few hundred years may have elapsed betwen the time of Lake Iroquois and the initiation of Early Lake Ontario. The lake at this time is hereby named the Duck-Galloo phase of Early Lake Ontario after the controlling sill located between Main Duck and Galloo Islands (Fig. 1).

The shallow-water, sand-silt sequence at site 17 is most likely not related to the 11 400 B.P. water-plane but possibly to an earlier, lower water-plane. However, to achieve a lower water-plane through site 17 parallel to the Iroquois and post-Iroquois water-planes requires that the Duck-Galloo outlet was at one time substantially lower than at present and was subsequently infilled by longshore sediment drift in suc-

ceeding lake phases. This interpretation is not substantiated at the present time because the postglacial evolution of the Duck-Galloo outlet is unknown. Alternatively, the sand-silt sequence at site 17 may have originated from sand deposits transported downslope from higher elevations in the steeply sloping eastern end of the Ontario basin as a result of longshore wave activity.

Lake-wide water levels were apparently low until at least 10 500 B.P. However, by 10 000 B.P. levels had risen by some 20 m in the western end of the lake based on pollen analysis of the stratified sand sequence at site 10 (Fig. 8). At the same time, sand and silt were deposited at site 19 in the St. Lawrence trough. The sand and silt are interpreted as signifying high-energy turbulent flow (discharge) through the St. Lawrence trough. As the lake back-flooded and deepened because of differential uplift by this time, flow diminished and clay, which had been maintained in suspension, was deposited.

Silty clay deposition commenced between 9000 and 10 000 B.P. (Fig. 5) indicating that lake-wide water levels had risen by this time. The post-10 000 B.P. water-planes, (see Fig. 8), demonstrate the progressive rise in lake levels from backflooding as a result of differential uplift of the Lake Ontario basin. Though the post-5000 B.P. water-planes are now sloped also, they are more parallel to the present water-plane of Lake Ontario signifying the diminishing rate of differential uplift.

Paleowater-Plane Analysis

As pointed out in the previous paragraph, younger waterplanes are progressively less tilted than older water-planes for similar intervals of time (Fig. 8). This suggests that the basin has rebounded differentially under the influence of glacio-isostatic crustal adjustment (Appendix 1). The exponential rate, k, for this adjustment was evaluated from water-planes defined in Figure 8 using Equation 6 from Appendix 1. The k values calculated from elevation differences between Kingston and Hamilton on pairs of the three best-controlled water-planes (Iroquois at 12 000, 8000, and 5000 B.P.) are shown in Table III. The mean value, $k = -0.404 \pm 0.006$ per thousand years, is similar to values obtained for sites in Arctic Canada ($k = -0.44 \pm 0.07$) by Andrews (1968a) and to values obtained for the Huron basin in the time period 10 500 to 4700 B.P. (Lewis and Anderson, 1985). The reciprocal of this k value − the relaxation time −

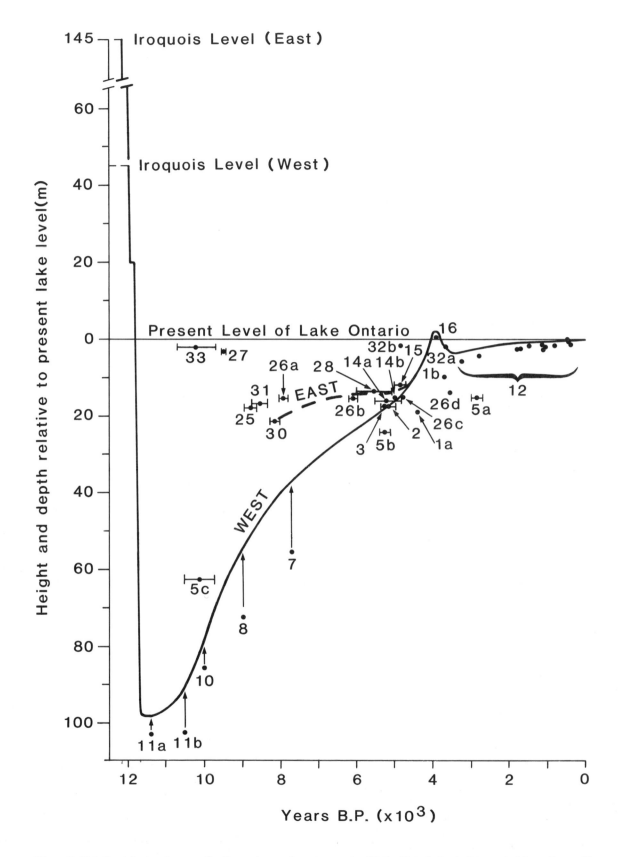

Figure 9. Relative lake-level curves for the eastern and western ends of Lake Ontario basin interpreted from the position of former water-planes in Figure 8.

suggests that, on average, after each 2470-year period, uplift remaining in the Ontario basin is reduced to 1/e (e = 2.71828) or 37 percent of its value at the commencement of each period.

A similar analysis of the same water-planes between Port Hope and Hamilton yielded a relaxation coefficient of k = -0.373 ± 0.045 and between Toronto and Hamilton k = -0.343 ± 0.072. These values, less than the coefficient for overall uplift between Kingston and Hamilton, suggests a slower rate of rebound in western Lake Ontario. A slower rate in this area is also suggested by the lesser slope of the Iroquois water-plane west of Port Hope (Fig. 8). However, this latter effect may be caused by beach-splitting during uplift in Lake Iroquois' lifespan as Port Hope lies close to the isobase through the lake outlet area at Rome, New York (Coleman, 1936). The Iroquois water-plane east of Port Hope would then be older than its counterpart to the west. Thus the relaxation coefficients calculated from data west of Port Hope where the age of the Iroquois water-plane is most likely closest to its youngest phase at 12 000 B.P. may describe uplift more accurately.

Relative Lake-Level Curves

Figure 9 shows the interpretative, relative lake-level (RLL) curves developed for the Lake Ontario basin. The left side of the curves represents the post-Iroquois draw-down; the right side denotes the rising lake phases from Early Lake Ontario to the present.

The profile for the western Lake Ontario basin shows a gradual rise in lake levels following the low-water stage at 11 400 B.P. Lake levels then rose more rapidly beginning about 10 000 B.P. but less so between 8000 and 5000 B.P. A second rise occurred after 5000 B.P. corresponding with the discharge into the Lake Ontario basin of Upper Great Lakes drainage at the time of the Nipissing Great Lakes. Lake levels, in fact, rose slightly higher than the present at or shortly after 4000 B.P.; levels then dropped 3 to 4 m before rising to the current level.

The best control points for the RLL curves are sites 2, 3, and 10 to 12 in the western end of the lake and sites 14 to 16, 30, and 32 in the eastern end of the lake. The stratified sand and silt deposits at sites 10 and 11 are explained on the basis that these sites were within the wave base at the time of deposition. Water depths over the sites may have been as low as 8 to 10 m. The peat beds at sites 2, 3, 14, and 15, on the other hand, suggest that water levels probably ranged to within 1 to 2 m of these sites. After passing through these sites, the curve rises steeply to site 16, a peat deposit at 75.3 m elevation on the eastern shore of Lake Ontario (Sutton et al., 1972). The presence of this peat suggests water levels rose close to 1 m above present lake level in the eastern end of the lake which is the North Pond phase of Sutton et al. (1972). Corresponding, higher-than-present water levels were dated at 3900 ± 100 B.P. (BGS-898) in the Lake Erie basin (Coakley and Lewis, 1985). Following the high-level stand, the RLL curve drops slightly to pass through site 32a, after which it rises gradually to the present level. Gyttja deposition, like the stratified sand-silt sequences, also requires a minimum depth of water estimated to be about 2 m

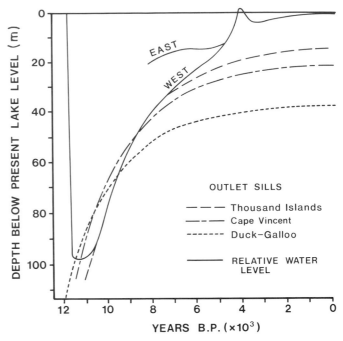

Figure 10. Interpreted relative lake-level curves for eastern and western Ontario basin compared with predicted uplift histories of Duck-Galloo, Cape Vincent, and Thousand Islands outlet sills.

on the basis of near-recent gyttja deposition in Lake Ontario lagoons (Otto and Dalrymple, 1983). The lake-level curve is thus drawn about 2 m above the dated gyttja intervals at site 12.

The large southwestward tilt of the early water-planes (Fig. 8) suggests that most of the postglacial lake-level rise in the western Ontario basin is due to uplift of lake outlets in eastern Lake Ontario and the upper St. Lawrence River. A review of detailed bathymetric charts for this area reveals two critical saddles and a restricted channel area which may have controlled outflow — the Duck-Galloo sill at 37 m below present lake level, the Cape Vincent sill at 21 m below lake level, and sills about 14 m below lake level in the Thousand Islands area (Fig. 1). The Duck-Galloo sill lies between Main Duck and Galloo Islands where it could have controlled drainage from the main basin of Early Lake Ontario into the downstream St. Lawrence trough. Drainage from the St. Lawrence trough into the upper St. Lawrence River would have been controlled by the Cape Vincent sill between Cape Vincent, New York, and Wolfe Island, Ontario. Channel restrictions and shoals in the Thousand Islands area between Ivy Lea, Ontario, and Alexandria Bay, New York, may have acted as a third downstream control on Lake Ontario water levels.

The uplift histories of these sills relative to present lake level in the western Ontario basin are plotted in Figure 10. The trends and cross-overs of these curves suggest that main Lake Ontario waters were controlled in succession by the Duck-Galloo, Cape Vincent, and Thousand Islands sills. The Duck-Galloo sill was dominant until the Cape Vincent sill overtook it about 10 500 B.P. The Cape Vincent sill prevailed for about 3000 years until the Thousand Islands sill surpassed it about 7500 B.P. and remained dominant to the

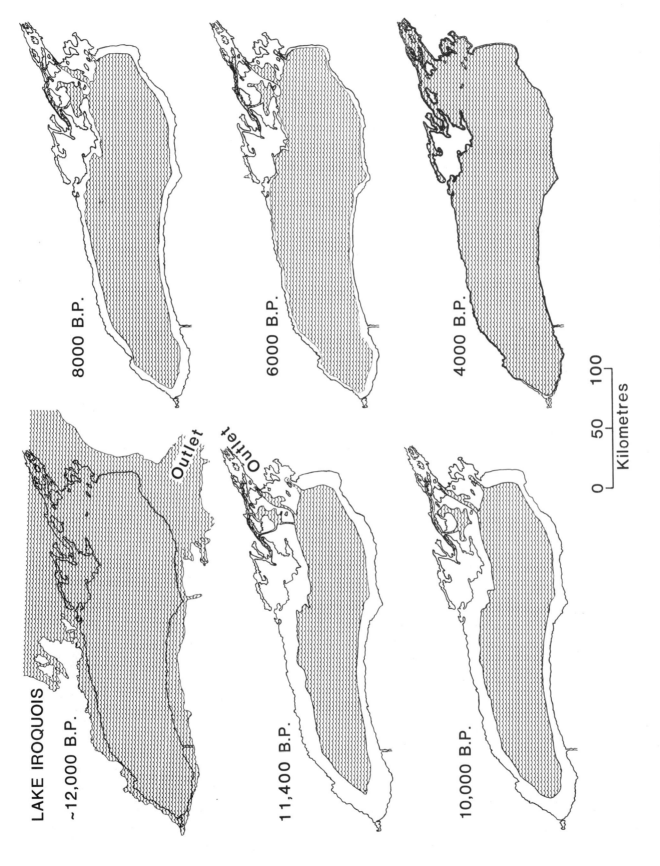

Figure 11. Areal extent of Lake Ontario basin at time of Lake Iroquois (ca. 12 000 B.P.) and at 11 400, 10 000, 8000, 6000, and 4000 B.P.

present day.

The foregoing results were obtained by relaxing the differential uplift on the Iroquois water-plane between each outlet area and western Lake Ontario in turn using the relaxation coefficient computed for the western basin area (k = -0.343 per thousand years). The relative elevation is estimated from the expression:

$$RLL = D + \triangle Ee^{k(t_1 - t)}$$

where RLL is lake level relative to present Lake Ontario,

    D is present water depth over an outlet sill,

    $\triangle E$ is elevation difference on the Iroquois water-plane between outlet sill and western Lake Ontario (Toronto-Hamilton area),

    t_1 is age of the Iroquois water-plane (12 000 B.P.),

    t is the age variable in thousands of years B.P., i.e., the time at which an RLL estimate is desired,

    k is the relaxation coefficient (Appendix 1).

Shore Outlines and Drainage History

Outlines of the shorelines of Lake Iroquois and Lake Ontario basin at 11 400, 10 000, 8000, 6000, 4000 B.P. are illustrated in Figure 11. These outlines were derived by projecting the respective depths of each water-plane (relative to the present level of Lake Ontario) along isobases perpendicular to the line of section (Fig. 8) to isobaths of equal value on a bathymetric map. Outlines of the Kingston Basin and St. Lawrence trough were determined by tracing the sequence of lowest control sills and projecting the respective depths of each water-plane (relative to the depth of the controlling sill below present lake level) to isobaths on a bathymetric map similar to Johnston (1978).

The drainage history of the Lake Ontario basin is deduced from the relative lake-level history and uplift histories of sills potentially controlling the Kingston basin, North Channel, and main Lake Ontario water levels. The present water depths for the analysis of the investigated sills (Cold Bath Shoal, Upper and Lower Gap, Main Duck-False Duck, Allan Otty, Charity Shoal, Duck-Galloo, and Cape Vincent) were read from detailed bathymetric charts.

At 11 400 B.P., while main Lake Ontario was draining into the St. Lawrence River and levels were controlled by the Duck-Galloo sill, a separate lake in the Kingston basin drained northward via Upper and Lower Gaps into North Channel which drained over Cold Bath Shoal sill. Increased outflow through the restricted Duck-Galloo outlet as a result of glacial Lake Algonquin drainage into Ontario basin (Mirynech, 1962) about this time may have allowed water levels to rise sufficiently high to flood across the Main Duck-False Duck sill into the Kingston basin.

About 10 500 B.P., North Channel waters rising behind the Cold Bath Shoal outlet back-flooded the Kingston basin through Upper Gap. At this time, the sill connecting main Ontario basin and Kingston basin between False Duck and Main Duck Islands (Fig. 1) was dry. The Allan Otty and Charity Shoal connections into the St. Lawrence trough were never significant controls for the Kingston basin.

By 10 000 B.P., differential uplift had substantially raised the Cold Bath Shoal outlet but it continued to control water levels in North Channel and the Kingston basin. Lower Gap and Main Duck-False Duck outlets were dry; the Kingston basin drained into North Channel via Upper Gap.

After 10 000 B.P., the more rapidly rising Cold Bath Shoal outlet directed North Channel and Kingston basin drainage southward to main Lake Ontario over the Main Duck-False Duck sill. By 9000 B.P., main Lake Ontario back-flooded Main Duck-False Duck outlet and brought waters in all basins − North Channel, Kingston basin, main Lake Ontario, and St. Lawrence trough − to a common level controlled by the Cape Vincent sill. From this time forward, Kingston basin levels were confluent with those of main Lake Ontario.

Peripheral areas of the Kingston basin would have been exposed since about 11 500 B.P. and apparently conditions were suitable in these areas for organic deposition as indicated by plant detritus at sites 21 to 25 and 30. Reduced flow in the upper St. Lawrence River area favoured peat growth as deduced at site 31. Bay of Quinte (site 26) and Henderson Harbour (site 28) were transgressed by about 6000 B.P. The trophic states of these embayments changed from restricted shallow lakes with marl deposition to deep lakes with gyttja deposition. Differential uplift of the Lake Ontario basin raised water levels along the south and southwest shores of the basin. The Sodus Bay and Hamilton Harbour lagoons were transgressed at or shortly after 5000 B.P. The trophic states of these embayments changed subsequently from lagoon and marsh-like habitats to deep lakes with silty clay deposition.

DISCUSSION AND CONCLUSIONS

Lake History and Relationship to Champlain Sea

Evidence in the offshore and embayment cores from Lake Ontario supports, and in some cases provides, new data on the late Wisconsinan history of the Lake Ontario basin. Lacustrine sedimentation commenced in the western Ontario basin prior to 12 500 B.P. The massive clay with inclusions of clay blebs below laminated clay at site 11 is believed to have originated from an ice shelf during the Peel Ponds stage and northeastward extension of the Erie-basin, high level lakes, Grassmere, and Lundy (Prest, 1970). Permanent ice eventually gave way to open-lake conditions which enhanced glaciolacustrine sedimentation on a seasonal basis. The earliest accumulations of laminated sediments which post-date 12 500 B.P. at site 11 (Fig. 5) thus mark the initiation of sedimentation in glacial Lake Iroquois. Ice retreat in the upper St. Lawrence River area created low outlets to the northeast and Lake Iroquois and the immediate post-Iroquois lakes drained to successively lower levels (Prest, 1970; Clark and Karrow, 1984). Ontario-basin waters were confluent with sea level (Gilbert Gulf of Fairchild, 1907) possibly as early as the post-Iroquois Trenton phase (Clark and Karrow, 1984) or more likely at a later lower phase. Relative lake levels continued to decline because the basin uplifted with respect to sea level. Once the upper St. Lawrence River area emerged from sea level, the decline of lake levels ceased (lowest-level Early Lake Ontario) and back-flooding commenced.

Early Lake Ontario is dated at 11 400 B.P. from pollen stratigraphy of the stratified sand and silt overlying laminated clay of Lake Iroquois at site 11. Lake Iroquois, therefore, drained a few hundred years previously. The date of 11 760 ± 310 B.P. (GSC-626) on basal gyttja in Biddy Lake near Brighton, Ontario, provides a minimum age for isolation of this lake from Lake Iroquois (Terasmae, 1980) and hence a minimum age for the draining of Lake Iroquois. This date is in agreement with an inferred age of 11 700 B.P. for the end of Ontario-basin glaciolacustrine deposition in Lambs Pond basin, near Brockville, Ontario (Anderson et al., 1985).

The presence of estuarine conditions in the Lake Ontario basin hau been suggested (Clark and Karrow, 1984) partly on the basis of high concentrations of acidic amino acids in the glaciolacustrine sediments of core 70-0-37-E30 from eastern Lake Ontario (Schroeder and Bada, 1978). Boron analysis as well as additional aspartic acid racemization studies on other cores seem desirable in order to substantiate the geochemical findings.

Had marine waters entered the Lake Ontario basin, they would have left a fossil record in the deepest basins of eastern Lake Ontario. However, an examination of the uppermost glaciolacustrine sediments of core 70-0-37-E30 in the deepest part of the main basin and core 68-0-18-28 (site 19, this study) in the St. Lawrence trough revealed that marine evidence is lacking in the benthic ostracode fauna (Anderson et al., 1985). The freshening influence of the glacial lakes and freshwater outflow may have been too predominant for a marine (or brackish) fauna or flora to become established. However, brief seasonal or intermittent underflows of saline waters into the deepest parts of the Ontario basin may account for the marine character of sedimentary amino acids but would have been insufficient to alter the established freshwater ostracode biota. It might be useful to examine the uppermost glaciolacustrine sediments for the presence of agglutinated rhizopods (thecamoebians) since these benthic organisms have proved successful as indicators of marine-freshwater transgressions in coastal studies in Atlantic Canada (Scott and Medioli, 1980).

Relative Lake Level Changes

The interpreted RLL curves of Figure 9 are considered to represent the most accurate indication available of lake-level change for main Lake Ontario. Several sites lie off the RLL curve for the eastern end of Lake Ontario and relate to basin changes that occurred separately from the main lake. The early onset of organic deposition in these basins relates to the low-water phase of Early Lake Ontario when eastern Lake Ontario was still glacio-isostatically depressed; peat deposition ceased when lake levels back-flooded these basins as a result of differential uplift. This is borne out by the early dates of 10 200 ± 500 B.P. on gyttja at site 33 in Cataraqui River, 9480 ± 70 B.P. on gyttja at Rossmore Bog (site 27) in interior Bay of Quinte, 8790 ± 170 B.P. on gyttja at site 25 in the island area of the Kingston basin, 8560 ± 200 B.P. on plant detritus at site 31 in the upper St. Lawrence River, and 7920 ± 120 B.P. on basal peat (site 26) in the Bay of Quinte.

Dated samples 5b and 5c (site 5) lie off the RLL curve for the western end of the lake. Wood sample 5c was probably reworked from shore deposits by longshore wave activity associated with the Early Lake Ontario period of rising lake levels rather than with the post-Iroquois interval of falling levels (Sandy Creek phase) as postulated by Sutton et al. (1972). In a similar way, the lower of two undated peat horizons and overlying lacustrine sequence in Irondequoit Bay, New York (Young, 1983) falls on the 8000 B.P. water-plane of Figure 8 and is likely associated with the rising lake phase of Early Lake Ontario. The upper Irondequoit Bay peat-sand and gravel sequence is believed to correspond with similar records discussed earlier for Sodus Bay and Hamilton Harbour.

The wood sample (5b), dated 5240 ± 140 B.P., was likely reworked from the marsh deposits in Hamilton Harbour by transgressive lake levels at this time. It was redeposited in the barrier beach deposits outside Hamilton Harbour by the action of longshore waves and sediment drift.

The predicted RLL based on outlet-uplift history agrees in a general way with the interpreted RLL (Fig. 10) confirming, as expected, that the greater part of postglacial water-level change is explained by differential uplift. Between 11 400 and 10 000 B.P. the predicted outlet elevations lie above the interpreted RLL curve, but after 9000 B.P., the predicted outlet sills pass beneath the RLL curve at progressively greater depths. The earlier anomaly suggests that rapid uplift was delayed or slowed in immediate post-Iroquois time, perhaps due to residual loads from glacial ice or Champlain Sea water northeast of the Ontario basin. With lake-level-controlling outlets uplifting as predicted there would be little opportunity for Early Lake Ontario to descend below 100 m as required by Sly and Prior (1984).

The progressive rise of the interpreted RLL curve above predicted elevations of controlling outlets between 9000 and 5000 B.P. probably reflects increasing flow resistance arising from decreasing bed slope and increasing complexity of the uplifting St. Lawrence River outlet and its channels. Other contributing factors are thought to be uncertainties in the RLL data and differential uplift processes. A full paleohydrological analysis is beyond the scope of this paper, but if done, might assist in explaining lake-level history.

The rise of lake levels to a peak at 4000 B.P. (above present lake level in eastern Lake Ontario) is attributed to the diversion of Upper Great Lakes drainage through Lakes Erie and Ontario at the Nipissing Great Lakes phase (Anderson and Lewis, 1982). The decline of lake level after 4000 B.P. presumably reflects the erosion of outlet channels and development of increased drainage capacity. Continuing uplift of the outlet region while carrying full Great Lakes drainage would account for the progressive lake-level rise over the past 3000 years to about 14 m above the shallowest sill in the Thousand Islands area.

Grimsby-Oakville Bar

The early development of the massive sand and gravel bar buried beneath postglacial mud between Grimsby and Oakville may have been aided by a probable slowdown in lake-level change just prior to Early Lake Ontario when lake levels were confluent with sea level. At this time, while basin levels were held above the eastern Ontario outlet sills by the Champlain Sea, the relative water-level changes were dependent upon the net effect of basin uplift and sea-level rise. As these processes operated in the same direction, the rate of relative lake-level change would have declined substantially compared with the earlier period of post-Iroquois drawdown and the subsequent period of outlet control under isostatic rebound. We tentatively suggest that this situation caused a near stillstand in the western Ontario basin, thereby inducing a prolonged period of wave action within a restricted vertical range in which longshore sediment drift may have contributed to early construction of the Grimsby-Oakville bar. The reworked, fossil-bearing lagoonal sediments cored at site 11 and dating about 11 500 B.P. are thought to have originated in this period. Once Ontario-basin and Champlain Sea waters separated, relative lake levels rose rapidly in western Lake Ontario under the influence of the isostatically rebounding, Duck-Galloo outlet sill.

The Grimsby-Oakville bar falls on the 10 000 B.P. water-plane (Fig. 8) and correlates in time with the uppermost coarse sand and gravel bed in the Niagara Gorge Whirlpool Park section (Calkin and Brett, 1978) where contained shells have been dated at 9770 ± 150 B.P. (BGS-274) and 9915 ± 165 B.P. (QC-117). Rapid erosion of the sand and gravel bed and underlying unlithified fill of the buried St. Davids Gorge possibly led to massive inputs of unconsolidated sediments by the Niagara River into Lake Ontario. Rising lake levels of Early Lake Ontario presumably reworked and redeposited these sediments to form the Grimsby-Oakville bar. Mud deposition in western Lake Ontario subsequently buried the bar.

Summary Model of Glacial and Postglacial Water-Level History, Ontario Basin.

Our proposed model of relative lake-level change for the Lake Ontario basin (Fig. 12) is based on new evidence of previous lake levels assembled in this paper, recent advances in our understanding of the relationship between the Ontario basin and the Champlain Sea (Clark and Karrow, 1984; Anderson et al., 1985), the acoustic stratigraphy of Ontario basin sediments (Sly and Prior, 1984), and the regional geology of the Great Lakes region. After initially high elevations controlled by glacier-damming, lake levels declined to their lowest level at sea level as glaciers retreated. After a short period of little change reflecting the balance of basin uplift and sea-level rise, relative lake levels rose with diminishing rates to the present under the influence of glacio-isostatic basin tilting and uplift of outlets. Fluctuations in lake level were superimposed on this rise due to increases in basin water supply and outlet adjustments when upper Great Lakes drainage resumed its flow through Lake Ontario. The stages of this water-level history are outlined with reference to Figure 12 in greater detail below:

AB (~12 500 to 12 000 B.P.) Glacial Lake Iroquois – glacier dam in northeast part of Ontario basin, drainage via Mohawk River at Rome, New York.

BC (~12 000 to 11 500 B.P.) Post-Iroquois falling lake phases – Frontenac, Sydney, Belleville (Sandy Creek), Trenton-Skinner Creek – retreat of glacier and release

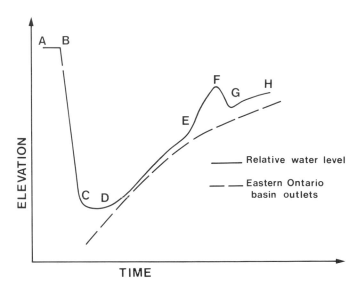

Figure 12. A proposed summary model of relative lake-level change for Ontario basin showing early rapid decline due to retreat of a glacial dam (ABC), near stillstand due to sea level control (CD), progressive rise at steadily diminishing rates due to differential uplift of outlets (DE), and superimposed flooding with outlet adjustments due to capture of upper Great Lakes drainage (E-H).

of lake waters by newly opened lower outlets, expansion of glacial lake waters into the Ottawa and upper St. Lawrence valleys.

C (~11 500 B.P.) Fall to sea level (Gilbert Gulf phase) – Trenton-Skinner Creek or later lower phases are confluent with Champlain Sea level. Relative lake-level changes are reduced, depending on net effect of basin uplift and sea-level rise.

D (~11 500 to 10 500 B.P.) Early Lake Ontario (Duck-Galloo phase) – separation from Champlain Sea.

DE (~10 500 to 5000 B.P.) Rising Early Lake Ontario – Following diversion of upper Great Lakes drainage to the Mattawa and Ottawa Rivers (drainage of glacial Lake Algonquin in the Huron basin), the Ontario basin experienced a long period of reduced water supply causing lake levels to follow the rising eastern outlets rather closely.

EF (5000 to 4000 B.P.) "Nipissing Flood phase" – With return of upper Great Lakes drainage through Lakes Erie and Ontario, increased outflow overtaxed the capacity of outlet channels, causing water levels to rise significantly. The "Nipissing Flood", peaking about 4000 B.P., surpassed present levels in eastern Lake Ontario. This stage probably corresponds with the North Pond phase of Sutton et al., (1972).

FG (4000 to 3500 B.P.) Levels subsided as outlet channels adjusted to increased outflow from upper Great Lakes discharge.

GH (3500 B.P. to present) Levels increase gradually but more slowly than in early Holocene under the influence of rising outlets.

The RLL interpretation of this study is similar to other recent models (Karrow et al., 1961; Sutton et al., 1972; Sly and Prior, 1984) in that all recognize a substantial and rapid decline to levels well below present following high glacial lake stages. However, the low stage is shallower in the Karrow *et al.* model, deeper in the Sly and Prior model, and much delayed in the Sutton *et al.* model compared with our proposed model. The Sutton *et al.* model, like the present model, predicts a period of sea-level control, though this persists much longer (to 5000 B.P.) than permitted by current evidence. Following the low stage, all three models exhibit rising levels at steadily diminishing rates with slight variations to the present day. A period of higher-than-present lake levels which is inferred by Sutton *et al.* (1972) but not by Karrow *et al.* (1961) or Sly and Prior (1984) is confirmed and explained in the present model. Refinements to the present model will likely be possible with further dating and paleoecological study and correlation with the stratigraphy of basin sediments, paleohydraulic analysis of outlet channels, and better geodynamic undertanding of postglacial earth movements.

ACKNOWLEDGEMENTS

Sponsorship of Geological Survey of Canada Projects for sample collection and radiocarbon dating, and the support of the Canada Centre for Inland Waters, Burlington, Ontario, for ship time, technical assistance, and office facilities are gratefully acknowledged.

We are also grateful to the following for identifying the faunal macrofossils in the Lake Ontario cores and for providing paleoecological interpretations: G. Mackie (University of Guelph) and M. Smith (National Museum Natural Sciences) for molluscs, L.D. Delorme (Canada Centre for Inland Waters) for ostracodes, and J.V. Matthews (Geological Survey of Canada) for insect remains. V.K. Prest (Geological Survey of Canada) kindly provided shoreline elevation and uplift data on Lake Iroquois and the post-Iroquois lake stages. Comments and constructive criticisms by B.R. Pelletier, G. Vilks, and I. Reid (Geological Survey of Canada), W.A. Gorman (Queens University), R.A. Young (SUNY College, Geneseo), and J.S. Street (St. Lawrence University) greatly improved the manuscript.

REFERENCES

Anderson, T.W., 1971, Postglacial Vegetative Changes in the Lake Huron-Lake Simcoe District, Ontario, with Special Reference to Glacial Lake Algonquin: Ph.D. Thesis, Waterloo, Ontario, University of Waterloo, 246 p.

Anderson, T.W., and Lewis, C.F.M., 1982, The Mid-Holocene Nipissing Flood into Lake Ontario: American Quaternary Association Program and Abstracts, Seventh Biennial Conference, Seattle, Washington, p. 60.

Anderson, T.W., Mott, R.J., and Delorme, L.D., 1985, Evidence for a pre-Champlain Sea Glacial Lake Phase in Ottawa Valley, Ontario, and its Implications: *in* Geological Survey of Canada Paper 85-1A, Current Research, Part A, p. 239-245.

Andrews, J.T., 1968a, Postglacial Rebound: Similarity and Prediction of Uplift Curves: Canadian Journal of Earth Sciences, v. 5, p. 39-47.

_____, 1968b, Pattern and Cause of Variability of Postglacial Uplift and Rate of Uplift in Arctic Canada: Journal of Geology, v. 76, p. 404-425.

_____, 1970, A Geomorphological Study of Postglacial Uplift with Particular Reference to Arctic Canada: Institute of British Geographers Special Publication 2, 156 p.

Berry, J.C., and Drimmie, R.J., 1982, University of Waterloo Radiocarbon Dates I: Radiocarbon, v. 24, p. 68-82.

Calkin, P.E., and Brett, C.E., 1978, Ancestral Niagara River Drainage: Stratigraphic and Paleotologic Setting: Geological Society of America Bulletin, v. 89, p. 1140-1154.

Clark, P., and Karrow, P.F., 1984, Late Pleistocene Water Bodies in the St. Lawrence Lowland, New York, and Regional Correlations: Geological Society of America Bulletin, v. 95, p. 805-813.

Clarke, A.H., 1973, The Freshwater Molluscs of the Canadian Interior Basin: Malacologia, v. 13, 509 p.

Coakley, J.P., and Lewis, C.F.M., 1985, Postglacial Lake Levels in the Erie Basin: *in* Karrow, P.F., and Calkin, P.E., eds., Quaternary Evolution of the Great Lakes: Geological Association of Canada Special Paper 30.

Coleman, A.P., 1922, Glacial and Post-Glacial Lakes in Ontario: University of Toronto Studies, Publications of the Ontario Fisheries Research Laboratory No. 10, Toronto, The University Library, 76 p.

_____, 1937, Lake Iroquois: Ontario Department of Mines, Annual Report, v. 45, pt. 7, 36 p.

Fairchild, H.L., 1907, Gilbert Gulf (Marine Waters in the Ontario Basin): Geological Society of America Bulletin, v. 17, p. 712-718.

Farrand, W.R., 1962, Postglacial Uplift in North America: American Journal of Science, v. 260, p. 181-199.

Fillon, R.H., 1972, Possible Causes of the Variability of Postglacial Uplift in North America: Quaternary Research, v. 1, p. 522-531.

Fullerton, D.S., 1980, Preliminary Correlation of Post-Erie Interstadial Events (16 000-10 000 Radiocarbon Years before Present) Central and Eastern Great Lakes Region and Hudson, Champlain and St. Lawrence Lowlands, United States and Canada: United States Geological Survey Professional Paper 1089, 52 p.

Johnston, L.M., 1978, Geolimnological Studies in the Kingston Basin-upper St. Lawrence River Region: Ph.D. Thesis, Kingston, Ontario, Queen's University, 243 p.

Karrow, P.F., Clark, J.R. and Terasmae, J., 1961, The Age of Lake Iroquois and Lake Ontario: Journal of Geology, v. 69, p. 659-667.

Lewis, C.F.M., 1969, Quaternary Geology of the Great Lakes: Geological Survey of Canada Paper 69-1A, Report of Activities, Part A, p. 63-64.

Lewis, C.F.M., and Anderson, T.W., 1985, Postglacial Lake Levels in the Huron Basin: Comparative Uplift Histories of Basins and Sills in a Rebounding Glacial Marginal Depression [Abstract]: *in* Karrow, P.F., and Calkin, P.E., eds., Quaternary Evolution of the Great Lakes: Geological Association of Canada Special Paper 30.

Lewis, C.F.M., and McNeely, R.N., 1967, Survey of Lake Ontario Bottom Deposits: Proceedings of the 10th Conference on Great Lakes Research, International Association for Great Lakes Research, p. 133-142.

Lewis, C.F.M., and Sly, P.G., 1971, Seismic Profiling and Geology of the Toronto Waterfront Area of Lake Ontario: Proceedings of the 14th Conference on Great Lakes Research, International Association for Great Lakes Research, p. 303-354.

Lowdon, J.A., Robertson, I.M., and Blake, W. Jr., 1977, Geological Survey of Canada Radiocarbon Dates XVII: Geological Survey of Canada Paper 77-7, 25 p.

McAndrews, J.H., 1971, Report to the Geological Survey of Canada on Work Done on Contract for 1969-71: 39 p.

————, 1973, Pollen Analysis of the Sediments of the Great Lakes of North America: Proceedings of the 3rd International Palynological Conference, Moscow, p. 76-80.

Miller, N.G., 1973, Late-Glacial and Postglacial Vegetation Change in Southwestern New York State: New York State Museum and Science Service Bulletin 420, 102 p.

Mirynech, E., 1962, The Pleistocene Geology of the Trenton-Campbellford Map-Area, Ontario: Ph.D. Thesis, Toronto, Ontario, University of Toronto, 240 p.

Mott, R.J., and Farley-Gill, L.D., 1978, A Late-Quaternary Pollen Profile from Woodstock, Ontario: Canadian Journal of Earth Sciences, v. 15, p. 1101-1111.

Muller, E.H., 1977, Late-Glacial and Early Postglacial Environments in Western New York: Annals of the New York Academy of Sciences, v. 288, p. 223-233.

Muller, E.H., and Prest, V.K., 1985, Glacial Lakes in the Ontario Basin: in Karrow, P.F., and Calkin, P.E., eds., Quaternary Evolution of the Great Lakes: Geological Association of Canada Special Publication 30.

Otto, J.E., and Dalrymple, R.W., 1983, Ontario Geoscience Research Grant Program, Grant No. 78, Terrain Characteristics and Physical Processes in Small Lagoon Complexes: Ontario Geological Survey Open File Report 5463, 89 p.

Peltier, W.R., 1980, Models of Glacial Isostasy and Relative Sea Level: in Bally, A.W., Bender, P.L., McGetchin, T.R., and Walcott, R.I., eds., Dynamics of Plate Interiors: American Geophysical Union, Geodynamics Series 1, p. 111-128.

Prest, V.K., 1970, Quaternary Geology of Canada: in Douglas, R.J.W., ed., Geology and Economic Minerals of Canada: Geological Survey of Canada, Economic Geology Series, No. 1, p. 676-764.

Schroeder, R.A., and Bada, J.L., 1978, Aspartic Acid Racemization in Late Wisconsin Lake Ontario Sediments: Quaternary Research, v. 9, p. 193-204.

Scott, D.B., and Medioli, F.S., 1980, Post-Glacial Emergence Curves in the Maritimes Determined from Marine Sediments in Raised Basins: Burlington, Ontario, Canadian Coastal Conference 1980 Proceedings, p. 428-446.

Sly, P.G., and Prior, J.W., 1984, Late-Glacial and Post-Glacial Geology in the Lake Ontario Basin: Canadian Journal of Earth Sciences, v. 21, p. 802-821.

Sutton, R.G., Rukavina, N.A., and Towle, E.L., 1965a, Lake Ontario Shoreline Processes and Evolution at Braddock Heights, New York: Report of Progress: Proceedings of the 8th Conference on Great Lakes Research; University of Michigan, Great Lakes Research Division Publication 13, p. 240-247.

————, 1965b, Changes in the Levels of Lake Ontario as Inferred from Offshore Sediments at Braddock Heights, New York: Proceedings of the Rochester Academy of Science, Inc., v. 11, p. 72-82.

Sutton, R.G., Lewis, T.L., and Woodrow, D.L., 1972, Post-Iroquois Lake Stages and Shoreline Sedimentation in Eastern Ontario Basin: Journal of Geology, v. 80, p. 346-356.

Terasmae, J., 1980, Some Problems of Late Wisconsin History and Geochronology in Southeastern Ontario: Canadian Journal of Earth Sciences, v. 17, p. 361-381.

————, 1981, Late-Wisconsin Deglaciation and Migration of Spruce into Southern Ontario, Canada: in Romans, R.C., ed., Geobotany II: New York, Plenum Press, p. 75-90.

Terasmae, J., and Mirynech, E., 1964, Postglacial Chronology and the Origin of Deep Lake Basins in Prince Edward County, Ontario: Proceedings of the 7th Conference on Great Lakes Research; University of Michigan, Great Lakes Research Division, Publication 11, p. 161-169.

Thomas, R.L., Kemp, A.L.W., and Lewis, C.F.M., 1972, Distribution, Composition and Characteristics of the Surficial Sediments of Lake Ontario: Journal of Sedimentary Petrology, v. 42, p. 66-84.

Walcott, R.I., 1970, Isostatic Response to Loading of the Crust in Canada: Canadian Journal of Earth Sciences, v. 7, p. 716-727.

Walton, Q., Trautman, M.A., and Friend, J.P., 1961, Isotopes, Inc. Radiocarbon Measurements 1: Radiocarbon, v. 3, p. 47-59.

Washburn, A.L., and Stuiver, M., 1962, Radiocarbon-Dated Postglacial Develevelling in Northeast Greenland and its Implications: Arctic, v. 15, p. 66-72.

Woodrow, D.L., Sutton, R.G., and Rukavina, N.A., 1967, A Drowned Beach in Lake Ontario west of Rochester, New York: Proceedings of the 10th Conference on Great Lakes Research, International Association for Great Lakes Research, p. 157-161.

Young, R.A., 1983, The Geologic Evolution of the Genesee Valley Region and Early Lake Ontario: A Review of Recent Progress: Proceedings of the Rochester Academy of Science, Inc., v. 15, p. 85-98.

APPENDIX 1

Evaluation of Exponential Relaxation from Differentially Uplifted Paleowater-Planes

It is assumed here that the rate of vertical motion in an uplifting deglaciated region decays exponentially with time. This follows from Farrand's (1962) observations, based on deformed beaches and shorelines, that at many sites in the Great Lakes and Arctic regions postglacial uplift proceded quickly at deglaciation, then more slowly at steadily decreasing rates through to the present. These observations were confirmed by other geologists working in similarly deglaciated areas (Andrews, 1968a; 1968b; 1970; Washburn and Stuiver, 1962; Fillon, 1972) and by geophysicists (Walcott, 1970; Peltier, 1980) consiering processes of crustal adjustment following glacial unloading. These workers show or agree that the decaying rate of vertical crustal motion in deglaciated uplifted areas can be characterized kinematically as a negative exponential function.

A lake basin lying in the rebounding marginal depression of a retreating ice sheet will experience faster uplift in areas closer to the retreating ice than in more distant areas. In such a basin, former water-planes are differentially uplifted in the direction of glacier retreat. Older water-planes are upwarped more than younger water-planes and are observed at present with higher shoreline gradients.

Following Andrews (1968a), exponentially decaying uplift of a point in the period following an initial time t_1 is given by

$$U_{(t)} = U_{t_1} e^{k(t_1 - t)} \qquad \text{(Eq. 1)}$$

where $U_{(t)}$ is uplift remaining from time t (variable). Its value is approximated by the uplift achieved from time t to the present.

U_{t_1} is uplift remaining from time t_1 (a known parameter) and is approximated by the uplift achieved from time t_1 to the present.

t_1 is a reference age or point in time, usually known, and is measured in thousands of years B.P.

t is any point in time measured in thousands of years B.P.

k is the relaxation coefficient.

$1/k$ the absolute value of $1/k$ is the relaxation time or time constant of the uplifting process. It is the period in thousands of years in which uplift remaining decays to $1/e$ or 37% ($e = 2.71828$) of its initial value.

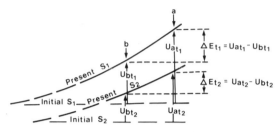

Figure A-1. Sketch showing the initial levels and present (uplifted) traces of two former water planes, S_1 and S_2. The total and differential vertical movements of each water plane at two arbitrary points, a and b, are defined.

The difference in elevation between any two points a and b on a former water-plane as a function of time (Fig. A-1) may be found by evaluating Equation 1 at the points and subtracting the two expressions.

$$\text{Thus } U_a(t) = U_{a_{t_1}} e^{k(t_1-t)} \qquad \text{(Eq. 2)}$$
$$\text{less } U_b(t) = U_{b_{t_1}} e^{k(t_1-t)} \qquad \text{(Eq. 3)}$$
$$\text{gives } (U_a - U_b)(t) = (U_{a_{t_1}} - U_{b_{t_1}}) e^{k(t_1-t)} \qquad \text{(Eq. 4)}$$

The difference in uplift remaining $(U_{a_{t_1}} - U_{b_{t_1}})$ between two points on a former water-plane equals their present difference in elevation $(\triangle E_{t_1})$ (Fig. A-1). Thus Equation 4 shows that the difference in elevation $\triangle E_t$ between any two points on a former water-plane is itself an exponentially decaying function operating on the present difference in elevation of the water-plane at the same two points.

That is, $\triangle E(t) = \triangle E_{t_1} e^{k(t_1-t)}$ \qquad (Eq. 5)

where $\triangle E(t)$ is the relative elevation as a function of time (age B.P.) of two points on a former water-plane of age t_1

$\triangle E_{t_1}$ is the present difference in elevation.

The relaxation coefficient k is evaluated by substituting in Equation 5 the relative elevations as defined in Figure A-1 of any two points on two former water-planes,

then $\triangle E_{t_2} = \triangle E_{t_1} e^{k(t_1-t_2)}$

and $k = \dfrac{1}{t_1-t_2} \log_e \left(\dfrac{\triangle E_{t_2}}{\triangle E_{t_1}} \right)$ \qquad (Eq. 6)

An identical value for k is obtained if shoreline gradients on the former water-planes S_1 and S_2 (Fig. A-1) are substituted in Equation 6 in place of the elevation differences. This result is easily shown by deriving an equation equivalent to 5 by dividing each of its sides with the horizontal distance, a-b, between the two points on former water-planes whose elevation differences are $\triangle E(t)$ and $\triangle E_{t_1}$. The resulting ratios, $\triangle E(t)/a-b$ and $\triangle E_{t_1}/a-b$, in the equivalent equation are also the shoreline gradients for the water-planes S_2 and S_1, respectively. Solving for k in the equivalent equation yields Equation 6.

INDEX

GEOLOGICAL ASSOCIATION OF CANADA

ASSOCIATION GEOLOGIQUE DU CANADA

SPECIAL PAPERS**

20 The Continental Crust and Its Mineral Deposits
Edited by D.W. Strangway, 1980, 804 p., $24/$30*

21 Cretaceous Rocks and Their Foraminifera in the Manitoba Escarpment
Edited by D.H. McNeil and W.G.E. Caldwell, 1981, 439 p., $24/$30*

22 The Buchans Orebodies: Fifty Years of Geology and Mining
Edited by E.A. Swanson, D.F. Strong and J.G. Thurlow, 1981, 350 p. (2 multi-coloured geological maps in separate binder), $29/$36*

23 Sedimentation and Tectonics in Alluvial Basins
Edited by A.D. Miall, 1981, 272 p., $22/$26*

24 Major Structural Zones and Faults of the Northern Appalachians
Edited by P. St. Julien and J. Beland, 1982, 250 p., $24/$29*

25 Precambrian Sulphide Deposits
(H.S. Robinson Memorial Volume), Edited by R.W. Hutchinson, C.D. Spence and J.M. Franklin, 1982, 791 p., $47/$57*

26 Glacial Lake Agassiz
Edited by J.T. Teller and L. Clayton, 1983, 451 p. (+ 2 maps in pocket), $28/$34*

27 Jurassic-Cretaceous Biochronology and Paleogeography of North America
Edited by G.E.G. Westermann, 1984, 315 p , $30/$36*

28 Evolution of Archean Supracrustal Sequences
Edited by L.D. Ayres, P.C. Thurston, K.D. Card, and W. Weber, 1985, 380 p., $35/$42*

29 The Carswell Structure Uranium Deposits, Saskatchewan
Edited by R. Lainé, D. Alonso, and M. Svab, 1985, 230 p., $35/$42*

30 Quaternary Evolution of the Great Lakes
Edited by P.F. Karrow and P.E. Calkin, 1985, 253 p., $35/$42*

*Members/Non-members
**For handling and postage to any address add $3.00 per publication.

Payments must accompany orders. **Make cheques payable to Geological Association of Canada.** Payments may also be made in U.S. funds. No refunds or exchanges.

Mail orders to: GAC Publications
Business and Economic Service Ltd.
111 Peter Street, Suite 509
Toronto, Ontario M5V 2H1
CANADA